EVERYTHING™ CIVIL WAR

The Ultimate Guide to

Civil War Products . . .

Services . . .

D0094258

Places of Interest . . .

Organizations . . .

Archives . . .

Accommodations . . .

1997 Edition

EVERYTHING CIVIL WAR

FIRST EDITION
Second Printing, July 1997

Price: $19.95

Willow Creek Press of Washington
P.O. Box 3730
Silverdale, WA 98383-3730
Phone: (360) 830-5612

Cover art by Willow Creek Press

Publisher's Cataloging-in-Publication
(Provided by Quality Books, Inc.)

Kope, Spencer

   Everything Civil War: the ultimate guide to Civil War products, services, places of interest, organizations, archives, accommodations / Spencer Kope. -- 1st ed.
   p. cm.
   Includes index.
   ISBN: 0-9647183-1-6

   1. United States--History--Civil War, 1861-1865--Miscellanea--Directories. I. Title.

E641.K67 1997   973.7'0216
                             QBI97-40643

Table of Contents

Please Note: This book is intended as a reference book. Willow Creek Press has no control over the companies and organizations represented here and is not responsible for negligence or fraud committed by these enterprises. While they all appear to be reputable, "buyer beware" always applies. Make sure you're getting what you paid for. If you experience a blatant case of fraud, please let us know. If the claim can be substantiated, the organization will be excluded from future editions of *Everything Civil War*.

Willow Creek Press of Washington, P.O. Box 3730, Silverdale, WA 98383

Introduction

Welcome to the first edition of **Everything Civil War**. A brief explanation of this book, how it was put together, and how to use it is in order. Willow Creek Press of Washington sent out requests for information to over 1,000 Civil War companies, parks, museums, organizations, associations, and various federal, state, and private archival sources. Of these requests, some were returned as undeliverable. The final result, however, was over 550 descriptive write-ups of products, places of interest, archival sources, and organizations, plus over 200 illustrations.

It is the policy of the **Everything Civil War** staff to include only those enterprises which responded to our request for information, *with one exception*. At the end of the *Places of Interest* section, we've added those museum, parks, and other sites which *did not* respond to our request. We've included their names and latest address information as a service to our readers, but, without a response, we cannot be sure that the information is correct.

The **Products & Services** section identifies companies and organizations which offer Civil War-related products and services. Below the address of each company is a product list that identifies the type of products and services offered by the company. This list is not meant to be all-inclusive, but instead, it identifies the *primary* products and services offered by each company. Many companies, especially sutlers, offer products that are not listed in their write-up. This was done because of space constraints. With the extensive inventories of many of the companies in this book, it would take too much space to list every single item.

At the end of the **Products & Services** section is the **Products & Services QuickFind Index**. This index takes each category of product and service and identifies those companies to which it applies. Keep in mind that products listed can include authentic as well as reproduced items, and in the case of weapons, it can include firing and non-firing, full-size and scaled weapons.

The **Places of Interest** section is also followed by a QuickFind Index. While the **Places of Interest** section is in alphabetic order, the index breaks the section into a state by state listing. The idea was to make it easier to identify museums and other sites by location, particularly if you don't know the name of the site. This way, if you're going to Tennessee on vacation (or business), you can quickly identify those sites in Tennessee that you may not have otherwise known about.

The rest of the book is pretty much self-explanatory. If you're having trouble finding something, you can always refer to the Master Index at the back of the book. It's here that you'll locate products like *Civil War Times Illustrated* (under Magazines). The Master Index is particularly helpful in this case because *Civil War Times Illustrated* is not listed in the **Products & Services** section under its own name, but under the publisher's name (Cowles Magazines). When in doubt, use the Master Index. Also, keep in mind that the Master Index is a key to products, places, and events that are actually *mentioned* in text. Many companies offer the Enfield rifle, but the Master Index points you only to those pages where "Enfield" was directly referenced. This, of course, is typical of all indexes.

Well, that's it. We had a lot of fun putting this book together and hope it leads you to new discoveries and a better appreciation of the events surrounding the Civil War.

Spencer Kope
Editor

*I'd like to say a special **"Thank You"** to all the Civil War companies, organizations, and institutions who helped make this book what it is. There are too many of you to thank individually, so instead, just imagine that after every entry in this book there's a big* **"Thanks for your help and encouragement"** *sprawled across the page. This book is as much your success as it is mine.*

The ***Golden Kepi Award*** was established by Willow Creek Press of Washington to recognize those companies, organizations, and associations which have made significant and lasting contributions to the Civil War community. Eleven recipients were selected for 1996. They are:

Association for the Preservation of Civil War Sites

The APCWS was selected because of the hard-fought battles they have won in the interest of preservation, particularly their recent victory in the fight for Brandy Station.

Civil War News

An invaluable source for thousands of reenactors and Civil War buffs, the Civil War News helps spread the word about upcoming reenactments, shows, and other events, helping the organizers make their events as good as they can be.

Civil War Trust

The Civil War Trust was selected for two reasons. First, they've done a great job putting together the Civil War Discovery Trail and the accompanying guide book. Second, their efforts in developing the Civil War Discovery System deserves special recognition. This system is an interactive, multimedia computer database, which will be located at Civil War sites, beginning with national and state park visitor centers.

Museum of the Confederacy

An exceptional organization that goes beyond simply being a museum. With educational programs and thousands of artifacts (including the White House of the Confederacy), the museum is responsible for bringing the Civil War to countless people who otherwise may not have cared to learn more.

National Park Service

The dedicated civil servants at the National Park Service deserve our thanks and appreciation for their hard work in keeping the parks accessible and enjoyable. They are the force behind stirring and memorable places such as Gettysburg National Military Park.

Pamplin Park

Pamplin Park was selected because they were willing to take a bold step in developing a private sector Civil War site. Federal and state funding for new Civil War sites will always be a challenge. Through efforts like Pamplin Park, additional Civil War sites can be established without government dependency.

Sons of Confederate Veterans
Sons of Union Veterans of the Civil War
Auxiliary to Sons of Union Veterans of the Civil War
United Daughters of the Confederacy

Four outstanding organizations that have contributed to the Civil War community and local communities for decades. Through their education programs, preservation efforts, and memorial services for fallen ancestors, they remind us all of the sacrifices that were made on both sides of the war.

United States Civil War Center

The United States Civil War Center was chosen as a recipient of the Golden Kepi Award for their efforts in bringing the Civil War to the Internet, and for providing what is quickly becoming a national center for Civil War research, discussion, and exchange.

Congratulations to all!

Future **Golden Kepi Award** recipients will be selected prior to the publication of each new edition of **Everything Civil War** (about every two year).

Editor's Choice

The Editor's Choice section of *Everything Civil War* is where I, as your trusted editor, am allowed to tell you about those companies, products, and organizations that I think every Civil War enthusiast should know about. Without wasting sentences on useless chatter, here are my picks.

Internet

Originally, *Everything Civil War* was going to have a special section for Internet addresses. After tossing this around, we decided that an easier approach would be to simply provide the Internet address for the United States Civil War Center at Louisiana State University (http://www.cwc.lsu.edu). This outstanding organization has built an Internet site with over 1,000 links to other Civil War sites. It's amazing the type of information you can access. Needless-to-say, this was an extremely valuable asset in researching this book. For this, I've selected the United States Civil War Center as an Editor's Choice Selection.

United States Civil War Center can be found on page 216

Civil War Round Tables

If you're looking for a Civil War Round Table to join, or thinking of starting your own Round Table, consider contacting Civil War Round Table Associates in Little Rock, Arkansas. Founded in 1968 by Jerry Russell, CWRT Associates is an umbrella organization that serves as a national "informational clearing house" for Civil War Round Tables and related groups. Though all Round Tables are locally autonomous, most of the 200+ active groups are members of CWRT Associates.

Civil War Round Table Associates can be found on page 192

Preservation

Two groups spring to mind when I think preservation. These are the Civil War Trust and the Association for the Preservation of Civil War Sites (APCWS). Both are outstanding and contribute greatly toward the preservation of our Civil War sites.

Civil War Trust can be found on page 195
APCWS can be found on page 187

Music

I'm not much of a country/western music fan, but I loved *Confederate Man*, the latest release from The Rebelaires. My favorite song was *Rebel Yell* - it made me tingle. You have to love something that makes you tingle, right? Check them out.

The Rebelaires can be found on page 73

Newspapers

When it comes to current events information (Civil War News) about the Civil War, there are a number (Civil War News) of publications that provide great coverage (Civil War News) of upcoming reenactments, shows, and other events (Civil War News), and though I'm not bias (Civil War News), I have to say that Civil War News is one of the finest sources of current events information available. I look forward to receiving my copy every month. But that's just my impartial opinion.

Civil War News can be found on page 29

Civil War Site Guides   *Editor's Choice* SELECTION

When it comes to locating interesting Civil War sites in your state or in other states you plan to visit, I can recommend two sources. You're reading the first source, which provides descriptive write-ups of *staffed* Civil War locations. Everything Civil War provides information on over 160 museums, battlefields, and other staffed Civil War sites. But since you already know that, I'll stop wasting your time and move to source number two; The Official Guide to the Civil War Discovery Trail, offered through The Civil War Trust. This is a great book that provides information on over 400 sites in 24 States. The Guide provides information on both staffed and unstaffed locations (such as cemeteries, monuments, and marked Civil War locations). An excellent reference!

The Civil War Trust can be found on page 195

Archives   *Editor's Choice* SELECTION

I've selected the U.S. Army Military History Institute as my Editor's Choice for archives and research. The institute is a treasure trove of invaluable Civil War research material. More importantly, they stress that they are a public institute and are eager to help visitors in their research efforts.

The U.S. Army Military History Institute can be found on page 246

> *Those are my picks. I hope you find them useful.*
>
> *Spencer Kope*
> Editor

Products&Services

An alphabetical listing of Civil War-related products and services

A & K Historical Art

P.O. Box 6521
Hamden, CT 06517
Phone: (203) 562-5212
Information/Orders: 1-800-286-3084

Product(s): Art

A & K Historical Art offers new issue and secondary market limited edition art. They have a large inventory of Civil War, military, and historical prints by leading artists such as Gallon, Kunstler, Neary, Rocco, Stivers, Strain, Troiani, and others. They'll even conduct searches for hard to find prints.

Abraham Lincoln Book Shop Inc.

357 West Chicago Avenue
Chicago, IL 60610
Phone: (312) 944-3085
Fax: (312) 944-5549

Product(s): Art, Books, CDVs, Lincolniana, Paper, Photographs, Statuary

Whether collecting Lincoln memorabilia, or autographs, letters, photos, and diaries of Civil War generals, The Abraham Lincoln Book Shop Inc. offers one of the most impressive selections of collectibles you will find. Browse through one of their catalogs and you will find documents signed by the likes of Abraham Lincoln, U.S. Grant, William T. Sherman, J.E.B. Stuart, R.E. Lee, Joshua Chamberlain, Jefferson Davis, and the list goes on. With 2-4 catalogs a year, each completely different from the last, your biggest problem will be whittling down your "gotta-have-it" list.

Photo Courtesy of Abraham Lincoln Book Shop Inc.

If you order a catalog, plan on spending some time looking through it. A sample catalog we examined had 745 items listed and described in detail. For example, item 492—one of the shorter entries—reads:

(1860 Campaign) Gilt stamped-metal campaign pin, in the shape of an axe; lettered on the helve "Honest Abe" and on the axe-head, in script, "The rail splitter." These pins were made in other varieties, one w/ "Wide Awake" on the helve in honor of that famed Lincoln campaign organization; this one, of course, utilizes Lincoln's best known nickname/images. Approx. 1-1/4 inches long; hinged pin and clasp on reverse.

Some wear to gilt but fundamentally fine and bright; a delightful campaign relic - and rare!
$1,250.00

This is just one example of the collectibles you will find in Abraham Lincoln Book Shop catalogs. They also offer items from the Black Hawk War, from other noted personalities (e.g. signatures from famous individuals like Daniel Boone or Albert Einstein, even a signed note from Helen Keller), and Americana in general. Prices range from under $20 into the thousands, offering something for every level of collector.

Catalog: $5 single copy
$15 two years (2-4 catalogs a year)

Aclamon Music

P.O. Box 10098
Rochester, NY 14610
Phone: (716) 654-9637
Fax: (716) 654-6613

Product(s): Music

Aclamon Music's release, "Battle Cry of Freedom," by Don Laird, is a beautifully performed collection of 19th century songs—plus a few newer tunes composed by Laird, which capture the spirit of the 19th century. Twenty-two songs are on the recording, including: *Sweet Bye and Bye, Johnny Get Your Gun, The Battle Cry of Freedom, Shall We Gather at the River, Santa Lucia, The Yellow Rose of Texas, Amazing Grace, Red River Valley,* and others. The CD jacket for "Battle Cry of Freedom" presents a short history for each piece. For example, the history of "Johnny Get Your Gun" reads: "like many good 19th century popular songs, this one, written under the pseudonym 'F. Belasco' by NYC newspaper

Photo Courtesy of Aclamon Music

reporter Monroe Rosenfeld, was later 'adaptively reused' in 1917 by none other than George F. Cohan. Cohan adapted the verses for his popular World War I tune 'Over There.'" This song's history continues for another paragraph.

Aclamon Music offers another collection of 19th century songs performed by Don Laird, titled "Grandfather's Clock."

Songs in this collection include: *Grandfather's Clock, When You and I Were Young, The Drunken Sailor, Oh My Darling Clementine,* and others.

Great music for anyone interested in a well-rounded collection of 19th cen-tury tunes. Current prices are $15 for CD, $10 for cassette. Orders can be placed di-rectly with Aclamon Music or through the Dynamic Record Store on the Internet (http://www.dynrec.com),or call Dynamic's toll-free at 1-800-816-4262.

Tim Allen

1429 Becket Rd.
Eldersburg, MD 21784
Phone: (410) 549-5145

Product(s): Hats

Tim Allen's period slouch hats are starting to show up just about everywhere; on actors portraying Confederate soldiers in the series *"Civil War Journal,"* on back-ground actors in movies such as *Gettysburg* and *Andersonville,* and at reenactments ev-erywhere.

Each hat is hand-blocked using only fur felt blanks. Hats are lined using 100% cotton thread and 100% polished cotton material. Mr. Allen has researched several labels from period hat makers which can be added to liners for more authentic-ity. Sweatbands are either pigskin leather or painted canvas. All hats are hand-sewn and made to order.

Amazon Drygoods

2218 East 11th Street
Davenport, IA 52803
Phone: (319) 322-6800
Fax: (319) 322-4003
Orders: 1-800-798-7979
Consultations: (319) 322-4138

Product(s): Accouterments, Books, Blankets, Brass, Clothing, Fabric, Fans, Flags, Footwear, Games, Glass, Hats, Instruments (Music), Millinery Findings, Music, Newspapers, Patterns, Tinware, Toi-letries, Toys, Woodenware, and more

The three catalogs available from Amazon Drygoods are packed with items of interest to the Civil War community. The Pattern Catalog illustrates 1,123 authentic patterns for men, women, children, and dolls. These patterns range from Medieval through 1950 with a heavy emphasis on

Photo Courtesy of Amazon Drygoods

Amazon Drygoods owner Janet Burgess and her husband Milan model a selection of their clothing

the Victorian and Edwardian eras. The 95-page General Catalog includes items such as shoes, stockings, garters, corsets, fabric, clothing, hoopskirts, fans, hats, millinery, toi-letries, tools & more for needlework, print-ing art, household & domestic matters, sten-cils & stained glass, woodenware, glass, tin-ware, brass, books (over 1,200), music, instru-ments, music arrangements, flags, toys, cookbooks, paper dolls, belts, buckles, buttons, and much more. The shoe catalog offers 158 styles of historic reproduction footwear from all eras, including Victorian.

General Catalog: $3
Shoes and Boots Catalog: $5
Patterns Catalog: $7

American Epic Studio

Karl Anderson, Sculptor
241 N. Stratton Street
P.O. Box 3994
Gettysburg, PA 17325
Phone: (717) 337-1814
Email: ka-epic@cvn.net

Product(s): Statuary

The work of Sculptor Karl Anderson is offered through American Epic Studio. Offerings include limited edition statuettes, portraits in relief, and busts in traditional bronze or cold cast bronze. These exceptional pieces of art were inspired by Karl's passion for military history and for the Civil War in particular. In 1994 he moved his studio to Gettysburg, Pennsylvania where he pursues sculpting full time. In our correspondence, Karl expressed his desire to produce accurate and moving sculptures. From what we've seen, he has succeeded on both counts. Write, call, or E-mail American Epic Studio for a free update of Karl's latest releases.

"The Pride of the South"

The American Historical Foundation

1142 West Grace Street
Richmond, VA 23286-0858
Phone: (804) 353-1812
Orders: 1-800-368-8080
Internet: http://www.ahfrichmond.com

Product(s): Collectibles

If you've ever opened the cover of a Civil War or historical magazine—as I'm sure you have, based on the exquisite taste and obvious intelligence you displayed when you purchased *Everything Civil War*—then you've no doubt noticed the advertisements for various pistols and rifles offered by The American Historical Foundation. These high-end collectibles come in limited numbers, usually ranging from 250 to 1000, and honor heroes of the North and

South with strikingly beautiful craftsmanship that will take center-stage wherever displayed. The pistols and rifles offered by The American Historical Foundation are fully functional and have been proof fired. And though average prices are between $2000 and $4000 dollars, the Foundation does offer payment terms which will make your purchase easier.

I have a particular weakness for the LeMat pistol and was impressed with The American Historical Foundation's "General J.E.B. Stuart" LeMat pistol in a limited edition of 500. In addition to firearms, the Foundation occasionally offers limited edition, reproduction "glass plate" portraits of Civil War generals. Their most recent promotion is the "Lee at Evelynton Plantation." Write or call The American Historical Foundation for more information on their beautiful line of products.

American Military Antiques

Courtney B. Wilson & Associates
8398 Court Avenue
Historic Ellicott City, MD 21043
Phone: (410) 465-6827

Product(s): Accouterments, Artifacts, Insignia, Paper, Uniforms, Weapons & Accessories

Appraisers and dealers in fine 18th and 19th Century Military Americana. Civil War is their specialty, particularly firearms, swords, accouterments, uniforms, insignia, letters, documents, personal memorabilia, and relics. Items from the American Revolution through 1900 are also kept in stock.

Appraisals of single items and collections are held in the strictest confidence. Highest prices are paid for single items and entire collections. Confederate material is especially sought.

American Social History and Social Movements

4025 Saline Street
Pittsburgh, PA 15217
Phone: (412) 421-5230
Fax: (412) 421-0903

Product(s): CDVs, G.A.R., Lincolniana, Memorabilia, Paper, Photographs

Though not exclusively Civil War, American Social History and Social Movements publishes a fully illustrated mail/phone/fax auction catalog twice per year (usually in June and December) which typically contains more than three dozen lots of interest to Civil War collectors.

Catalog: $30 (3 issues/18 months)

An Early Elegance

39 N. Washington Street
Gettysburg, PA 17325
Phone: (717) 338-9311

Product(s): Boxes, Buttons, Collectibles, Fabric, Lanterns

Specializing in American made items and authentic reproductions, An Early Elegance offers products for the gentleman or lady reenactor. Writing boxes, camp chairs, ammunition boxes, wool, cotton, brocades, buttons, lanterns, and other items are available. The shop is open seven days a week, it's easy to locate and away from the crowds. A swatch book is available for $2.50, and a free product guide is available if you send a large, self-addressed stamped envelope.

The Antique Center of Gettysburg

7 Lincoln Square
Gettysburg, PA 17325
Phone: (717) 337-3669

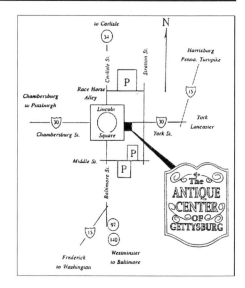

Product(s): Art, Artifacts, Books, Collectibles, Memorabilia

The Antique Center of Gettysburg is actually composed of 85 showcases which feature fine antiques and collectibles. The center represents dealers from ten states and is conveniently located on Lincoln Square. Closed on Tuesdays.

Appalachian Art Stamps

P.O. Box 1405
Norcross, GA 30091-1405
Phone: (770) 962-2669
Fax: (770) 962-2669
Email: Aplchnarts@aol.com

Product(s): Rubber Stamps

If you want to dress up your correspondence, a newsletter, envelopes, or just about anything else, consider a Civil War stamp from Appalachian Art Stamps. Prices range from $4.95 to $8.25—a fraction of the cost of custom-made stamps, which typically run $25 and up. The company's catalog "The Heritage Collection" offers a decent selection, including the Confederate Seal and the United States of America War Office seal. Stamps of various personalities are available, as well as a variety of eagles, cannons, flags, and others. Stamp accessories are available, including ink pads and special stamping paper (note cards, bookmarks, gift tags, envelopes, etc.).

Catalog: FREE

Archive Arts

P.O. Box 2455
Fallbrook, CA 92088
Phone: (619) 723-2119
Fax: (619) 723-2119

Product(s): Computer Software (Clipart)

Archive Arts currently offers eight editions (450 illustrations) of Civil War clipart.

Selected for the quality and uniqueness of the original artists' work, each image was scanned at 300 dots-per-inch (dpi), allowing the image to be scaled while maintaining high resolution.

Civil War Editions Include:
Edition 31: Civil War Leaders
Edition 32: Civil War Scenes
Edition 48: Civil War Battle Scenes

Edition 49: Civil War Battle Scenes
Edition 51: Iron Clads and The Navies
Edition 52: Maps of The American Civil War

Available in .PCX, .TIF, or .WPG file formats for IBM-compatible PCs, or .TIFF file format for MacIntosh.

Armistead Civil War Collections, Ltd.

8306 Wilshire Blvd., Suite 684
Beverly Hills, CA 90211
Phone: (310) 280-3507
Fax: (310) 472-6081

Product(s): Art, Paper

An extremely rare ink and oil masterpiece, probably completed in 1864

Armistead Civil War Collections, Ltd., based in Beverly Hills, California, offers a variety of exceptional Civil War maps and authentic 19th century Civil War related art. Examples include an exceedingly rare ink and oil image of General Robert E. Lee in full dress uniform. Painted circa 1864, this masterpiece is the only known example. It is being offered for $55,000. Map and art prices start at several hundred dollars and venture into the tens of thousands. These high end collectibles are perfect for those looking for a crown jewel to place at the forefront of their Civil War collection.

Arsenal Artifacts

486 West Main Street
Sylva, NC 28779
Phone: (704) 586-1061

Product(s): Art, Artifacts, Bullets, Buttons, Clothing, Dug Items, Weapons & Accessories

Arsenal Artifacts and Prints offers a large selection of dug artifacts and limited edition prints. Dug artillery shells are a specialty. They disarm some artillery shells and perform professional electrolysis.

Custom framing is another house specialty (using only acid-free products) and a wide selection of art is available from artists such as Michael Gnatek, Dale Gallon, Rick Reeves, Mort Kunstler, Dan Nance, Jeremy Scott, Robert Summers, and others. Call to have your name placed on their mailing list.

Associated Video Productions

2511 Kingswood Drive, Suite K
Marietta, GA 30066-6256
Phone: (770) 425-1530
Fax: (770) 425-0392
Email: kone@vivid.com

Product(s): Video

Mastering Reenacting by Associated Video Productions is the first video I would want to see if I were new to the world of reenacting. And if I was an experienced reenactor ... well, I'd watch it again. The most impressive aspect of the video is the depth of knowledge displayed by the presenters. Both the Union and the Confederate reenactor knew their gear and were passionate about their impression. The result is a video that almost anyone can learn from.

Mastering Reenacting sells for $24.95, plus $4 shipping and handling.

Barry'd Treasure

P.O. Box 16569
Louisville, KY 40256
Phone: (502) 448-8772
Internet:
  http://www.iglou.com/btreasure/

Product(s): Accouterments, Artifacts, Artillery, Books, Bullets, Camp Relics, Cartridges, Dug Items

Excellent web site. Barry does a lot of business through the Internet and, because of this, he offers a nice illustrated catalog on-line. You can easily view available stock and keep current as he adds new items to his inventory. Just another fine reason to join the cyber community and take a ride on the information super highway.

Baton Rouge Arsenal

P.O. Box 40512
Baton Rouge, LA 70835
Phone: (504) 667-1861

Product(s): Cannon, Carriages, Gatling Guns

Rod Pyatt founded Baton Rouge Arsenal with the goal of producing the strongest tubes on the market, great carriages, limbers, etc., and providing these at a price that makes them more affordable, even for people on a limited budget. Baton Rouge Arsenal does not limit its products to the more popular gun tubes, but will custom build any piece the customer desires. Every full-scale tube is machined from a solid billet of 1018-grade carbon steel which is blind-bore gun-drilled to the ap-

propriate diameter and depth. Cast iron is never used. Gun tubes are available in both standard smoothbore for reenacting, display, etc., or as rifled competition bores.

Baton Rouge Arsenal also manufactures carriages, kits, cannon hardware, and the Model 1 Gatling Revolving Battery Gun – the patent model Gatling Gun. This is a fully functional .50 caliber brass and steel reproduction of Richard J. Gatling's original gun.

Send SASE for standard price sheet

A fine example of Baton Rouge Arsenal's craftsmanship

Battlefields Revisited

P.O. Box 231
New Cumberland, PA 17070

Service(s): Research

Battlefields Revisited offers a number of research services for those interested in tracing their Civil War ancestors. These services include searches for pension records, military records, regimental histo- ries, complete searches, and other customer specific research. Most research is offered at a fixed price, such as $45 for a military records search, which would include available muster rolls, medical records, and POW information. Additional research is available at an hourly rate. A brochure is available with current rates and includes a simple form for submitting your search request.

Bellinger's Military Antiques

P.O. Box 76371-WC
Atlanta, GA 30358
Phone: (404) 252-0267

Product(s): Accouterments, Belts & Buckles, Books, Weapons & Accessories

Bellinger's Military Antiques is a full-time dealer of antique firearms, edged weapons, belt plates, leather goods, scarce books & miscellaneous items from the 17th through the 19th century, with the American Civil War being a specialty.

Catalog: $10 a year (4 issues) or $3 for a single issue.

Brian & Maria Green, Inc.

P.O. Box 1816
Kernersville, NC 27285-1816
Phone: (910) 993-5100
Fax: (910) 993-1801

Product(s): Paper

Brian & Maria Green offer a nice selection of autographs, signed letters and documents, diaries, signed books, and currency. A recent catalog included signatures (on letters, note cards, etc.) from Confederate Generals P.G.T. Beauregard, Breckinridge, R.E. Lee, N.B. Forrest, Jubal Early, James Longstreet, J.E.B. Stuart, and CSA President Jefferson Davis. Union Generals included Anderson, Burnside, Butterfield, Garfield, Halleck, Hancock, Hooker, McClellan, Meade,

Sheridan, Sherman, Sykes, Webb, and many more. All material is guaranteed to be genuine.

Catalog: $5 per year (4 issues)   **Stonewall Jackson signature**

Brigade Bugler

P.O. Box 165
Pitman, NJ 08071

Product(s): Music (bugle calls)

Brigade Bugler offers a book and cassette tape of 49 bugle calls, including written and verbal explanations of each.

Also included are spoken commands, a brief history of the bugle and the calls, and actual accounts and anecdotes by Civil War Soldiers. The cost of the book and cassette tape is $19.95 (postage paid).

Butternut and Blue

3411 Northwind Road
Baltimore, MD 21234
Phone: (410) 256-9220
Fax: (410) 256-8423

Product(s): Books

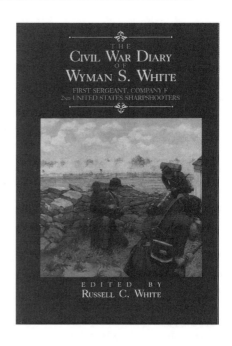

With an extensive inventory of in-print and out-of-print books, as well as over 50 titles of its own, Butternut and Blue is an excellent source for your research and literary needs. Five or six comprehensive Civil War catalogs are issued each year, offering scarce titles, as well as the most recent publications. In addition to the regular book list, two Civil War series are currently being offered by Butternut and Blue. The *Army of the Potomac Series* (APS) contains 13 titles which include reprints of hard-to-find classic regimentals, memoirs, letter collections, and biographies. The *Army of Northern Virginia Series* (ANV) is similar to the APS and contains six titles. These series are published by Butternut and Blue and, based on the sample book we examined, promise to be handsome, high-quality books. Anyone ordering from the Butternut and Blue catalog will be included in future mailings at no charge.

Catalog: $2 within the U.S., $5 foreign

Camp Chase Publishing Company, Inc.

240 Seventh Street
P.O. Box 707
Marietta, OH 45750
Phone: (614) 373-1865
Fax: (614) 374-5710
Email: civilwar@campchase.com
Internet: http://nemesis.cybergate.net/
~civilwar

Product(s): Magazines

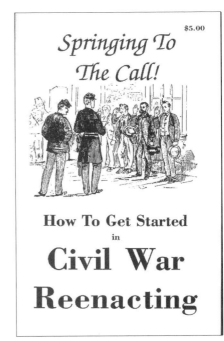

$5.00

Springing To The Call!

How To Get Started in Civil War Reenacting

The Camp Chase Publishing Company, Inc., publishes two important magazines and a handbook. Their flagship publication is the *Camp Chase Gazette*, known and loved by countless reenactors. This 68-page magazine is published ten times per year and contains a wealth of information vital to the Civil War reenactor. Over 350 Civil War events were listed during 1995. *The Citizens' Companion*, a 40-page magazine, is Camp Chase Publishing Company's second magazine. Published six times per year, this magazine serves the particular needs of those who participate in Civil War reenacting as civilians. Articles focus on the material culture of the mid-19th century, social customs, and life on the home front during the Civil War. *Springing To The Call* is Camp Chase's 36-page handbook which provides information to those who are interested in becoming a reenactor. Chapters cover topics such as the history of reenacting, how reenacting is organized, description of a typical reenacting event, various types of impressions, tips on finding just the right unit for you in your area of the country, where, when, and how to buy your gear, plus useful lists of organization contacts and equipment suppliers. *First Impressions* is the 36-page handbook that serves as the civilian version of *Springing To The Call*. Handbooks sell for $5.00 each, postpaid.

Subscriptions:
Camp Chase Gazette - $24 per year
The Citizens' Companion - $20 per year

Camp Pope Bookshop

P.O. Box 2232
Iowa City, IA 52244
Phone: (319) 351-2407
Fax: (319) 339-5964
Orders: 1-800-204-2407
Internet: http://members.aol.com/
ckenyoncpb/index.htm

Product(s): Books, Newsletters

Another fine Civil War publisher. Reprints available include: *The Lyon Campaign in Missouri*, *With Fire and Sword*, and *Reminiscences of the Twenty-Second Iowa Volunteer Infantry*. Camp Pope Bookshop car-

Camp Pope

25

Bookshop

ries an extensive line of regional books (Iowa, Missouri, the Trans-Mississippi, and Western Theater) from other publishers.

Not ones to shrink from duty, the Camp Pope Bookshop also publishes the Trans-Mississippi News (a quarterly newsletter).

Book Catalog: FREE
Newsletter: $15 year (four issues)

Campaign Tours
435 Newbury Street
Danvers, MA 01923
Phone: 1-800-343-6768

Service(s): Battlefield Tours

Campaign Tours offered a number of enticing tour packages for 1996, including "The First Stride of the Giant," which explored the opening of McClellan's Peninsula Campaign; "The Confederate Invasion of New Mexico," which takes participants to places like Fort Craig and Glorieta Pass; "Nathan Bedford Forrest: The Wizard of the Saddle;" and "The Campaign for Atlanta," among others.

Interestingly, Campaign Tours is headquartered in Danver, Massachusetts, formerly known as Salem Village. It's not surprising then, that they also offer a tour called "The Devil Hath Been Raised: Witch Hunt in 1692 Salem." When I first saw the title I thought someone was alluding to General Nathan Bedford Forrest again. My mistake.

Call or write for information on upcoming tours.

Cannon Ltd.
2414 Bethel Church Road
Coolville, OH 45723
Phone: (614) 667-6896

Product(s): Cannon

Photo Courtesy of Cannon Ltd.

First, let me just say that there is nothing "limited" about Cannon Limited. Whether you're looking for a full scale 1-pounder bronze swivel gun, a full scale 24-pounder Coehorn Mortar, or anything in between, chances are that Cannon Ltd. can fill your needs. All barrels (except the poured, solid bronze models) have seamless D.O.M. steel liners. Bronze tubes are cast from solid ingots of #225 bronze, yielding a casting of uniform quality. Keep in mind that even though bronze tube casting costs 3 times as much as iron, the appearance and safety of a bronze tube is significantly better than that of iron.

Aside from their extensive line of artillery, Cannon Ltd offers a selection of artillery books, implements, and accessories.

Catalog & 2-hour Video:
$12 U.S. ($14 to Canada, $15 to other foreign addresses)

Canon Prints

P.O. Box 45
Canonsburg, PA 15317
Phone: (412) 746-1573
Orders: 1-800-303-6086

Product(s): Art

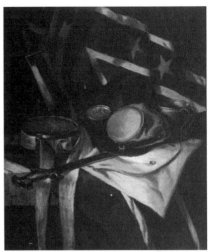

"Southern Glory" by James M. Sulkowski

Canon Prints features the work of award-winning artist James M. Sulkowski, creator of such work as *Civil War Memories*, *Southern Glory*, and *My Brother, My Son*. Though his passion is the Civil War, Mr. Sulkowski's artistic endeavors cover a much broader spectrum, including still lifes, landscapes, contemporary portraits, and sculptures. His works grace numerous private and public collections in the U.S. and abroad, including that of President & Mrs. George Bush.

Cantrell, Isaac & Company

Chas. A. Cantrell
933 Westedge Drive
Tipp City, OH 45371
Phone: (513) 667-3379
Email: CAC309@aol.com

Product(s): Clothing, Haversacks, Uniforms

Cantrell & Company offers historically accurate, museum-quality uniforms and clothing for the Confederate enlisted man. They specialize in Western Theatre uniforms, but also offer the Richmond Depot Type II Jacket and Richmond Depot trousers. Their clothing is constructed with all the visible stitching done by hand. Linings, collars, and cuffs are sewn by hand. All top-stitching and buttonholes are hand-done. All garments are patterned after originals and all jeans and satinet, and most cottons are woven on original period looms.

Catalog and fabric samples: $2

Caps & Kepis

2665 Longfellow Drive
Wilmington, DE 19808
Phone: (302) 994-6428

Product(s): Belts & Buckles, Clothing, Hats, Haversacks, Uniforms

Photo Courtesy of Caps & Kepis

Don't let the name fool you, Caps & Kepis does more than just hats. They offer distinctive, custom-made Civil War uniforms and period civilian attire, plus accouterments such as a soldier's billfold, carpet bag, cap pouch, and cartridge box and sling. Forage caps and kepis are the house specialties.

Catalog: $2

23

CARA

P.O. Box 302
West Nyack, NY 10994

Product(s): Collectibles

Photo Courtesy of CARA

Necessity is the mother of invention, or so the saying goes. Either way, CARA deserves a word of praise for identifying a Civil War need and filling it. Their Civil War stamp frames are the perfect solution for displaying the U.S. Postal Service Civil War series of stamps. Each frame (they come in pewter or brass-colored metal) has a celluloid front and back to protect the stamp from damage. The frame backing offers an unobstructed view of the descriptive text on the back of each stamp. Because of their size and their built-in stands, these frames can be displayed just about anywhere.

Carole Thompson Fine Photographs

1515 Central Avenue
Memphis, TN 38104
Phone: (901) 278-2741
Fax: (901) 726-5533
Email: ctfp@ix.netcom.com

Product(s): Photographs

Specialists in vintage Southeastern American photography of the 1860s, including the works of Alexander Gardner, Timothy O'Sullivan, and others. Carole Thompson buys, sells, and appraises. By appointment only.

Photo Courtesy of Carole Thompson

Cartridges Unlimited

Mike Watson, Sutler
4320-A Hartford Street
St. Louis, MO 63116
Phone: (314) 664-4332

Product(s): Boxes, Cartridges, Hardtack

No matter what your ammunition requirements are, Cartridges Unlimited is sure to have what you need. Whether you need blanks, dummy cartridges (made with railroad ballast), or live rounds, they can fill your order. Union and Confederate labels are available, as are ammunition boxes, cast bullets, tubes (with or without wadding), and souvenir items. Cartridges Unlimited even offers a number of miscellaneous items, including hardtack, cigars, matches (5 different labels), nitrate paper, and more.

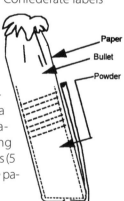

Paper
Bullet
Powder

Artwork Courtesy of Cartridges Unlimited

Cavalier Shoppe

205 East Calhoun
Bruce, MS 38915
Orders: 1-800-227-5491

Product(s): Belts & Buckles, Clothing, Flags, Hats, Videos

The Cavalier Shoppe has a great catalog filled with T-shirts, hats, ties, skirts, buckles, socks, clocks, golf balls, lamps, pins, flags, even peanut brittle – all with a Confederate theme. They also have memo pads, scratch pads, and bookmarks with Confederate Treasury notes on one side—a great way to get someone's attention.

Gift Certificates are available.

WARNING TO ALL YANKS: The Confederate clothing and novelty items in the Cavalier Shoppe's catalog are extremely tempting and may create an urge to secede. Be strong. Join with other such afflicted souls and start a support group. You can then wear your Confederate T-shirts, hats, and buckles to support group meetings and no one will be the wiser.

Cavalry Regimental Supply

P.O. Box 64394
Lubbock, TX 79464
Fax: (806) 798-8867

Product(s): Footwear

Offering cavalry footwear for periods ranging from the Renaissance to the present, Cavalry Regimental Supply's Civil War period footwear includes the J.E.B. Stuart Style Hip Boot, the 1861 Model Cavalry Boot, the 1862 Model Cavalry Knee Boot, the 1840 style Dragoon Ankle Boot, and the 1859 Jefferson Boot.

Artwork Courtesy of Cavalry Regimental Supply

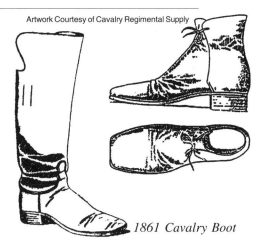

1861 Cavalry Boot

Catalog: $2

Centennial General Store

Servant & Company
230 Steinwehr Ave.
Gettysburg, PA 17325
Phone: (717) 334-9712
Fax: (717) 334-7482
Orders: 1-800-GETTYS-1
Voice Mail: (717) 337-5082
Internet: http://www.servantandco.com

Product(s): Accouterments, Belts & Buckles, Books, Buttons, Camp Gear, Canteens, Clothing, Fabric, Flags, Footwear, Games, Hats, Haversacks, Insignia, Instruments, Jewelry, Lanterns, Pipes, Tents, Tinware, Toys, Uniforms, Weapons & Accessories

One of the finest catalogs available for Civil War reproductions is Servant & Company's Centennial General Store catalog. This nicely illustrated catalog contains two sections (or two separate catalogs, depending how you look at it). On one side you'll find an excellent assortment of uniforms and military accouterments. On the other side you'll find lady's things.

The list of military reproductions available through Servant & Company is extensive. A partial listing includes: bayonets, brass hat insignia, brass spurs, breast plates, brogans, bull's-eye canteens, bummer hats, C.S.A. buckles, C.S.A. buttons, C.S.A. shoulder boards, cartridge boxes, cavalry boots, chevrons, Civil War clothing patterns, cravats, cross straps, cap boxes, drums, embroidered hat insignia, enamel ware, fifes, flags, frogs, gauntlets, hardee hats, hardtack, hat cords, hat pins, haversack stuffers, haversacks, holsters, jaw harps, kepi hats, knives, musket caps, musket slings, pewter buttons, pistol boxes, pistols, ponchos, rag gloves, rag socks, rifles, sashes, scabbards, slouch hats, state buckles, state buttons, sword belts, swords, tinware, tin whistles, U.S. buckles, U.S. eagle buttons, U.S. shoulder boards, utensils, waist belts, wooden lanterns, and yard goods for uniforms.

Lady's things include: gloves, drawstring bags, fans, chemises, corsets, drawers, under-the-hoop petticoats, stockings, hoop skirts, over-the-hoop petticoats, underskirts, work dresses, day dresses, cloaks, ballgowns, period footwear, jewelry, accessories, outerwear, hats, bonnets, parasols, and much more.

So next time you're in Gettysburg, make time to stop by the Centennial General Store. It's easy to find, just head out of town on Steinwehr Avenue and the store is on your left. If you pass the Civil War Wax Museum on the right, then you've gone too far.

Catalog: $6

Photo Courtesy of Servant & Co.

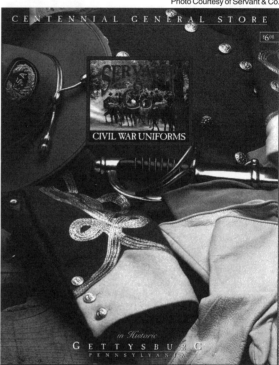

Chilmark

Hudson Creek
321 Central Street
Hudson, MA 01749

Product(s): Collectibles

Exquisite, finely detailed pewter and bronze sculptures are the trademark of Hudson Creek's Chilmark line. The Chilmark Civil War collection includes such works as Francis Barnum's *Rebel Yell*, *The High Tide* (now sold out), *Clashing Sabers*, *The Swinging Gate*, *Last Resort*, and *Confederate Pride*. Write Hudson Creek for a list of dealers in your area and a catalog.

Chris & Jackie's

P.O. Box 717
Dunkirk, MD 20754
Phone: (410) 741-1909

Product(s): Collectibles

Chris & Jackie offer a unique item which will provide the finishing touch to any "Civil War Room." In fact, the decorative light switch plates they make are called "The Finishing Touch." Chris and Jackie have been making decorative light switch plates for five years and expanded their line to include Civil War designs a couple years ago. Their selection is impressive and they can handle custom orders, whether for the individual or for historical societies, reenactment groups, etc. This is another one of those creative ideas I like to trumpet, so if you have a special room for your Civil War items, or if you're just looking for a unique and interesting idea for decorating, give Chris and Jackie a call. Plates range in price from $9.95 to $14.95 (the large triple-switch plates can be made with a single switch-hole to allow for full battle scenes).

Civil War Antiques

David W. Taylor
P.O. Box 87
Sylvania, OH 43560
Phone: (419) 878-8355
Fax: (419) 878-8365

Purveyor of Fine Historical Americana

Product(s): Antiques, Artifacts, Paper

David Taylor buys, sells, and appraises Civil War antiques, artifacts, and paper. Items bought and sold include: quality guns, uniforms, buckles, insignia, flags, drums, letters, diaries, autographs, etc. Catalogs are issued semiannually, or you can visit their shop in Waterville, Ohio – five minutes from Toledo. Call for hours and directions. All items are fully guaranteed.

Photo Courtesy of Civil War Antiques

Catalog subscription: $10 year (two issues)

Civil War Antiquities

P.O. Box 1411
Delaware, OH 43015
Phone: (614) 363-1862

Product(s): Artifacts, Books, Memorabilia

Civil War Antiquities specializes in books covering the Civil War through the Indian Wars. A variety of relics and display cases are also available.
Catalog: FREE

Civil War Artifacts

Dale S. Snair
2737-7 Briarcliff Road, N.E.
Atlanta, GA 30329
Phone: (404) 633-3519
(Phone orders taken after 6:30 p.m.)

Product(s): Artifacts, Photographs

Dale S. Snair offers a quarterly descriptive catalog of original Civil War photographs, documents, letters, books, weapons, and other equipment and accouterments. Civil War photography is a specialty. Catalogs may include a limited selection of militaria from other eras.

Catalog: $3 per year

Civil War Designs

P.O. Box 646
Arvada, CO 80001
Phone: (303) 424-6414
Fax: (303) 424-6414

Embroidered Civil War Apparel

Product(s): Clothing

If you're looking for caps, jackets, or shirts with custom Civil War embroidering, Civil War Designs just might have what you're looking for. They can embroider flags, names of campaigns, individuals, and battles—or customer designs—on your choice of apparel. Their designs have a high stitch count and are made with top quality, colorfast thread on industrial machines.

Civil War Education Center

308 W. College
Roswell, NM 88201

Service(s): Education

The Civil War Education Center offers a series of tests designed to test (and challenge) ones knowledge of the Civil War.

A score of 70 or higher on the initial test (50 questions) will earn an "expert" certificate. Those scoring 90 or better will be allowed to proceed to the next level (senior expert). The truly dedicated can ultimately pursue certification as a "Master Expert." Cost of the initial test is $14.95.

Civil War Labels Unlimited

Paul Wilson
46 Saw Mill Rd.
Springfield, MA 01118

Product(s): Mailing Labels

Spice up your correspondence with personalized labels, customized with an image of your favorite Civil War personality, battlefields, reenactment photo, or badge. A five-page list of personalities and battlefields is available, but since most of the better-known sites and personalities are available you may not need the list. Current cost for a sheet of 30 labels is: Personalities, $5; Battles, $6.50; Battlefield views, $5.50 (postpaid). Be sure to include your name and address as you want it to appear on the labels (Make checks payable to Paul Wilson). For personalized scanning of reenactment photos, etc., please write for information.

List: $1

The Civil War Music Store

13621 Powder River Avenue
Bakersfield, CA 93312
Phone: (805) 589-5544
Internet: http://lsnt7.lightspeed.net/
~cwms/order.htm

Product(s): Music

Offering a selection of U.S.A. and C.S.A. music on compact disc or cassette. An on-line catalog and order form is available on the Internet.

The Civil War News

36 Monarch Hill Road
Tunbridge, VT 05077
Mail:
RR1 Box 36
Tunbridge, VT 05077
Phone: (802) 889-3500
Fax: (802) 889-5627
Orders: 1-800-777-1862

Product(s): Newspapers

The Civil War News is a monthly newspaper produced by a professional staff of writers and photographers. It is the only Civil War current events publication, and gives extensive coverage of battlefield and site preservation issues. Each issue includes a dozen or more book reviews, photo coverage of living history and reenactment programs, a calendar of coming events, letters to the editor, columns on images, preservation, collecting and firearms, as well as numerous news and feature stories and photos. Many Civil War-related products such as books, art, artifacts and collectibles, reproduction reenactor gear and weapons, miniatures, music tapes and videos are advertised, as well as services, tours, seminars, book and relic shows, reenactments, and membership opportunities. The annual subscription rate for 11 issues is $27.00 for U.S., Canada and overseas surface mail ($50 for foreign air mail).

Note: If you are interested in Civil War shows, organizations, reenactments, preservation efforts, or anything else dealing with current Civil War news and events, *The Civil War News* is simply the finest source available. An outstanding newspaper.

—The Editors

Civil War "Things 'n Frames"

P.O. Box 422
Kingston Springs, TN 37082
Phone: (615) 952-3672
Email: Sonny@viponline.com
Internet:
http://www.antiquerow.com/civil/

Product(s): Art, Artifacts, Medical

A country-style store offering Civil War artifacts, prints, medical equipment, and other miscellaneous items. If you're looking for something special, the folks at Civil War "Things 'n Frames" will help you find it.

Civil War Tours of Tennessee, Inc.

P.O. Box 1298
Fairview, TN 37062
Phone: (615) 356-7537

Service(s): Battlefield Tours

Civil War Tours of Tennessee offers daily tours that examine the Battles of Franklin and Nashville, and General John Bell Hood's failed invasion of Middle Tennessee.

Tours depart at 9 am and return around 12:30. All-day trips to Shiloh and Chickamauga Battlefields are also available, as are "step-on" guides for groups traveling on their own bus. Special tours can be arranged to meet the needs of any Civil War enthusiast.

Special tours can be arranged to meet the needs of any Civil War enthusiast.

Collectors Antiquities, Inc.

60 Manor Road
Staten Island, NY 10310
Phone: (718) 981-0973

Product(s): Antiques, Artifacts, CDVs, Memorabilia, Paper

If you succumb easily to temptation, as I do, you may want to hide your credit cards before checking out Collectors Antiquities. They publish three catalogs a year featuring collectibles from the Civil War and other American wars.

Since each catalog is entirely different, it's hard to predict what you'll find— but that's half the fun. The catalog we examined had everything from bugles and Carte-de-Visites (CDVs), to a stick pin commemorating the 50th anniversary of the Battle of Gettysburg and a letter written and signed by President Buchanan.

Layaway is available.

Catalog: $12 a year (3 issues)/$15 overseas
(free to purchasers of $75 or more)

Collector's Armoury

P.O. Box 59, Dept. ECW
Alexandria, VA 22313-0059
Phone: (703) 684-6111
Fax: (703) 683-5486
Orders: 1-800-544-3456 Ext. 515
Internet:
  http://www.armoury.com

Product(s): Belts & Buckles, Bugles, Cannons (miniature, non-firing), Canteens, Flags, Hats, Insignia, Weapons & Accessories (non-firing)

The 1996 Collector's Armoury catalog presents an assortment of reproduction, non-firing pistols, rifles, and miniature cannon. While they have a respectable assortment of Civil War items, they also carry Roman, Viking, Medieval, Old West, and WWII weapons. A large selection of edged weapons is also available.

Catalog: $4

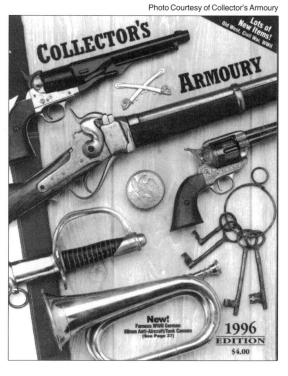

Photo Courtesy of Collector's Armoury

Collector's Library

P.O. Box 263
Eugene, OR 97440
Phone: (503) 937-3348

Product(s): Books

> *...a wide selection of reference books dealing with antique arms and related militaria*

Collector's Library offers a wide selection of reference books dealing with antique arms and related militaria. Available titles include: *American Military Belts and Related Equipment; Serial Numbers of U.S. Martial Arms, Volume 4; Gun Tools: Their History and Identification; Spencer Repeating Firearms; The American Sword 1775-1945; United States Military Saddles, 1812-1942;* and *The Horse Soldier, 1776-1943,* among others. In addition to retail sales, Collector's Library sells to dealers and distributors. Price and ordering information are included with their book list.

Columbia Games, Inc.

P.O. Box 3457
Blaine, WA 98231
Phone: (360) 366-2228
Fax: (360) 366-3313
Orders: 1-800-636-3631

Product(s): Games (historical strategy)

    If you're looking for Civil War trading cards that double as a strategy game, Columbia Games currently offers three designs to choose from: *Dixie: Bull Run, Dixie: Shiloh,* and *Dixie: Gettysburg.* The cards are colorful, well-designed, and highly portable, fitting easily into a shirt or coat pocket. Columbia Games also manufactures board games, including *Bobby Lee* and *Sam Grant.*

Catalog: FREE

Combined Books, Inc.

151 East 10th Ave.
Conshohocken, PA 19428
Phone: (610) 828-2595
Fax: (610) 828-2603
Orders: 1-800-4-1860-65
Email: combined@dca.net.
Internet:
   http://www.dca.net/combinedbooks

Product(s): Books

    One of the more interesting Civil War books on my *already-read-it* shelf is *The Civil War Book of Lists,* by Combined Books. Though, in truth, it doesn't deserve to be classified as an its *already-read-it* book, because I find myself coming back to it again and again, treating it more like a reference book than a list of intriguing facts and figures. Maybe it's time a created a *read-it-again* shelf.

    The Civil War Book of Lists is only one of the many titles available from Com-

bined Books. With over 180 backlist titles and 45 new titles dealing with Military and General History subjects, particularly the Civil War, Combined Books has established itself as a premier publisher. Backlist Civil War titles include: *The Antietam Campaign, The Atlanta Campaign, The Chancellorsville Campaign, The Civil War Notebook, Civil War Quotations, Civil War Sea Battles, Civil War Wordbook, Confederate Monuments at Gettysburg, The Court Martial of Robert E. Lee, General John Buford, The Gettysburg Campaign, Jackson's Valley Campaign, Opening Guns, The Petersburg Campaign, The Shiloh Campaign, The Vicksburg Campaign, War On Two Fronts,* and *The Wilderness Campaign.*

    New Civil War titles include: *In Search of Robert E. Lee, Gettysburg July 1, Civil War Firearms,* and *The Second Bull Run Campaign.*

The Confederate States Armory & Museum

529 Baltimore Street
Gettysburg, PA 17325
Phone: (717) 337-2340

Product(s): Collectibles

Primarily a museum, The Confederate States Armory & Museum also has a quality gift shop where you'll find the best in Civil War collectibles. So come for the museum, but don't forget the gift shop.

See listing under *Places of Interest* for more information.

C.S.A. Confederate States Arsenal

1305 Spring Avenue
Spring Lake, NC 28390
Phone: (910) 960-2466

Product(s): Weapons & Accessories
Service(s): Weapons Restoration

The Confederate States Arsenal deals in Civil War-era antique artillery reproductions, parts and accessory items— including steel or bronze tubes. Restoration work is available for original pieces.

Price List: FREE on request

Confederate States Military Antiques

2905 Government Street
Baton Rouge, LA 70806
Phone: (504) 387-5044

Product(s): Accouterments, Artifacts, Belts & Buckles, Books, Buttons, Dug Items, Leather Goods, Weapons & Accessories

Specializing in Civil War artifacts, Confederate State Military Antiques is open to the public Tuesday through Saturday, of-fering an assortment of muskets, swords, carbines, revolvers, belt buckles, buttons, leather goods, books, maps, and other items of interest to the Civil War collector. A selection of artifacts from the Revolutionary War and other military engagements prior to the Civil War is also available.

Catalog: $10 per year (3 catalogs)

The Confederate Treasury

1100 North Main St.
Tennessee Ridge, TN 37178
Phone: (615) 721-3303
Fax: (615) 721-4155
Orders: 1-800-632-2383 (M-F, 8am-5pm)
Internet: http://confederatetreasury.com

Product(s): Currency

> *This collection includes* all seventy *(Confederate) notes*

The Confederate Treasury has put together a wonderful collection of authentically reprinted Confederate Treasury Notes. This collection includes *all seventy* notes (even the rare ones) printed and issued for the Confederate States Treasury Department (1861-1865). Now everyone can experience the intricate craftsmanship and rich history surrounding these bills.

The notes come nicely displayed in a burgundy leather-look album with gold-foil stamp. The album cover can be personalized with a gold-foil stamp of your name for a modest fee. A great conversation piece. The Confederate treasury album is as educational as it is beautiful. A color brochure is available upon request.

Countryside Prints, Inc.

35 W. Prospect Avenue
Washington, PA 15301
Phone: (412) 228-2461

Product(s): Art

Countryside Prints, Inc., founded in 1980, and solely owned by artist Ray W. Forquer, publishes collector quality, limited edition, offset lithographs. Historical subjects from various time periods, with a special emphasis on the American Civil War, are available. Strict control of the printing process is maintained by the artist. Images are reproduced on the finest papers using superior inks.

Ray Forquer's works have appeared in a variety of magazines, newspapers, and history books. His *Wiskey Rebellion Series* was used to illustrate the PBS television series *America's Battlegrounds* in 1994. Recent works include *Mine Eyes Have Seen the Glory*, a stirring portrait of Lincoln, *The Fight for Sharpshooter's Ridge*, which vividly illustrates the desperate fight at Glorieta Pass in the New Mexico Territory (one of the lesser known battles of the Civil War), *Christmas on the Rappahannock*, and *The Ringgold Cavalry*.

Information available upon request.

Cowles Magazines, Inc.

6405 Flank Drive
Harrisburg, PA 17112-2753
Orders: 1-800-829-3340

Product(s): Magazines

Cowles Magazines is responsible for a number of outstanding magazines, including *Civil War Times Illustrated*, *America's*

Civil War, *American History*, and *Military History*. Best known among these is *Civil War Times Illustrated*, which has earned an ever-expanding readership base because of its outstanding scholarly articles and beautiful original art.

Other magazines published by Cowles which may be of interest to Civil War enthusiasts include *Great Battles*, *Historic Traveler*, and *Wild West*.

Crescent City Sutler
17810 Hwy. 57 N.
Evansville, IN 47711
Phone: (812) 983-4217

A Civil War Store At Your Front Door

Product(s): Accouterments, Artifacts, Belts & Buckles, Blankets, Books, Bugles, Buttons, Camp Gear, Canteens, Clothing, Hardtack, Hats, Haversacks, Insignia, Instruments, Lanterns, Music, Pipes, Tents, Tinware, Uniforms, Weapons & Accessories

Crescent City Sutler's 64-page catalog offers up a treasure chest of museum quality reproduction Civil War uniforms and equipment. Reenactors will find this catalog to be another excellent resource in creating their impression.

Weapons offered include the 1851 Navy Revolver, 1860 Army Revolver, First, Second, and Third Model Dragoons, 1847 Walker Revolver, 1863 Sharps Black Powder Carbine, 1861 Springfield Musket, 1853 3-Band Enfield, and the Remington Model 1863 "Zouave." The selection of sabers includes the M1850 Staff & Field Officer's Sword, M1850 Foot Officer's Sword, U.S. 1860 Cavalry Saber, 1840 Musician's Sword, Texas Dragoon Saber, USN 1861 Naval Cutlass, CSA Froelich Staff Officer's Sword, Confederate N.C.O. Sword, Confederate Foot Officer's Sword, and the Confederate Nashville Plow Works Saber.

A wide variety of insignia, hats, clothing, uniform items, and music add to Crescent City Sutler's impressive line of products. Haversack items such as scissors, a wooden comb, straight razor, pocket knife, Generals playing cards, poke bags, twist tobacco, pipes, bottles, and hardtack are available. Camping essentials include Dog Tents, Wedge or "A" Tents, Wall Tents, Sibley Tents, Skillets, Folding Fire Grill, and others.

Catalog: $3

CSA Galleries, Inc.
2401 Mall Drive, A-4
North Charleston, SC 29406
Phone: (803) 744-1003

Product(s): Art, Collectibles, Uniforms

CSA Galleries features the art of Kunstler, Stiver, Reeves, Gnatek, Phillips, Amirian, J.P. Strain, Troiani, Wilson, Umlbe, Rocco, Gallon, and others. Gifts, collectibles, uniforms, and framing are also available.

Cump and Company

Doris R. McCann
118 Hastings Avenue
Oakdale, PA 15071
Phone: (412) 693-8755

A Newsletter for Friends and Fanciers of General William Tecumseh Sherman

Product(s): Newsletter

Cump and Company is a newsletter devoted entirely to General William T. Sherman. The publication is informal and encourages articles from readers who share an interest in Sherman. Cump and Company is published bimonthly. A free sample copy is available upon request.

Subscription: $12 per year (6 issues)

Dale Gallon Historical Art Gallery

9 Steinwehr Avenue
Gettysburg, PA 17325
Phone: (717) 334-0430
Fax: (717) 334-1017

Product(s): Art

Civil War military history comes alive at Dale Gallon's art gallery. You'll find the complete collection of Mr. Gallon's works, including spectacular battle scenes of Gettysburg and Antietam, captured by Mr. Gallon's talented hands. A knowledgeable staff can help you with any questions you may have from the art itself to the research that went into it.

Catalog: $1

Henry Deeks
Dealer/Historian

P.O. Box 2260
Acton, MA 01720
Phone: (508) 263-1861

Product(s): CDVs

One look at Henry Deeks' sales catalog was enough to convince us that the man is passionate about his work. Specializing in vintage photographic prints of Civil War persons in the Carte-de-Visite (CDV) format, Henry researches each subject thoroughly, adding a sense of familiarity to each face. For example, the description of item #8 in catalog No.12 reads:

Robert H. Walker. Captain. Company "K" 65th Indiana Infantry. Head and shoulder view as 2nd Lieutenant. Inscribed on reverse "Robert" and "taken from life 1863" Wearing slouch hat turned up at side with hint of a device. Clearly seen is hat cord, plume, and on front an infantry device with numerals "65" within. Commissioned and mustered 2nd Lieutenant December 1862. Promoted and commissioned 1st Lieutenant July 1864, mustered September 1864, Promoted and commissioned Captain, September 1864, mustered November 1864, mustered out with regiment [June 1865]. F.W. Knight, photographer, Henderson Ky. Price $150.

With 162 items listed in catalog No. 12 (and two catalogs issued each year), Henry spends a lot of time doing research—to the benefit of his customers. Each described item includes an illustration. All material is unconditionally guaranteed to be genuine and efforts are made to describe defects fully. Material is returnable for any reason within seven days of receipt. Postage is included in the purchase price.

Catalog: FREE

Deer Valley Game Company

P.O. Box 87886
Phoenix, AZ 85080-7886
Internet: http://www.getnet.com/~dvgc

Product(s): Games

SQUARES, the Civil War Battle Game, is currently being offered by Deer Valley Game Company for those interested in a strategy game of military maneuvers and tactics. The game has no dice, no spinners, and no chance cards. Instead of relying on chance, like most games, SQUARES allows you to match wits with your opponent. Deer Valley emphasizes that the game has no complicated rules to memorize, no tables and charts to study. The entire game centers on implementing the principles of maneuver and attack. The game includes 32 game pieces, a 12 x 13½ inch, six-color gameboard, and rules. Price is $24.95 per game, plus $3.50 shipping and handling per game (Arizona residence add 7.05% sales tax).

Different Drummer

Kirk D. Lyons
1112 ½ Montreat Road, Suite 1
P.O. Box 1411
Black Mountain, NC 28711
Phone: (704) 669-0097
Fax: (704) 669-5191
Email: UnreConfed@aol.com

Product(s): Clothing, Photographs, Uniforms
Service(s): Historical Consultation

Different Drummer offers clothing reproductions for men and women for the period 1607-1865, and specializes in Confederate Officer impressions. They are purveyors of quality original Victorian clothing and photographs. Additionally, they provide a consultation service for movie/TV productions, museums, and educational institutions. Their areas of expertise include European and American Military and social history, folk music, dance, militaria, and photography.

Dixie Leather Works

306 N. 7th Street
Paducah, KY 42001-1020
Phone: (502) 442-1058
Fax: (502) 442-1049
Orders: 1-800-888-5183

Purveyors of 19th Century Military Leather Goods

Product(s): Accouterments, Belts & Buckles, Books, Buttons, Currency, Hats, Haversacks, Knapsacks, Leather Goods, Medical, Paper (reproduction), Saddlebags, Trunks, Weapons & Accessories

While Dixie Leather Works specializes—obviously—in leather items, they also have a noteworthy selection of stationery,

Confederate currency, books, weapons, and other interesting items. The Bawdy House Tokens (from houses of ill repute in New Orleans, New York, Atlanta, and Chicago) were particularly interesting. Other unusual items included period nails for box construction, a Jaw Harp, a selection of 19th century tin can labels, reproduction Confederate war bonds, wax impression equipment for sealing documents with your initial, and Civil War camp fire song books.

Dixie Leather Works makes 90% of the leather items in their fully illustrated 68-

page catalog, including 75 hard-to-find items. The products they are most pleased with, and which have been well received throughout the country, are their authentically reproduced folded leather officer sword belts, fine period trunks, and field glass cases. One look at their catalog, however, will tell you they have a great many other products to be proud of as well.

Catalog: $6 (within the U.S.)
$10 (outside the U.S.)

fully illustrated 68-page catalog, including 75 hard-to-find items

Don Meredith's Civil War Art

P.O. Box 370020
Tampa, FL 33697
Phone: (813) 962-1225

Product(s): Art

Don Meredith's Civil War Art (and Wild West Art) presents enthusiasts with the unique opportunity to have their portrait drawn or painted in Civil War theme. Using sharp, ordinary photos, Mr. Meredith can add Civil War uniforms, hats, beards, and an almost limitless variety of settings. The portrait can be done using pencil, pen & ink, colored pencil, watercolor, acrylic, oils, and more. Prices start at $75 and reenactors receive a 15% discount.

Don Meredith also offers a selection of fine art prints, including the original signed and numbered limited edition, "Old Times Are Not Forgotten," shown here. Call or write for a free color brochure.

Photo Courtesy of Don Meredith

Old Times Are Not Forgotten

R. Stephen Dorsey Antique Militaria

P.O. Box 263
Eugene, OR 97440
Phone: (541) 937-3348

Product(s): Accouterments, Artifacts, Belts & Buckles, Leather Care (Pecard), Saddles, Weapons & Accessories

R. Stephen Dorsey deals in U.S. antique militaria, with a heavy emphasis on the Civil War and the Indian War period. Items covered include: guns, edged weapons, accouterments of all kinds, saddles and related equipment, antique ammunition, belts, holsters, cap pouches, cartridge boxes, sabre knots, and others. For those interested in bringing antique leather goods back to life, Mr. Dorsey is a distributor of Pecard Antique Leather Care, a colorless, odorless, museum quality product that moisturizes, softens, and preserves old leather.

As the publisher of *Collector's Library*, Mr. Dorsey also offers a wide selection of reference books dealing with antique arms and related militaria. See the listing under *Collector's Library*.

Du Page Military Flag Company

20 Chester Avenue
Westwood, MA 02026

Product(s): Flags

Du Page Military Flag Company manufactures museum quality flags, many of which have been (or currently are) displayed at an impressive list of government buildings, forts, museums, as well as in the movie "Last of the Mohicans," and in A&E presentations of "Civil War Journal," and "The American Revolution." All flags are individually made to proper specifications for the particular regiment or unit being portrayed. Design and details are based on originals of individual unit colors, or on appropriate representative types where the originals have been lost. A selection of Civil War finials (ornamental caps) is available, including some cast from the original and some made by hand. Since each flag is made to individual specifications, please allow several months for delivery. Quality takes time.

Dyestone Company

320 Dyestone Springs
Hohenwald, TN 38462
Phone: (615) 796-7364

Service(s): Boot Resoling, Leather Repair

With a combined experience of 30 years in the business of restoring cavalry boots and brogans, Dyestone Company is a small company that replicates the original process of soling, complete with lemon wood pegs and old fashioned handstitches. As far as leather repair goes, they've pretty much seen it all, so don't be afraid to ask.

Eastern Muzzleloader Supply

78 Clinton Street
P.O. Box 551
Delaware City, DE 19706
Phone: (302) 836-3488
Fax: (302) 836-8206

Product(s): Accouterments, Leather Goods, Weapons & Accessories

Just about anything the beginning or experienced muzzleloaders might need can be found at Eastern Muzzleloader Supply. Their catalog includes weapons ranging from the 1861 Springfield, cal. 58 rifled musket to the 1858 New Model Army Revolver. Weapon accessories include bayonets and swords, powder flasks/horns, powder, caps, flints, ball pullers, ramrods, bore cleaner, leather goods, bullet molds, nipple wrenches, and sights, plus much more. Eastern Muzzleloader Supply even offers a modest selection of Civil War memorabilia (T-shirts, coffee mugs, and a selection of cassette tapes).

Fall Creek Suttlery

A.J. Fulks
P.O. Box 92
Whitestown, IN 46075
Phone: (317) 482-1861 or 769-5355
Fax: (317) 482-1848
Email: AJF5577@aol.com
Internet: http://www.cybergate.net/
    ~civilwar/falcreek.html
or
A.D. Fulks
P.O. Box 530
Freedom, CA 95019
Phone: (408) 728-1888
Fax: (408) 728-1853

Product(s): Accouterments, Belts & Buckles, Books, Bugles, Buttons, Canteens, Clothing, Eyewear, Footwear, Hats, Haversacks, Insignia, Music, Patterns, Pipes, Tents, Tinware, Uniforms, Video, Weapons & Accessories

In business for over 18 years, Fall Creek Suttlery travels to 30-38 Civil War Reenactments, Civil War Shows, and other living history events each year. There 32-page photo illustrated catalog is packed full of items for the

> *currently reproducing several styles of Civil War-period State buttons*

reenactor and Civil War enthusiast. Many of the items sold by Fall Creek are manufactured in their own facility, or under their control at other facilities, allowing for quality control that insures their strict standards of uniformity and authenticity are met. They are currently reproducing several styles of Civil War-period State buttons heretofore unavailable.

While half their business is done by phone or mail, Fall Creek Suttlery does have a retail outlet, located at 917 E. Walnut Street, Lebanon, IN 46052, where they offer their complete line of products in a convenient, friendly, atmosphere. Hours are Monday through Friday, 9:00 to 4:00. They recommend, however, that you call first.

Illustrated Catalog: $3

Farnsworth House Inn

401 Baltimore St.
Gettysburg, PA 17325
Phone: (717) 334-8838
Fax: (717) 334-5862

Showplace of the Civil War

Product(s): Art, Artifacts, Books, Paper

     Farnsworth House Inn has something for just about everyone. Their catalog is issued three times a year and offers a nice assortment of artifacts (mostly dug items)

and books. The Farnsworth House Civil War Gallery offers works by Troiani and other major Civil War artists. Still, the nicest aspect of the Farnsworth House is its friendly staff—quite common to the hospitable town of Gettysburg.

Also available: A five-room Bed & Breakfast, restaurant, custom framing, and nightly Civil War ghost stories (in-season)

Catalog: $2

Fields of Glory

55 York St.
Gettysburg, PA 17325
Fax: (717) 337-9315
Email: FOGlory@aol.com
Orders: 1-800-517-3382

Product(s): Books, Memorabilia

     Nice selection of books and memorabilia. Conveniently located near Lincoln Square in the heart of Gettysburg.

Catalog: $10 year (12 issues)

First Corps Books

42 Eastgrove Court
Columbia, SC 29212-2404
Phone: (803) 781-2709 (9am - 10pm)

Product(s): Books

     Open by appointment only, First Corps Books specializes in both new and out-of-print material and offers a search service for hard to find volumes. Catalogs are issued four times a year and they attend the major eastern Civil War shows and re-enactments.

Catalog: $2

search service for hard to find volumes

The Flag Guys

283 Windsor Hwy, Dept 311
New Windsor, NY 12553
Phone: (914) 562-0088, ext. 311
Fax: (914) 562-6172 (24 hours)
Hours: Mon-Fri 9-5, Sat 10-2 EST

Product(s): Books, Flags, Hats, Music, Weapons & Accessories

     Whether looking for a reproduction of the Bonnie Blue Flag, the C.S.A. Navy Jack, or the 34-star 1861-1863 Union flag, there's a good chance The Flag Guys have what you want. If you need a custom regimental flag for reenactments or other living history presentations, you can submit a sketch or photo, plus size and finishing details and The Flag Guys will give you a quote. They do ask that you allow 5 - 10 weeks for custom orders, so plan ahead. Good selection of stock flags. Other Civil War-related items you'll find in The Flag Guys' catalog include car antenna flags, stickers, patches, lapel pins, an assortment of books & music cassettes, and Civil War edged weapons. Not bad for a company described as "Very friendly as far as Yankees usually go."

Music selections include several volumes of Civil War songs by Bobby Horton, including tunes such as *The Battle Hymn of the Republic*, *Skedaddle*, *Vicksburg is Taken*, *Virginia's Bloody Soil*, *The Cross of the South*, *Pat Murphy of the Irish Brigade*, and others. Of course, The Flag Guys don't just deal in Civil War items. You'll also find a wide selection of international, state, and specialty flags—plus flag accessories.

Catalog: FREE

Framing Fox Art Gallery

148 Main Street
P.O. Box 679
Lebanon, NJ 08833
Phone: (908) 236-6077
Fax: (908) 236-7088
Orders: 1-800-237-6077

Product(s): Art

Offering signed and numbered limited edition prints, Framing Fox Art Gal- lery handles the works of leading Civil War artists such as Troiani, Kunstler, Gallon, Strain, and others. Layaway is available.

The Gamers

500 W. 4th Street
Homer, IL 61849
Phone: (217) 896-2145
Fax: (217) 896-2880
Orders: 1-888-TGAMERS (toll free)

Product(s): Games

The Gamers offer military histori- cal simulations covering the American Civil War, WWII, and some modern situations. Their Civil War Brigade Series covers sev- eral different battles in separate games. The games are moderately complex and range in size from one to two maps. A quarterly support magazine called *Operations* is also available.

GDR Enterprises

P.O. Box 807
Hollywood, SC 29449
Phone: (803) 889-6360

Purveyors of quality wood furnishings for the field and garrison since 1982.

Product(s): Boxes, Furniture

GDR Enterprises has been producing historically correct wood products of the Civil War and Indian War era since 1982. Products include ammunition boxes, artillery boxes, commissary boxes, regimental desks, traveling chests, Indian war boxes, and Steamboat Bertrand boxes. Appropriate items are stenciled with authentic markings.

Catalog: $2

The General's Armory
61 Debbie Drive
South Windsor, CT 06074

Product(s): Cannon (miniatures, firing), Dioramas, Living History Presentations

The General's Armory offers a selection of miniature cannon (1/10th scale to 1/2 scale) which fire black powder, plus hand-painted decorator cannon miniatures. Civil War dioramas and Union General Living History Presentations are also available.

List: $3 (includes color pictures and is refundable with purchase.)

The Gettysburg Gift Center
297 Steinwehr Avenue
Gettysburg, PA 17325
Phone: (717) 334-6245

Product(s): Art, Artifacts, Books, Clothing, Collectibles, Flags, Hats, Video

Located in the lobby of the National Civil War Wax Museum, the Gettysburg Gift Center offers one of the finest collections of Civil War collectibles, clothing, art, and souvenirs in Gettysburg. The employees, from management on down, are friendly and helpful, making your visit that much more enjoyable. The Gift Center is also your source for the AAA approved Auto Tape Tour of The Battle of Gettysburg. This 90-minute cassette tape (complete with music and sound effects) allows you to tour the battlefield at your own pace as a knowledgeable guide describes the highlights of the three-day battle. Tour tapes can be purchased or rented.

During the summer, you'll often find Civil War reenactors camped in front of the Wax Museum or performing drill on the lawn. A great place to visit.

Catalog: FREE upon request

Photo Courtesy of the Gettysburg Gift Center

Gettysburg Magazine

260 Oak Street
Dayton, OH 45410
Phone: 1-800-648-9710
Fax: (937) 461-4260
Email: msbooks@erinet.com
Internet:
    http://www.morningsidebooks.com

Product(s): Magazines

For those interested in the Gettysburg Campaign of 1863, The Gettysburg Magazine answers the call. Concentrating solely on the Gettysburg Campaign, the magazine provides an in-depth study of the events that took place at America's most famous battlefield. Filled with 128 pages of editorial and no advertising, The Gettysburg Magazine is a must for Civil War enthusiasts. The magazine is published twice a year and sells for $4.95 an issue, plus shipping. Subscriptions are available, as are copies of all back issues.

Gettysburg Railroad Passenger Service

106 N. Washington Street
Gettysburg, PA 17325
Phone: (717) 334-6932
Fax: (717) 334-7350

Service(s): Civil War Train Raids

In addition to their 16-mile weekend rail trips (and some weekday trips) offered April through October, and a 5 hour, 50-mile trip from Gettysburg to Mt. Holly Springs, the Gettysburg Railroad Passenger Service offers "Special Events" which include Civil War train raids (currently offered two weekends each year) and a Lincoln Train event (offered one weekend each year). The fare is modest at $8 for adults and $4 for children (3 to 12 years of age) for the special events, and $7.50 for adults and $3.50 for children (3 to 12 years of age) for the regular rail trips to Biglerville and back (16 miles). Of course you'll want to call for current prices and information on other special events such as the Moonlight Dinner Trip, Apple Blossom Dinner Trip, the Santa Christmas Train, and others.

Goodson Enterprises, Inc.

150 A Watson Divide Road
Snowmass, CO 81654
Phone: (970) 923-0063
Phone: (303) 838-1357

Product(s): Books

The latest offering by Goodson Enterprises is *Georgia Confederate 7,000*. This book presents new research on the Army of Tennessee and includes ALL names (including rank, and regiment) of the men who fought with the Georgia Infantry Brigade (40th, 41st, 42nd, 43rd, and 52nd Georgia Regiments) under Brigadier Generals Seth M. Barton and Marcellus A. Stovall. This softcover book contains 150 pages with maps and pictures, and retails for $27.00 plus $3.00 shipping and handling. Wholesale discounts are available to dealers.

Will Gorges Civil War Antiques

2100 Trent Boulevard
New Bern, NC 28560
Phone: (919) 636-3039
Fax: (919) 637-1862
Email: rebel!@abaco.coastalnet.com
Internet: http://www.collectorsnet.com/
cvdealer/gorges/wgnwbrn.html

Product(s): Artifacts, Buttons, Flags, Paper, Photographs, Uniforms, Weapons & Accessories
Service(s): Textile Conservation and Restoration, Appraisals

Open Mon-Fri, 9am - 5pm

"Largest Active Inventory in the Southeast."

Will Gorges specializes in original authentic uniforms, rifles, swords, pistols, muskets, flags, battlefield excavated artifacts, historical documents, buttons, letters, artillery implements and ammunition, gold coins, quilts, and more. Professional services include textile conservation and restoration, and insurance/estate appraisals.

Catalog: $10 a year (FREE to walk-ins)

The Gospel Truth and Civil War Room

228 W. Main Street
Ligonier, PA 15658
Phone: (412) 238-7991

Product(s): Art, Books, Music, Newspapers, Patterns, Videos

Aside from being a full-service Christian bookstore, The Gospel Truth offers a Civil War Room with a variety of Civil War products, including copies of The Civil War News, Kunstler Calendars, and Civil War books. Though some might find a combination Christian bookstore and Civil War Room to be an unusual paradox, consider the number of soldiers who carried their Bibles, dare I say "religiously," into battle. Throughout history, Religion and War have always marched in the same column. Sometimes at opposite ends of the column, but the same column nonetheless.

Grafica Multimedia, Inc.

1777 Borel Place, Suite 500
San Mateo, CA 94402
Phone: (415) 358-5555
Fax: (415) 358-5556
Email: graficamm.com
Internet: http://www.graficamm.com

Product(s): Computer Software

"A House Divided" by Grafica Multimedia provides an interactive look at America in the years just prior to the Civil War. The CD offers indexed and footnoted video reenactments (over an hours worth), evocative photo essays, narrated slave diary excerpts, a political cartoon gallery, games, the complete transcript of the Lincoln-Douglas debates, and a selection of period music. Lab Pack and School Edition versions are also available. The price of "A House Divided" is currently $49.95, plus 7% shipping and handling (California residents must add applicable sales tax). The Lab Pack version is $159.95, and the School Edition is $79.95 (distributed through Broderbund Software, phone 1-800-521-6263).

Grand Illusions

108 A East Main St.
Newark, DE 19711
Phone: (302) 366-0300
Fax: (302) 738-1858

Makers of Quality Reproduction Clothing for Over 23 Years

Product(s): Belts & Buckles, Buttons, Canteens, Clothing, Haversacks, Insignia, Patterns, Tinware, Uniforms, Weapons & Accessories

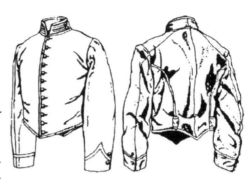

Grand Illusions has the distinction of having researched and manufactured uniforms for over thirty motion pictures and TV productions, including *Gettysburg*, *Andersonville*, and the *Custer mini-series*. They offer period-correct military uniforms and civilian attire for men, women, and children. Each garment is well-researched and made from authentic, natural fibers and the correct period fasteners. Patterns are drafted by Grand Illusions using existing garments in private collections and museums. Owners Sunny and Maurice Whitlock will be happy to dress you for the ballroom, the kitchen, or anything in between.

Catalog: $4

The Grand Spectacle

528 W. Water Street
Elmira, NY 14905
Phone: (607) 732-7500
Fax: (607) 732-6045

Product(s): Eyewear

Reenactors with less-than-perfect vision face an extra challenge when it comes to presenting an authentic impression. Frankly, it's a little difficult to look 19th century when sporting 20th century Eyewear. Contacts sound like a solution, and in some cases they are. But if you're roughing it in camp, the last thing you need to worry about is packing disinfectant, saline solution, a contact case, and daily cleaner. After you drop your contacts in the dirt a few times, you'll probably be ready for a sensible solution. That's where Optician Richard S. Buchanan at The Grand Spectacle comes into play. Mr. Buchanan offers a complete line of reenactor Eyewear. Every frame that he sells is authentic to the time period that you request and your prescription is inserted in period glass, plastic, or polycarbonate lenses. A period case is included with each purchase. If you already have a period frame, or purchase one from a dealer or sutler, The Grand Spectacle will insert your prescription into the frame for the price of the lenses plus shipping. Also, period cases may be purchased individually at $15.00 per case.

Great Expeditions Limited

81 High Path Road
Guildford GU1 2QL
England
Phone: 1-800-353-8256
Internet:
   http://www.astanet.com/get?grtexpd

Service(s): Battlefield Tours

        Based in England, Great Expeditions Limited offers several Civil War tours each year, lasting nine to twelve days. Four tours were offered in 1996, each featuring Edwin Bearss as the tour leader. Day-by-day itineraries are available upon request, along with booking details. Though based in England, Great Expeditions maintains a 1-800 number in the U.S., along with a United States Operations Director to handle your inquiries or concerns.

Green River Trading Corporation

Box 2
Bonnieville, KY 42713
Phone: (502) 531-3115
Fax: (502) 531-3115
Email: ekelle@scrtc.blue.net
   or ekelle@scrtc.net

Product(s): Accouterments, Belts & Buckles, Books, Clothing, Hats, Uniforms, Weapons & Accessories

        Green River Trading Corporation manufactures, imports, and sells (both wholesale and retail) original and reproduction items for Civil War enthusiasts, collectors, and reenactors. Items for other periods of military reenacting and collecting are also available.

Catalog: $1

Grolier Interactive, Inc.

90 Sherman Turnpike
Danbury, CT 06816
Phone: (203) 797-3530
Internet: http://www.grolier.com

Product(s): Computer Software, Games

        Grolier Interactive is now offering a new game called *Battle of the Ironclads,*

Photo Courtesy of Grolier Interactive

available for both PC and MacIntosh. The game is based on the historic battle between the Monitor and the Merrimack. Gamers can play from either the Union (Monitor) or Confederate (Merrimack) perspective. In their quest for historical accuracy, Grolier Interactive meticulously recreated the ships, weapons, and equipment using blueprints, plans, and maps from the National Archive. This promises to be an exciting game.

H-Bar Enterprises
1442 Davidson Loop
Oakman, AL 35579
Phone: (205) 622-2444
Fax: (205) 622-3040
Orders: 1-800-432-7702
1-800-770-3250
Email: hbaral@aol.com
Internet: http://www.hbar.com

Product(s): Computer Software

H-Bar Enterprises is one of those innovative companies helping to bring the Civil War into the era of cyberspace. As one of the premier electronic publishing companies dealing with the Civil War, they have succeeded in placing the entire *Official Record* on CD ROM—but that's only the beginning. They also have 12 volumes of

the entire Official Record *on CD ROM*

Confederate Military History, 4 volumes of *Battles and Leaders of the Civil War*, 6 volumes of *Roster of the Confederate Soldiers of Georgia*, 9 volumes of *Abraham Lincoln: His Life and Works*, 10 volumes (ten years worth) of *Confederate Veteran Magazine*, and many individual titles.

Non-Civil War titles encompass World War I, World War II, General History titles, Genealogy, Biographies, and many more. I was happy to see that H-Bar has taken the next step towards the ultimate electronic library by placing all their publications—including the *Official Record*—on the Internet. For a fee of $10 a month, researchers can access *all* electronic publications produced by H-Bar.

Hallowed Ground Prints
P.O. Box 61322
Raleigh, NC 27661
Phone: (919) 872-7111
Orders: 1-800-576-7409

Product(s): Art

Featuring the work of Jeremy L. Scott, Hallowed Ground Prints offers a se-lection of beautiful signed and numbered limited edition prints. Examples include *To The Last*, which depicts the 26th North Carolina at the Highwater Mark, Gettysburg, July 3, 1863, and *Uncommon Valor*, which portrays the 75th Indiana and the 58th Alabama at Chickamauga, September 19, 1863. A limited number of artist's proofs and publisher's proofs are also available.

The Haversack Store

The Museum of The Confederacy
1201 East Clay St.
Richmond, VA 23219
Fax: (804) 644-7150
Orders: (804) 644-4936

Product(s): Art, Clothing, Collectibles, Computer Software, Flags, Music, Video

No trip to The Museum of The Confederacy would be complete without stopping at The Haversack Store. Select from an assortment of items with a Confederate theme, including: books, pictures, clothing, a trivet, ornaments, watches, coasters, even a mouse pad printed with "The Last Meeting of Lee and Jackson."

Catalog: FREE

Jim Hayes, Antiquarian

Drawer 12560
James Island, SC 29422
Phone: (803) 795-0732
Fax: (803) 795-9001

Product(s): Paper (Letters, Documents, and Autographs)

Jim Hayes specializes in letters, documents, and autographs from The War Between the States. Aside from collecting and selling, he offers appraisal and authentication services. He prints a sixteen-page list every two months.

Subscription: $10 year (six issues)

Heartfelt Designs

P.O. Box 206
Pinto, MD 21556
Phone: (301) 729-2974

Product(s): Cross-Stitch Designs

Heartfelt Designs specializes in samplers depicting major battles of the Civil War. All samplers are stitched in Rebel gray and Yankee blue with gold and green accents and are suitable for framing in a 10 x 14 inch frame.

At present, major battles that are available include: First Manassas, Second Manassas, Antietam, Gettysburg, Vicksburg, Chickamauga, Fredericksburg, Chancellorsville, and Shiloh. Additional battles are being designed.

Patterns are available for $4.50 (specify battle), kits, which include cloth, thread, needle, color chart, and beads, are available for $24.50.

Brochure: $2

Heidi Marsh Patterns

3494 N. Valley Road
Greenville, CA 95947

Product(s): Belts & Buckles, Books, Buttons, Fabric, Insignia, Patterns

While Heidi Marsh offers a nice selection of fashion accessories, her strong point is patterns—and I mean strong. You'll find patterns for camp dresses, working dresses, ballgowns, skirts, blouses, bonnets, girdles, wraps, jackets, petticoats, underpinnings, and uniforms, plus much more. Books are available on many subjects and are compiled from original sources. Accessory items include an assortment of boxes, purses, fans, gloves, and reproduction Civil War playing cards, among others.

Catalog: $3

49

Heritage Drum Company

Terry Cornett
4021 Apollo Drive SW
Huntsville, AL 35805
Phone: (205) 533-5498
Internet: http://fly.hiwaay.net/~tpalmer/

additional options are available which will allow you to customize a drum to your liking. An on-line catalog is available on the Olde Towne Brass web page (see Internet address to the left).

Product(s): Drums

With 20 years in the drum manufacturing and repair business, Terry Cornett offers hand-crafted, period reproduction drums on a custom order basis. Snare drums and Bass drums are offered in a variety of sizes and

The Historian's Gallery

Perimeter Mall
Upper Level - Rich's Wing
Atlanta, GA 30346
Mail:
3232 Cobb Parkway, Suite 207
Atlanta, GA 30339
Phone: (770) 522-8383
Fax: (770) 522-8388
Email: history@atl.mindspring.com
Internet: http://www.nr-net.com/history/

Product(s): Art, Artifacts, Paper

An outstanding source for authentic, rare, and antique maps, selected relics, historically significant signed documents/manuscripts, and autographs, The Historian's Gallery offers service and selection that goes beyond the norm. A unique search system, designed by The Historian's Gallery, allows them to track the inventories of over 1,000 collectors and dealers worldwide. An exceptional, effort-saving tool—and their search services are free of charge (though a

Confederate Officer's Frock Coat

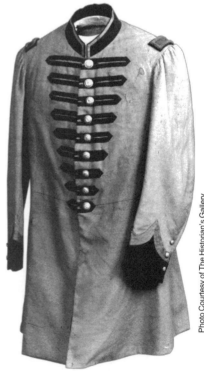

Photo Courtesy of The Historian's Gallery

$50 refundable deposit is required). All items sold by The Historian's Gallery have been inspected, researched, photographed, numbered, and registered by trained experts to insure authenticity and provide protection from loss or theft. They also provide an unconditional lifetime guarantee of authenticity on everything they sell.

The Confederate Officer's Frock Coat shown on the previous page belonged to a Lieutenant who was mortally wounded at Port Hudson. The doctor who treated him, Doctor T. Thatcher Graves, saved the coat and sent it home as a remembrance of the event. The coat made its way into A.E. Brooks' collection and was recorded on page 111 (bottom right) of Sylvia and O'Donnell's "Illustrated History of Civil War Relics." This item offers an excellent example of the quality items available from The Historian's Gallery. Impressive.

Historic Jonesborough Visitors Center

117 Boone Street
Jonesborough, TN 37659
Phone: (423) 753-1012

Service(s): Tours

The Historic Jonesborough Visitors Center offers a guided walking or buggy ride through Jonesborough, during which the headquarters, hospitals, prisons, cemeteries, and other Civil War sites of Jonesborough are pointed out. The tour begins at the visitors center. Self-guided tour maps are also available.

Historical Enterprises

571 West 1400 North
Centerville, UT 84014

Product(s): Books

Publications produced by Historical Enterprises include: *The Battle of Fayetteville, Arkansas, April 18, 1863*, and *Federal Outpost at Fayetteville: The First Arkansas Union Cavalry*. Both are softcover, 55-page, 8 1/2 x 11 format, and retail for $10.95 postpaid.

Historic Framing and Collectibles

8344 Main Street
Ellicott City, MD 21043
Phone: (410) 465-0549

Product(s): Accouterments, Art, Artifacts, Uniforms, Weapons & Accessories
Service(s): Custom Matting & Framing

Specializing in the Civil War, Historic Framing and Collectibles buys, sells, and trades military and other antiques. A full line of military art (framed or ready to frame) is available featuring all major artists from Civil War to WWII.

Historic Richmond Foundation Tours

707-A East Franklin Street
Richmond, VA 23219
Phone: (804) 780-0107
Fax: (804) 788-4244

Service(s): Battlefield Tours

Offering a five-hour guided riding tour titled Civil War Battlefields, Historic Richmond Foundation Tours operates from May through October on the 2nd, 3rd, and 4th Sunday afternoon of each month. The tour takes participants to the site of the Seven Days Battles of the 1862 Peninsula Campaign, including Chickahominy Bluff, Beaverdam Creek, Savage Station, Gaines Mill, Malvern Hill, and Cold Harbor (1864). Cost of the tour is $22 for adults and $12 for children six through 12. Reservations are required and there must be four reservations by 11 a.m. the day of the tour for the tour to take place. As a convenience, the tour meets participants at the Hyatt Richmond, Marriott, Jefferson, Berkeley, Commonwealth Park, and Radisson Hotels, at Linden Row Inn, and at the Metro Richmond Visitor Center.

Richard T. Hoober, Jr.

P.O. Box 3116
Key Largo, FL 33037
Phone: (305) 853-0105
Fax: (305) 853-0105

Product(s): Currency, Newspapers, Paper

Specializing in Civil War paper collectibles, Richard Hoober offers autographs, letters, currency, bonds, documents, engravings, newspapers, and other paper collectibles from the war. Completely new descriptive price lists are published three times a year.

The Horse Soldier

777 Baltimore Street
Gettysburg, PA 17325
Mail:
P.O. Box 184
Cashtown, PA 17310
Phone: (717) 334-0347
Fax: (717) 334-5016
Email: hsoldier@cvn.net

Product(s): Accouterments, Art, Artifacts, Books, CDVs, Collectibles, Currency, Dug Items, Medical, Memorabilia, Paper, Photographs, Video, Weapons & Accessories
Service(s): Appraisals, Research

Photo Courtesy of The Horse Soldier

dug items, soldier letters, weapons, art, and books, among other things. With the variety and quantity of artifacts available, it's just a fun place to visit. An illustrated catalog is offered semiannually containing over 90 pages of weapons, paper, dug items, and other artifacts. For those interested in researching their ancestors, The Horse Soldier offers a Soldier Research Service for a competitive fee.

I make a point of visiting The Horse Soldier whenever I'm in Gettysburg because they offer a truly impressive assortment of

Catalog: $10 per year (2 issues)

Craig Howell

1825 T Street NW
Washington, DC 20009-7135
Phone: (202) 462-0535

Service(s): Battlefield Tours

Craig Howell conducts tours—walking tours, auto tours, or motorcoach tours—of various Eastern Theater Battlefields, from Manassas to Appomattox. Tours can be half-day, full day, or multiple days. Especially good for those who are just catching the Civil War bug.

Hudson's Hobby Games

P.O. Box 121503
Arlington, TX 76012-1503
Phone: (817) 461-0126
Email: HudsonGame@aol.com

Product(s): Computer Software, Games

Serving the gaming community since 1983, Hudson's Hobby Games offers a game line which includes the products of around 200 companies. Among these are 65 boardgames and 10 software titles dealing with the War Between the States. Game-related books and magazines are also available. Discounts as high as 38% are offered, as well as free shipping in the United States. For a catalog, provide them with a mailing address and indicate whether you're interested in the Software or Boardgame catalog (or both).

Catalog: FREE

I.C. Mercantile

122 E. Jewel Street
Republic, MO 65738
Phone: (417) 732-8495 after 7:00 p.m.

Product(s): Footwear

If custom-made boots are in your future, check out I.C. Mercantile. Working with an experienced, family-operated boot company in Juarez, Mexico, I.C. Mercantile produces boots based on an original pair of U.S. M1876 cavalry boots (construction details of this boot are typical of earlier 19th century military and civilian boots). They are made with a two-piece upper with leather welts and pull loops over the boot tops. Leather soles are machine sewn to the uppers. Standard heels are flat "military" heels about one inch high. Leather used is standard weight with a calf lining. Toes are squared.

Photo Courtesy of I.C. Mercantile

I.C. Mercantile provides a paper ruler and measuring instructions so that your boot can be made per your specifications. Also, you can designate the height of the uppers (e.g. M1859 boots were 12 inches with no front flap, M1872 boots were 14 inches with a 2-inch flap, and M1876 boots were 16 inches including a 3-inch flap).

Infinop

P.O. Box 934
Frisco, TX 75034
Orders: 1-800-816-4774

Product(s): Computer Software

Infinop offers four War Between the States screen saver series for the home computer. Volume One contains 35 im-

ages of Confederate flags, Volume Two contains 22 images of Confederate leaders and generals, Volume Three contains 13 images of Union leaders, and Volume Four contains 17 images of Confederate currency. Volumes are $14.95 each plus $1.50 shipping and handling (write or call for current prices and system requirements).

ISI Prints

2821 Minot Lane
Waukesha, WI 53188

Product(s): Art

Rather than concentrating on battle scenes or historic figures as the inspiration for her work, artist J.B. Collins, working with ISI Prints, has created two exceptional renditions of Civil War battle flags. Specifically, the flags of the 2nd Wisconsin Infantry and the 4th Virginia Infantry.

The 2nd Wisconsin Infantry was part of the Army of the Potomac's famed Iron Brigade. The flag depicted is of the unit's Stars and Stripes, received in 1863 as a replacement for the regiment's original flag—which was weather worn and combat torn by 1863. The regiment's Stars and Stripes was carried into combat at Mine Run, Laurel Hill, the Wilderness, and Spotsylvania. It was carried home to Wisconsin when the regiment was mustered out in 1864. The flag is currently in remarkably good shape and Collins was able to base her work off of a photograph of the relic.

The 4th Virginia Infantry was one of the five regiments which composed the Army of Northern Virginia's Stonewall Brigade. After earning its nickname at First Manassas, the brigade would remain a potent fighting force for most of the war. The numerous battle honors which appear on the flag are testament to the heavy fighting

the 4th saw. The relic now resides in the Museum of the Confederacy and is in very tattered condition. For this flag, Collins worked off reconstruction information supplied by Civil War flag expert Howard Michael Madaus. The flag was a third bunting pattern and was produced at the Richmond Clothing depot in 1863. It was issued to the regiment in September 1863 and would eventually be lost to Union forces, most likely when the Stonewall Brigade was overrun at the "Mule Shoe" on 12 May, 1864.

Both prints are limited editions (s/n 1,000) and measure fifteen inches square. They are available through mail order at a very reasonable price of $28.50 for the unframed, $98.50 framed, plus $5 shipping and handling. Future prints will include the 10th Tennessee (CSA), 36th Illinois, the Irish Brigade, and others. With luck, the success of these prints will encourage J.B. Collins and ISI Prints to continue with their battle flag series.

James Country Muzzleloading and Mercantile

P.O. Box 364
111 North Main
Liberty, MO 64068
Phone: (816) 781-9473
Fax: (816) 781-1470
Email: jamescntry@aol.com

Product(s): Accouterments, Belts & Buckles, Books, Buttons, Clothing, Fabric, Hats, Haversacks, Insignia, Jewelry, Music, Patterns, Tobacco Goods, Uniforms, Weapons & Accessories

In business since 1986, James Country Mercantile supplies information and merchandise for 19th Century living history enthusiasts. "Our customers are people who recreate the life and times of the 1800s. They might be Mountain Men, Fur Traders, Civil War Reenactors, members of Old West groups, or Buffalo Soldier units, - or they may just love the 1800s and want to learn more about it," says owner Del Warren. Aside from his duties as proprietor, Del is a practiced gunsmith who specializes in black-powder and period weapons; he frequently serves as an on-site gunsmith at living history events such as Civil War reenactments and Old West events.

The mercantile offers an impressive variety of items, including a large selection of patterns, over 2100 different books dealing with American history and the 1800s (including a 23-page list of Civil War titles), uniforms, clothing, kepis and hats, buttons, music (Bobby Horton, Wayne Erbsen, 12th Louisiana Band, 97th Regimental String Band, and others), rifles, pistols, sabers, tobacco goods, weapon accessories, and parts for most reproduction weapons.

Catalog: $6
Price List: $1

"Our customers are people who recreate the life and times of the 1800s. They might be Mountain Men, Fur Traders, Civil War Reenactors, members of Old West groups, or Buffalo Soldier units, - or they may just love the 1800s and want to learn more about it," says owner Del Warren.

JEBCO Clocks

301 Industry Lane
Carlisle, OH 45005
Phone: (513) 746-2268
Fax: (513) 746-9836
Orders: 1-800-635-3226

Product(s): Clocks, Plaques

Using reproductions of works by Civil War artists Mort Kunstler and Michael Gnatek, Jebco is able to offer a selection of impressive and stylish clocks and plaques. The clocks are offered as limited edition collectibles (total of 5000) and come individually numbered with an official Jebco collectible seal.

JM Comics

P.O. Box 56982
Jacksonville, FL 32241-6982

Product(s): Comic Books

Southern Blood is a new series of Civil War comic books offered by JM Comics. The comics are offered by subscription for $22.50 (12 issues), less than $2 each. The series follows the plight of the Austins, a South Carolina family, as they fight for the Southern cause. Major engagements of the Army of Northern Virginia, such as Sharpsburg, Chancellorsville, Gettysburg, and Spotsylvania are covered.

Character Alexander Samuel Austin from the series **Southern Blood**

J.W. Carson Company

130 Myrtle Street, Dept WCP
Le Roy, NY 14482
Phone: (716) 768-4949
Fax: (716) 768-6334

Product(s): Maps

J.W. Carson Company specializes in topographical watercolor Civil War battle-field maps. A 17-page essay titled "Re-writing the Maps of the American Civil War" is provided with the company's product catalog. Prices start at $8.95 for folded maps and go up to $24.00 for the map prints.

Catalog: $1

K & P Valley Collectibles

499 Osprey Lane
Front Royal, VA 22630
Phone: (540) 635-8564
Email: fournier @ rma.edu

Product(s): Accouterments, Artifacts, Paper, Weapons & Accessories

Located in the historic Shenandoah Valley, K & P Valley Collectibles offers a fine collection of original Civil War accouterments, firearms, swords, artifacts, and newspapers. They have a large selection of relics that were excavated from camps and battlegrounds located throughout the Valley.

Original Civil War issues of Harper's Weekly are the house specialty. These newspapers provided the country with pictorial and printed news of the war. Famous artists who contributed to Harper's Weekly included Winslow Homer, Thomas Nast, and A.R. Waud, among others. The artists would send in their sketches which were then engraved on the woodblocks used to make prints for the newspapers. Most issues of the paper have five or six such prints. K & P sells individual prints that have been professionally matted on acid-free mats and backboards and are ready for framing. Most of Winslow Homer's prints are available, including the famous "Sharpshooter."

All items are guaranteed authentic and can be returned for a full refund if not satisfied. Call, write, or Email for a current list of available items.

K & P Weaver

P.O. Box 1131
Orange, CT 06477
Phone: (203) 795-9024

Product(s): Clothing, Haversack Items, Uniforms

Ken & Paula Weaver use their ongoing research and examination of Civil War-era clothing and accessories to help create period reproductions as close to the original as possible. Historically accurate men's clothing is offered for both military and civilian impressions. Clothing is custom made using period construction techniques, such as hand sewn buttonholes. Accessories include such items as oak campstools, a pivoting cherry mirror, shaving kits, and much more.

Catalog: $1

Richard A. LaPosta

154 Robindale Drive
Kensington, CT 06037
Phone: (203) 828-0921

Product(s): Books

Richard A. LaPosta buys, sells, and trades Civil War Books, with a specialization in Regimental Histories.

Lee-Grant, Inc.

Rt. 4, Box 102
Appomattox, VA 24522
Phone: 1-800-350-5234

Product(s): Artifacts, Currency, Flags, Memorabilia, Paper

Located on Highway 460 just two miles from Appomattox Court House National Park, Lee-Grant, Inc., is the largest Civil War gift shop in Appomattox. They specialize in relics and flags, though a variety of other items are also available.

Legendary Arms, Inc.

P.O. Box 299
Dunellen, NJ 08812-0299
Fax: (908) 424-2303
Orders: 1-800-528-2767

Product(s): Accouterments, Belts & Buckles, Canteens, Footwear, Gauntlets, Hats, Haversacks, Insignia, Uniforms, Weapons & Accessories

Legendary Arms has an excellent assortment of cutlasses, sabers, and swords common to the Civil War era. Though they offer weapons and equipment from other periods and wars (Roman, Viking, Conquistador, Samurai, etc.), Civil War items occupy a good portion of their full-color catalog.

Levi Ledbetter, Sutler

7032 Mineral Springs Road
Oakboro, NC 28129
Phone: (704) 485-4746
    (Noon - 10 p.m.)

Quality Reproduction Civil War Uniforms and Equipage

Product(s): Accouterments, Bayonets, Belts & Buckles, Blankets, Books, Buttons, Canteens, Flags, Footwear, Hats, Haversacks, Insignia, Instruments, Knapsacks, Leather Goods, Tents, Tinware, Uniforms, Weapons & Accessories

Offering an extensive list of leather goods, uniform items, and other equipment needed by both reenactors and Civil War enthusiasts, the 12-page Levi Ledbetter, Sutler, catalog includes standard equipment, along with an assortment of miscellaneous items. So if you're looking for uniform items, spurs, rosewood fifes, or a Barlow knife, check out Levi Ledbetter. They'll send their catalog free of charge as long as you provide a LONG self-addressed stamped envelope.

Catalog: FREE

Lodgewood Manufacturing

P.O. Box 611
Whitewater, WI 53190-0611
Phone: (414) 473-5444

Product(s): Weapons & Accessories

William V. Osborne II, proprietor of Lodgewood Manufacturing, specializes in U.S. marital arms from 1780 to 1898, particularly Civil War guns and parts.

Catalog: $1

Longstreet House

P.O. Box 730
Hightstown, NJ 08520
Phone: (609) 448-1501

Product(s): Books

Longstreet House is a Civil War publisher specializing in Gettysburg and Unit Histories. Recent releases include: *Regimental Strengths and Losses at Gettysburg (Third Edition), Reminiscences of the Thirteenth New Jersey Infantry in the Civil War*, and *Charlie Mosher's Civil War: From Fair Oaks to Andersonville with the Plymouth Pilgrims (85th N.Y. Infantry)*.

Martin's Mercantile

4566 Oakhurst Drive
Sylvania, OH 43560-1736
Phone: (419) 474-2093
Fax: (419) 474-2093

Product(s): Clothing, Millinery, Patterns

Period Clothing (1850-1865) for the Discriminating Woman

*An Example of
Mrs. Martin's Bonnet Designs*

Mrs. Martin's Mercantile & Millinery offers an excellent selection of custom-made clothing for women (they also have an assortment of clothing for men and children). Selection includes day & camp dresses, fan-front dresses, ballgowns, waists, capes, underpinnings, accessories, and millinery (bonnets, Glengarry hats, straw hats). The bonnet illustrations in their catalog are particularly impressive.

Each piece is designed for historical authenticity and is crafted to Mrs. Martin's high standards of quality.

Catalog: $4.50

Mary Ellen & Company

100 North Main Street
North Liberty, IN 46554
Phone: (219) 656-3000
Fax: (219) 656-3000
Orders: 1-800-669-1860
Email: 71562,2136@compuserve.com

Be Whisked Back to the Victorian 1800's!

Product(s): Books, Clothing, Fans, Footwear, Hats, Parasols, Patterns

Mary Ellen & Company's impressive selection of 1800's fashion items includes a wide assortment of patterns, including some inspired by *Gone With the Wind*. All the standard women's clothing items are available (from corsets and bonnets to ball gowns) plus accessory items such as wooden thimbles, hand mirrors, pill boxes, wooden combs, and palm fans. Mary Ellen & Company carries books on clothing, costuming, customs, cooking, needlecraft, dolls, photography, architecture, and 1800's history. Titles include: *Civil War Gentlemen: 1860s Apparel, Arts & Uniforms; Children's Fashions 1860-1912; History of Underclothes; Wedding Fashions, 1862-1912; Hearts of Fire ... Soldier Women of the Civil War;* and *Who Wore What: Women's Wear 1861-1865.*

One item in particular caught my attention while examining Mary Ellen & Company's products, and that was an authentic replica of an Eagle-At-Bay Daguerreotype case. Suitable for modern as well as antique picture, the case is lined with red velvet and has an embossed gold-color frame. Wholesale prices are available on this and other Mary Ellen & Company items to museums, the National Park Service, theatre groups, sutlers, dealer stores, and living history groups.

Catalog: $3 (refundable with any order)

Mary Lou Productions
Gift of Heritage

P.O. Box 17233
Minneapolis, MN 55417
Phone: (612) 726-9432
Fax: (612) 727-2705
Orders: 1-800-774-8511

Product(s): Video

Photo Courtesy of Mary Lou Productions

Gift of Heritage, an instructional video by Mary Lou Productions, offers organizational techniques and timesaving tips to those interested in recording their family history on video tape. Gift of Heritage will take you through the process of beginning the research, planning and organizing materials, combining family-tree information, photographs, slides, home-movies and video footage, interviewing, and effectively telling the family's story. Gift of Heritage sells for $29.95, plus $3.00 shipping and handling (MN residents add 6.5% sales tax, plus any appropriate city tax).

Frank Matuszek - Civil War Antiques

126 E. Wing Street, #210
Arlington Heights, IL 60004-6064
Phone: (847) 253-4685

Product(s): Accouterments, Artifacts, Uniforms, Weapons & Accessories

Frank Matuszek specializes in Civil War and Indian War antiquities. He buys, sells, and trades muskets, carbines, leather goods, cartridges, artillery, uniforms, sabers, shells, and other authentic items. Fully illustrated, high quality catalogs are available. All items are authentic with a 30-day return policy if not satisfied—though Frank is sure you will be.

Catalog: $8 (two editions)

McGowan Book Company

39 Kimberly Drive
Durham, NC 27707
Phone: (919) 403-1503
Fax: (919) 403-1506
Orders: 1-800-449-8406

Product(s): Books, Currency, Memorabilia, Paper, Photographs

McGowan Book Company has specialized in the Civil War since 1987. They offer the finest in rare and out-of-print books, autographs, currency, documents, photographs, veterans memorabilia, postal history items, and objects of the period. They are active buyers in the marketplace and, from past experience, they feel confident that you will be pleasantly surprised by the prices paid for top material.

Catalog: $3 (3 issues)

Mechanical Baking Company

P.O. Box 513-W
Pekin, IL 61555-0513

Product(s): Hardtack

If you're looking for more authenticity in your reenactments, or if you want to provide a memorable interactive experience for students, Mechanical Baking Company has just what you need: Hardtack. That's all they do and they do it well. The company was started in 1990 and has continued to grow—thanks to the support of enthusiastic reenactors.

Samples are available for $1.50. A price list and additional information are also available, but plan ahead. After baking, hardtack requires a week to a week and a half to cure, so the good bakers at Mechanical ask that you allow 4-6 weeks for delivery.

Note: Weevils and maggots, customarily found with hardtack, are **not** included as part of Mechanical Baking Company's packaging. We regret to say we were unable to locate a weevil/maggot supplier, but hope this shortcoming doesn't take away from your "almost" authentic hardtack experience.

—The Editors

Michaels & Perrin

414 Main Street, Box 29
Hartleton, PA 17829
Phone: (717) 922-1065 or 922-1245
Email: tperrin@sunlink.net

Product(s): Clothing, Uniforms

Michaels & Perrin provides custom made period clothing and uniforms. They can supply everything from Sack Coats to Lady's gowns. They are also a supplier of reenactor equipment.

Catalog: Available upon request

Military Historical Tours, Inc.

1800 Diagonal Road, Suite 600
Alexandria, VA 22314
Phone: (703) 739-8900
Fax: (703) 684-0193
Information: 1-800-722-9501
Email: PJ4MHT@aol.com

Service(s): Battlefield Tours

Offering tours with an impressive lineup of Civil War authorities, Military Historical Tours takes their guests on a multi-day journey into the very soul of the Civil War. Their 1996 tour, "Lee's Greatest Successes and Defeats," began in Manassas, proceeded to Fredericksburg, Chancellorsville, The Wilderness, Spotsylvania, Harpers Ferry, Antietam, and Gettysburg (where all three days of the battle were examined in detail).

Mr. James Kushlan, Editor of Civil War Times Illustrated, served as Tour Host for 1996, while Mr. Dale Floyd, author, Civil War historian, and historian for the National Park Service's American Battlefield Protection Program, served as the Tour Leader. Guest speakers included Mr. Edwin Bearss, Mr. John Hennessey, Mr. A. Wilson Greene, Mr. Robert Krick, and Dr. Richard Sommers.

Military Images

RD1, Box 99A, Lesoine Drive
Henryville, PA 18332
Phone: (717) 629-9152
Email: milimage@csrlink.net

Product(s): Magazines

Established in 1979, Military Images (MI) is a quality magazine that examines Civil War-era military figures through the photographer's lens. Each issue (six a year) is filled with an impressive selection of military photos. Most images are courtesy of MI's readers, thus providing a glimpse at hundreds of previously unpublished military photos.

Photo Courtesy of Military Images

MI also boasts a prominent list of regular contributors, providing scholarly articles on everything from photo analysis to uniforms, insignia, and equipment recognition. Advertising is available at reasonable rates.

Subscription: $24 one year (six issues); $40 two years (twelve issues).

Photographic History of the U.S. Fighting Man, 1839-1900

Morningside Bookshop

260 Oak Street
Dayton, OH 45410
Phone: 1-800-648-9710
Fax: (937) 461-4260
Email: msbooks@erinet.com
Internet:
http://www.morningsidebooks.com

Product(s): Art, Books, Magazines

Morningside Bookshop is the premiere seller of Civil War books. In addition to the nearly one hundred books Morningside currently has in print, they sell and keep in stock well over two thousand titles from other publishers. A full catalog of these books is issued twice a year, and supplemented monthly.

Morningside is also the publisher of the *Gettysburg Magazine*, a biannual, scholarly publication devoted to the Battle of Gettysburg. Look for them on the World Wide Web.

Catalog: $3 (for shipping)

Mr. "K" Products

P.O. Box 5234 Dept. W
Fairlawn, OH 44334-0234

Product(s): Miniatures

Mr. "K" Products is a dealer in American Civil War miniatures. Products

American Civil War miniatures

include soft plastic soldiers, infantry, cavalry, artillery, and accessory items in 1/32 (54mm) scale and 1/72 (25mm) scale.

Catalog: $1

Mrs. Eddins' Fine Sewing Emporium

186 Hayes Circle
Rex, GA 30273
Phone: (770) 389-1470

Product(s): Clothing, Uniforms

Custom sewing and hand-knitting is the hallmark of Mrs. Eddins' Fine Sewing Emporium. Items available include Confederate trousers, Richmond Depot jackets, Columbus Depot jackets, Confederate enlisted frock coat, Federal Sack Coats (lined and unlined), Schyukill Arsenal trousers, military vests, Federal issue shirts, Gentleman's Sack Coat, civilian vests, socks (Echoes of Glory, Southern Confederacy, and Beauvour), slat sunbonnets, pinner aprons, Constance dresses, petticoats, drawers, chemises, corsets, day dresses, traveling dresses, wrappers, ballgowns, and more.

Catalog: $2 (refundable with order)

MultiEducator, Inc.

244 North Avenue
New Rochelle, NY 10801
Phone: (914) 235-4340
Fax: (914) 235-4367
Orders: 1-800-866-6434

Product(s): Computer Software

MultiEducator recently announced the release of "Civil War: America's Epic Struggle." This two CD ROM set brings the drama of the "War between the States" to the computer as nothing ever before. "Civil War: America's Epic Struggle" contains over 3,000 photos and drawings chosen from the collections of the Library of Congress and the National Archives (comprising the majority of the Brady Civil War collection). Most of these images are full screen. Also included in this set are substantial excerpts from the memoirs of Grant, Sheridan, Davis, and the correspondence of R.E. Lee, President Lincoln, McClellan, as well as numerous articles by other participants in the conflict.

The heart of "Civil War: America's Epic Struggle," however, is over two hours of original narrated audiovisual presentations on each of the major battles and events of the war. These presentations combine photos, animated maps and some period music, together with voice-overs to dramatize the passion of America's internal struggle. Another program highlight is its extensive section dealing with the causes of the war. Users trace the war from the first shots fired at Ft. Sumter, to Lee's surrender at Appomattox Court House and Lincoln's assassination.

The comprehensive photo archive includes thousands of images divided by subject. An extensive section of photos on the camp life brings vividly to the screen the day to day life in army camps (including dozens of color drawings). Other photo sections focus on the railroads, medical care, women, supplies, and much more.

Other sections include a chronology of the events that took place in Washington and Richmond, short biographies and photos of over 300 Confederate and Union Generals, force statistics, and Naval action during the war (including over 200 photos).

Available for both Macintosh and Windows.

Museum of Historic Natchitoches

840 Washington
Natchitoches, LA 71457
Phone: (318) 357-0070

Product(s): Video

The last major victory for the Confederacy came with the battles of Sabine Crossroads and Pleasant Hill, two small communities in Northwest Louisiana. The largest campaign ever fought west of the Mississippi River, and one of the Union's worst fiascoes,

THE FORGOTTEN MARCH

A VIDEO DOCUMENTARY of the LARGEST CIVIL WAR CAMPAIGN FOUGHT WEST OF THE MISSISSIPPI RIVER

began a retreat from these little known battles. *The Forgotten March*, a documentary of the Red River Campaign, follows the Union forces from south Louisiana as they travel north to these lesser-known battlefields and, ultimately, to defeat. The video sells for $19.95, plus $2.50 shipping and handling.

Photo Courtesy of Musket Miniatures

Musket Miniatures, LLC

P.O. Box 1976
Broomfield, CO 80038

Product(s): Miniatures

A wide range of miniature infantry, cavalry, artillery, wagons, and accessories in 15mm and 20mm scale is available from Musket Miniatures. In business for twenty years, they are fully prepared to fill your diorama, train layout, and wargaming needs, including buildings, fortifications, terrain, and a full line of scenery.

Illustrated Catalog: $3 (refundable with purchase)

Susan A. Nash

Paper Conservator
P.O. Box 1011
Shepherdstown, WV 25443
Phone: (304) 876-3772

Service(s): Paper Conservation

Susan Nash offers a very specialized service in the arena of conservation. Her expertise is in the conservation and restoration of artifacts on paper: documents, photographs, maps, prints and drawings, watercolors, and historic wallpapers. Her conservation treatments can include cleaning, washing and buffering, mending tears and repairing losses, and museum matting and framing.

Trained at the Cooperstown Graduate Program in Conservation of Historic and Artistic Works, and with twenty-five years of field experience (including four years with the National Park Service at Harpers Ferry) Susan Nash offers considerable experience and expertise.

Navy Arms Company

689 Bergen Boulevard
Ridgefield, NJ 07657
Phone: (201) 945-2500
Fax: (201) 945-6859
Cable Address:
        Serarmament, Ridgefield, N.J.
Telex: 134619 SER ARM RIDE

Product(s): Accouterments, Belts & Buckles, Books, Hats, Video, Weapons & Accessories

When you sell more reproduction Confederate-type revolvers than the Confederate States of America did during the entire Civil War, you must be doing something right. And that's exactly what Navy Arms Company has done. They've also sold

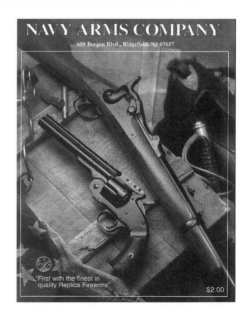

65

more percussion Remingtons than Remington ever produced, and more Harpers Ferry flintlocks than the Harpers Ferry Arsenal ever made.

Their catalog of reproductions is impressive and includes:

Rifles & Carbines:

Smith Cavalry Carbine, .50; Smith Artillery Carbine, .50; 1859 Sharps Cavalry Carbine, .54; 1859 Sharps Infantry Rifle, .54; Zouave Rifle, .58; 1861 Springfield Rifle, .58; 1863 Springfield Rifle, .58; 1841 Mississippi Rifle, .54 & .58; 1863 Richmond Rifle, .58; Navy Arms 1853 and 1858 Enfield Muskets, .58; and the Navy Arms 1861 Musketoon, .58.

Revolvers:

LeMat (Army, Navy, 18th Georgia, Beauregard, and Cavalry models); 1851 Army & Navy;

Reb Model 1860; .36 & .44; 1847 Walker Dragoon, .44; 1847 Walker Single; 1860 Army, .44; 1858 Remington-Style, .44; Stainless Remington-style, .44; Brass Frame Remington-style, .44; Rogers and Spencer, .44; Spiller and Burr, .36; and others.

Navy Arms Company also offers a number of kits for those wishing to assemble their own gun. Other available items include muzzle loading accessories, actions & locks, hats, buckles and insignia, bayonets, swords, tomahawks, weapons-related books, video tapes, military surplus arms, leather accouterments, and a variety of ammunition.

Catalog: $2

Neddle & Thread

2215 Fairfield Rd.
Gettysburg, PA 17325
Phone: (717) 334-4011

Product(s): Fabric, Patterns

Aside from supplying standard sewing materials, Needle & Thread provides an assortment of Civil War patterns and fabrics for those talented enough to create their own clothing.

New Vision Productions

P.O. Box 511
Holidaysburg, PA 16648
Phone: (814) 695-9893

Product(s): Video

Take an insider's look at historic Gettysburg with Historian/Author Gregory A. Coco via New Vision Production's 1995 video release: *Secrets of the Battlefield — Gettysburg*. This video takes you to rock carvings made by soldiers during and after the battle, shows you battle damage that still scars Gettysburg's architecture, and takes you to the actual grave sites of Confederate soldiers buried in National Cemetery.

Future releases by New Vision Productions will include: *Secrets of the Battlefield — Antietam*, *Between the Bullet and the Battlefield*, and *Some Mothers Son*. *Secrets of the Battlefield-Gettysburg* sells for $19.95, plus $3 shipping and handling.

Dr. F. Don Nidiffer

P.O. Box 8184
Charlottesville, VA 22906
Phone: (804) 296-2067

Product(s): Paper

Dr. Nidiffer buys and sells American historical documents from the Colonial period to WWII. Items available include documents, letters, and other papers, signed by Civil War generals and military/political figures; signed documents from U.S. Presidents; documents from other military periods; and Native American ethnographic art, including pre-1900 weapons, headwork, clothing, etc.

Northcoast Miniatures

311 Boyle Drive
Eureka, CA 95503
Phone: (707) 443-8915

Product(s): Miniatures

As a manufacturer of 54mm painted metal figures, Bob and Judiann O'Connell offer an extensive line of the finest Civil War figures, cannons, and wagons. Sets are sold in limited editions and shipped with the set number and serial number on the end of the box. Northcoast Miniatures also carries Napoleonic figures, Victorian figures, carousels, wagons, and Christmas figures.

Catalog: $1

Northwest Reenactments
Civil War Adventures, Inc.

1532 Lakeway Pl
Bellingham, WA 98226
Phone: 1-800-624-4421

Service(s): Travel (special)

There are many people out there who find themselves wondering what it would be like to be a reenactor. Most consider their thoughts to be nothing more than an intriguing daydream because they're not sure they would like reenacting and they don't want to make a commitment they can't live up to. For these people, Civil War Adventures may be a daydream come true.

Still in the start-up phase, Civil War Adventures hopes to offer the opportunity for individuals to experience reenacting

Training in the use of weapons and period combat tactics

without the long-term commitment of time and money. Three-day programs are being designed during which participants will be provided with a Union or Confederate uniform, accouterments (including cartridge box and sling), replica rifle, accommodations in period tents, and meals. Training in the use of weapons and period combat tactics will be included, along with daily reenactments and evening entertainment. This is a great idea, but it's also one which will require a lot of preparation on the part of Civil War Adventures, so the sooner you let them know of your interest, the better. At present, the first camp is scheduled for June of 1997.

Olde Soldier Books, Inc.

18779 B North Frederick Road
Gaithersburg, MD 20879
Phone: (301) 963-2929
Fax: (301) 963-9556

Product(s): Books, CDVs, Paper, Photographs

Offering a fine collection of new, old, out-of-print, and rare books, Olde Soldier Books also carries a nice selection of autographs, photographs, and general memorabilia. A catalog listing recent acquisitions is available.

Old West Saddle Shop

6854 Hummingbird Lane
P.O. Box 4300
Casper, WY 82604
Phone: (307) 577-1356
Email: mattsee@trib.com
Internet:
   http://www.trib.com/SADDLESHOP/

Product(s): Accouterments, Leather Goods, Saddles

A variety of saddles are offered through the Old West Saddle Shop, including the 1859 McClellan Saddle, the 1874 McClellan Saddle, and the Confederate "McClellan" Saddle.

Original Frameworks

1300 S. Main Street - Gables
Blacksburg, VA 24060
Phone: 1-800-654-1861
Email: civilwar@nrv.net
Internet: http://www.ptiweb.com/
   ~civilwar
Product(s): Art, Artifacts, Paper

Original Frameworks buys, sells, trades, and appraises Civil War-related paper, documents, and autographs. Their art offerings include period works, as well as present-day limited editions. Proprietor Jay Rainey also buys and sells anything used by the soldier during the Civil War. Internet catalogs are available.

Owens Books

2728 Tinsley Drive
Richmond, VA 23235
Phone: (804) 272-8888
Email:
   mramsey@rmond.mindspring.com
Internet: http://www.skytec.com/web/
   owensbooks

Product(s): Books

Owens Books deals in First Editions, Out-of-Print, Scarce, and Rare Books on the American Civil War. Their catalog is mailed monthly and is also available on the World Wide Web. If you're having trouble finding a particular book, give them a call.

Catalog: FREE

First Editions, Out-of-Print, Scarce, and Rare Books on the American Civil War.

Palmetto Presence

Jim Arnett, Proprietor
P.O. Box 527
Montmorenci, SC 29839
Phone: (803) 641-2382
Email: jarnett@csra.net
Internet: http://www.21mall.com/
            ppresence/ppresence.htm

Product(s): Artifacts, Artillery Items, Belts
& Buckles, Books, Buttons, Dug Items,
Paper

catalog on the Internet

Specializing in things Confederate, particularly South Carolina relics and paper, Palmetto Presence has a catalog on the Internet and conducts business primarily through mail order, Civil War shows, and gun shows. Check out their web site and give Jim a call, especially if you're looking for a piece of South Carolina's Civil War past.

Panther Lodges

P.O. Box 32WC
Normantown, WV 25267
Phone: (304) 462-7718
Orders: 1-800-487-2684

Product(s): Buttons, Camp Gear, Fabric, Instruments, Patterns, Pipes, Tents, Tinware, Tobacco

cookware, wool blankets, candle lanterns, enamelware, hand forged items, knives, tomahawks, brass bugles, and many different types of canvas bags. Their catalog includes items from the French & Indian War, Revolutionary War, Fur Trade, and, of course, the Civil War.

When I received Panther Lodges' catalog in the mail, I must admit that I was pleasantly surprised. Having seen their advertisements, which appear regularly in various Civil War publications, I assumed—wrongly so—that they sold tents and only tents. Their 140-page catalog quickly destroyed that notion. Yes, tents are still their specialty and they can easily fill whatever Civil War tentage requirement you have, but that's only the beginning. They also deal in tent accessories, tinware, oak kegs, cast iron

Illustrated Catalog: $2
Civil War Tent Flyer w/prices: FREE

Photo Courtesy of Panther Lodges

Sibley Tent from Panther Lodges

Peter Evans Pipes

285 West Mashta Drive, Dept. P
Key Biscayne, FL 33149
Phone: (305) 361-5589
Email: GSA00008@mail.wvnet.edu

Product(s): Pipes

Peter Evans Pipes are handmade-to-order, carved to your specifications from

General John Buford Pipe as seen in the motion picture **Gettysburg**

Briar, Meerschaum, and other materials of your choice. Each pipe is period-correct in style, materials, and workmanship. Examples of General James Longstreet and General John Buford pipes can be seen in the motion picture *Gettysburg*.

Information: $1

General James Longstreet Pipe

Phalanx Studio
414 Oak Street
Mr. Horeb, WI 53572
Phone: (608) 437-6739

Product(s): Art

Featuring the work of artist Mike Thorson, Phalanx Studio offers stirring images of the Civil War. Recent works include "Black Hat Baptism" and "The Skirmishers." "Black Hat Baptism" depicts Company B of the 7th Wisconsin at Brawner Farm on August 28, 1862. This is a limited edition print (750 signed and numbered). "The Skirmishers" is also a limited edition (450 signed and numbered) and depicts skirmishers from the Army of the Cumberland in the Summer of 1864. Since "Black Hat Baptism" is the first in a series of Iron Brigade prints, we'll keep our eyes open for other works by Mr. Thorson.

H.J. Popowski
Union Capsule Histories
158 North Chase Avenue
Columbus, OH 43204-2603
Phone: (614) 276-4993

Product(s): Unit Histories

Each Unit History Capsule offered by H.J. Popowski contains three sections, specifically a service record of the unit, an order of battle placing the unit in its larger context, and a bibliography of sources. Unit History Capsules are currently $10.00 per unit. Due to the scarcity and scattered nature of Southern records, Confederate capsules are not available.

The Powder Horn Gunshop, Inc.
Box 1001
200 West Washington Street
Middleburg, VA 20118-1001
Phone: (540) 687-6628
Fax: (540) 687-6431

Product(s): Artifacts, Weapons & Accessories

Photo Courtesy of The Powder Horn Gunshop

Antique arms and militaria are the house specialty at The Powder Horn Gunshop. Catalogs, which are issued quarterly, include a nice description of each item. A sample from the May 1996 catalog reads:

220. CIVIL WAR GENERAL OFFICERS BELT AND BUCKLE WITH HANGERS. Found in a barn in the village of Bloomfield in Loudoun County, Virginia. Beautiful M1851 rectangular Eagle sword belt plate in superb condition. The sword belt is of folded stitched and sewn construction with three bands of gold wire running the full length of it. The belt is in two pieces as might be expected from its storage, but is otherwise intact. Retains its leather sword hangers with the gold wire decoration and "S" shaped hook for shorting the swords level. One of these is attached to the belt and one is detached. Complete and very scarce. $950.00

Illustrated Catalog: $20 a year (four issues)

Publisher's Press, Inc.

P.O. Box 631
Orange, VA 22960
Phone: (540) 672-4845
Fax: (540) 672-7283
Email: nstcw@msn.com
CompuServe: 71764,1311
(71764.1311@compuserve.com)

Product(s): Books, Magazines

Publisher's Press is a publisher and distributor of Civil War reference books for the collector. With over twenty years in the business, their crisp photography, authoritative text, and stylish graphics and design have become a hallmark of their products.

First and foremost among their publications is *North South Trader's Civil War* magazine. This 74-page, heavily illustrated bimonthly periodical specializes in detailed articles on artifacts of the war, from buttons and buckles to uniforms and weaponry. The articles are written by some of the nation's most knowledgeable and renowned collectors. The magazine also contains a comprehensive calendar of upcoming collectors' events.

Publisher's Press also compiles, publishes, and distributes the biannual North South Trader's Civil War Collector's Price Guide, which lists current market values in all the major categories of Civil War collectibles. In addition to current price information, the *Price Guide* contains recommended readings, contacts and catalogues, and collecting tips.

Magazine subscription: $30 per year (domestic) $40 per year (foreign)

Price Guide: $25 plus $3 shipping and handling

Current Book List: FREE

The Quartermaster Shop

5565 Griswold Road
Kimball, MI 48074
Phone: (810) 367-6702 (8 to 4 EST)
Fax: (810) 367-6514

Product(s): Clothing, Hats, Insignia, Uniforms

Offering a large inventory of 1860-65 period Union and Confederate Enlisted Uniforms in stock (ready for immediate shipment) and taking custom orders for Officer's Uniforms and men's period civilian clothing on a limited basis, The Quartermaster Shop is an excellent source for men getting involved in Living History. Their nicely illustrated black and white catalog includes fabric samples.

Catalog: $4.00

Confederate General's Frockcoat

R & K Sutlery

1015-1200th Street
Lincoln, IL 62656
Phone: (217) 732-8844

Product(s): Accouterments, Belts & Buckles, Buttons, Canteens, Clothing, Fabric, Hats, Haversacks, Tents, Tinware, Uniforms

Robert and Kay Coons offer a nice selection of period clothing for men, women, and children. Items for women include fans, parasols, girdles & stomachers, jewelry, aprons, pantaloons, petticoats, slippers, corsets, bonnets, and others. Tents include the officer's wall tent, 6 foot "A" tents, 9 foot "A" tents, dog tents, Sibley tents, etc. R & K also offers a nice selection of men's hats, including kepis and bummers, toppers, derby hats, planters hats, and tall hats. Uniform items include everything from pants and mounted trousers, to great coats.

Reb Acres

Route 2, Box 314
Raphine, VA 24472
Phone: (540) 377-2057

Product(s): Accouterments, Artifacts, Memorabilia, Newspapers, Paper

Four times each year, Reb Acres publishes their 32-page catalog of authentic Civil War artifacts. In an attempt to satisfy the needs of all collectors, from the beginner to the high art collector, their detailed catalog includes a variety of items. These include documents, letters, music, Confederate and slave papers, newspapers, personal items, items from the home front, medical, dental, religious articles, camp items, regulation items from uniform accouterments to cavalry, artillery, and navy items, edged weapons, pistols, revolvers, carbines, and muskets.

An excerpt from catalog Volume IX, Number Two, reads:

D258   Original Fort Sumter Brick: This is the second one of these historic bricks we have had. The first is still in our personal collection where it has been for more than ten years, and we hope to have it a while longer! Both bricks are almost identical in texture and size (@ 8" x 4" x 2-3/4" and weighing @5 lbs). This brick comes with an affidavit of authenticity from the gentleman who originally obtained it from Fort Sumter. A great display item!
$187.50

Reb Acres will provide a complimentary copy of their catalog for three First Class stamps. Current buyers receive a yearly subscription at no charge; non-buyers may subscribe for $10 a year.

The Rebelaires
950 Sunset Lane
Waycross, GA 31503
Phone: (912) 285-8191

Product(s): Music

What do you get when you take four guys from Georgia whose ancestors all fought in the same company for the Confederacy, mix in some obvious talent, and stir with heartfelt emotion? The Rebelaires and their great music, that's what. The group's original compositions have a modern sound, mixing acoustic and bass guitars with the more traditional 19th century instruments. The result is a sound that borders on Country/ Folk/Bluegrass, but with lyrics that are Civil War. Recordings currently available include: *Carry the Memories On*, *For the Cause*, and *Confederate Man* (one of my favorite CDs). All titles are available on cassette at $11.00 each, postpaid. *Carry the Memories On/For the Cause* is available on double-length CD at $21.00 postpaid. *Confederate Man* is available on CD at $16.00 postpaid. The Rebelaires are also available for balls, conventions, reenactments, and private parties.

Editor's Choice
SELECTION

Sutlers! Call or write for wholesale information.

The Rebel Company

P.O. Box 15191
Atlanta, GA 30333
Phone: (770) 947-1863

Product(s): Gift Packs (Georgia Preserves, Syrups, Dressings)

Photo Courtesy of The Rebel Company

If you're looking for a gastronomical gift idea, take a look at The Rebel Company's fine selection of Georgia preserves (blackberry jam, spiced peach chutney, vidalia onion relish, wild honey, and others), Dressings (Vidalia onion and peppercorn and Vidalia onion honey mustard dressing), and Syrups (strawberry, peach, blackberry, and blueberry). Ship one to a friend, relative, or to yourself today and enjoy a tasty combination of fresh produce and traditional Southern recipes.

Red Willow Clothing and Canvas Shelters

Box 188 - 131 West Main St.
Oxford, IA 52322
Phone: (319) 628-4815

Product(s): Fabric, Tents

Red Willow offers a selection of Civil War tents (Guard tents, Officer tents, common shelters, The Sibley Tent, and pup tents). Tents are available in untreated cotton, cotton treated for water and mildew, cotton treated for water, mildew and fire, and 50/50 cotton/poly treated for water, mildew, and fire.

Note: Pup tents are available in olive green temper tent fabric only

Reenactment Eyewear

RR 4, Box 62
Williamsport, PA 17701
Phone: (717) 322-9849

Product(s): Eyewear

Reenactment Eyewear is a family business with 21 combined years of optical experience. They are American Board of Opticianry certified and all their eyewear is made according to ANSI standards and passes all FDA requirements on impact resistance. Prescription lenses are available for Civil War reenactors and for those creating impressions of the Revolutionary War and WWI.

The Regimental Band

37th Georgia Volunteer Infantry, CSA
766 Riverhill Drive
Athens, GA 30606
Phone: (706) 543-4559

Photo Courtesy of The Regimental Band

Product(s): Music

The 37th GVI's brass band, fife-and-drum corps, and songsters have appeared in two award-winning movies (*Glory* and *The Rose and the Jackal*). They also perform at conventions, parades, cotillions, reenactments, and patriotic/civic ceremonies. All tunes—USA and CSA—are performed in mid-19th-century style on antique wind and percussion instruments. Five 1-hour cassettes are available at $13.50 each, postpaid. CDs will be available soon.

Volumes available include:

Vol. I: Serenade in Gray (out of stock)
Vol. II: Memories of Home, Camp, and Field
Vol. III: A Southern Celebration–Live (out of stock)
Vol. IV: Serenade in Blue
Vol. V: Rebel Rousers & Concert Classics

Donations/contributions are federally tax-exempt. Sales proceeds from recordings help the 37th Georgia preserve our great American tradition of military band music.

The Regimental Quartermaster

P.O. Box 553
Hatboro, PA 19040
Phone: (215) 672-6891
Fax: (215) 672-9020

Product(s): Accouterments, Belts & Buckles, Blankets, Books, Buttons, Clothing, Hats, Haversacks, Insignia, Leather Goods, Music, Uniforms, Weapons & Accessories

An extensive line of reproduction Civil War military goods can be found in The Regimental Quartermaster catalog. Shooting supplies, gun parts, and weapons (muskets, swords, etc) are well represented, as are uniform items and accessories.

The Regimental Quartermaster maintains a shop at 540 Newtown Road, Warminster, Pennsylvania, but they ask that you call ahead to insure someone is available to assist you. Gift certificates are available.

Catalog: $2 post paid

Resurgence Outfitters

56 East Uwchlan Ave #405
Exton, PA 19341

Product(s): Clothing, Uniforms

Custom Civil War-era clothing is the specialty at Resurgence Outfitters. They make the basic enlisted man's uniform (shirt, shell jacket, trousers, and drawers) and are expanding their line all the time. RO recently finished an illustrated brochure of their products and will send it out free to anyone sending a self-addressed stamped envelope.

Photo Courtesy of Resurgence Outfitters

Basic Shell Jacket

Richmond Arsenal

7605 Midlothian Turnpike
Richmond, VA 23235
Phone: (804) 272-4570

Items are both excavated and non-excavated

The Civil War Shop

Product(s): Accouterments, Artifacts, Buttons, Canteens, Uniforms, Weapons & Accessories

Richmond Arsenal buys, sells, and trades Civil War artifacts. They carry a line of original muskets, carbines, accouterments, buttons, canteens, uniforms, leather goods, bullets, artillery shells, prints, and relics. Items are both excavated and non-excavated and each comes with a 100 percent guarantee.

Catalog: $10 (three issues)

Richmonville Tinware

21328 Highway 99E
P.O. Box 407
Aurora, OR 97002
Phone: (503) 678-1675
Orders: 1-800-501-1675 Pin #2000

Product(s): Canteens, Tinware

Maybe I'm easily impressed, but I loved the catalog published by Richmonville Tinware. It's old-fashioned- newspaper look and interesting side-bars make for a truly outstanding presentation. You can tell right away that proprietor James Richmond is another one of those passionate craftsmen.

Richmonville Tinware has been doing business for over 30 years and offers a variety of handmade tinware from 1720 thru about 1865. They have worked with museums across the country, Civil War reenactors, the Buckskin Crowd, and special orders. Their list of tin products is impressive and includes: a wide variety of lanterns, candle holders, and lamps; Chandeliers; sconces; political campaign torches; mess gear; water buckets; a cream pitcher; a hardtack cutter; a water dipper; camp kettles; match safes; a wash pan; medicine containers; the Hope Camp Stove; the Sibley Stove; coffee pots and unit coffee pots; canteens; flasks; a flint and steel set; tinderbox; cookie cutters; cartridge tins; pie safe panels; cuspidors; and even a Civil War field secretary. So if you're interested in tinware, order their catalog today—you'll thank me for it later.

Catalog: $3

RSV Products

P.O. Box 26
Hopkins, MN 55343
Phone: (612) 936-0400

History's Soundtrack ...

Product(s): Music (bugle calls)

RSVProducts was started a number of years ago with the goal of providing unique, program-enhancing material for Scout Leaders. The company has grown since then and now offers several bugle call packages that teach calls from Reveille to Taps and beyond. All calls are recorded in both the keys of G and C to allow either regulation Army or Cavalry bugles to play along. The packages are designed for a number of uses, including: training beginners, accompanying performers, testing and training for recognition, having a recorded call on standby for most any situation or ceremony when a live bugler is unavailable, and simply for enjoyment.

Bugle packages (book and cassette/CD) currently available include:

The Basic Bugler - 15 essential calls, sequenced from Reveille to Taps.
Bugler Harmony - 7 arrangements for duet or trio.
Specialty Bugler - 36 calls that explore our bugling heritage.

Individual packages are $8.99 (cassette version) or $13.99 (CD version) plus shipping. *The Complete Bugler Series* is $24.99 (cassette) or $39.99 (CD version) plus shipping. Write or call the company for ordering instructions.

J.M. Santarelli

Civil War Books & Publishing
226 Paxson Ave.
Glenside, PA 19038-4612
Phone: (215) 576-5358

Product(s): Books

specializes in antique, reprint, and out-of-print books

J.M. Santarelli Civil War Books & Publishing specializes in antique, reprint, and out-of-print books. While stocking over 300 Civil War titles, they still keep an eye out for new material to publish. Two recent publications are *"This War Is An Awful Thing ..." The Civil War Letters of the 19th and 90th Pennsylvania Volunteers*, and *A Pennsylvania Quaker In Andersonville: The Diary of Charles Smedley.*

Catalog: $2

Schneider Enterprises

1252 N. Brownslake Road
Burlington, WI 53105-9794
Phone: (414) 534-6813
Fax: (414) 534-6813

Product(s): **Cannon, Carriages, Gatling Guns**

Photo Courtesy of Schneider Enterprises

Offering scale model cannons and full scale Gatling guns, Schneider Enterprises currently offers a Bronze Coehorn Mortar, 1/2 scale Parrot Rifle (12-pounder), 1/3 scale Napoleon 12-pounder, English Swivel Gun, 1/4 scale No. 1 trail carriage, 1/3 scale Whitworth Howitzer, 1/3 scale 1841 6-pounder, and others. My favorite, though, is their full scale Gatling gun. Invented and patented by Richard Gatling in 1862, the original Gatling gun was capable of firing 350 rounds per minute through rotating barrels. Though the Gatling gun saw some limited use during the Civil War, it didn't achieve the status of official Army weaponry until 1866.

Brochure: $2

The Scholar's Bookshelf

110 Melrich Road
Cranbury, NJ 08512
Phone: (609) 395-6933
Fax: (609) 395-0755
Email: jgreen4@ix.netcom.com
Internet: http://www2.scholarsbookshelf.com/scholars/

Product(s): Books

A major book catalog company that produces three 88-page Military History catalogs each year. Catalogs feature a substantial variety of Civil War books and videos, including new, backlist, and many sale books.

Catalog: FREE

Scotty's Scale Soldiers

1008 Adams Street
Bay City, MI 48708
Phone: (517) 892-6177

Product(s): Miniatures

With a large scale (54mm to 125mm) and small scale (6mm to 30mm)

catalog exclusively for Civil War miniatures, Scotty's Scale Soldiers offers an impressive selection of over 2000 items from more than 50 manufacturers, enough to satisfy the needs of almost any miniatures gamer or collector. The February 1995 small scale catalog we examined featured 76 pages of Civil War miniatures. The large scale catalog was similar in size and selection, offering 64 pages from which to choose. Paints, game rules, books, terrain items, and other accessories are also offered in the catalogs.

120MM Union Zouave Officer

Catalogs: Small Scale $6.00
            Large Scale $5.00

Second/II Corps Civil War Books

209 High Street
Petersburg, VA 23803
Phone: (804) 861-1863

Second/II Corps Books specializes in Civil War books, but also offers guided Civil War tours of the Petersburg area. Hours are Monday-Saturday, 10-6, or by appointment.

Product(s): Battlefield Tours, Books

Slide-A-Fact

P.O. Box 66085
St. Peterburg Beach, FL 33736-6085

Product(s): Reference Material

Slide-A-Fact's "101 Civil War Battles" is a nicely constructed, handy reference tool that provides instant data regarding the battles, dates, commanders, casualties, and victors of the well-known and lesser known battles of the Civil War. Sliding the data card through the Slide-A-Fact frame, you can quickly find that on June 3, 1861, Union General McClellan faced Confederate General Garnett at Philippi, West Virginia (before West Virginia was officially a state). Casualties were light: two on the U.S. side, 15 on the Confederate side. Slide-A-Fact offers a simple way of keeping the facts straight—especially with so many battles, commanders, dates, and casualty figures to remember. "101 Civil War Battles" sells for $6.95 postpaid, plus applicable sales tax. Special rates are available for bulk purchases and for dealers and distributors.

Somewhere In Time Studio

P.O. Box 7
Zion Hill, PA 18981
Phone: (215) 536-0143

Product(s): Art

Featuring the work of Deborah George, Somewhere In Time Studio is currently offering a duotone pencil sketch (11" x 14") of Confederate General Nathan Bedford Forrest and his horse Highlander. A second equestrian sketch is in the works, this one featuring Joshua Lawrence Chamberlain and his horse Charlemagne. The 500 limited edition prints are signed and numbered by the artist.

South Bend Replicas, Inc.

61650 Oak Road
South Bend, IN 46614
Phone: (219) 289-4500

Product(s): Cannon

Pile of lathe turned guns for Fort Pillow, Tennessee

Photo Courtesy of South Bend Replicas, Inc.

The 1992-96 *Catalog of Antique/Replica Ordnance* by South Bend Replicas, Inc., is packed with photos and useful information. Anyone with an interest in artillery will benefit from this catalog because, in addition to providing product information, it packs in a lot of cannon-related history, safety tips, and other valuable information. A sure sign of the passion South Bend Replicas, Inc. has for its products—and ordnance in general.

The catalog provides an extensive list of products, including: the 12-pounder Whitworth; Noble Brothers Confederate 6-pounder; 1/4 scale sea service 12-pounder; 12-pounder Mountain Howitzer; Carronades; 9-inch Dahlgrens; 3/4 scale 10-pounder Parrott; Model 1841 6-pounder; 3" Ordnance Rifle; Ordnance seal; and much more.

Catalog: $7

Anyone with an interest in artillery will benefit from this catalog because, in addition to providing product information, it packs in a lot of cannon-related history, safety tips, and other valuable information.

Southern Heritage Press

P.O. Box 347163
Atlanta, GA 30334

Product(s): Books

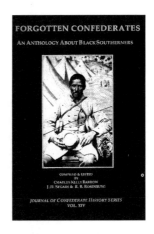

Southern Heritage Press currently offers a number of Civil War books, including *Forgotten Confederates: An Anthology About Black Southerners*; *They Sleep Beneath The Mockingbird*; *Andersonville: The Southern Perspective*; *For The Sake Of My Country: The Diary of Colonel W.W. Ward*; *Black Southerners in Gray*; and *A Nation of Sovereign States*, among others.

SPEERIT Strategy Games

10612-D Providence Road #325
Charlotte, NC 28277
Phone: (704) 849-7777
Fax: (704) 849-7777
Orders: 1-800-831-1155

Product(s): Games

Photo Courtesy of SPEERIT Strategy Games

With one Civil War game already on the market and three more on the way, SPEERIT Strategy Games is quickly implementing its own strategy for success. *Gettysburg: Three Days in July* is currently available from SPEERIT and comes with two foldout boards that, when joined together, create an impressive and accurate map of Gettysburg in 1863. Toss in 137 double sided, upright playing pieces and you have the makings (or remaking) of one of the most important battles of the Civil War.

Gettysburg: Three Days in July is a well-thought-out, well-designed interactive board game that offers hours of enjoyment.

As with all board games, plan on spending a few minutes acquainting yourself with the rules—then dive in. And keep your eyes open for other Civil War games from SPEERIT, including *Antietam: Bloody Harvest* (spring 1997), *Shiloh: The Coming Fury* (fall 1997), and *Manassas: Lightning Strikes Twice* (spring 1998).

Free color brochure upon request.

> *Gettysburg: Three Days in July* is a well-thought-out, well-designed interactive board game

Staley's Sundries

710 Caroline Street
Fredericksburg, VA 22401-5904
Phone: (540) 899-6464
Fax: (540) 373-2469

Product(s): Belts & Buckles, Books, Buttons, Cannon (non-firing), Clothing, Flags, Hats, Insignia, Instruments, Medals, Miniatures, Music, Patterns, Video, Weapons & Accessories (non-firing)

Located in Old Town Fredericksburg, just three doors from the city visitor's center, Staley's Sundries offers a variety of American Revolution, Civil War, and Indian War items. Their selection of merchandise includes military miniatures, both painted and kits, and all the necessary paints, brushes, glues, etc.; reference books; miniature and full size military, state, and international flags; T-shirts, music cassettes and CDs; reproduction buttons, belt buckles, and cartridge box plates; Civil War coffee mugs; neckties; spoons; magnets; and the list goes on.

A pattern catalog (*Period Impressions*) containing a selection of extensively researched patterns drawn from original patterns or clothing is available. These patterns have illustrated, easy to follow instructions for the best possible results.

Staley's Sundries offers a particularly wide selection of music cassettes and CDs, including the works of Bobby Horton, Camelot Records, George Carroll, Billy Ray Reynolds, Keith & Rusty McNeil, Songs of the Seventh Cavalry, 97th Regimental String Band, The Regimental Band of the 11th NC Troops, 12th Louisiana String Band & Benevolence Society, Southern Horizon, Wayne Erbsen, Dr. Horsehair's Old Time Minstrels, First Brigade Band, Heritage Americana Brass Band, Jim Morgan, The Gettysburg Vocal Ensemble, Starline Productions, The Regimental Band 37th Georgia Volunteer Infantry, Jimmy Arnold, Americus Brass Band, 8th Georgia Regimental, Jim Taylor, and scores from movies and TV (*Glory*, the 11-hour *Civil War* mini-series by Ken Burns, *Music of the Civil War*, and *Dances With Wolves*).

Pattern Catalog: $1

Stan Clark Military Books

915 Fairview Avenue
Gettysburg, PA 17325
Phone: (717) 337-1728 (9am - 9pm EST)
Fax: (717) 337-0581

Product(s): Art, Books, Paper

Stan Clark Military Books specializes in Civil War and other U.S. Military books, whether new or used, including out-of-print. Based in Gettysburg, the company operates exclusively as a mail-order business. Stan Clark also publishes a selection of Civil War titles. Their books are high-quality and attractive. I was particularly moved by the introduction Stan Clark offered in "Bayonet!

Photo by Willow Creek Press

Forward. My Civil War Reminiscences" by Joshua Lawrence Chamberlain. As a Chamberlain admirer, I was impressed that Mr. Clark could so effectively portray the character and quality of General Chamberlain in two short pages. Paper items, autographs, documents, U.S. Marine Corps books, and other items are also available.

Catalog: $2

Stone Mountain Miniatures, Inc.

P.O. Box 675, Dept. ECW
Brighton, CO 80601
Phone: (303) 654-7989
Fax: (303) 659-9024
Email: StonMtnMin@aol.com

Where History Meets the Future

Product(s): Books, Miniatures

Providing pewter Civil War miniatures in 6mm, 15mm, and 54mm scales, Stone Mountain Miniatures has an extensive product line they can be proud of. Their 15mm Civil War line won the Origins™/H.G. Wells award in 1987 for best historical miniatures line. They have the only line of American Civil War figures to win this prestigious award in its 25-year history. If it's U.S.A. or C.S.A. ships and ironclads you're looking for, they have a nice selection to choose from. The company also offers Napoleonic, Seven Years War, WWI, Foreign Ships, British Colonial, French Colonial, Wild West, and American Revolution miniatures. Terrain material, paper flag sets, paints, scenery accessories, buildings, and forts can be ordered for the more elaborate displays and for finishing touches. Rule sets and a selection of books are also available.

Catalog: $4.00

Photo by Willow Creek Press

StrataMax, Inc.

6238 Raintree Lane
Oaklandon, IN 46236

Product(s): Games

Rebs & Yanks, a Civil War card game, is the brainchild of Max Michael, president of StrataMax, Inc. Unlike many card games which require additional purchases, *Rebs & Yanks* comes complete and ready to play (though you will need a pair of dice). Designed to be a two-player game, you'll need about forty minutes to annihilate your enemy (or be annihilated). This is an easy pack-along game for reenactments, road trips, waiting rooms, lunch breaks, or anywhere else that two Civil War buffs gather with time on their hands. *Rebs & Yanks* sells for $18, plus $2 shipping and handling.

TalonSoft

P.O. Box 632
Forest Hill, MD 21050
Phone: (410) 821-7282
Orders: 1-800-211-6504
AOL: Talonsoft1
CompuServe: 75162,373
Prodigy: ZGAK37A
Internet: http://www.talonsoft.com

Product(s): Computer Software, Games

Captured Screen Image Courtesy of TalonSoft

If you've been waiting for a good excuse to buy a computer "Battleground Gettysburg" by TalonSoft is here. TalonSoft takes you back to the three-day conflict at Gettysburg and lets you call the shots (Confederate or Union) at places like the Wheatfield, Little Round Top, Culp's Hill, during Pickett's Charge, and others. Battleground Gettysburg also has an Artificial Intelligence (AI) button that will finish a scenario for you—insuring that all your units have fired or moved before moving to the next phase of the battle. Whether playing with a friend or against the computer, you're in for a fun ride.

An exceptional game

Taylor Design, Inc.

P.O. Box 956
Harpers Ferry, WV 25425
Phone: (304) 876-3871
Fax: (304) 876-1666
Orders: 1-800-371-9452

Product(s): Art

Photo Courtesy of Taylor Design

Taylor Design offers limited and open edition prints by nationally recognized artist, Tom Taylor. Each print comes with a handy reference guide that describes the historical significance of the images shown—creating works that are educational as well as artistic.

Limited edition prints focus on particular battles, while the open series, *A Journey Through The Civil War*, portrays the many people, places, and events that helped shape this chapter of American history.

Portion of **Gettysburg, The Triumph and Tragedy,** *by Tom Taylor*

TDC Interactive

2716 Ocean Park Blvd.
Suite 3085
Santa Monica, CA 90405
Phone: (310) 452-6720
Fax: (310) 452-6722
Orders: 1-800-832-0032

Product(s): Computer Software

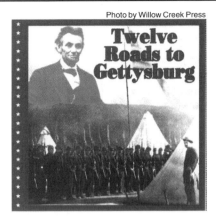
Photo by Willow Creek Press

With over 30 CD-ROM titles under its belt, including art libraries, multimedia storybooks, interactive music education titles, and a variety of games and children programming, TDC Interactive is also the producer of the award-winning *Twelve Roads to Gettysburg*. This outstanding CD brings narration, animated maps, biographical sketches, unit histories, period music, organizational charts, illustrations, and photographs together to tell the story of Gettysburg in a new and exciting format. The suggested retail price of *Twelve Roads to Gettysburg* is $29.95, and it is available for both PC and Macintosh.

Timefarer Footwear

P.O. Box 1237
Bristol BS18 5BY
United Kingdom

Handmade reproduction boots & shoes

Product(s): Footwear

Photo Courtesy of Timefarer Footwear

American Civil War Mounted Boots

Committed to historical accuracy, Timefarer Footwear supplies handmade reproduction footwear to historical reenactors, living historians, and museums worldwide. Their footwear is carefully researched to ensure that construction methods and styles used are appropriate to each period. Whatever your period of interest may be, from prehistoric to present day, civilian or military, ladies or mens, Timefarer Footwear can provide the correct footwear.

> *carefully researched to ensure that construction methods and styles used are appropriate to each period*

Trans-Mississippi Militaria

Charles Brecheisen
1004 Simon Drive
Plano, TX 75025-2501
Phone: (214) 517-8111
Fax: (214) 517-8111

Product(s): Artifacts, Books, CDVs, G.A.R., Medical, Paper, Photographs, Stereoviews, U.C.V.

> *authentic Civil War medical equipment*

Trans-Mississippi Militaria offers a nice selection of books, papers, G.A.R. & U.C.V. collectibles, and authentic Civil War medical equipment.

They regularly attend shows in Memphis, TN; Tulsa, OK; Chicago, IL; Vicksburg, MS; Mansfield, OH; Wheaton, IL; Louisville, KY; Houston, TX; and Nashville, TN.

Catalog: $1

Troubadour Interactive

P.O. Box 12
Northfield, MA 01360
Phone: (413) 498-2758
Orders: 1-800-497-0042
Email: trubador@crocker.com
Internet: http://www.wp.com/trubador/

Product(s): Computer Software

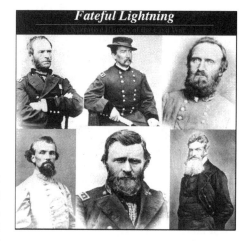

Centered on a 175,000-word text by William Hillenbrand, FATEFUL LIGHTNING: A NARRATIVE HISTORY OF THE CIVIL WAR, by Troubadour Interactive, is an exciting example of how computers are changing the study of the Civil War. From a broad overview of socio-political affairs, the CD shifts to close analysis of the major campaigns. Detailed accounts of individual engagements are directly linked to maps providing animated, narrated views of the action. In addition, a series of pop-up maps provide instant map reference from related text pages. Other multimedia features include color photos of the major battlefields as they appear today, archival images of key political and military figures, recordings of twelve popular songs of the Civil War-era (with songbook and lyrics), and video clips of recent reenactments. Check their Web site for sample text and graphics.

For Macintosh and Windows.

> *From a broad overview of socio-political affairs, the CD shifts to close analysis of the major campaigns*

Uniforms of Antiquity

610 Mena Street
Mena, AR 71953
Phone: (501) 394-7288
Email: Pbradley @ cswnet.com

Photo Courtesy of Uniforms of Antiquity

Product(s): Clothing, Hats, Insignia, Uniforms

Proprietors Mike and Bette Bradley offer a nice selection of 1800's time period uniforms and civilian clothing, recreated for collectors, historians, and skirmishers. They have supplied uniforms throughout the U.S. to museums, reenactors, for motion pictures and television programs, and to state and national parks.

No order too small.
No size too large.

Upper Mississippi Valley Mercantile Company

1607 Washington Street
Davenport, IA 52804
Phone: (319) 322-0896
Fax: (319) 383-5549

Quality Civil War Supplies

Product(s): Books, Camp Gear, Leather Goods, Patterns, Tents, Tinware, Uniforms, Weapons & Accessories

Established in 1980, The Upper Mississippi Valley Mercantile Company has been supplying the reenactor for sixteen years. Their current catalog (the Seventh Edition) is highly illustrated and contains more than 800 individual items for the Civil War enthusiast, whether serious reenactor or casual hobbyist. The catalog also provides valuable information on all items carried by the mercantile.

Catalog: $3 (Illustrated, 100 pages)

U.S. Flag Service

5741 Elmer Derr Rd.
Frederick, MD 21703-7411
Orders: 1-800-USA-FLAG (M-F, 4-6pm)

Product(s): Flags

In business for over 17 years, the U.S. Flag Service claims the distinction of being the largest U.S. historical flag dealer. A strong supporter of the Civil War community, they sponsored the Battle of Monocacy Reenactment in September 1995, an event attended by over 12,000 people.

All flags are made in America.

List: $3 (nylons only)

largest U.S. historical flag dealer

Valley Framing Studio & Gallery

328 W. Main Street
Waynesboro, VA 22980
Phone: (540) 943-7529
Fax: (540) 949-7525
Internet: http://www.pointsouth.com/
valframe.htm
Orders: 1-800-821-7529

Product(s): Art, Framing, Statuary

Valley Framing offers the works of Mort Kunstler, John Paul Strain, Robert Summers, David Wright, and Aubrey Hayden, as well as sculptures by Ron Tunison and Carl McClesky. Art related items, such as books and calendars, are also offered.

Village Tinsmithing Works

P.O. Box 189
Randolph, OH 44265
Phone: (330) 325-9101

Purveyors of Fine Copper, Brass, and Tin Ware

Product(s): Canteens, Lanterns, Tinware

What reenactment would be complete without period tinware manufactured by the same type of tinsmithing machines that crafted the coffee pots, tin plates, mess tins, and other mess gear found in every Civil War camp? That's exactly what you get from Tinsmith Bill Hoover at the Village Tinsmithing Works. Bill uses the same early to mid-1800s tinsmithing machines, hand tools, stakes, and swedges to individually craft each item. Many of the items available in their catalog are reproductions of artifacts loaned to them by individuals and museums, including some "non-issue" items found as Civil War relics and in camp pictures.

For your safety and in accordance with Food and Drug Administration guidelines and Federal Regulations, all potable items are manufactured using lead-free solder. The Village Tinsmithing Works recommends that you inquire about the solder used on the tinware you are purchasing.

Catalog: FREE (send long SASE)

Walden Font

P.O. Box 871
Winchester, MA 01890
Fax: (619) 933-7859
Email: SCHWABE@AOL.COM
Internet: http://home.navisoft.com/scrolls/
walden/index.htm

Purveyors of Fine Historic Fonts & Clipart

Product(s): Computer Software (Fonts & Clipart)

Walden Font offers a collection of original fonts and clipart as part of their Civil War Press, a publishers kit which reproduces the typefaces used in the 1860s. Two signature fonts are included, along with digitized autographs of prominent war time personalities (e.g. R.E. Lee and Abraham Lincoln). Seventy clipart images come with the Civil War Press — perfect for creating newsletters or flyers for reenactments and other living history events. Or, give your business cards, letterhead, and envelopes a Civil War flavor.

Clipart Courtesy of Walden Font

Walkala Home Video

P.O. Box 191
Parrish, AL 35580
Phone: (205) 686-7495
Fax: (205) 686-7495
Orders: 1-800-598-8243

Product(s): Video

Praise continues to mount for Walkala Home Video's production of *Co.*

Aytch (Company H) Memoirs of a Confederate Soldier. Based on the autobiography of Sam Watkins (*Co. Aytch, A Side Show Of The Big Show*), the video stars actor Bob Funk and music is provided Bobby Horton. Through Sam Watkins we see the pain, joy, and longings of the average Confederate soldier. The video sells for $24.95, plus $4.95 shipping and handling.

War Between The States Memorabilia

Len Rosa - Proprietor
P.O. Box 3965
Gettysburg, PA 17325
Phone: (717) 337-2853

Product(s): Artifacts, Books, CDVs, Memorabilia, Newspapers, Paper, Photographs, Tintypes

Len Rosa buys and sells memorabilia of the War Between the States and offers a nice catalog five times a year. Items available include Union and Confederate soldiers' letters, covers, patriotic envelopes, documents, autographs, C.D.V.'s, ambrotypes, tintypes, albumens, U.C.V. and G.A.R. badges and ribbons, newspapers such as Harpers Weekly, currency, slavery documents, relics, framed display items, and other memorabilia. The excerpt below was taken from catalog 47 and is one of 482 items offered.

83. Captain John L. Worden: commander of the famous Union ironclad, "Monitor," when it engaged its Confederate counterpart, the "Merrimac," in Hampton Roads, Va., Mar. 9, 1862. During the battle, Worden was wounded and partially blinded. In 1863, while commanding the "Montauk," he sunk the C.S.S.

Color Sergeant, 4th New Hampshire Infantry

Nashville. Clipped signature with rank, John L. Worden, Rear Admiral, U.S. Navy, 3 3/4 x 1. Closely cut, mounting traces on reverse. Very nicely signed in ink. Desirable C.W. naval autograph. Getting scarce. $150.00

Catalog: $10 per year (five issues)

Whitacre's Machine Shop

519 Turtle Meadow Drive
Winchester, VA 22602
Phone: (540) 877-1468

Product(s): Weapons & Accessories (barrels)

Manufacturer of Civil War-era barrels, particularly 1842 Springfield, 1855-1863 Springfield, Enfield, and Zouave. Will also reline 58 cal. barrels - one piece barrels.

Wildman's

2879 South Main
Kennesaw, GA 30144
Phone: (770) 422-1785

The Best Little War House in Kennesaw

Product(s): Art, Artifacts, Books, Weapons & Accessories

Wildman's specializes in pro-Southern items and will gladly mail a list of "sporadic goodies" for $2 (Federal currency accepted). Check them out, they don't call themselves the Best Little War House in Kennesaw for nothing.

Willow Creek Press of Washington

P.O. Box 3730
Silverdale, WA 98383-3730
Phone: (360) 830-5612
Fax: (360) 830-5612
Email: kope@sincom.com

publisher of
Everything Civil War

Product(s): Books

Yes, the publisher of *Everything Civil War* reserves the right to include themselves in their own book. Though *Everything Civil War* is only the second Civil War title published by Willow Creek Press of Washington, we hope we're establishing a trend. At present, the company plans to publish an updated edition of *Everything Civil War* every two years. Other *Everything* books are also planned. Subjects discussed so far include *Everything Dogs, Everything Guns, Everything Women, Everything Auto Racing, Everything College, Everything Government, Everything Conservative, Everything Romantic,* and a slew of others.

If you like a good ghost story, one that's more heartwarming and adventurous than scary, you might consider reading *When The Drummer Falls; A Gettysburg Ghost Story,* by Spencer Kope (hey, that's me). I wrote this book partly because it gave me an excuse to visit Gettysburg as often as I wanted, and partly because I'm fascinated by the many ghost stories that have risen from the Gettysburg National Military Park and the Civil War era buildings in town.

When The Drummer Falls sells for $17.95 (hardback). Willow Creek Press will pay the postage and, at your request, they'll make sure you get a signed copy.

Warning: *When The Drummer Falls* has a tendency to leave readers misty-eyed. Also, I've received *many* complaints from people who stayed up half the night because they couldn't put it down.

The Winchester Sutler, Inc.

270x Shadow Brook Lane
Winchester, VA 22603
Phone: (540) 888-3595
Fax: (540) 888-4632

Quality Civil War
Reproductions

(Store open by appointment only)

Product(s): Accouterments, Belts & Buckles, Books, Buttons, Camp Gear, Canteens, Fabric, Flags, Footwear, Hardtack, Haversacks, Hats, Insignia, Music (bugle calls), Paper, Patterns, Pipes, Uniforms, Weapons & Accessories

Nice catalog! Instead of simply presenting their products and prices and hoping for the best, the folks at the Winchester Sutler have gone a step beyond. Their catalog contains page after page of insightful and useful information that anyone serious about the Civil War will appreciate. The 87-page catalog identifies items that were common or uncommon during the war. It provides a history for uniforms and accouterments and even gives instructions for such things as cleaning oil-tanned leather or loading a black powder musket.

Accouterments include such items as wallets, bone toothbrush with hog bristles, tobacco products, razor with horn handle, hardtack, period cards, and a Barlow-type pocket knife—among other items.

Catalog: $4

A great source for anyone interested in reenacting.

Winsome Games

515 West Hutchinson Ave., Suite 6
Pittsburgh, PA 15218
Phone: (412) 244-0599
Fax: (412) 486-3157

Product(s): Games

Winsome Games has added a Civil War card game to its line of products. Called *Damn the Torpedoes*, this Civil War Naval Battles Card Game is comprised of a fully illustrated 114-card Action Deck. The 40 Union and 27 Confederate Ship Cards offer a side profile drawn to 1:1000 scale. Casement Ironclads, turreted Monitors, stealthy submarines, blockade runners, commerce raiders, and torpedo boats, among others, are represented in the deck. Designed for 2 to 6 players, playing time is 1 to 2 hours. Price is $25.00 plus $5 shipping and handling (PA residents add 6% sales tax).

Wisconsin Veterans Museum

30 W. Mifflin Street
Madison, WI 53703
Phone: (608) 266-1680

Product(s): Blankets, Canteens, Certificates, Tinware

The Wisconsin Veterans Museum sells a number of items that would be of interest to Civil War enthusiasts and reenactors, primarily tinware and period blankets. The one outstanding item that caught my eye, however, was a Certificate of

Service available for Wisconsin Veterans of the Civil War. This is the perfect gift idea for those Civil War buffs who have Wisconsin relatives who fought in the War Between the States. The certificate is on parchment-style paper, suitable for framing, and includes personal information, such as dates of service and a list of battles fought. It also includes a thorough regimental history for the particular soldier's unit. This type of documentation is made possible because of a Civil War database created by the museum using data from *Roster of Wisconsin Volunteers* (1866, The State of Wisconsin). The price is quite reasonable at $6.25 (plus tax and $2 shipping and handling). If you have a relative who served from Wisconsin you really should consider one of these certificates. I'm thinking about adopting a Wisconsin Volunteer so I can get one.

Yankee Camp Studio

404 East Main Street
Ligonier, PA 15658
Phone: (412) 238-2776

Product(s): Art

Founded in October of 1995, Yankee Camp Studio is a small art company offering limited edition original art prints and photographs. The studio is not part of a large publishing company and they don't produce thousands of copies of their works. Instead, they offer very limited edition art, signed and numbered by the artist. All items are currently priced under $100. A complete presentation package is available for $3.00.

Photo Courtesy of Yankee Camp Studio

Robert E. Lee Charcoal
by Karen Parson Cumberledge

Products & Services QuickFind Index

The *Products & Services QuickFind Index* is an alphabetical guide intended to identify the primary products or services of each company listed. Many companies offer additional products not listed here, this is especially true of the sutlers.

Accouterments: Amazon Drygoods, American Military Antiques, Barry'd Treasure, Bellinger's Military Antiques, Centennial General Store, Confederate States Military Antiques, Crescent City Sutler, Dixie Leather Works, R. Stephen Dorsey Antique Militaria, Eastern Muzzleloader Supply, Fall Creek Suttlery, Green River Trading Corporation, Historic Framing and Collectibles, The Horse Soldier, James Country Muzzleloading and Mercantile, K & P Valley Collectibles, Legendary Arms, Levi Ledbetter, Frank Matuszek Civil War Antiques, Navy Arms Company, Old West Saddle Shop, R & K Sutlery, Reb Acres, The Regimental Quartermaster, Richmond Arsenal, The Winchester Sutler

Ammunition: See *Cartridges*

Antiques: Civil War Antiques, Collectors Antiquities

Appraisals: Will Gorges Civil War Antiques, The Horse Soldier

Art: A&K Historical Art, Abraham Lincoln Book Shop, The Antique Center of Gettysburg, Armistead Civil War Collections, Arsenal Artifacts, Canon Prints, Civil War "Things 'n Frames," Countryside Prints, CSA Galleries, Dale Gallon Historical Art Gallery, Don Meredith's Civil War Art, Farnsworth House Inn, Framing Fox Art Gallery, The Gettysburg Gift Center, The Gospel Truth and Civil War Room, Hallowed Ground Prints, The Haversack Store, The Historian's Gallery, Historic Framing and Collectibles, The Horse Soldier, ISI Prints, Morningside Bookshop, Original Frameworks, Phalanx Studio, Somewhere In Time Studio, Stan Clark Military Books, Taylor Design, Valley Framing Studio & Gallery, Wildman's, Yankee Camp Studio

Artifacts: American Military Antiques, The Antique Center of Gettysburg, Arsenal Artifacts, Barry'd Treasure, Civil War Antiques, Civil War Antiquities, Civil War Artifacts, Civil War "Things 'n Frames," Collectors Antiquities, Confederate States Military Antiques, Crescent City Sutler, R. Stephen Dorsey Antique Militaria, Farnsworth House Inn, The Gettysburg Gift Center, Will Gorges Civil War Antiques, The Historian's Gallery, Historic Framing and Collectibles, The Horse Soldier, K & P Valley Collectibles, Lee-Grant, Frank Matuszek Civil War Antiques, Original Frameworks, Palmetto

Presence, The Powder Horn Gunshop, Reb Acres, Richmond Arsenal, Trans-Mississippi Militaria, War Between The States Memorabilia, Wildman's

Artillery (also see **Cannon**): Barry'd Treasure, Palmetto Presence

Autographs: See **Paper**

Battlefield Tours (also see **Tours**): Campaign Tours, Civil War Tours of Tennessee, Great Expeditions Limited, Historic Richmond Foundation Tours, Craig Howell, Military Historical Tours, Second/II Corps Civil War Books

Belts & Buckles: Bellinger's Military Antiques, Caps & Kepis, Cavalier Shoppe, Centennial General Store, Collector's Armoury, Confederate States Military Antiques, Crescent City Sutler, Dixie Leather Works, R. Stephen Dorsey Antique Militaria, Fall Creek Suttlery, Grand Illusions, Green River Trading Corporation, Heidi Marsh Patterns, James Country Muzzleloading and Mercantile, Legendary Arms, Levi Ledbetter, Navy Arms Company, Palmetto Presence, R & K Sutlery, The Regimental Quartermaster, Staley's Sundries, The Winchester Sutler

Blankets: Amazon Drygoods, Crescent City Sutler, Levi Ledbetter, The Regimental Quartermaster, Wisconsin Veterans Museum

Books: Abraham Lincoln Book Shop, Amazon Drygoods, The Antique Center of Gettysburg, Barry'd Treasure, Bellinger's Military Antiques, Butternut and Blue, Camp Pope Bookshop, Centennial General Store, Civil War Antiquities, Collector's Library, Combined Books, Confederate States Military Antiques, Crescent City Sutler, Dixie Leather Works, Fall Creek Suttlery, Farnsworth House Inn, Fields of Glory, First Corps Books, The Flag Guys, The Gettysburg Gift Center, Goodson Enterprises, The Gospel Truth and Civil War Room, Green River Trading Corporation, Heidi Marsh Patterns, Historical Enterprises, The Horse Soldier, James Country Muzzleloading

and Mercantile, Richard A. LaPosta, Levi Ledbetter, Longstreet House, Mary Ellen & Company, McGowan Book Company, Morningside Bookshop, Navy Arms Company, Olde Soldier Books, Owens Books, Palmetto Presence, Publisher's Press, The Regimental Quartermaster, J.M. Santarelli, The Scholar's Bookshelf, Second/II Corps Civil War Books, Southern Heritage Press, Staley's Sundries, Stan Clark Military Books, Stone Mountain Miniatures, Trans-Mississippi Militaria, Upper Mississippi Valley Mercantile Company, War Between The States Memorabilia, Wildman's, Willow Creek Press of Washington, The Winchester Sutler

Boot Resoling: Dyestone Company

Boxes: An Early Elegance, Cartridges Unlimited, GDR Enterprises

Brass: Amazon Drygoods

Bugles: Collector's Armoury, Crescent City Sutler, Fall Creek Suttlery

Bullets: Arsenal Artifacts, Barry'd Treasure

Buttons: An Early Elegance, Arsenal Artifacts, Centennial General Store, Confederate States Military Antiques, Crescent City Sutler, Dixie Leather Works, Fall Creek Suttlery, Will Gorges Civil War Antiques, Grand Illusions, Heidi Marsh Patterns, James Country Muzzleloading and Mercantile, Levi Ledbetter, Palmetto Presence, Panther Lodges, R & K Sutlery, The Regimental Quartermaster, Richmond Arsenal, Staley's Sundries, The Winchester Sutler

Camp Gear: Centennial General Store, Crescent City Sutler, Panther Lodges, Upper Mississippi Valley Mercantile Company, The Winchester Sutler

Camp Relics: Barry'd Treasure

Cannon (also see **Artillery**): Baton Rouge Arsenal, Cannon Ltd., Collector's Armoury, The General's Armory, Schneider Enterprises, South Bend Replicas, Staley's Sundries

Canteens: Centennial General Store, Collector's Armoury, Crescent City Sutler,

Fall Creek Suttlery, Grand Illusions, Legendary Arms, Levi Ledbetter, R & K Sutlery, Richmond Arsenal, Richmonville Tinware, Village Tinsmithing Works, The Winchester Sutler, Wisconsin Veterans Museum

Carriages: Baton Rouge Arsenal, Schneider Enterprises

Carte-de-Visite: See **CDVs**

Cartridges: Barry'd Treasure, Cartridges Unlimited

CDVs: Abraham Lincoln Book Shop, American Social History and Social Movements, Collectors Antiquities, Henry Deeks Dealer/Historian, The Horse Soldier, Olde Soldier Books, Trans-Mississippi Militaria, War Between The States Memorabilia

Certificates: Wisconsin Veterans Museum

Civil War Train Raids: Gettysburg Railroad Passenger Service

Clipart: Archive Arts, Walden Font

Clocks: JEBCO Clocks

Clothing: Amazon Drygoods, Arsenal Artifacts, Cantrell & Company, Caps & Kepis, Cavalier Shoppe, Centennial General Store, Civil War Designs, Crescent City Sutler, Different Drummer, Fall Creek Suttlery, The Gettysburg Gift Center, Grand Illusions, Green River Trading Corporation, The Haversack Store, James Country Muzzleloading and Mercantile, K & P Weaver, Martin's Mercantile, Mary Ellen & Company, Michaels & Perrin, Mrs. Eddins' Fine Sewing Emporium, The Quartermaster Shop, R & K Sutlery, The Regimental Quartermaster, Resurgence Outfitters, Staley's Sundries, Uniforms of Antiquity

Collectibles: The American Historical Foundation, An Early Elegance, The Antique Center of Gettysburg, CARA, Chilmark, Chris & Jackie's, The Confederate States Armory & Museum, CSA Galleries, The Gettysburg Gift Center, The Haversack Store, The Horse Soldier

Comic Books: JB Comics

Computer Software: Archive Arts, Grafica Multimedia, Grolier Interactive, H-Bar Enterprises, The Haversack Store, Hudson's Hobby Games, Infinop, MultiEducator, TalonSoft, TDC Interactive, Troubadour Interactive, Walden Font

Cross-Stitch Designs: Heartfelt Designs

Currency: Brian & Maria Green, The Confederate Treasury, Dixie Leather Works, Richard T. Hoober, The Horse Soldier, Lee-Grant, McGowan Book Company

Diaries: See **Paper**

Dioramas: The General's Armory

Documents: See **Paper**

Drums: Heritage Drum Company

Dug Items: Arsenal Artifacts, Barry'd Treasure, Confederate States Military Antiques, The Horse Soldier, Palmetto Presence

Education: Civil War Education Center

Eyewear: Fall Creek Suttlery, The Grand Spectacle, Reenactment Eyewear

Fabric: Amazon Drygoods, An Early Elegance, Centennial General Store, Heidi Marsh Patterns, James Country Muzzleloading and Mercantile, Neddle & Thread, Panther Lodges, R & K Sutlery, Red Willow Clothing and Canvas Shelters, The Winchester Sutler

Fans: Amazon Drygoods, Mary Ellen & Company

Flags, Amazon Drygoods, Cavalier Shoppe, Centennial General Store, Collector's Armoury, Du Page Military Flag Company, The Flag Guys, The Gettysburg Gift Center, Will Gorges Civil War Antiques, The Haversack Store, Lee-Grant, Levi Ledbetter, Staley's Sundries, U.S. Flag Service, The Winchester Sutler

Footwear: Amazon Drygoods, Cavalry Regimental Supply, Centennial General Store, Fall Creek Suttlery, I.C. Mercantile, Legendary Arms, Levi Ledbetter, Mary Ellen & Company, Timefarer Footwear, The Winchester Sutler

Framing: Historic Framing and Collectibles, Valley Framing Studio & Gallery

Furniture: GDR Enterprises

Games: Amazon Drygoods, Centennial General Store, Columbia Games, Deer Valley Game Company, The Gamers, Grolier Interactive, Hudson's Hobby Games, SPEERIT Strategy Games, StrataMax, TalonSoft, Winsome Games

G.A.R. (Grand Army of the Republic): American Social History and Social Movements, Trans-Mississippi Militaria

Gatling Guns: Baton Rouge Arsenal, Schneider Enterprises

Gift Packs: The Rebel Company

Glass: Amazon Drygoods

Hardtack: Cartridges Unlimited, Crescent City Sutler, Mechanical Baking Company, The Winchester Sutler

Hats: Tim Allen, Amazon Drygoods, Caps & Kepis, Cavalier Shoppe, Centennial General Store, Collector's Armoury, Crescent City Sutler, Dixie Leather Works, Fall Creek Suttlery, The Flag Guys, The Gettysburg Gift Center, Green River Trading Corporation, James Country Muzzleloading and Mercantile, Legendary Arms, Levi Ledbetter, Mary Ellen & Company, Navy Arms Company, The Quartermaster Shop, R & K Sutlery, The Regimental Quartermaster, Staley's Sundries, Uniforms of Antiquity, The Winchester Sutler

Haversacks: Cantrell & Company, Caps & Kepis, Centennial General Store, Crescent City Sutler, Dixie Leather Works, Fall Creek Suttlery, Grand Illusions, James Country Muzzleloading and Mercantile, Legendary Arms, Levi Ledbetter, R & K Sutlery, The Regimental Quartermaster, The Winchester Sutler

Haversack Items: K & P Weaver

Historical Consultation: Different Drummer

Insignia: American Military Antiques, Centennial General Store, Collector's Armoury, Crescent City Sutler, Fall Creek Suttlery, Grand Illusions, Heidi Marsh Patterns, James Country Muzzleloading and Mercantile, Legendary Arms, Levi Ledbetter, The Quartermaster Shop, The Regimental Quartermaster, Staley's Sundries, Uniforms of Antiquity, The Winchester Sutler

Instruments (music): Amazon Drygoods, Centennial General Store, Crescent City

Sutler, Levi Ledbetter, Panther Lodges, Staley's Sundries

Jewelry: Centennial General Store, James Country Muzzleloading and Mercantile

Kepis: See **Hats**

Knapsacks: Dixie Leather Works, Levi Ledbetter

Lanterns: An Early Elegance, Centennial General Store, Crescent City Sutler, Village Tinsmithing Works

Leather Care: R. Stephen Dorsey Antique Militaria

Leather Goods: Confederate States Military Antiques, Dixie Leather Works, Eastern Muzzleloader Supply, Levi Ledbetter, Old West Saddle Shop, The Regimental Quartermaster, Upper Mississippi Valley Mercantile Company

Leather Repair: Dyestone Company

Letters: See **Paper**

Lincolniana: Abraham Lincoln Book Shop, American Social History and Social Movements

Living History Presentations: The General's Armory

Magazines: Camp Chase Publishing Company, Cowles Magazines, Gettysburg Magazine, Military Images, Morningside Bookshop, Publisher's Press

Mailing Labels: Civil War Labels Unlimited

Maps: J.W. Carson Company

Medical: Civil War "Things 'n Frames," Dixie Leather Works, The Horse Soldier, Trans-Mississippi Militaria

Memorabilia: American Social History and Social Movements, The Antique Center of Gettysburg, Civil War Antiquities, Collectors Antiquities, Fields of Glory, The Horse Soldier, Lee-Grant, McGowan Book Company, Reb Acres, War Between The States Memorabilia

Millinery: Amazon Drygoods, Martin's Mercantile

Miniatures: Mr. "K" Products, Musket Miniatures, Northcoast Miniatures, Scotty's Scale Soldiers, Staley's Sundries, Stone Mountain Miniatures

Music: Aclamon Music, Amazon Drygoods, Brigade Bugler, The Civil War Music Store, Crescent City Sutler, Fall Creek Sutlery, The Flag Guys, The Gospel Truth and Civil War Room, The Haversack Store, James Country Muzzleloading and Mercantile, The Rebelaires, The Regimental Band, The Regimental Quartermaster, RSVProducts, Staley's Sundries, The Winchester Sutler

Newsletters: Camp Pope Bookshop, Cump and Company

Newspapers: Amazon Drygoods, The Civil War News, The Gospel Truth and Civil War Room, Richard T. Hoober, Reb Acres, War Between The States Memorabilia

Paper: Abraham Lincoln Book Shop, American Military Antiques, American Social History and Social Movements, Armistead Civil War Collections, Brian & Maria Green, Civil War Antiques, Collectors Antiquities, Dixie Leather Works, Farnsworth House Inn, Will Gorges Civil War Antiques, Jim Hayes, The Historian's Gallery, Richard T. Hoober, The Horse Soldier, K & P Valley Collectibles, Lee-Grant, McGowan Book Company, Dr. F. Don Nidiffer, Olde Soldier Books, Original Frameworks, Palmetto Presence, Reb Acres, Stan Clark Military Books, Trans-Mississippi Militaria, War Between The States Memorabilia, The Winchester Sutler

Paper Conservation: Susan A. Nash

Parasols: Mary Ellen & Company

Patterns: Amazon Drygoods, Fall Creek Suttlery, The Gospel Truth and Civil War Room, Grand Illusions, Heidi Marsh Patterns, James Country Muzzleloading and Mercantile, Martin's Mercantile, Mary Ellen & Company, Needle & Thread, Panther Lodges, Staley's Sundries, Upper Mississippi Valley Mercantile Company, The Winchester Sutler

Photographs: Abraham Lincoln Book Shop, American Social History and Social Movements, Carole Thompson Fine Photographs, Civil War Artifacts, Different Drummer, The Horse Soldier, McGowan Book Company, Olde Soldier Books, Trans-Mississippi Militaria, War Between The States Memorabilia

Pipes: Centennial General Store, Crescent City Sutler, Fall Creek Suttlery, Panther Lodges, Peter Evans Pipes, The Winchester Sutler

Plaques: JEBCO Clocks

Reference Material: Slide-A-Fact

Research: Battlefields Revisited, The Horse Soldier

Rubber Stamps: Appalachian Art Stamps

Saddles: R. Stephen Dorsey Antique Militaria, Old West Saddle Shop

Saddlebags: Dixie Leather Works

Statuary: Abraham Lincoln Book Shop, American Epic Studio, Valley Framing Studio & Gallery

Stereoviews: Trans-Mississippi Militaria

Tents: Centennial General Store, Crescent City Sutler, Fall Creek Suttlery, Levi Ledbetter, Panther Lodges, R & K Sutlery, Red Willow Clothing and Canvas Shelters, Upper Mississippi Valley Mercantile Company

Textile Conservation and Restoration: Will Gorges Civil War Antiques

Tintypes: War Between The States Memorabilia

Tinware: Amazon Drygoods, Centennial General Store, Crescent City Sutler, Fall Creek Suttlery, Grand Illusions, Levi Ledbetter, Panther Lodges, R & K Sutlery, Richmonville Tinware, Upper Mississippi Valley Mercantile Company, Village Tinsmithing Works, Wisconsin Veterans Museum

Tobacco Goods: James Country Muzzleloading and Mercantile, Panther Lodges

Toiletries: Amazon Drygoods

Tours: Historic Jonesborough Visitors Ctr.

Toys: Amazon Drygoods, Centennial General Store

Travel: Civil War Adventures (see Northwest Reenactments)

Trunks: Dixie Leather Works

U.C.V. (United Confederate Veterans): Trans-Mississippi Militaria

Uniforms: American Military Antiques, Cantrell & Company, Caps & Kepis, Centennial General Store, Crescent City Sutler, CSA Galleries, Different Drummer, Fall Creek Suttlery, Will Gorges Civil War Antiques, Grand Illusions, Green River Trading Corporation, Historic Framing and Collectibles, James Country Muzzleloading and Mercantile, K & P Weaver, Legendary Arms, Levi Ledbetter, Frank Matuszek Civil War Antiques, Michaels & Perrin, Mrs. Eddins' Fine Sewing Emporium, The Quartermaster Shop, R & K Sutlery, The Regimental Quartermaster, Resurgence Outfitters, Richmond Arsenal, Uniforms of Antiquity, Upper Mississippi Valley Mercantile Company, The Winchester Sutler

Unit Histories: H.J. Popowski

Video: Associated Video Productions, Cavalier Shoppe, Fall Creek Suttlery, The Gettysburg Gift Center, The Gospel Truth and Civil War Room, The Haversack Store, The Horse Soldier, Mary Lou Productions, Museum of Historic Natchitoches, Navy Arms Company, New Vision Productions, Staley's Sundries, Walkala Home Video

Weapons & Accessories: American Military Antiques, Arsenal Artifacts, Bellinger's Military Antiques, Centennial General Store, Collector's Armoury, Confederate States Arsenal, Confederate States Military Antiques, Crescent City Sutler, Dixie Leather Works, R. Stephen Dorsey Antique Militaria, Eastern Muzzleloader Supply, Fall Creek Suttlery, The Flag Guys, Will Gorges Civil War Antiques, Grand Illusions, Green River Trading Corporation, Historic Framing and Collectibles, The Horse Soldier, James Country Muzzleloading and Mercantile, K & P Valley Collectibles, Legendary Arms, Levi Ledbetter, Lodgewood Manufacturing, Frank Matuszek Civil War Antiques, Navy Arms Company, The Powder Horn Gunshop, The Regimental Quartermaster, Richmond Arsenal, Staley's Sundries, Upper Mississippi Valley Mercantile Company, Whitacre's Machine Shop, Wildman's, The Winchester Sutler

Weapons Restoration: Confederate States Arsenal

Woodenware: Amazon Drygoods

P laces I of I nterest

An alphabetical listing of Museums, Historic Homes & Sites, Parks, and Attractions with Civil War themes or displays

Abraham Lincoln Birthplace National Historic Site

2995 Lincoln Farm Road
Hodgenville, KY 42748
Phone: (502) 358-3137

Hours: Daily, 8am - 6:45pm
(Memorial Day through Labor Day)
Daily, 8am - 4:45pm
(early September through late May)

Thomas and Nancy Lincoln settled on the 348-acre Sinking Spring Farm in the fall of 1808. In a one-room log cabin near the Sinking Spring, the future president of the United States was born on February 12, 1809. Today the park contains 116.5 acres, roughly one-third the size of the original Lincoln homestead. An early 19th century Kentucky cabin, symbolic of the one in which Lincoln was born, is preserved in a memorial building at the site of his birth.

Facilities at the site include a visitor center, 2.2 miles of hiking trails, and an 18-minute film titled "Lincoln: The Kentucky Years." The visitor center also offers exhibits, such as tools and utensils representative of the period, and the Lincoln Family Bible.

Abraham Lincoln's Boyhood Home

Knob Creek Farm
U.S. 31E
Hodgenville, KY 42748
Phone: (502) 549-3741

Hours: Daily *(April 1 - November 1)*

The first home that Abraham Lincoln remembered was the 228-acre Knob Creek Farm. The future president lived on this farm from the time he was two until he was eight years old. He recalled in later years numerous memories from his childhood on the farm, including that of a favorite tree, of the old homestead, a stone house he had passed while taking corn to Hodgen's Mill, and of a baby brother who was born and died on the farm.

The original cabin, which was Lincoln's home during this time, was torn down in 1870 by Steve Thompson and his son Robert. The cabin had been used as a corn crib until that time. Many years later, in 1931, Robert Thompson rebuilt the cabin on the original site. Today the cabin is furnished with relics donated by the descendants of the early settlers of Knob Creek. A museum is at the site, as well as a pavilion which can be rented for private parties.

The Abraham Lincoln Museum

Lincoln Memorial University
Box 2006, Cumberland Gab Parkway
Harrogate, TN 37752
Phone: (423) 869-6235
Fax: (423) 869-6350

Hours: Monday - Friday, 9am - 4pm
         Saturday, 11am - 4pm
         Sunday, 1pm - 4pm

> *Exhibits include . . . the silver-topped cane Lincoln carried the night of his assassination*

The Abraham Lincoln Museum houses one of the largest and most complete Lincoln and Civil War collections in the country. Exhibited are many rare items, such as the silver-topped cane Lincoln carried the night of his assassination, two life masks made of Lincoln, and numerous personal belongings. Over twenty thousand books, manuscripts, photographs, paintings, and sculptures tell the story of President Lincoln and the Civil War period in America. This treasure trove serves as a great attraction to students, researchers, and the general public. The museum also serves as a teaching facility for the University, hosting numerous school groups, lectures, and special programs throughout the year.

A.H. Stephens State Historic Park

P.O. Box 283
Crawfordville, GA 30631
Phone: (706) 456-2602

Hours: Daily, 7am - 10pm (park)
         Tuesday - Saturday, 9am - 5pm
         Sunday, 2pm - 5pm (site)

> *home of Vice President of the Confederacy and Governor of Georgia, A.H. Stephens*

Photo Courtesy of A.H. Stephens State Historic Park

The A.H. Stephens State Historic Park includes Liberty Hall, the home of Vice President of the Confederacy and Governor of Georgia, A.H. Stephens, and the Confederate Museum. The park occupies 1,200 acres which offer nature trails, picnic shelters, fishing lakes, and camping facilities. The Confederate Museum houses an excellent collection of Confederate artifacts. Annual events include a Stephens homecoming in April and a Civil War reenactment in September.

Andersonville National Historic Site

Route 1, Box 800
Andersonville, GA 31711
Phone: (912) 924-0343

Hours: Daily, 8am - 5pm (Park Grounds)
         Daily, 8:30am - 5pm (Visitor Ctr)

DIRECTIONS: Andersonville is ten miles north of Americus on Highway 49, park entrance will be on your right.

Established in 1970, the 475-acre Andersonville National Historic Site consists of a national cemetery and the site of the Andersonville prison, where Union soldiers died by the thousands due to malnutrition and the diseased environment of the overcrowded prison. Today, the site is unique in that is serves as a memorial to all Americans ever held as prisoners of war.

The visitor center offers an orientation film and a number of exhibits. On weekends, guided cemetery walks and prison site talks are given by Park Rangers. The National Prisoner of War Museum/Visitor Center is planned for the near future.

Other park features include research facilities for those studying the history of American prisoners of war, historic monuments located throughout the Park, and a picnic area. A cassette tape for individual driving tours can be rented at the visitor center for $1.00. Reservations for school groups, other educational groups, tour buses, and special interest groups should be made at least two weeks prior to the planned visit.

On Memorial Day, ceremonies are conducted honoring American veterans from all wars. These ceremonies include music, guest speaker, and the Laying of Wreaths by civic and patriotic organizations. An American flag is placed on each of the 18,000 graves in the national cemetery, honoring their service, and in most cases, their sacrifice. Also, the burial flags of American veterans are displayed in the traditional Avenue of Flags.

Other area attractions include the Civil War Village of Andersonville.

Admission: FREE (Donations accepted)

Antietam National Battlefield

P.O. Box 158
Sharpsburg, MD 21782-0158
Phone: (301) 432-5124

Hours: Daily, 8:30am - 6pm *(summer)*
         Daily, 8:30am - 5pm *(winter)*

Located 10 miles south of Hagerstown on Md. 65, Antietam National Battlefield was established by Act of Congress on August 30, 1890. With landmarks such as Dunker Church, Bloody Lane, The Cornfield, and Burnside Bridge, this site commemorates one of the fiercest, bloodiest days of the Civil War. The battle claimed over 23,000 men killed, wounded and missing in one single day combat, September 17, 1862, and led to Lincoln's issuance of the Emancipation Proclamation.

The park features a Visitors Center and museum, a book store, a nine mile self-guided tour by car, bike, or foot, and, during the summer, guided walks and talks conducted by Park Rangers. An audio cassette tape may be rented or purchased to supplement the driving tour. The museum offers a 26-minute film called "Antietam Visit" which is offered every hour on the hours. Reservations for school groups or tour groups should be made at least two weeks prior to visiting.

Annual events include an Independence Day Commemoration, complete with symphony and fireworks display, the Anniversary Commemoration around the 17th of September, and the very touching and beautiful Memorial Illumination, where over 500 volunteers place 23,000 candles on the battlefield, one for every Antietam casualty. Special tours, lectures, Living History programs, and Ranger hikes are available at various times throughout the year

A research library is available, but only by appointment. Please contact the battlefield for further information.

Admission charged.

Appomattox Court House National Historical Park

P.O. Box 218
Appomattox, VA 24522
Phone: (804) 352-8987

Hours: Daily, 9am - 5:30pm *(Summer)*
         Daily, 8:30am - 5pm *(Winter)*

Directions: Two miles north of Appomattox on Va. 24

Photo Courtesy of Appomattox Court House NHP

The McLean House

The National Historic Park's visitor information center, located in the courthouse building, offers a slide presentation and knowledgeable Park personnel to help visitors relive the irony and drama of the final days of the Civil War. Park highlights include a visit to the McLean House, site of Lee's surrender to Grant, the Clover Hill Tavern, where parole passes were printed for the defeated Confederate forces, and the stage road where Confederate soldiers stacked their arms.

Admission charged.

Arlington House

The Robert E. Lee Memorial
George Washington Memorial Parkway
Turkey Run Park
McLean, VA 22101
Phone: (703) 557-0613

Hours: Daily, 9:30am - 6pm
         (April - September)
         Daily, 9:30am - 4:30pm
         (October - March)

Located in Arlington National Cemetery, Arlington House was home to Robert E. Lee and Mary Custis Lee from 1831 until the outbreak of Civil War in 1861 Mrs. Lee inherited the house and property from her father, George Washington Parke Custis, Martha Washington's grandson. It was at Arlington that Robert E. Lee declined Lincoln's offer of field command of U.S. forces and resigned his commission to defend his native Virginia.

Arlington National Cemetery was established on the site in 1864, after the property was seized for nonpayment of taxes. Lee's eldest son, George Washington Custis Lee, fought to get the property back, but it wasn't until 1882 that the Supreme

Court ruled in his favor. By then, thousands of graves covered the family estate, and Lee chose to sell the property to the U.S. government.

Restored to its 1861 appearance, the Lee memorial itself occupies 28 acres and contains some of the original Custis and Lee furnishings .

Augusta-Richmond County Museum

560 Reynolds Street
Augusta, GA
Phone: (706) 722-8454

Hours: Tuesday - Saturday, 10am - 5pm
Sunday, 2pm - 5pm

The Confederate display rooms of the Augusta-Richmond County Museum feature uniforms, weaponry, photographs, paintings, and a mural depicting Sherman's march across Georgia.

The Battles for Chattanooga Museum

3742 Tennessee Ave.
Chattanooga, TN 37409
Phone: (615) 821-2812

Hours: Year-round, 9am - 5pm
(8:30am - 8:30pm, June - Labor Day)

Admission charged (group rates available)

The Battles for Chattanooga Museum offers a three-dimensional presentation of Chattanooga's Civil War history, featuring 5,000 miniature figures, 650 lights, sound effects and details of major battles in 1863. Before exploring Lookout Mountain, Missionary Ridge, Orchard Knob, Wauhatchie, or Brown's Ferry, stop by The Battles for Chattanooga Museum for an overview. You'll be better informed and enjoy your visit that much more.

The "Battle of Carthage" Civil War Museum

205 Grant Street
Carthage, MO 64836
Phone: (417) 358-6643

Hours: Monday - Saturday, 8:30am - 5pm
Sunday, 1pm - 5pm

Thirteen battles and skirmishes raged in or near Carthage during the Civil

War, including the July 5, 1861 Battle of Carthage, which preceded First Bull Run by sixteen days as the first full scale land battle. As the war progressed, Carthage suffered guerrilla attacks from both sides, destructive battles and skirmishes, and Missouri-wide neighbor-on-neighbor violence that was unprecedented in American history. On September 22, 1864, Confederate guerrillas rode into Carthage and burned the city to the ground. The only building left intact was the Kendrick House, which still stands. As the war progressed, the county population steadily declined from the 6,883 residents recorded in the 1860 census, to only 30 by the end of the war. Almost seven thousand residents had either been killed or had fled.

The "Battle of Carthage" Civil War Museum features a wall-sized mural which depicts the battle, period clothing, a diorama which presents the Battle of Carthage in miniature, a video about the Civil War in the Ozarks, displays of rifles, pistols, sabers, and other artifacts, and a Belle Starr "Queen of the Bandits" exhibit.

"Petticoat Flag"
by Andy Thomas

Admission: FREE

Battle of Carthage State Historic Site

East Chestnut Street, next to Carter Park
Carthage, MO

Site of the first major land battle of the Civil War on July 5, 1861. The battle pitted a force of 6,000 Missouri State Guards-

men led by Missouri's pro-Southern Governor Claiborne Fox Jackson against an outnumbered Union force of 1,100 troops from St. Louis led by Colonel Franz Sigel. The Battle of Carthage State Historic Site preserves this important location. A kiosk at the site highlights events of the battle through text and graphic illustration.

Battle of Lexington State Historic Site

P.O. Box 6
Lexington, MO 64067
Phone: (816) 259-4654

Hours: Daily, Dawn - Dusk (Park)
Monday - Saturday, 10am - 4pm
Sunday, Noon - 4pm *(winter)*
Sunday, Noon - 5pm *(summer)*

The Anderson House

Located on 13th Street in Lexington, The Battle of Lexington State Historic Site occupies 105 acres of the original battlefield, offering a visitor center and the restored Anderson House, which was used as a hospital by both Union and Confederate forces.

It was during this battle that Confederate General Sterling Price instructed his men to use hemp bales as shields. These bales were conveniently sitting on a wharf below the battlefield awaiting shipment. With three Confederate soldiers behind each bale, the Rebel army used the bulky hemp as moveable breastworks and approached to within 100 yards of the Union entrenchments. The Union forces finally capitulated and the Confederates took 3,000 prisoners.

A visit to the site offers the opportunity to explore the weathered Union earthworks and entrenchments, to learn more about the hemp bales, and to explore the battle-damaged Anderson House.

Beauregard-Keyes House

1113 Chartres Street
New Orleans, LA 70116
Phone: (504) 523-7257

Hours: Monday - Saturday, 10am - 3pm
          (Tours on the hour)

If it were possible for a house to have a split personality, the Beauregard-Keyes House would be a good candidate. Such is the fate of homes that have offered shelter to more than one famous individual, even when these individuals shared the home more than a half century apart from one another.

Built in 1826, the home's first famous resident was Confederate General P.G.T.

Beauregard, who lodged here for eighteen months after the war. It was because of the Beauregard connection that the house was saved from demolition in 1925 by a collection of Southern ladies who raised funds to save the structure. In 1944, the second famous personality, novelist Frances Parkinson Keyes, moved into the house. Eventually, Mrs. Keyes took over the house and began its restoration. It was in this house that Mrs. Keyes wrote several of her books.

Of particular interest to Civil War enthusiasts is the Beauregard Chamber, which features furniture and other heirloom pieces that belonged to the General and his family.

Admission charged.

Belle Boyd Cottage

101 Chester Street
Front Royal, VA
Phone: (540) 636-1446

Operated by the Warren Heritage Society, this is the house where Confeder-

ate spy Belle Boyd lived during her visits to Front Royal. Belle is most noted for her actions prior to and during the Battle of Front Royal on May 23, 1862, during which she supplied information to General Thomas "Stonewall" Jackson.

Belle Boyd House

126 East Race Street
Martinsburg, WV 25401
Phone: (304) 267-4713

Hours: Wed - Sat, 10am - 4pm
          (closed last two weeks of Dec.)

Purchased by the Berkeley County Historical Society in 1992 after nearly being razed by its former owner, the Belle Boyd

House is the only house in Martinsburg (still standing) which is known to have been lived in by Confederate spy Belle Boyd. Though this isn't the house where Belle shot and killed a Union soldier on July 4, 1861 (that house was located in the 500 block of S. Queen Street), it was built by Ben Boyd, Belle's father, and served as the family residence for a number of years.

The Belle Boyd House now features the Ben Boyd Book Store, named after Belle's father, The Berkeley County Museum, and The Boyd Mason Civil War Museum.

Belle Grove Plantation

P.O. Box 137
Middletown, VA 22645
Phone: (540) 869-2028

Hours: Mon - Sat, 10:15am - 3:15pm (Tours)
Sunday, 1:15am - 4:15pm (Tours)
Mid-March - October

Located south of Middletown on U.S. Route 11, Belle Grove Plantation is a National Trust Historic Site with a rich, 200-year history rooted in the Shenandoah Valley. Annual events include a Civil War Reenactment & Living History Weekend presented by the Cedar Creek Battlefield Foundation.

Photo Courtesy of Belle Grove Plantation

Bentonville Battleground State Historic Site

5466 Harper House Road
Four Oaks, NC 27524
Phone: (910) 594-0789

Hours: Monday - Saturday, 9am - 5pm
Sunday, 1pm - 5pm
(April 1 through October 31)
Tuesday - Saturday, 10am - 4pm
Sunday, 1pm - 4pm
(November 1 through March 31)

For three days in March 1865, Confederate troops under General Joseph E. Johnston attempted to prevent General Sherman's army from joining with General Grant's forces in Virginia. The battle erupted near the village of Bentonville and would be the largest engagement ever fought in North Carolina, occupying over 6,000 acres, fielding 80,000 Union and Confederate troops, and consuming 4,000 killed, wounded, or missing. The Battle of Bentonville was the last full-scale action of the Civil War and the last battle in which the Confederacy was able to mount an offensive. As the fighting ensued, Union casualties were taken to the home of John and Amy Harper, now known as Harper House, where a field hospital had been established.

The Harper House still stands at Bentonville Battleground and is furnished as a field hospital. The historic site occupies 125 acres of state-owned property. Reminders of the battle are displayed in the visitor center. A Confederate cemetery and a section of Union trenches are located nearby. Roads in the Park are marked with plaques highlighting events of the battle.

Membership in the Bentonville Battleground Historical Association (B.B.H.A.) is available to those interested in the preservation of this site. Identified as a Priority I, Class A Civil War battlefield by the Civil War Sites Advisory Commission, the site ranked number six out of 384 historically important Civil War sites, giving it a high priority for coordinated preservation action. Membership ($20) includes an honorary certificated of ownership for one square foot of Bentonville. For membership or information write: B.B.H.A., P.O. Box 432, Newton Grove, NC 28366, or phone (910) 594-0789.

Park Admission: FREE
B.B.H.A. Membership: $20

Bessemer Hall of History

1905 Alabama Avenue
Bessemer, AL 35020
Phone: (205) 426-1633

Hours: Tuesday - Saturday, 10am - 4pm

Housed in the renovated Southern Railway Terminal, the Bessemer Hall of History contains artifacts, documents, photographs, and unique items such as Hitler's typewriter. Of interest to Civil War enthusiasts is the Hall's collection of items relating to the 28th Alabama Regiment.

Admission: FREE

Blandford Church & Cemetery

111 Rochelle Lane
Petersburg, VA 23803
Phone: (804) 733-2396

Dating to 1735, Blandford Church became a lasting memorial to Confederate soldiers when 15 stained glass windows (one donated by each Southern state) where designed for the church by Louis Comfort Tiffany. The first Memorial Day was observed here in June, 1866, honoring the 30,000 Confederate soldiers buried in the church cemetery.

Boonsborough Museum of History

113 North Main Street
Boonsboro, MD 21713-1007

Hours: Sunday, 1pm - 5pm
         (May through September)
         Other times by appointment

The Boonsborough Museum has been shaped by one man's passion for history. Owner Doug Bast has spent a lifetime collecting everything from stone artifacts

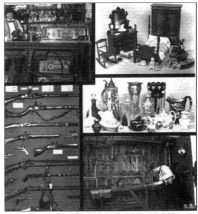

Photo Courtesy of Boonsborough Museum

(dating to 30,000 B.C.) to lead bullets hand-carved into various shapes by the idle hands of Civil War soldiers. Many of the Civil War relics in the museum come from the local battlefields of South Mountain, Antietam, and Harpers Ferry.

Civil War displays at the museum include personal items such as accouterments, musical instruments, games, writing material, and tobacco products. You'll also see a flower that was seized from President Lincoln's coffin, a sharpshooter's rifle from Devil's Den, a number of cannons, fractional currency, personal documents of Confeder-

ate Officer Henry Kyd Douglas, a piece of original rail fence from Bloody Lane, rare Hanes and Ketchum hand grenades, an original order issued by Stonewall Jackson, a piece of hardtack brought back from the war, and a drum carried by a local soldier.

Non-Civil War displays include Roman, Egyptian, Chinese, and Native American items (including a cane carved by Chief Geronimo), antique china and glassware, 19th century dolls and toys, and over 500 edged weapons from around the world.

Modest admission charged.

Boyhood Home of Robert E. Lee

607 Oronoco Street
Alexandria, VA 22314
Phone: (703) 548-8454

Hours: Monday - Saturday, 10am - 4pm
Sunday, 1pm - 4pm
December 15 through January 31,
by appointment only

Built in 1795, this elegant mansion served as the boyhood home of Robert E. Lee from the time he was five years old until he entered West Point at the age of 18. The house is a mix of Federal and Georgian styles and is furnished with period antiques. A boxwood garden adjoins the house.

The home was visited often by George Washington, and it was here that the Marquis de Lafayette paid a formal call on Ann Hill Carter Lee, the mother of Robert

E. Lee and widow of General Henry "Light Horse Harry" Lee. In the drawing room of the mansion Mary Lee Fitzhugh married George Washington Parke Custis, grandson of Martha Washington, and builder of Arlington. Their daughter, Mary Ann Randolph Custis, married Robert E. Lee twenty-seven years later. The house is now owned by The Lee-Jackson Foundation, P.O. Box 8121, Charlottesville, VA 22906.

Modest admission charged.

Britton Lane Battlefield

Britton Lane Battlefield Association
199 Carriage House Drive
Jackson, TN 38305
Phone: (901) 784-4227

Hours: Daily

Site of conflict on September 1, 1862, Britton Lane Battlefield features a Civil War-era cabin which was used as a field hospital during the battle, monuments which mark the site of a Confederate mass grave and the site where 213 Federal prisoners were captured, and other amenities. The Denmark Presbyterian Church, located near the battlefield, was used to imprison Federal troops after the battle. Graffiti left by these soldiers can still be seen in the structure.

Camp Moore

Confederate Museum & Cemetery
70640 Camp Moore Road
P.O. Box 25
Tangipahoa, LA 70465
Phone: (504) 229-2438

Hours: Tuesday - Saturday, 10am - 4pm

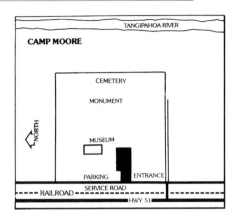

Established in the summer of 1861 and completely destroyed by Union forces in the fall of 1864, Camp Moore enjoyed a short, though colorful history. After its establishment it became one of the largest Confederate training bases in the southern states, while also serving as a principal base of operation in eastern Louisiana and southwestern Mississippi. Four efforts were made to destroy Camp Moore during the course of the war, finally resulting in the destruction of the Camp and the scattering of its forces in the fall of 1864.

Today, Camp Moore boasts a Confederate Museum and a cemetery where at least 440 of the camp's soldiers are buried (eighty percent died of disease). The museum contains many distinct artifacts, including: The Wall family diary which contains the signature of Colonel John S. Scott (last Confederate commander of the region), letters form Louisiana and Mississippi Confederate soldiers based at Camp Moore, the saddle used by Governor Thomas Overton Moore (for whom the camp was named), weapons, an example of the uniform worn by the Louisiana Tigers, jewelry fashioned from coins by soldiers based at Camp Moore, a list of Confederate dead buried at the camp, military orders, photographs of Camp Moore soldiers, war period maps, Confederate and Louisiana state issue canteens, pistols, belt buckles, buttons, and power horns, contemporary newspaper accounts of local fighting, uniforms, and scores of other artifacts found at Camp Moore. The 6.2 acre site also offers a walking tour.

Membership in the Camp Moore Conservancy is available for those interested in supporting the preservation and maintenance of the site. Membership includes free access to the museum.

Membership: $20 per year

Camp Nelson

P.O. Box 1170
Nicholasville, KY 40356

Hours: Daily, Dawn - Dusk

Located five miles south of Nicholasville, Kentucky, off US 27, Camp Nelson once served as a major Union supply depot and recruiting/training center for African-American troops (in fact, it was the third largest African-American recruiting base in the Union). At its height, the camp covered 4,000 acres and had 300 buildings and fortifications. The office of the Camp

Nelson National Cemetery currently serves as a visitors center, offering a video which highlights the history of the camp (shown on request). The Camp Nelson Preservation & Restoration Foundation is raising funds and making plans for a museum and interpretive center. Membership is available (see *Organizations*).

Admission: FREE

The Carter House

1140 Columbia Avenue
Franklin, TN 37065
Phone: (615) 791-1861

Hours: Daily

The Carter House, a National Historic Landmark, was at the very center of the Battle of Franklin, serving as the Union command post. The house offers a museum, video presentation, and guided tours of the house and grounds.

Casemate Museum

P.O. Box 51341
Bldg 20, Bernard Rd.
Fort Monroe, VA 23651-0341
Phone: (757) 727-3391
Fax: (757) 727-3886

Hours: Daily, 10:30am - 4:30pm

The Casemate Museum was established in 1951 to display the prison cell

Photo Courtesy of the Casemate Museum

where Confederate President Jefferson Davis was confined in 1865. The museum's mis-

sion has since been expanded to depict the history of Fort Monroe and Old Point Comfort, with special emphasis on the Civil War period. The exhibit area includes many displays of uniforms, weapons, photographs, drawings by Frederick Remington and R.F. Zogbaum, and other items relating to the war (including the 49,000-pound Lincoln Gun which overlooks the parade field).

The museum is housed in a series of casemates built in the 1820s. The building is handicap accessible, with free parking across the street. Facilities include a reference library (weekdays only, by appointment) and a gift shop. Within walking distance are the quarters occupied by 1st Lt. Robert E. Lee in 1831-34, and the quarters where President Abraham Lincoln was a guest in May 1862.

There is no admission charge. Guided tours for groups between ten and 150 people are available with at least two weeks notice.

> *prison cell where Confederate President Jefferson Davis was confined . . . quarters occupied by 1st Lt. Robert E. Lee in 1831-34*

Photo Courtesy of the Cavalry Museum

Cavalry Museum

Mail:
298 W. Old Cross Road
New Market, VA 22844
Phone: (703) 740-3959
Directions:
Take exit 264 off I-81. Go west on Route 211 to Collins Drive (Route 305). Museum is on the northwest corner of I-81 and 211.

Hours: Daily, 9am - 5pm
          (April to November)

With three distinct galleries of cavalry history, this privately owned historic site and museum houses the largest interpreted collection focused on the American Horse Cavalry available for public viewing. Situated on the New Market Battlefield, The Cavalry Museum is on the estate of Major Chris-

tian Shirley, 12th Virginia Cavalry, CSA. Gallery #2 is of primary interest to Civil War enthusiasts, as it covers the period from 1860 through 1865, with an emphasis on the Shenandoah Valley. Museum displays include art, equipment, arms, armor, maps, personal items, and memorabilia.

For those interested in additional cavalry displays, Gallery #1 covers the period from 1607 to 1848, and Gallery #3 covers 1865 to Vietnam.

Cedar Creek Battlefield

Visitors' Center & Bookshop
P.O. Box 229
Middletown, VA 22645
Phone: (540) 869-2064
Fax: (540) 869-1438

Hours: Monday - Saturday, 10am - 4pm
          Sunday, 1pm - 4pm

Established in 1988 by the Cedar Creek Battlefield Foundation, Inc., the Cedar Creek Battlefield now boasts 158 acres, the historic Heater House on the battlefield, and a new 5,000 square foot visitors center. The Foundation is continuing its efforts to interpret the battlefield

with trails and signs (making it accessible to the public all the time). Plans are also underway to purchase more land. The Foundation has started a program whereby individuals can "purchase" a square foot of the battlefield. The program costs $25 and the "property owner" receives a personalized certificate suitable for framing. A great gift idea.

The Battle of Cedar Creek took place October 19, 1864, with battle casualties totaling 8,824. After his victory at Cedar Creek, Confederate General Jubal A. Early declared "This is glory enough for one day," after deciding not to pursue routed Federal troops.

Cedar Creek Battlefield now boasts 158 acres, the historic Heater House on the battlefield, and a new 5,000 square foot visitors center.

Chattanooga Regional History Museum

400 Chestnut Street
Chattanooga, TN 37402
Phone: (423) 265-3247
Fax: (423) 266-9280

Hours: Monday - Saturday, 10am - 4:30pm
Sunday, 11am - 4:30pm

With over 1,000 items related to the Chattanooga and Chickamauga campaigns, the Chattanooga Regional History Museum offers an special look at these significant battles. Exhibits include photographs, weapons, uniforms, diaries, accouterments, and documents. A gift shop with Civil War items is also available.

The Civil War Library and Museum

1805 Pine Street
Philadelphia, PA 19103
Phone: (215) 735-8196
Fax: (215) 735-3812

Hours: Wed - Sun, 11am - 4:30pm

library of more than 13,000 volumes

Founded in 1888, The Civil War Library and Museum is America's oldest chartered Civil War institution. Three floors of exhibits are on display at the Library and Museum; exhibits which include original uniforms, weapons, accouterments, photographs and images, flags, and other artifacts related to the "War of the Rebellion."

Unique artifacts include the uniform worn by Major General George Meade as commander of the Army of the Potomac at the battle of Gettysburg, the saddle upon which Major General John F. Reynolds was riding when killed at the battle of Gettysburg, a superb collection of material related to Lieutenant General U.S. Grant, and an entire room dedicated to President Abraham Lincoln. The institution's research collection includes a library of more than 13,000 volumes, 200+ feet of archival/manuscript material, and 5,000 photographs. Old Baldy Civil War Round Table meets at the Library and Museum the second Thursday of every month.

Membership is available for those wishing to join the *Friends of The Civil War Library and Museum*. Membership privileges include unlimited free admission, a subscription to the quarterly newsletter, 10% discount at the Museum Shop, and discounts to special events.

Admission charged.

Clarksville-Montgomery County Museum

P.O. Box 383
Clarksville, TN 37041-0383
Phone: (615) 648-5780

Located in downtown Clarksville at the corner of Commerce and South Second Streets, the Clarksville-Montgomery County Museum offers a small Civil War exhibit, along with a variety of art, science and other history exhibits. The museum store carries books by local authors such as Ordeal by Fire, by C. Wallace Cross, Jr., and Clarksville, Tennessee in the Civil War: A Chronology, by Richard Gildrie, Phillip Kemmerly, and Thomas H. Winn.

Columbus-Belmont State Park

P.O. Box 8
Columbus, KY 42032-0008
Phone: (502) 677-2327

Hours: Daily, 9am - 5pm (Museum)
        May - September

        (weekends only, April & October)

Known as "The Gibraltar of the West," this 156 - acre site was witness to the 1861 Battle of Belmont. The park features a museum with Civil War artifacts and a video presentation, cannon used to shell Union troops, hiking trails, camping, an activity center (available for private functions), miniature golf, picnic areas and special events such as Civil War Days at Columbus-Belmont in October.

Confederate Armory

Contact: *Tallasse Chamber of Commerce*
301-A King Street
Tallassee, AL 36708
Phone: (334) 283-5151

Hours: By appointment

In the spring of 1864 the decision was made to move the Richmond Carbine Factory from Richmond to a more secure location in Tallassee. The factory soon occupied the 1844 cotton mill in Tallassee and began manufacturing cavalry carbines. The factory stands as the only Confederate armory to survive the Civil War.

Admission: FREE

Confederate Memorial Hall

3148 Kingston Pike
Knoxville, TN 37919
Phone: (423) 522-2371

Hours: Tuesday - Friday
        Afternoons

Headquarters of General James Longstreet during the Confederate occupation of Knoxville in 1862, this antebellum mansion now serves as a Confederate memorial and museum.

Headquarters of General James Longstreet

Confederate Memorial Park

437 County Road 63
Marbury, AL 36051
Phone: (205) 755-1990
Internet: http://members.aol.com/
          wwhitby/cmp.html

Hours: Daily, Dawn - Dusk (park gates)
        Daily, 9am - 5pm (museum)

Located off U.S. Highway 31, near I-65, Confederate Memorial Park was the site of Alabama's only home for Confederate veterans. The park cemetery contains the burial sites of more than 300 Southern soldiers and widows. The Park museum features a large collection of Civil War memorabilia, including uniforms, weapons, and other artifacts.

Admission: FREE

The Confederate Memorial State Historic Site

c/o Confederate Memorial
Friend's Association
P.O. Box 332
Higginsville, MO 64037

Located 13 miles south of Lexington on Highway 13, the Confederate Memorial State Historic Site is situated on 191 acres which were once part of the grounds surrounding the Confederate Soldier's Home of Missouri. The site features The Chapel of the Confederate Home of Missouri, Confederate Memorial Cemetery, the 20-foot granite monument of the Lion of Lucerne, erected by the United Daughters of the Confederacy in 1906, Memorial Park, the last cottage from Cottage Row, a Farmhand's House, picnic areas, seven lakes, and a playground.

The Confederate Museum

2740 Farm Road #359
Richmond, TX 77469
Mail:
P.O. Box 179
Richmond, TX 77469
Phone: (713) 342-8787

Hours: Tuesday - Thursday, 10am - 3pm
Saturday & Sunday, 1pm - 4pm
Other times by appointment

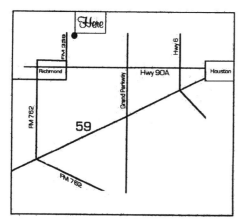

Located on the Old South Plantation grounds, The Confederate Museum offers a broad assortment of artifacts ranging from an antique antebellum bed to a varied collection of Civil War firearms. Read from the memoirs of Southern statesmen and generals such as Jefferson Davis, Robert E. Lee, Stonewall Jackson, and Nathan Bedford Forrest; view historical events captured forever on canvas by famous artists; and visit the home of Jane Long (the mother of Texas).

Membership in the Confederate Museum on the Old Plantation is available to those wishing to help preserve the history of the old South and present educational programs for residents and visitors of Richmond and the greater Houston area.

Membership: $35 (Individual)
$45 (Family)

> *Read from the memoirs of Southern statesmen and generals such as Jefferson Davis, Robert E. Lee, Stonewall Jackson, and Nathan Bedford Forrest*

The James W. Woodruff, Jr.

Confederate Naval Museum

202 - 4th Street
P.O. Box 1022
Columbus, GA 31902
Phone: (706) 327-9798

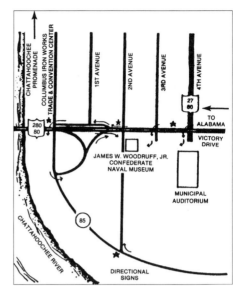

Hours: Tuesday - Friday, 10am - 5pm
Saturday & Sunday, 1pm - 5pm

The prime exhibits of the Confederate Naval Museum are the remains of two Confederate warships; the 225-foot ironclad ram Jackson ("Muscogee") and the 130-foot gunboat Chattahoochee. Considering the scarcity of Civil War ships available for display, the salvaged remains of the C.S.S. Jackson and the C.S.S. Chattahoochee represent a rare opportunity to glimpse this facet of naval history. Other displays at the museum include ship models, weapons, relics, and other exhibits dealing with the Confederate Navy.

Confederate Officers Quarters

Contact: *Tallassee Chamber of Commerce*
301-A King Street
Tallassee, AL 36708
Phone: (334) 283-5151
Fax: (334) 283-2940

Hours: Monday - Friday, 9am - 1pm

The three Confederate officers homes on King Street were built when the Confederate Armory was moved to Tallassee from Richmond. Two of the original three homes remain and are of particular interest because it is believed they are the only house ever built by the Confederate government.

Admission: FREE

The Confederate Research Center and Museum

Hill College
P.O. Box 619
Hillsboro, TX 76645
Phone: (817) 582-2555

Hours: Monday - Friday, 9am - 3pm

The Confederate Research Center and Museum offers displays which include .

Photo Courtesy of The Confederate Research Center and Museum

3/4, 1/3, and 1/6 scale Confederate artillery pieces, Confederate flags carried during the war, framed letters and documents concerning C.S.A. and U.S.A. military and civilian leaders, military art, battle dioramas, bronzes and a completely furnished antebellum doll house—TARA from *"Gone With The Wind."*

The Center and Museum also offers an extensive collection of research material including capsule histories of all 3,220 Confederate regiments and special units, and Confederate ships (see separate listing under *Archives & Libraries*).

The Confederate States Armory & Museum

529 Baltimore Street
Gettysburg, PA 17325
Phone: (717) 337-2340

The collection of weapons and memorabilia in The Confederate States Armory & Museum are fine examples of Southern manufacturing efforts during the Civil War. With no major arms makers in the South at the beginning of the war, the newly formed Confederate States of America was faced with the daunting task of supplying a growing army. The Confederate States Armory & Museum serves as a testament to their accomplishments. While there, be sure to visit their gift shop.

Admission fee (group rates available).

CSS Neuse State Historic Site

2612 W. Vernon Avenue (US70 Business)
Kinston, NC 28502
Mail:
P.O. Box 3043
Kinston, NC 28502-3043
Phone: (919) 522-2091

Hours: Monday - Saturday, 9am - 5pm
        Sunday, 1pm - 5pm
        (April 1 through October 31)
        Tuesday - Saturday, 10am - 4pm
        Sunday, 1pm - 4pm
        (November 1 through March 31)

Take an up-close look at the remains of the ironclad gunboat *CSS Neuse*, a key vessel in the Confederate Navy's ill-fated attempt to take control of the lower Neuse river and retake the city of New Bern. The 158-foot *Neuse* was one of 22 ironclads commissioned by the Confederate Navy. Launched in 1863, the still incomplete *CSS Neuse* was floated downstream to Kinston

Photo Courtesy of CSS Neuse State Historic Site

Remains of the CSS Neuse

where it was to be fitted with armor, guns, and machinery. The *Neuse* saw little action during the war because of obstructions in the river and the lack of troop support. In March of 1865, as Union forces approached Kinston, the *Neuse* was burned by its crew to prevent its capture. A large explosion in the port bow sank the ship. Almost a hundred years later, in 1963, the gunboat was raised and transported to the site where it sits on display.

Guided tours of the remains of the ironclad are available, as well as a thirteen-minute slide program that details the history and recovery of the ship. The exhibit room displays artifacts recovered from the gunboat and also offers an excellent scale model of the vessel. Living history programs are presented annually.

Delaware History Museum
504 Market Street
Wilmington, DE 19801
Phone: (302) 656-0637

Hours: Tuesday - Friday, Noon - 4pm
         Saturday, 10am - 4pm

         The Delaware History Museum has a major exhibit on Delaware in the Civil War which begins September 28, 1996 and continues through Summer 1997. The museum also has regimental flags, a draft wheel, weapons, and other artifacts of the Civil War in its collection and available to researchers by appointment. Call (302) 655-7161 for information on collections.

Dickson-Williams Mansion
114 W. Church Street
Greeneville, TN
Phone: (423) 638-8144

Hours: Monday - Saturday

         Used as a headquarters for both Union and Confederate troops, this home, called the "Showplace of East Tennessee," was where Confederate General John Hunt Morgan spent his last night before being killed in a surprise cavalry encounter. The room in which Morgan spent the night still has its original furnishings.

Drum Barracks Civil War Museum
1052 Banning Blvd.
Wilmington, CA 90744
Phone: (310) 548-7509
Fax: (310) 548-2946

Tours: 10:00, 11:00, 12:00, and 1:00
         Tuesday - Thursday
         11:30, 12:30, 1:30, and 2:30
         Saturday and Sunday

         With all the Civil War literature available these days, most people are still uneducated regarding California's part in the war. In fact, from 1861 to 1865, about 17,000 Californians served in volunteer regiments in the West and the East. Drum Barracks, also known as Camp Drum, served as Army Headquarters in the Southwest form 1861 until 1871.

In 1862, as Texas volunteers took control of territory in present-day Arizona and New Mexico, Colonel James Henry Carleton, first commander of Drum Barracks, marched The California Column towards Santa Fe. On the way, the 2,350-man column fought the Battle of Picacho Pass, the westernmost battle of the Civil War.

The Drum Barracks Civil War Museum is housed in the last remaining major structure of Camp Drum. The museum helps explain the role played by California soldiers, shows what life was like in Army Camps during the 1860's, tells the real story of the

117

U.S. Army Camel Corps., and describes the Battle of Picacho Pass.

Membership in The Drum Barracks Garrison & Society is available for those wishing to enlist. Membership benefits include a copy of *Reveille*, the newsletter of the Drum Barracks Garrison & Society, plus opportunities to socialize with others who are interested in preserving California's Civil War history. The Los Angeles Civil War Round Table holds its monthly meetings at Drum Barracks.

Exchange Hotel Civil War Museum

400 S. Main Street
Gordonsville, VA 22942
Mail:
P.O. Box 542
Gordonsville, VA 22942
Phone: (540) 832-2944

Hours: Tuesday - Saturday, 10am - 4pm
        (mid-Mar through mid-Dec)
        Sundays, 12:30pm - 4:30pm
        (June through September)

Photo Courtesy of the Exchange Hotel Civil War Museum

ness. Special exhibits include medical instruments, military collections (uniforms, arms, equipment, etc.), railroad memorabilia, and local history. Living History Weekends are held in April and September featuring military reenactors and medical personnel. Gordonsville is located in the heart of Central Virginia's battlefields of Brandy Station, Cedar Mountain, Chancellorsville, The Wilderness, Fredericksburg, Mine Run, Richmond, and Trevilian Stations.

Membership in Historic Gordonsville, Inc., is available to those interested in supporting the Exchange Hotel & Civil War Museum. Benefits include free annual admission to the Exchange Hotel, 10% discount on all gift shop purchases, membership card, and a subscription to the organizations quarterly newsletter. To join or for more information, contact Historic Gordonsville, Inc., at the mail address above.

Gordonsville's Exchange Hotel Civil War Museum is a beautifully restored Greek Revival structure originally built in 1860 as a railroad hotel. It served as a Confederate Receiving Hospital during the Civil War and was especially active with wounded during the Battle of the Wilder-

Admission charged.

Membership: $10 Individual
               $15 Family

Farnsworth House Inn

401 Baltimore St.
Gettysburg, PA 17325
Phone: (717) 334-8838
Fax: (717) 334-5862

Attraction: Ghost Stories

Descend the staircase into the darkness of a stone cellar and, by the light of a flickering candle, listen to haunting tales of Civil War spirits believed to still walk the town and surrounding battlefields.

Groups welcome.

First White House of the Confederacy

644 Washington Avenue
Montgomery, AL 36130
Phone: (334) 242-1861

Hours: Monday - Friday, 8am - 4:30pm

As the name implies, this 1835 house served as the White House of the Confederacy from February, 1861, when representatives from seven southern states met in Montgomery to form the Confederate government, until April, 1861, when Virginia seceded and the capital was moved to Richmond. Newly appointed Confederate President Jefferson Davis and his wife lived in the house during this period, thus lending it the distinction of being the First White House of the Confederacy. Period furnishings adorn the home.

Admission: FREE

Ford's Theatre National Historic Site

511 10th Street N.W.
Washington, DC
Phone: (202) 426-6924

Hours: Daily, 9am - 5pm

On April 14, 1865, Ford's Theatre became part of history when John Wilkes Booth fatally shot President Abraham Lincoln. With General Robert E. Lee surrendered at Appomattox only a few days before, the president could finally see an end to the four year war. But he would not live to enjoy the peace that followed.

The museum, located in the basement of the theatre, offers a collection of art, photographs, artifacts, and memorabilia related to President Lincoln. Of particular interest is the gun used by Booth and other artifacts from the trial of Booth's conspirators. The National Park Service lists over 12,000 objects and specimens (including documentation) at the Ford's Theatre NHS. Note: After visiting Ford's Theatre, be sure to visit the Peterson House across the street. Lincoln was taken to this house after being shot and it was there that he died, April 15, 1865.

Of particular interest is the gun used by Booth and other artifacts from the trial of Booth's conspirators.

Fort Clinch State Park

2601 Atlantic Avenue
Fernandina Beach, FL 32034
Phone: (904) 277-7274
Fax: (904) 277-7225

Hours: Daily, 9am - 5pm

Located at the mouth of the St. Marys River between Florida and Georgia, Fort Clinch was held by the Confederacy from the beginning of the Civil War until March 3, 1862, when the Union captured the fort and held it until the end of the war.

Living history interpreters gather the first weekend of each month and provide weapons demonstrations, as well as demonstrations of the more mundane aspects of the soldier's life, such as guard duty, fireplace cooking, and fatigue duty (splitting firewood, cleaning the kitchen, sandbagging ramparts, etc.). Signal Corps, sutlers, paymasters, and civilians are also demonstrated and the infirmary offers medical interpretation. A candlelight viewing of Fort Clinch is offered the first Saturday evening of every month (time varies with sundown), and soldier-led candlelight tours are available after sundown on Fridays and Saturdays, May through Labor Day, but you must call for reservations.

The park also features camping facilities, a salt-water fishing pier, and picnicking.

Fort Davidson State Historic Site

P.O. Box 509
Pilot Knob, MO 63663
Phone: (573) 546-3454

Hours: Daily, Sunrise to Sunset (Park)
          Monday - Saturday, 10am - 4pm
          Sunday, Noon - 5pm (Visitors Ctr)

Located at Highway 21 and Highway "V" in Pilot Knob, Fort Davidson State Historic Site occupies thirty acres which include the original earthen walls of the fort and a Visitor's Center. The Visitor's Center has a small library devoted to local Civil War history, and a small museum which displays artifacts found in the area. A slide program and a fiber optics battle map provide details of the Battle of Pilot Knob, 1864. Picnic tables and grills are nearby.

Fort Donelson National Battlefield

174 National Cemetery Drive
Dover, TN 37058
Mail:
P.O. Box 434
Dover, TN 37058
Phone: (615) 232-5706

Hours: Daily

A six-mile self-guided auto tour of Fort Donelson (an earthen fort), river batteries, outer earthworks, Dover Hotel, and National Cemetery is available. The battlefield also features a visitors center and museum with artifacts and a slide show. The Dover Hotel, site of Confederate General Buckner's surrender to U.S. Grant, now serves as park headquarters.

It was at Fort Donelson that General U.S. Grant earned his nickname, "Unconditional Surrender" Grant, upon offering no terms to General Buckner and stating "I propose to move immediately upon your works." The capture of Fort Donelson pro- pelled Grant into the national spotlight and provided a much needed victory for the Lincoln administration.

Fort Fisher Civil War Museum

P.O. Box 169
Kure Beach, NC 28449
Phone: (910) 458-5538

Hours: Monday - Saturday, 9am - 5pm
Sunday, 1pm - 5pm
(April 1 - October 31)
Tuesday - Saturday, 10am - 4pm
Sunday, 1pm - 4pm
(November 1 - March 31)

Located southwest of Kure Beach, off Route 421, and overlooking Cape Fear River, Fort Fisher served as one of the last strongholds of the Confederacy, protecting Cape Fear River and the Port of Wilmington and allowing safe passage for blockade runners. The earthen fort didn't fall until January 15, 1865. The site now offers access to the remains of the fort, a visitor center (with an orientation slide show), and guided tours.

Fort Gaines Historic Site

P.O. Box 97
Dauphin Island, AL 36528
Phone: (334) 861-6992

Hours: Daily, 9am - 5pm

Located at the east end of Bienville Blvd. on Dauphin Island, Fort Gaines was a key stronghold guarding Mobile Bay prior to and during the Battle of Mobile Bay. On August 5, 1864, Rear Admiral David G. Farragut said "Damn the torpedoes," which were early versions of the naval mine, and passed Fort Gaines and Fort Morgan. In the southern part of Mobile Bay, Farragut engaged and defeated the ironclad *Tennessee* and a small Confederate fleet. Though the port of Mobile was now closed, the city itself didn't surrendered until April 13, 1865. Visitors can explore the battlements, living quarters, tunnels, and bastions of Fort Gaines. Cannons used during the battle are also on display.

Admission charged.

Fort James Jackson Historic Site

1 Fort Jackson Road
Savannah, GA 31404
Phone: (912) 232-3945

Hours: Monday - Sunday, 9am - 5pm

Located on the Savannah River, Old Fort Jackson was used as the headquarters for the Confederate river defenses during the Civil War. The fort was a strategic location because any ship entering or leaving Savannah's Port must pass within reach of Fort Jackson's guns.

Georgia's first ironclad, the C.S.S. Georgia, was scuttled at the fort the night of Savannah's evacuation to prevent her from falling into Union hands. Her final resting place is marked by a red buoy in the Savannah River at Fort Jackson.

Fort McAllister State Historic Park

3894 Fort McAllister Road
Richmond Hill, GA 31324
Phone: (912) 727-2339

Hours: Daily, 7am - 10pm (park)
         Tuesday - Saturday, 9am - 5pm
         Sunday, 2pm - 5:30pm (site)

Home of the best preserved earthwork fortification of the Confederacy, Fort McAllister State Historic Park occupies 1,690 acres on the south bank of the great Ogeechee River. The earthworks have been restored to their 1863-64 appearance and a museum with Civil War artifacts is at the site.

Fort Morgan

51 Highway 180 West
Gulf Shores, AL 36542
Phone: (334) 540-7125

Hours: Daily, 9am - 5pm

Prominent during the Battle of Mobile Bay, Fort Morgan was one of the last Confederate forts to fall. A museum at the site provides a glimpse of the fort's history; its beginning in 1819 and completion in 1834, its contribution to the Confederacy, and its service into the 20th century (ending in 1945).

Admission charged.

Fort Pillow State Historic Site

Route 2
Henning, TN 38041
Mail:
P.O. Box 109
Henning, TN 38041
Phone: (901) 738-5581

Hours: Daily (site)
         Monday - Friday (visitor center)

Overlooking the Mississippi River north of Memphis, Tennessee, Fort Pillow was an important Confederate river defense until its capture by Union forces in 1862. The fort remained in Union hands until April 12, 1864, when troops of Confederate General Nathan B. Forrest's Cavalry Corps attacked and captured the earthworks.

Battle casualties for the Confederates were light, with 14 killed and 86 wounded. Union troops, especially black troops, suffered much greater losses, with 231 killed, 226 captured, and roughly 100 wounded. The unusually high ratio of killed versus wounded instantly created controversy and raised charges of a massacre. Union troops stated that black troops who had already surrendered and thrown down their weapons were killed, along with the wounded. At the time of the assault, 262 black troops occupied Fort Pillow, composing the 11th U.S. Colored Troops, and Battery F of the 4th U.S. Colored Light Artillery. At battle's end, only 58 were taken prisoner. Some would later claim (on both sides) that the high casualty rate was due to the 11th U.S.C.T.'s hard-fought defense of the earthworks and their refusal to fall back. The controversy has continued for over thirteen decades and will likely continue for as many more.

The fort is open to the public, courtesy of the State of Tennessee, and features a visitors center and other amenities.

Fort Towson Military Park

HC 63, Box 1580
Fort Towson, OK 74735-9273
Phone: (405) 873-2634

Hours: Tuesday - Friday, 9am - 5pm
         Saturday - Sunday, 1pm - 5pm

Fort Towson, Oklahoma's second oldest military outpost, was officially aban-doned in 1856, but saw new life during the Civil War as the command post of Confederate General Sam Bell Maxey. After the war the fort became a dispersal point for Confederate veterans.

Remains of the fort can be seen at the site, as well as the reconstructed Suttler's Store.

Fort Ward Museum & Historic Site

4301 West Braddock Road
Alexandria, VA 22304
Phone: (703) 838-4848

Hours: Tues - Sat, 9am - 5pm (Museum)
         Sunday, Noon - 5pm
         Daily, 9am - sunset (site)

Of the sixty-eight forts surrounding Washington, D.C. during the Civil War, Fort Ward was the fifth largest. Named for Commander James Harmon Ward, the first Union naval officer killed in the war, Fort Ward had 36 guns mounted in 5 bastions. The historic site occupies 45 acres and includes picnic facilities and an open-air amphitheater.

The museum is patterned after a Union headquarters building. Exhibits cover such topics as Civil War medicine, the art of the artilleryman, the life of the common soldier, and local Alexandria Civil War history. Tours, lectures, and living history activities are offered throughout the year. A research library is also available.

Membership in *The Friends of Fort Ward* is available. Founded in 1982, this organization is composed of private citizens dedicated to helping historic Fort Ward with fund raising and promotion. Members will be invited to special receptions and programs at Fort Ward, receive a 10% discount in the Museum Shop, may participate in Friends' bus tours to other Civil War sites at discount rates, and will receive the *Fort Ward Dispatch* which is published quarterly.

Admission: FREE (donations appreciated)

Named for Commander James Harmon Ward, the first Union naval officer killed in the war, Fort Ward had 36 guns mounted in 5 bastions.

Fort Zachary Taylor State Historic Site

P.O. Box 6560
Key West, FL 33041
Phone: (305) 292-6713

Occupied by Union forces under Captain John Brannon when the Civil War broke out, Fort Zachary Taylor remained in Union hands throughout the war and proved to be a tremendous deterrent to the Confederate Navy.

Beginning in 1968, volunteers excavating for old armaments in the gun room uncovered a number of Civil War era guns and some ammunition. The unearthed cannon represent only a fraction of the arsenal buried at Fort Zachary Taylor. It was this which prompted the fort's placement on the National Register of Historic Places in 1971.

The fort's museum offers a display of artifacts and models of the original guns and facilities. Original Civil War cannon are also on display and guided tours are available daily.

For information on the preservation of Fort Taylor, see Friends of Fort Taylor, Inc., in the *Organizations* section.

Fortification Hill

Portsmouth Road/S.R. 141
Mail:
Ohio Valley Visitors Center
45 State Street
Gallipolis, OH 45631

Phone: 1-800-765-6482

Fortification Hill overlooks Gallipolis, the Ohio River, and West Virginia with a breathtaking view for about 10 miles. Receiving its name when it was fortified with cannons during the Civil War to protect Gallipolis from a then Confederate Virginia. The cannons were melted down during World War II.

Frederick Douglass National Historic Site

1411 W Street NW
Washington, DC 20020
Phone: (202) 426-5961

Hours: Daily, 9am - 5pm
        (April - September)
        Daily, 9am - 4pm
        (rest of year)

Last home of Frederick Douglass, the former slave who became a prominent statesman and equal rights activist. The site contains objects, furnishings, paintings, books, newspapers, and prints related to Douglass and his family. A film documents the life of Frederick Douglass and interpretive exhibits are available.

Fredericksburg Area Museum & Cultural Center

907 Princess Anne Street
Fredericksburg, VA 22401
Mail:
P.O. Box 922
Fredericksburg, VA 22404
Phone: (540) 371-3037

Hours: Monday - Saturday, 10am - 5pm
        Sunday, 1pm - 5pm

Located in the 1816 Town Hall/ Market House, the Fredericksburg Area Museum has permanent displays that cover the history of Fredericksburg and the surrounding area from dinosaurs to the 1960s. The Civil War exhibits emphasize the civilian experience—though attention is also paid to the soldier. Military items on display include a Henry rifle, a sword with "CSA" carved into the basket, and a Confederate Officer's coat, among others. Most weapons and accessories were found on local battlefields. A museum gift shop is also available.

Museum membership is available. Benefits include: free admission to the museum; 10% discount at the gift shop; discounts on special programs, workshops, and lectures; annual subscription to Museum's newsletter; invitations to exhibit openings and special events.

Admission charged.

The Galena-Jo Daviess County Historical Society & Museum

211 South Bench Street
Galena, IL 61036
Phone: (815) 777-9129
Fax: (815) 777-9131

Hours: Daily, 9am - 4:30pm

The small town of Galena claims no fewer than nine residents who became Union Generals during the Civil War, including Ulysses S. Grant. The Museum honors this part of the town's history with an exhibit that features original Civil War weaponry, prints, letters, tools, and more. Of particular interest is the 9' x 12' oil painting by Civil War artist Thomas Nast, which depicts Lee's surrender to Grant at Appomattox in 1865. The painting was presented to the City of Galena in 1895.

The Museum also offers a gift and book shop, a step-on guide service and tours (advance reservations required), events throughout the year, and membership in the Historical Society.

Photo Courtesy of The Galena-Jo Daviess County Historical Society & Museum

Lee's Surrender to Grant at Appomattox, by Thomas Nast

Admission charged.

Gallia County Civil War Soldiers Homecoming: A Federal Reunion

Gallipolis City Park and Our House Tavern State Memorial
Gallipolis, OH 45631
Phone: 1-800-765-6482

Time: Last weekend in April

The Federal Army Homecoming, a weekend living history encampment, is held at the original Union Army campsite in historic Downtown Gallipolis, Ohio during the last weekend in April. Authentic Union infantry, artillery, medical, signal corp, engineering, civilian impressions, and sutlers are welcomed. Highlights of the event include skirmishes, artillery night firing, special Civil War exhibit on loan from the Ohio Historical Society at the Our House Tavern State Memorial, and Ladies High Tea for participants as well as an evening of entertainment at the Ariel Theatre, a restored 19th-century opera house. Registration fee of $3 for participants is for the upkeep of the Our House Tavern State Memorial, an army hospital at the time of the rebellion. The event is free to the public.

General Joe Wheeler Home

12280 Alabama Hwy 20
Hillsboro, AL 35643
Phone: (205) 637-8513

Built in the 1870s, this home is located 15 miles west of Decatur on Highway 20. It served as the residence of General Joseph Wheeler, Confederate cavalry officer. The home contains many of the original furnishings and memorabilia of General Wheeler and his family. The 15 acre site features a family cemetery and a number of outbuildings.

Admission charged.

General Lloyd Tilghman House

631 Kentucky Avenue
Paducah, KY 42002

The home of Confederate General Lloyd Tilghman, who was killed in action near Vicksburg on May 16, 1863, is currently being restored as the Tilghman Military Heritage Center. This center will serve as a museum of American military history.

General Sweeny's Civil War Museum

5228 S. State Highway ZZ
Republic, MO 65738
Phone: (417) 732-1224
Fax: (417) 732-1224

Hours: Wednesday - Sunday, 10am - 5pm
         (March through October)
         Saturday & Sunday, 10am - 5pm
         (November & February)

Explore the Ozark Mountain Country's rich Civil War heritage at General Sweeny's Museum of Civil War History. With artifacts and weapons displays of the war in the Trans-Mississippi, General Sweeny's has won praise from historians like Mr. Ed Bearss, former chief historian of the National Park Service, who wrote "General Sweeny's Civil War Museum is a must for anyone interested in the Civil War in the Trans-Mississippi," and "A few hours there will enrich a visit to related historic sites in a four-state region."

Located adjacent to Wilson's Creek National Battlefield Park, the museum collection includes thousands of artifacts that were collected over a twenty-five year period. These artifacts are presented in 51 professionally designed display cases which tell the story of the war in the West.

Items of interest include the sword belt and sash of General Patrick Cleburne, the "Stonewall Jackson" of the West, a number of flags, including a rare Cherokee Indian Confederate Flag, medical displays, a wide variety of weapons used by the infantry, cavalry, and artillery, and weapons of the fresh water navy which operated on the Mississippi and other rivers.

Admission charged.

The Gettysburg Headquarters of General Robert E. Lee

U.S. 30 West, 401 Buford Avenue
Gettysburg, PA 17325

conveniently located eight blocks west of Lincoln Square

Hours: Daily, 9am - 9pm
        (mid-March through November)

Chosen for its location (at the center and rear of Lee's battle lines) and its safety (the stone walls on the first floor are more than 20" thick), this old house served as General Lee's headquarters during the three-day Battle of Gettysburg. Items on display include Union and Confederate rifles, carbines, pistols, sabers, bullets, bullet molds, powder flasks, uniforms, buttons, belt buckles, personal items, surgical instruments, saddles and cavalry equipment, rare photographs, documents, and the original kitchen with Civil War-period furnishings. The museum is conveniently located eight blocks west of Lincoln Square.

Grand Army of the Republic Civil War Museum and Library

4278 Griscom Street
Philadelphia, PA 19124-3954
Phone: (215) 289-6484

Hours: First Sunday each month and
Each Sunday in January,
Noon - 5pm
Open by appointment for out-of-town visitors or groups

Dedicated to the preservation of the heritage and history of the Civil War, the G.A.R. Museum and Library offers a variety of historical programs, forums, and exhibitions designed to promote a better understanding of American history. Located in the historic Ruan House, the museum collection includes unique and historic artifacts, battle relics, personal memorabilia, paintings, documents, and photographs of the Civil War. Filling three floors of the Ruan mansion, this extensive, historically significant collection was initially assembled by the veterans who formed Post 2 of the Grand Army of the Republic.

Displayed artifacts include: tree stumps from the Chickamauga Battlefield, each embedded with a cannonball; an original section of the stockade from Andersonville Prison; personal possessions of General George G. Meade; and the handcuffs owned by John Wilkes Booth—which he planned to use in the kidnaping of President Lincoln.

The Ruan House Library contains a 2,000-volume archive available to researchers, students, and those engaged in genealogical research. Approved researchers may examine the actual *Harper's Weekly* and *Philadelphia Inquirer* newspapers for the entire period of the war, the official records of the War of the Rebellion, as well as many magazines, regimental and unit histories, and other related historical volumes and accounts.

Membership in the *Friends of the G.A.R. Museum* is available to those interested in supporting the continued work of this outstanding organization. As a registered non-profit organization all donations are tax deductible. With no paid staff, the museum relies upon the dedicated members who volunteer their time, both at the museum and at programs presented to local schools and community groups.

Admission: FREE (donations appreciated)

Grand Army of the Republic Memorial Museum

629 South Seventh Street
Springfield, IL 62703
Phone: (217) 522-4373

Hours: Tuesday - Saturday, 10am - 4pm

Photo Courtesy of the GAR Memorial Museum

Just a few blocks from Lincoln's home in historic Springfield is the Grand Army of the Republic Memorial Museum, established and maintained by the National Woman's Relief Corps, Auxiliary to the Grand Army of the Republic. The museum is designed as a living memorial to the Civil War veterans who constituted the G.A.R., therefore a majority of the museum's displays are Civil War oriented.

Through the years various artifacts, documents, and historical items have been donated to the museum by the Civil War veterans of the Grand Army, their relatives, friends, and members of the National Woman's Relief Corps.

Admission: FREE

Gray & Blue Naval Museum

1102 Washington Street
Vicksburg, MS
Phone: (601) 638-6500

Hours: Monday - Saturday, 9am - 5pm

Housing the world's largest collection of Civil War gunboat models, the Gray & Blue Naval Museum offers an opportunity to study the many different designs of warships used in the Civil War. The museum also offers a collection of paintings, reference files, and artifacts—plus a Civil War bookstore.

Admission charged.

Hall of Valor Civil War Museum

New Market Battlefield State Historical Park
8895 Collins Drive
P.O. Box 1864
New Market, VA 22844
Phone: (540) 740-3101

Hours: Daily, 9am - 5pm

Established in 1970, the Hall of Valor Civil War Museum is a monument to the Virginia Military Institute (VMI) cadets who fought in the Battle of New Market on May 15, 1864. The museum's 125-seat theater presents two award winning films, one on the battle, the other on "Stonewall" Jackson's 1862 Shenandoah Valley Campaign. One admission ticket includes the Battlefield, Hall of Valor Museum, and Bushong Farm (the Bushong family saw their home turned into a hospital as the land around it was churned into a bloody battlefield).

Admission charged.

Tune your radio to AM 530 for Park info.

The museum's 125-seat theater presents two award winning films, one on the battle, the other on "Stonewall" Jackson's 1862 Shenandoah Valley Campaign.

Harpers Ferry NHP

P.O. Box 65
Harpers Ferry, WV 25425
Phone: (304) 535-6298

Hours: Daily, 8am - 6pm *(summer)*
             Daily, 8am - 5pm *(winter)*

Directions: Located along Route 340, approximately 20 miles southwest of Frederick, Maryland.

Harpers Ferry National Historical Park was established in 1944 and encompasses 2,300 acres in the states of Maryland, Virginia, and West Virginia. Facilities and exhibits include the Information Center, Industry Museum, Restoration Museum, Wetlands Exhibit, John Brown Museum and Fort, Storer College Museum, Black Voices Museum, Civil War Museum, and the Harper House. Numerous trails are available for the more industrious, including the Jefferson Rock Trail, Maryland Heights Trail, and Bolivar Heights Trail.

Annual events include "Election Day - 1860" which is held in October, and living history presentations at various times throughout the year.

Admission charged.

Harriet Beecher Stowe Center

also the home of Mark Twain

77 Forest Street
Hartford, CT 06105
Phone: (860) 522-9258
Fax: (860) 522-9259

Hours: Tuesday - Saturday, 9:30am - 4pm
             Sunday, Noon - 4pm

DIRECTIONS

Exit 46 from I-84. Right onto Sisson Avenue. Right onto Farmington Avenue. Right onto Forest Street. Free Parking.

Perhaps no other period book is more associated with slavery and, ultimately, the Civil War, than Harriet Beecher Stowe's *Uncle Tom's Cabin*. First published in serial form in 1851, and then as a book in 1852, the novel graphically revealed the emotional realities of American slavery for the first time to a world-wide reading audience, prompting many to support a war to abolish the "peculiar institution."

The Harriet Beecher Stowe Center operates the Harriet Beecher Stowe House, its Visitors Center and shop, and the Stowe-Day Library located in the Katharine S. Day House. The Stowe House, residence of Harriet Beecher Stowe from 1873 until her death in 1896, was also the home of Mark Twain, suffragist Isabella Beecher Hooker, Civil War general and senator Joseph R. Hawley, and actor/playwright William Gillette. The restored home features a "modern" 19th-century kitchen, period furnishings, some of Mrs. Stowe's paintings, her writing table, memorabilia, and historical gardens. All tours are guided and begin at the Visitors Center.

The Stowe-Day Library offers a collection of 160,000 original manuscripts, 15,000 volumes on 19th-century cultural history, photographs ranging form daguerreotypes to modern prints, and a selection of artifacts.

Hollywood Cemetery

412 South Cherry Street
Richmond, VA 23220
Phone: (804) 648-8501

Hours: Mon - Sat, 8:30am - 4:30pm (Office)

Hollywood Cemetery is the oldest active cemetery in the Richmond area. It is rich in Civil War history with over 17,000 soldiers interred here, as well as Jefferson Davis and his family. Hollywood is the final resting place for General Pickett, JEB Stuart, 25 Civil War Generals, and Presidents James Monroe and John Tyler.

The Cemetery is a not-for-profit, non-stock corporation that is actually owned by its lot owners. You can become a part owner of Hollywood Cemetery by arranging to purchase space for ground burial or entombment in the Hollywood Chapel Mausoleum located above the James River. Ground burial space near the Confederate Soldier's Section will be available for purchase in the near future.

A number of items can be purchased in the office, including a tour map ($1), Historic brochure ($5), *Register of Confederate Dead Interred in Hollywood Cemetery*

Photo Courtesy of Hollywood Cemetery

90-foot Confederate Monument

($10), and *Hollywood Cemetery: The History of a Southern Shrine* ($25). These items may also be purchased by mail. Please add $2.00 shipping and handling per item (not including tour map). Make check or money order payable to Hollywood Cemetery Company.

Hunt-Phelan Home

533 Beale Street
Memphis, TN 38103
Phone: (901) 344-3166

Hours: Daily *(spring and summer)*
          Tuesday - Wednesday
          (Labor Day - March 1)

The Hunt-Phelan Home played host to many dignitaries before and during the Civil War, among them President Andrew Jackson, Jefferson Davis, General Forrest, General Polk, and General Grant. It was in this house that Confederate General

> *General Grant used the home as his headquarters. It was here, in the home's library, that he planned the Vicksburg Campaign.*

Leonidis Polk laid out his strategy for the Battle of Corinth. Later, General Grant used the home as his headquarters. It was in the home's library that he planned the Vicksburg Campaign. At war's end, one of the first schools for freed slaves was built at the Hunt-Phelan Home by the Freedman's Bureau.

Hupp's Hill Battlefield Park and Study Center

Route 11 North
P.O. Box 31
Strasburg, VA 22657
Phone: (540) 465-5884

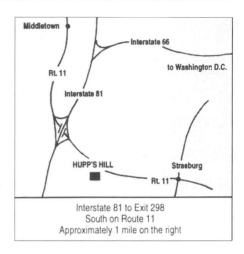

```
Middletown
                        Interstate 66
Rt. 11                            to Washington D.C.
      Interstate 81
         HUPP'S HILL         Strasburg
            ■          Rt. 11
```

Interstate 81 to Exit 298
South on Route 11
Approximately 1 mile on the right

Hours: Monday - Friday, 10am - 4pm
Saturday & Sunday, 11am - 5pm

Located on the southern end of Cedar Creek Battlefield, Hupp's Hill museum and learning center offers a glimpse of the Shenandoah Valley during the Civil War. Earthworks dug by General Sheridan's men can still be seen here and the hill offers a view of other historic sites, such as signal Knob and Fisher's Hill. The museum displays include weapons, men's and women's clothing, medical equipment, dug relics, documents, and other artifacts, and the center offers a unique hands-on approach to learning in their reproduction area.

The reproduction area of the museum offers a place where both children and adults can handle reproduction equipment from the Civil War period. Children can try on clothing, sit in Civil War saddles, or crawl into Civil War tents. The center also offers a Civil War Day Camp, held each year at the end of school. This intense hands-on program is designed for children ages 8 to 12, who play the part of new recruits in the Infantry, Cavalry, Artillery, and as Civilians. The program teaches them the duties and responsibilities of the Civil War era.

Admission charged.

> *Children can try on clothing, sit in Civil War saddles, or crawl into Civil War tents.*

John Brown Wax Museum

Harpers Ferry, WV 25425
Phone: (304) 535-2792

Hours: Daily, 9am - 5pm
(mid-March to December)
Weekends, 10am - 5pm
(mid-December to mid-March)

The life story of abolitionist John Brown is dramatically recreated at the John Brown Wax Museum, beginning when Brown was still a youth and ending with his death on the gallows. Located in one of the historic buildings that was standing during Brown's famous, yet ill-fated Harpers Ferry raid, the museum takes advantage of the latest developments in electronic lighting, sound, and animation.

Admission charged.

Johnsonville State Historic Area

Route 1, Box 37-4
New Johnsonville, TN
Phone: (615) 535-2789

Hours: Daily

The Johnsonville State Historic Site commemorates the November 4, 1864 destruction of the Federal depot at Johnsonville by "That devil" Nathan Bedford Forrest. General Forrest had the pleasure of reporting the capture and destruction of 4 gunboats, 14 transports, 20 barges, 26 pieces of artillery, $6.7 million in property, and 150 prisoners captured (see Civil War Times Illustrated, August 1996, pages 24-30). He estimated Union casualties at 500 killed, wounded, and captured. His own loses amounted to two killed and nine wounded.

Kennesaw Civil War Museum

2829 Cherokee Street
Kennesaw, GA 30144
Phone: (770) 427-2117
Fax: (770) 429-4538

Hours: Mon - Sat, 9:30am - 5:30pm
Sunday, Noon - 5:30pm

On April 12, 1862 Union volunteers lead by civilian James Andrews seized a locomotive known as *The General* in Big Shanty, Georgia (now Kennesaw, Georgia). The result was a chase that became known as *The Great Locomotive Chase*. Running the train north, Andrews' men tore up tracks, cut telegraph lines and burned bridges in an attempt to destroy the Confederate's main supply line. In hot pursuit of *The General* was another locomotive, *The Texas*, which had been commandeered by *The General's* conductor, Captain William A. Fuller. Near the Tennessee/Georgia border Andrews and his men were forced to abandon *The General*. Despite this, Andrews' Raiders were not able to escape the pursuing Confederates. All of the Raiders were captured. Eight of the twenty-two volunteers were hanged along with James Andrews, six were exchanged and eight escaped. These Union soldiers became the first recipients of the Congressional Medal of Honor. Andrews, a civilian, did not receive this honor.

Home of "The General"

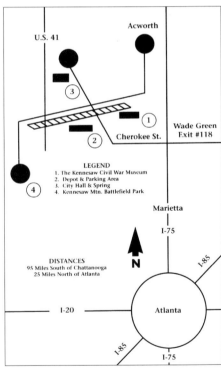

Kennesaw Civil War Museum now houses *The General* in an authentic cotton gin only a hundred yards from the site where *The General* was stolen. The museum also offers descriptive exhibits and a video reenactment of the raid.

LeMoyne House and the Military Museum of Southwestern Pennsylvania

Washington County Historical Society
49 East Maiden Street
Washington, PA 15301
Phone: (412) 225-6740

Hours: Tuesday - Friday, 11am - 4pm
Saturday - Sunday, Noon - 4pm
Closed mid-December to January

The LeMoyne House is the 1812 home of Dr. F. Julius LeMoyne, a physician, abolitionist, and humanitarian. The house was a stop on the Underground Railroad and served as a place for abolitionist meetings. Dr. LeMoyne was a candidate for governor of Pennsylvania on the anti-slavery platform, while his son, Dr. Frank LeMoyne, served as a surgeon for the Union during the Civil War. The military museum occupies one room of the house and contains a core collection of Civil War artifacts, including military equipment, uniforms, and a military history library.

The Lincoln College Museum

McKinstry Memorial Library
300 Keokuk Street
Lincoln, IL 62656
Phone: (217) 732-3155

Hours: Monday - Friday, 9am - 4pm
Saturday & Sunday, 1pm - 4pm
(Closed mid-Dec to Feb 1)

The Lincoln College Museum houses and displays over 2,000 items of Lincolniana, items relating to Illinois and Logan County History, and American Presidential Memorabilia. Holdings include items from the Beckwith Collection (left by Robert Todd Lincoln Beckwith, the last living descendant of Abraham Lincoln, who died Christmas Eve, 1985). This important collection contains china, books, and mourning clothing that belonged to Mary Todd Lincoln. Hundreds of documents relating to Lincoln, his family, members of his cabinet, and Civil War military leaders are available. Artifacts include the desk and chair used by Lincoln during his service in the Illinois House of Representatives, a table on which young Lincoln studied grammar and surveying, and tassels from the covering of his coffin, among other items.

Just outside the main museum area is The Hall of the Presidents. Here, documents signed by every U.S. president are on display, along with pictures and commemorative medals. Documents signed by almost every first lady are also available. *The Lincoln Newsletter*, an informative quarterly publication which includes news and feature articles about Lincoln, is available from the Lincoln College Museum for $10 per year.

Hundreds of documents relating to Lincoln, his family, members of his cabinet, and Civil War military leaders are available.

The Lincoln Museum

200 East Berry
Fort Wayne, IN 46802
Phone: (219) 455-3864
Fax: (219) 455-6922
Internet:
   http://www.TheLincolnMuseum.org

Hours: Tuesday - Saturday, 10am - 5pm
         Sunday, 1pm - 5pm

Photo Courtesy of The Lincoln Museum

Though The Lincoln Museum was begun in 1931, it recently re-opened a spectacular new $6 million, 30,000 square foot facility. The museum has a permanent exhibit called "The American Experiment," as well as two temporary exhibits each year. "The American Experiment" includes 11 exhibit galleries, featuring hundreds of artifacts and artworks from Lincoln's era; four theaters; and touchscreen computer exhibits that let you read Lincoln's mail, decorate the White House as Mary Todd Lincoln did, fight a Civil War battle, or take a history quiz. The world's largest private collection of Lincolniana is held by the museum, including over 200 documents signed by Lincoln, family belongings, family photos and a lock of the President's hair taken from his deathbed. A research facility is also available (by appointment only). With 18,000 books, 7,000 19th century prints, engravings, newspapers, and music sheets, 200,000 newspaper and magazine clippings, and 5,000 original photographs, the museum is a wealthy repository of Lincoln era information.

The museum publishes *Lincoln Lore*, the oldest continual publication on Abraham Lincoln, and the museum store offers nearly 1000 different items and books, mostly dealing with Abraham Lincoln and the Civil War. A full catalog and book listing is in the works and a 1-800 number and web page are planned for the near future.

Membership in The Lincoln Museum is available to those wishing to support this exceptional institution. Membership benefits include free admission to the museum, 10% discount on all merchandise from The Lincoln Museum Store, invitations to special events, including members' previews, subscription to *Lincoln Lore*, and reduced rental rates for both lobbies and meeting areas.

Admission charged.
Membership: $20 per year (individual)
              $35 per year (family)

> *The world's largest private collection of Lincolniana is held by the museum, including over 200 documents signed by Lincoln, family belongings, family photos and a lock of the President's hair taken from his deathbed.*

> *18,000 books, 7,000 19th century prints, engravings, newspapers, and music sheets, 200,000 newspaper and magazine clippings, and 5,000 original photographs*

The Lincoln Museum, Inc.

66 Lincoln Square
Hodgenville, KY 42748
Phone: (502) 358-3163

Hours: Monday - Saturday, 8:30am - 5pm
Sunday, 12:30pm - 5pm

Located three miles north of Sinking Spring Farm where Abraham Lincoln was born 1809, The Lincoln Museum building is on The National Register of Historic Places and located on the town square overlooking the original bronze statue of Lincoln by A.A. Weinmann. The first floor of the museum features twelve dioramas of great importance in Lincoln's life, including The Cabin Years, The Rail Splitter, The Lincoln-Douglas Debates, The Gettysburg Address

LINCOLN MUSEUM

and Ford's Theater. The second level of the museum presents exhibits, memorabilia, a film, and The Lincoln Day's Art Collection.

The Lincoln Room Museum

12 Lincoln Square
Gettysburg, PA 17325
Phone: (717) 334-8188

Hours: Sunday - Thursday, 9am - 7pm
(in season)
Friday & Saturday, 9am - 8pm
(in season)
Open in off season at
reduced hours

Located in the Historic Wills House in Gettysburg Square, the Lincoln Room Museum offers a glimpse at the bedroom where Abraham Lincoln completed the Gettysburg Address. Owned by Judge and Mrs. David Wills during Lincoln's 1863 visit, the museum still displays most of the original furniture that occupied the president's bedroom. During your visit you'll learn about and view copies of the five drafts of the Gettysburg Address that still exist. These named copies are known as the Nicolay, Hay, Everett, Bancroft, and Bliss copies. The museum also boasts a collection of Lincoln and Gettysburg related items located in the Archives Room, including a life mask that was made when Abraham Lincoln was a lawyer.

Photo Courtesy of The Lincoln Room Museum

Longwood

140 Lower Woodville Road
Natchez, MS 39121
Phone: (601) 446-6631

Photo Courtesy of Natchez Pilgrimage Tours

Designed for Dr. Haller Nutt, construction on this eight-sided southern palace began in 1860. With the outbreak of civil war, the craftsmen fired by Nutt headed back to their native Pennsylvania to enlist. The thirty-two room home was never completed and stands as a reminder of the hardships Natchezians endured during the war. Even Dr. Nutt, a Union sympathizer, suffered the destruction or confiscation of millions of dollars of cotton land. Longwood is maintained by Natchez Pilgrimage Tours. Contact them for further information on tours of Longwood and other Natchez sites.

Looney's Tavern Amphitheater & Park

US Hwy 278 East
Mail:
P.O. Box 70
Double Springs, AL 35533
Phone: (205) 489-5000
Fax: (205) 489-3500

Staged in the 1,500-seat amphitheater overlooking Bankhead National Forest, Looney's Tavern offers performances Thursday through Saturday at 8:00 p.m. which tell the story of locals caught between Union and Confederate forces during the Civil War. The park also features a Civil War show in its indoor theater, Looney's two-hour Riverboat cruises, a restaurant, miniature golf, and a gift shop.

Lotz House War Between the States and Old West Museum

1111 Columbia Avenue
Franklin, TN 37064
Phone: (615) 791-6533
Email: LotzRebel@aol.com
Internet:
    http://www.phoenix.w1.com/lotz

Hours: Monday - Saturday, 9am - 5pm
          Sunday, Noon - 5pm

Located in the historic Lotz House, the War Between the States and Old West Museum exhibits the largest and most comprehensive collection of War Between the States related artifacts in the area. Visi-

Photo Courtesy of the Lotz House

tors are encouraged to wander through the museum and spend as much time as they wish examining the museum's collection of rare and unique artifacts. A tour of the house is available to museum guests, during which the history of the house is discussed, along with its role in the November, 1864 Battle of Franklin. Other amenities include genealogical services and museum gift shop.

The Lotz House

The Loudoun Museum
14-16 Loudoun Street, SW
Leesburg, VA 20175
Phone: (703) 777-7427

Located near the Ball's Bluff Battlefield Regional Park, site of the largest Civil War engagement in Loudoun County, The Loudoun Museum offers the opportunity to examine this small, though significant battle. Discover artifacts from the battle— and from smaller Loudoun County skirmishes.

Other exhibits will give a glimpse of Colonial and 19th Century lifestyles in Loudoun County. Lectures and workshops are offered, as are walking tours, audio-visual presentations, school programs, and genealogical research material. A gift shop is also available.

Museum membership is available to those interested in supporting the museum's programs. Benefits of membership include: free admission to the Loudoun Museum; subscription to *The Heritage Review*, a quarterly museum newsletter; 10% discount at the museum gift shop; discounts and/or free admission to selected museum programs and events; and eligibility for the Museum Travel Program and for "members only" events and programs.

Mabry-Hazen House

1711 Dandridge Avenue
Knoxville, TN 37915
Phone: (423) 522-8661

Hours: Daily

Occupied by both Union and Confederate troops during the war, the house contains thousands of artifacts. Of particular interest are the sketches Mrs. Mabry made of the trenches surrounding her house. Along with the other artifacts, these sketches offer powerful insights into what it must have been like to live in the home during the Civil War.

The Manassas Museum

9101 Prince William Street
Manassas, VA 20110
Mail:
P.O. Box 560
Manassas, VA 20108
Phone: (703) 368-1873

Hours: Tuesday - Sunday, 10am - 5pm

Photo Courtesy of The Manassas Museum

Five miles from the Manassas National Battlefield Park, The Manassas Museum offers a local look at two of the most important battles of the Civil War. The museum's Civil War holdings include uniforms, weapons, flags, and—more significantly—the earthworks of Mayfield Fort (Confederate) and Cannon Branch Fort (Union), both of which are being restored. When complete, these earthworks will have interpretive trails and markers, reproduction cannon, and amenities such as benches and brochure racks. The museum also sponsors Civil War Weekends which feature living history encampments of Union and Confederate soldiers, artillery and musket firing, and demonstrations of soldier life.

Those interested in supporting the museum can become a Manassas Museum Associate. Benefits include: subscription to *Word From the Junction*, the Manassas Museum bimonthly newsletter; free lectures, guided tours, audiovisual programs and special events; 10% discount at *Echoes*, the Museum store; free admission to the museum; and special invitation to receptions and events.

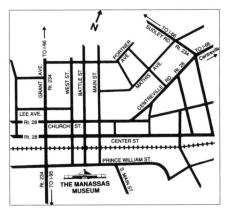

Mansfield State Commemorative Area

15149 Hwy 175
Mansfield, LA 71052
Phone: (318) 872-1474

climax point of the Red River Campaign

Located in DeSoto Parish, four miles south of Mansfield on Highway 175, the 178-acre Mansfield State Commemorative Area was the climax point of the Red River Campaign. The site features a museum with Civil War weapons, uniforms, letters, diaries, and other artifacts. An interpretive trial is available.

The Mariners' Museum

100 Museum Drive
Newport News, VA 23606-3759
Phone: (804) 596-2222
Fax: (804) 591-7320
Internet: http://www.mariner.org/mariner

Hours: Daily, 10am - 5pm

With 77,000 square feet of exhibit space and more than 35,000 maritime artifacts, the Mariners' Museum is a treasure trove of nautical history. Of particular interest to Civil War enthusiasts is the *Clash of Armor* gallery. Here, visitors will see artifacts recovered from the wreck of the ironclad *Monitor*, which sank off Cape Hatteras, North Carolina, on December 31, 1862. Discovered in 1973, the wreck of the *Monitor* has yielded more than 100 artifacts, many of which are on display at the Mariners' Museum.

Exhibit highlights include: the *Monitor's* 1,450-pound anchor, the navigation lantern that possibly sent the distress signal as the ship sank, a video which takes visitors on an underwater tour of the *Monitor* shipwreck site, models of the *Merrimack*, *Virginia*, and *Monitor*, blueprints and charts which compare the *Monitor* and *Virginia* (*Merrimack*), the *Virginia's* steering wheel and a section of armor plate, and other artifacts from the *Monitor*.

The museum's 75,000 volume research library and archives includes material on the *Monitor's* officers and crew, technical and historical reports, videotapes, photographs, slides, news articles, and information about the CSS *Virginia*. The museum also sponsors an annual Civil War family overnight camp-over, graduate courses and Elderhostel programs related to the *Monitor*, and *Monitor* Days with Civil War naval encampments on the Museum grounds and living history interpreters in the *Clash of Armor* gallery.

Admission charged.

Photo Courtesy of The Mariners' Museum

Crew members on the deck of the Monitor

Discovered in 1973, the wreck of the Monitor *has yielded more than 100 artifacts, many of which are on display at the Mariners' Museum.*

McCook House Museum

Carroll County Historical Society
P.O. Box 174
Carrollton, OH 44615
Phone: (216) 627-3345

Hours: Fri - Sat, 9am - Noon/1pm - 5pm
Sunday, 1pm - 5pm

Located on The Square in Carrollton, the home of Major Daniel McCook and his family, known as the "Fighting McCooks," stands as a monument to one family's sacrifice and dedication. During the Civil War, fourteen McCooks offered their services to the Union, nine from Daniel McCook's family and five from his brother John's family. Thirteen of the fourteen served as officers, and of these, four became major generals, three became brigadier generals, one was a colonel, and two were majors.

The museum contains the discharge certificate of Alexander M. McCook signed by Abraham Lincoln and Edwin Stanton, the sword of Brigadier General Robert Latimer McCook, who was wounded and died on a march in northern Alabama, and a Springfield rifle with a butt plate engraved "Charles M. McCook, 2nd Ohio Volunteer Infantry."

Home of "The Fighting McCooks"

Memorial Hall Confederate Museum

929 Camp Street
New Orleans, LA 70130
Phone: (504) 523-4522

Hours: Monday - Saturday, 10am - 4pm

Owned and operated by the Louisiana Historical Association, Memorial Hall (known as the Confederate Museum) opened its doors on January 8, 1891, thanks to Louisiana philanthropist Frank T. Howard. Mr. Howard constructed the hall as a meeting place for Confederate veterans to reflect on their Civil War stories. The hall was also intended as a repository for records, reports, artifacts, and memorabilia of the Civil War and many of the items on display were donated by the soldiers who used them. For example, a large iron cannon (an eight-inch Columbiad) mounted on the terrace in front of the building was donated in 1899 by survivors of the 5th Company,

Slocomb's Battery Battalion, Washington Artillery. The cannon serves as a monument to the thirteen members of the 5th who were killed or wounded around the gun during the Union siege of Mobile, Alabama. Varina Howell Davis, wife of Jefferson Davis, donated a large collection of Davis memorabilia.

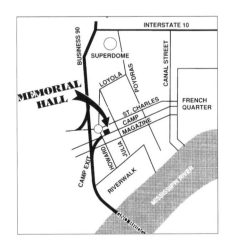

Personal items of famous figures such as Robert E. Lee, P.G.T. Beauregard, Jefferson Davis, Braxton Bragg, and Franklin Gardner on display, along with items used by the common soldier.

Though the museum attracts thousands of visitors each year, the largest turnout was on May 27 - 28, 1893, when over 50,000 paid their respects to Jefferson Davis (who died in New Orleans and was buried in that city from 1889 to 1893) as his body lay in state at Memorial Hall before being moved to Hollywood Cemetery in Richmond, Virginia for reburial.

Membership in the Memorial Hall Foundation is available for those wishing to support this exceptional museum. Benefits include free admission for one calendar year, a 10% discount at the Memorial Hall Gift Shop, a subscription to the Memorial Hall Foundation Newsletter, and admission to "members-only" specials, including exhibit previews.

Membership: $20 Individual
               $10 Student

Mississippi River Museum at Mud Island
125 N. Front Street
Memphis, TN 38103-1713
Phone: (901) 576-7241

Hours: Tuesday - Sunday, 10am - 5pm
         (April 5 - May 25)
         Daily, 10am - 8pm
         (May 26 - September 1)
         Tuesday - Sunday, 10am - 5pm
         (September 2 - October 31)

> *life-sized replica of an ironclad gunboat*

Featuring five galleries dedicated to the Civil War and the role of the mighty Mississippi River in that war. Of particular interest is a life-sized replica of an ironclad gunboat, complete with audio-visual programming. Outside, a five-block long model of the lower Mississippi River offers visitors the opportunity to trace significant battles along the river.

Monocacy National Battlefield
4801 Urbana Pike
Frederick, MD 21704-7307
Phone: (301) 662-3515
Fax: (301) 662-3430

Hours: Daily, 8am - 4:30pm
         (Memorial Day to Labor Day)
         Wed - Sun, 8am - 4:30pm
         (Labor Day to Memorial Day)

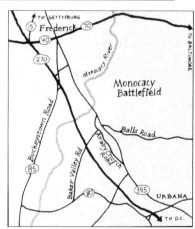

Known as the "Battle That Saved Washington," the Battle of Monocacy played out on July 9, 1864 between a Confederate force of 18,000 men lead by General Jubal Early, and a much smaller Union force of 5,800 men lead by General Lew Wallace. Fought on the road to Washington at the Monocacy river just south of Frederick, the battle marked the last attempt by the Confederacy to carry the war to the north. This time the Confederate commander was shooting for the big prize—Washington, D.C. Though the battle was a military victory for the Confederates, it forced a delay in their march on the federal capital, allowing time to reinforce Washington. After the battle, Early pushed his troops on toward the capital, but after a brief engagement with federal troops at Fort Stevens, Early withdrew and return to Virginia, recrossing the Potomac River at White's Ford, near Leesburg.

Facilities at Monocacy National Battlefield include the Gambrill Mill Visitor Center, which offers an electric map orientation program, an interactive computer program, interpretive displays, and artifacts from the battle. A 1/2 mile loop trail is available near the visitor center.

The Museum of the Confederacy

1201 East Clay St.
Richmond, VA 23219
Phone: (804) 649-1861
Fax: (804) 644-7150

Hours: Monday - Saturday, 10am - 5pm;
Sunday, Noon - 5pm

The Museum of the Confederacy maintains over 15,000 Confederate items, including Robert E. Lee's Appomattox sword, Thomas "Stonewall" Jackson's bible, and the personal effects of J.E.B. Stuart. The museum's crown jewel is the White House of the Confederacy, war-time residence of Jefferson Davis. The White House is adjacent to the museum and open for guided tours.

This museum is outstanding —a must see!

Museum of Culpeper History

140 E. Davis Street
Culpeper, VA 22701
Phone: (703) 825-1973

Hours: Monday - Saturday, 11am - 5pm

The Museum of Culpeper History offers a variety of displays ranging from dinosaur tracks, Revolutionary War items,

offers a variety of displays ranging from dinosaur tracks, Revolutionary War items, Indian artifacts, and Civil War relics.

Indian artifacts, and Civil War relics. Though not strictly a Civil War museum, Culpeper say its share of military action from 1861 to 1865. Relics from these actions are now on display, eagerly revealing their part in Culpeper's Civil War struggles.

Museum of East Tennessee History

600 Market Street
Mail:
P.O. Box 1629
Knoxville, TN 37901

Hours: Tuesday - Saturday, 10am - 4pm
          Sunday, 1pm - 5pm

The Museum of East Tennessee History opened in 1993. Each year thousands of visitors learn of the region's history through the museum's temporary exhibits and "The East Tennesseans" permanent exhibit. One of the most moving stories told in "The East Tennesseans" is that of the Civil War experience. Both Union and Confederate soldiers are represented, as are those that witnessed the war on the home front. Highlights include Civil War portraits, uniforms, and a Confederate battle flag. Equally interesting, however, is the small wooden heart carved by a Confederate prisoner of war and a miniature set of dice carried by a Union soldier. These are the artifacts that remind us how real these men were.

Membership in The East Tennessee Historical Society is available to those interested in supporting the museum and the organizations mission. Annual benefits include four newsletters, three genealogical periodicals, one historical journal, and a 10% discount on all purchases at the museum shop (which carries many Civil War books).

Membership: $35 per year (individual)
               $45 per year (family)

The Museum of Fife & Drum

62 North Main Street
Mail:
P.O. Box 525
Ivoryton, CT 06442
Phone: (203) 767-2237

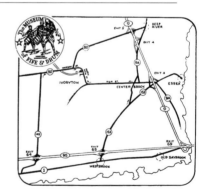

Hours: Saturday & Sunday, 1pm - 5pm
          (June, July, and August)

From the Revolutionary War to the present, The Museum of Fife & Drum offers one of the most unique collections of artifacts in the world. Included among the major exhibits is one dedicated to the American Civil War which included photographs, musical instruments, uniforms and weapons of the period. Group tours are available by appointment.

The museum is owned and operated by The Company of Fifers & Drummers, an international organization which coordinates the activities of more than 150 traditional fife and drum corps throughout the U.S., Canada, and parts of Europe (see *Organizations* for more information).

Small admission fee charged.

Museum of Southern History

4304 Herschel Street
Jacksonville, FL 32210
Phone: (904) 388-3574

Hours: Tuesday - Saturday, 10am - 5pm

The Museum of Southern History was established in 1975 by the Kirby Smith Camp No. 1209, Sons of Confederate Veterans (SCV). The original museum occupied small quarters, however, on February 26, 1994, the museum opened the doors of its new 4000 square foot facility.

The museum's presentation and interpretation of the history and culture of the South emphasizes the quality of life of a bygone era. Themes and displays present artifacts and memorabilia relating to politics, fashion, medicine, relics, personal items, camp life, uniforms, weapons, flags, and local history. The museum also offers a 3000 volume research library, including genealogical research assistance free of charge.

The Florida Depot, the retail arm of the Museum, is located at the facility and offers only original Revolutionary War, War of 1812, Seminole War, Civil War, Indian War, Spanish-American War, WWI, and WWII memorabilia. Available items include: weapons, accouterments, leather, uniforms, buttons, insignia, flags, headgear, canteens, medical items, camp gear, personal items, musical items, signatures, images, art, and other related military items. Emphasis is on the War Between the States.

Membership in the museum is available and allows an individual unlimited free admission and check-out privileges from the research library.

Membership: $20 Individual
                 $30 Family
                 $40 Booster

National Civil War Wax Museum

297 Steinwehr Avenue
Gettysburg, PA 17325
Phone: (717) 334-6245

Prominently located along Steinwehr Avenue in Gettysburg, the National Civil War Wax Museum has enjoyed millions, yes, millions of visitors in its years of operation. With over 230 life-sized action figures depicting the Civil War, including an animated President Lincoln giving the Gettysburg Address, its no wonder people make a point of visiting the museum during their stay at Gettysburg. The Gettysburg Gift Center is co-located with the museum, offering the opportunity to pick up some souvenirs during your visit. The staff is friendly and helpful, something I've started to take for granted at Gettysburg.

National Museum of Civil War Medicine

48 East Patrick Street
Mail:
P.O. Box 470
Frederick, MD 21705
Phone: (301) 695-1864
Internet: http://www.CivilWarMed.org

Hours: Tuesday - Friday, 10am - 5pm
         Saturday & Sunday, Noon - 5pm

The National Museum of Civil War Medicine takes a look at the war from the side of the caregivers. The legacy of Civil War medicine is explored, including the first widespread use of anesthesia, embalming, reconstructive surgery, triage, sanitation, ambulance corps, hospital ships, and women as nurses. The museum reminds visitors of the thousands of forgotten heroes who tended the wounded, giving hope, and in some cases life, back to men shattered by battle.

A museum store, annual conference, and an interesting variety of special programs are offered, such as *The Ransoming of Frederick -1864*, and *The War Between the Sheets: Sex in the Civil War*. The museum also sponsors Civil War Walking Tours of Frederick. These tours depart the museum at 2pm on Saturdays and Sundays and last

about 90 minutes. Call for more information or to arrange group tours.

Natural Bridge Battlefield State Historic Site

1022 Desoto Park Drive
Tallahassee, FL 32301
Phone: (904) 922-6007

Hours: Daily, 8am - Sunset

On March 6, 1865, as Union forces under General Newton approached the Natural Bridge, Confederate forces pre-vented their passage with the assistance of a rag-tag group of volunteers (old men and young boys) from Tallahassee. As a result of this desperate action, Tallahassee was preserved as the only Confederate capitol east of the Mississippi River never to fall into Union hands. Natural Bridge State Historic site now serves as a monument to the men who fought this battle. The Battle for Natural Bridge is re-enacted every year in March on a weekend near the anniversary of the actual battle.

New Bern Civil War Museum

301 Metcalf Street
New Bern, NC
Phone: (919) 633-2818

Hours: Tuesday - Sunday, 10am - 4pm

The New Bern Civil War Museum, located at the corner of Pollock and Metcalf Streets, houses an extensive collection of Civil War weapons and uniforms, both Union and Confederate. Their award-winning displays have been named "Best of Show" at exhibitions year after year.

New Market Battlefield Military Museum

9500 Collins Parkway
New Market, VA 22844
Phone: (540) 740-8065
Fax: (540) 740-3663

Hours: Daily, 9am - 5pm
          March 15 - December 1

The New Market Battlefield Military Museum occupies the crest of a gently-sloped hill where the Battle of New Market began in mid-May, 1864. This highly praised museum offers up a collection of over 2,500 original artifacts which are arranged in 130 displays and housed in a beautiful rendition of General Lee's famed Arlington House. The museum's focus is primarily Civil War, though the collection includes military memorabilia from the American Revolution to the present. Personal items that belonged to Alexander Hamilton, Stonewall Jackson, R.E. Lee, U.S. Grant, George A. Custer, Jefferson Davis, George S. Patton, D.D. Eisenhower, Audi Murphy, and Norman Schwarzkopf give a hint of the museum's impressive variety. A special section, including maps, is devoted to the battle fought at New Market. The museum contains memorabilia, relics, uniforms, headgear, edged weapons, flags, personal items, weapons, letters, maps, artwork, currency, stamps, medals, and other items that tell the story of past battles and past lives. Also offered is a 32 minute film on the Civil War. The museum offers a personal glimpse into the lives of the famous and the not so famous—men and women who passed their legacy of freedom to all of us.

The book shop has over 1,200 Civil War and military history titles, many out of print, some first editions, and current titles. The gift shop offers relics and rare pieces of memorabilia, including long arms, swords, CDV's, and currency (Colonial, Confederate, and others).

Around the museum, fourteen marble and granite markers dot the landscape, forever marking the Union and Confederate troop positions on this National Historic Site. Walking paths give access to these markers, as well as a wooded picnic area.

Modest admission charge.

North House Museum

301 W. Washington Street
Lewisburg, WV 24901
Phone: (304) 645-3398

Hours: Monday - Saturday, 10am - 4pm
         Thursday & Saturday, 1pm - 4pm

Built in the historic district of Lewisburg in 1820, the North House Museum holds the collections of the Greenbrier Historical Society, including artifacts and documents from the Civil War. An archives and library is available during limited hours on Thursdays and Saturdays.

Northeast MS Museum Association

P.O. Box 993
Corinth, MS 38834
Phone: (601) 287-3120

Hours: Monday - Saturday, 10am - 5pm
         Sunday, 2pm - 5pm
         (March - October)
         Mon - Sat, 10:30am - 4:30pm
         Sunday, 2pm - 4:30pm
         (November - February)

Not specifically a Civil War museum, the Northeast MS Museum does offer a collection of Civil War artifacts, pictures, maps, reference materials, and tales. Maps are available for self-guided tours of historical sites and homes. A souvenir shop is also available. The museum is located on Fourth Street, one block west of Business 45 (Polk Street).

Old Cahawba Archaeological Park

9518 Cahaba Road
Orrville, AL 36767
Phone: (334) 872-8058
Internet: http://www.olcg.com/selma/cahawbah.html

Hours: Daily, 9am - 5pm

Operated by the Alabama Historical Commission, Old Cahawba once served as the first capital of Alabama. During the Civil War Cahawba played host to Castle Morgan, a prison for Union soldiers. The town also had a hospital (formerly The Bell Tavern) which treated both Confederate and Union soldiers. Cahawba was a Civil War boom town and home to the Cahawba Rifles. Soon after the war, the once lively town faded, quickly becoming a ghost town.

Today the site offers the remains of the prison, markers with the name and regiment of each Union soldier that died in Cahaba's prison, and a nature trail. Pick up a free nature trail brochure and let Anna Gayle Fry, a resident of Cahaba during the War, take you along the half mile Clear Creek Nature Trail. Anna will show you how the women survived the long Union naval blockade. She'll even show you how they made the Confederate Gray dye for uniforms.

The Old Cahawba Welcome Center carries books on the Civil War and, in particular, Old Cahawba's part in the War. Anna Gayle Fry's *Memories of Old Cahaba* (1908) is available for $6, and William Bryant's *Cahaba Prison and the Sultana Disaster* (1990) is available for $20.

Old City Cemetery

Fourth & Taylor Streets
Lynchburg, VA
Phone: (804) 847-1811
(Lynchburg Visitors Center)

Hours: Daily, Dawn to Dusk

The Confederate Section of the historic Old City Cemetery serves as the final resting place for over 2200 individually marked graves of Confederate soldiers from 14 states. Nearby is the Pest House Medical Museum. One room depicts conditions in the House of Pestilence quarantine hospital during the Civil War. The second room is furnished as Dr. John J. Terrell's office when he practiced medi-cine in the area in the late 1800's. A monument to the memory of the 99 soldiers who died of smallpox in the Pest House during the war is located near the entrance to the adjacent Confederate Section.

Many self-interpretive tablets and brochures are available at no charge. Interior tours of the Pest House are available by appointment for a small fee.

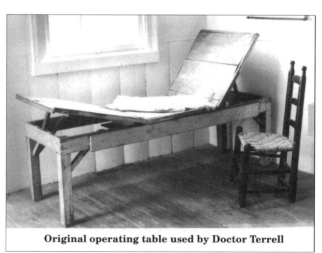

Original operating table used by Doctor Terrell

Organ Cave

Information:
Rt. 2, Box 381
Ronceverte, WV 24970
Phone: (304) 647-5551/1-800-258-CAVE/
1-800 CALL WVA

Directions: Ten miles south of Lewisburg, I-64 Harts Run Exit 175. Seven miles south of WV State Fair.

This National Historic Landmark features the "Rock Organ," a stone formation, as one of its main attractions. During the Civil War, however, it was known as General Robert E. Lee's powder works because it served as an ammunition factory. In fact, the cave still houses 37 original saltpeter hoppers. A gift shop, rock shop, picnic shelter, and playground are available.

Our House Tavern State Memorial

432 First Avenue
Gallipolis, OH 45631
Phone: 1-800-765-6482

Hours: Tuesday - Saturday, 10am - 5pm
Sunday, 1pm - 5pm
(Memorial Day - Labor Day)
Weekends in May, September, and October

From 1819-1860, guests such as the Marquis de Lafayette, a visitor in 1825, were entertained in this restored inn originally called the Cushing Tavern. During the War between the States, Our House, as it became known, became a hospital as well as a mustering-in point for the 91st OVI, Co. B. Original papers and artifacts are now on display. The museum is owned by the Ohio Historical Society and operated by Friends of Our House.

Pamplin Park Civil War Site

6523 Duncan Road
Petersburg, VA 23803
Phone: (804) 861-2408
Fax: (804) 861-2820

Hours: Daily, 9am - 5pm
(extended summer hours)

Pamplin Park Civil War Site is a private historical park, owned and managed by the Pamplin Foundation of Portland, Oregon – and from what we've seen, they're doing an excellent job. The site offers an Interpretive Center, complete with original battle flags, uniforms, and weapons; interactive games that make learning about the Civil War fun and exciting; and a 1.1 mile trail system that leads through the battlefield and provides a first hand look at what have been described as some of the finest

Photo Courtesy of Pamplin Park

original Civil War fortifications in existence. Along the trail you'll see a reconstructed soldier hut like those used by Confederate soldiers in the winter of 1864-65. You'll also see artillery emplacements, and original picket posts. Throughout the year, park guides offer tours and special programs on the life, weapons, and uniforms of the Civil War soldier.

Tudor Hall, built in 1812, is the original plantation home owned by the Boisseau family at the time of the battle. Renovated and open to the public, Tudor Hall represents itself in two forms: as the comfortable home of the Boisseau family, and as the headquarters of Confederate General Samuel McGowan. Future plans for the Pamplin Park Civil War Site include establishment of the *National Museum of the Civil War Soldier*. Finally, the site has a Civil War gift shop you'll want to visit before your day is complete.

A modest admission fee is charged.

Petersburg National Battlefield

Rt. 36, East of Petersburg
Mail:
P.O. Box 549
Petersburg, VA 23804
Phone: (804) 732-3531

Six major areas containing some 2,460 acres comprise the Petersburg National Battlefield. Administered by the National Park Service, the battlefield includes a visitors center, the City Point Unit and National Cemetery in Hopewell, Five Forks Battlefield in Dinwiddie County, Poplar Grove Cemetery in Dinwiddie County, and preserved fortifications along the siege line.

A four-mile driving tour includes: The Visitors Center, where you can see exhibits, maps and, a short walk away, Battery 5 and the Dictator (a huge Union mortal); Battery 8, renamed Fort Friend after its capture by black U.S. Troops; Battery 9, captured by black U.S. troops of Hink's Division; Harrison Creek, where Confederate forces dug in after being driven from their original battle lines; Fort Stedman; Fort Haskell; Taylor Farm; and The Crater, where a massive Union mine was planted by Pennsylvania coal miners under a Confederate fort and detonated. The 170-foot long, 30-foot deep crater that resulted was soon filled with bodies and blood as eager Union troops quickly threw away the advantage of their surprise attack by plunging into the gaping hole left by the explosion, rather than going around it. From above them, Confederate fire took a deadly toll, costing the Union 4,000 men before the soldiers were able to get back up the side of the crater.

For those interested in seeing all of Petersburg National Battlefield, a 16 mile driving tour, which begins on Crater Road, is recommended. This drive includes: Fort Sedgwick (site); Fort Wadsworth; Poplar Grove Cemetery, which contains the graves of more than 6,100 Union soldiers and a handful of Confederates; Forts Urmston and Conahey; Fort Fisher; Confederate Fort Gregg; and Five Forks.

As one would expect, Petersburg is rich in Civil War history and offers many sites which are not part of the national battlefield. Some of these sites are identified in the National Park Service map. Additional information is available at the Visitors Center.

> *For those interested in seeing all of Petersburg National Battlefield, a 16 mile driving tour, which begins on Crater Road, is recommended.*

The Peterson House/ House Where Lincoln Died

516 10th Street N.W.
Washington, DC
Phone: (202) 426-6924

Hours: Daily, 9am - 5pm

Built in 1849, the Peterson House has been restored to its 1860s appearance, looking as it did when President Lincoln was carried there after being mortally wounded at Ford's Theatre, across the street. Lincoln died in the Peterson House the next day, April 15, 1865, prompting Secretary of War Edwin Stanton to say "Now he belongs to the ages."

Pickett's Mill State Historic Site

2640 Mt. Tabor Road
Dallas, GA 30132
Phone: (770) 443-7850

Hours: Tuesday - Saturday, 9am - 5pm
         Sunday, Noon - 5pm

On May 27, 1864, a force of 14,000 Union troops under General O.O. Howard were sent in search of Confederate flank. They found it at Pickett's Mill. After a five hour march, Howard's men engaged 10,000

Confederates under the command of General Patrick Cleburne. Fighting began around 5:00 p.m. and raged into the night, resulting in 1,600 Federal and 500 Confederate casualties. The Confederate line held.

The site is considered one of the best preserved Civil War battlefields in the nation, looking very much today as it did in 1864. The roads and earthworks used by both Union and Confederate soldiers still exist. Annual events include the Battle of Pickett's Mill Commemoration and a Candle Lantern tour. Other living history programs are often available.

Pope's Tavern Museum

203 Hermitage Drive
Florence, AL 35630
Phone: (205) 760-6439

Hours: Tuesday - Saturday, 10am - 4pm

One of the oldest structures in Florence, Pope's Tavern Museum has a colorful history that includes service as a stagecoach stop and as a field hospital for both Union and Confederate forces. The museum features an extensive collection of Civil War artifacts upstairs, and antiques downstairs.

Admission charged.

Port Hudson State Commemorative Area

756 West Plains-Port Hudson Road
Zachary, LA 70791
Phone: (504) 654-3775

The 909-acre State Commemorative Area at Port Hudson is significant for a number of reasons. It was the last Confed-

erate stronghold on the Mississippi (Vicksburg having fallen five days before), it was the longest siege in American military history (during which Confederate soldiers were reduced to eating mules, horses, and rats), and it was here that black soldiers in the regular United States Army first participated in an assault. It was also the bloodiest battle for the Union during the Civil War, with 267 casualties per 1,000 troops.

The site offers a new Interpretive Center which includes a museum with displays of original Civil War artifacts and an audiovisual program which introduces visitors to the siege of Port Hudson. A wooden boardwalk offers a view of the original breastworks of Fort Desperate and three viewing towers offer an overall view of the battle site. Several living history events are hosted at Port Hudson each year, allowing visitors the opportunity to view weapons and equipment demonstrations by authentically costumed personnel. Specifically, the Park sponsors an annual reenactment the fourth weekend in March, and weapons firing demonstrations the first Sunday of every month.

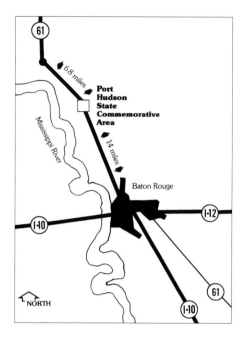

Prairie Grove Battlefield State Park

P.O. Box 306
Prairie Grove, AR 72753
Phone: (501) 846-2990

Hours: Daily, 8am - 10pm (Park)
        Daily, 8am - 5pm (Museum)

Located eight miles west of Fayetteville off US 62 (at the eastern edge of Prairie Grove), this state park offers a look at the effect the Civil War had on the people of the Ozarks. The park sites on 360 acres of the original battlefield and has a collection of buildings which depict life before and after the Civil War.

The Battle of Prairie Grove took place December 7, 1862, as Confederates under Major General Thomas Hindman clashed with Union divisions under Brigadier Generals Francis Herron and James Blunt. After an afternoon of bitter fighting, the Confederate Army, their ammunition nearly exhausted, retreated south under cover of darkness.

Park facilities include the Battlefield Museum and Visitor Center (with an audiovisual program and displays), a picnic area, and several historic structures (Borden House, Morrow House, Latta House, schoolhouse, church, store, blacksmith shop, sorghum mill, and others).

The park sites on 360 acres of the original battlefield and has a collection of buildings which depict life before and after the Civil War.

Rhodes Hall

Georgia Trust for Historic Preservation
1516 Peachtree Street, N.W.
Atlanta, GA 30309
Phone: (404) 881-9980

Hours: Monday - Friday, 11am - 4pm

Photo Courtesy of Rhodes Hall

Built in 1902-04 for Atlanta businessman Amos Giles Rhodes and his family, Rhodes Hall can fairly be called one of America's castles. The significance of this mansion for Civil War enthusiasts lies in the magnificent stained glass tribute to the Confederacy. Rhodes commissioned the Von Gerichten Art Glass Company to create a series of painted and stained glass windows a memorial to the Confederacy. Titled "The Rise and Fall of the Confederacy," this stained glass display surrounds the carved mahogany staircase as it winds from the first floor reception hall to the second floor hall. The nine panel display takes you from Jefferson Davis's oath of office to Robert E. Lee's surrender at Appomattox. The

The magnificent stained glass tribute to the Confederacy at Rhodes Hall.

work includes portraits of 15 Confederate generals and statesmen and the seals of the 13 Confederate states. A spectacular tribute to the Confederacy. Rhodes Hall is available for receptions, meetings, and other gatherings.

Robert Toombs House State Historic Site

216 East Robert Toombs Avenue
Mail:
P.O. Box 605
Washington, GA 30673
Phone: (706) 678-2226

Hours: Tuesday - Saturday, 9am - 5pm
         Sunday, 2pm - 5:30pm

The restored home of Robert Toombs, legislator, U.S. congressman, senator, Confederate Secretary of State, and General in the Army of Northern Virginia, presents exhibits and a film which help bring the life of the jingoistic General into focus.

Photo Courtesy of Robert Toombs House State Historic Site

Home of Confederate Secretary of State, Robert Toombs as it appears today in its restored condition.

153

Rosehill Cemetery & Mausoleum

5800 N. Ravenswood
Chicago, IL 60660
Phone: (312) 561-5940

Hours: Monday - Friday, 9am - 5pm
        Saturday & Sunday, 10am - 4pm

Rosehill Cemetery is the final resting place for five hundred Union soldiers and sailors, including fourteen Union Generals and two Medal of Honor recipients. A self-paced Civil War walking tour is available during normal operating hours. Guided walking tours are available the 1st and 3rd Saturday of each month at 10am.

Sailor's Creek Battlefield Historical State Park

Route 2, Box 70
Green Bay, VA 23942
Phone: (804) 392-3435

Operated by the Virginia Department of Conservation and Recreation, Division of State Parks, Sailor's Creek Battlefield was the scene of the last major battle of the Civil War in Virginia. Here on April 6, 1865, General Robert E. Lee, Commander of all armies of the Confederate States of America, lost over 8,000 men plus valuable supplies. This site of approximately 230 acres includes battlefield areas and the Hillsman House.

The house served as a Federal field hospital where the wounded of both the northern and southern commands were treated. The grounds are open year round for visitation at no cost. The Hillsman House is open selected times of the year, and for special events and tours. Additional special programming including living histories and reenactments are scheduled on a yearly basis.

Sailor's Creek Battlefield State Park is located in Amelia County on Route 617. The park can be reached from Highway 460 or 360 by following the signage. The site is also a stop along the *Route of Lee's Retreat Auto Tour* from Petersburg to Appomattox.

Saint-Gaudens National Historic Site

R.R. 3, Box 73
Cornish, NH 03745-9704
Phone: (603) 675-2175
Internet: http://www.nps.gov/saga

Hours: Daily, 9am - 4:30pm (late May through late October)

Located 12 miles north of Claremont, NH, on route 12A, and 2 miles northeast of Windsor, VT, the Saint-Gaudens National Historic Site is the former home and studio of renowned American sculptor Augustus Saint-Gaudens. The works of Saint-Gaudens include the Shaw Memorial, the "Standing Lincoln," the General John A.

The works of Saint-Gaudens include the Shaw Memorial, the "Standing Lincoln," the General John A. Logan monument, Admiral David G. Farragut monument, William T. Sherman monument...

Logan monument, Admiral David G. Farragut monument, William T. Sherman monument, and reliefs of Confederate surgeon Dr. Henry Shiff, and Union surgeon Dr. Silas W. Mitchell.

The Shaw Memorial and Farragut monument can be seen at the Saint-Gaudens NHS. The Shaw Memorial gained recognition after the making of *Glory*, a powerful movie which tells the story of Colonel Robert Gould Shaw and his 54th Massachusetts, the first black combat infantry regiment raised in the north to fight for the Union. The 54th gained fame for their heroism and sacrifice at Fort Wagner, South Carolina, July 18, 1863.

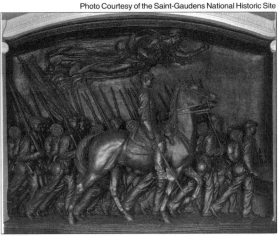

The Shaw Memorial

Sam Davis Home

1399 Sam Davis Road
Smyrna, TN 37167
Phone: (615) 459-2341

Hours: Daily

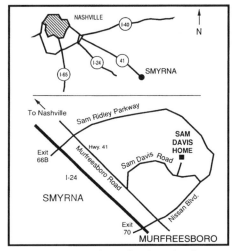

Family home and farm of Sam Davis, the Boy Hero of the Confederacy. After recovering from a wound inflicted at Shiloh while serving with the 1st Tennessee, young Sam Davis became one of Coleman's Scouts. In November of 1863, Davis was captured and found to be in possession of intelligence on Union troop movements. After interrogations failed to extract any information from Davis, he was tried and hanged on November 27, 1863. The manner in which he carried himself on the gallows and his refusal to divulge information to his Union interrogators made the 21-year old Davis a hero throughout the South.

Sherman House

137 East Main Street
Lancaster, OH 43130
Phone: (614) 687-5891

Hours: Tuesday - Sunday, 1pm - 4pm
(April through Mid-December)
By appointment January, February,
and March

Owned and operated by the Fairfield Heritage Association, the Sherman House stands as Ohio's sole memorial to the Shermans. While William Tecumseh Sherman gained great prominence during and after the Civil War, his younger brother John also achieved a great deal of fame. John served as a U.S. Congressman, Senator,

Secretary of Treasury, and Secretary of State. The Sherman Antitrust Act carries his name.

The Sherman House includes a restored dining room, master bedroom, children's bedroom, study, and family parlor. On the second floor is a recreation of General Sherman's field tent with Civil War exhibits and a room filled with Sherman family memorabilia. The Sherman House is available for private parties, receptions, and meetings.

Modest admission charged.

Photo Courtesy of The Sherman House

Shiloh National Military Park

Highway 22
Mail:
Route 1, Box 9
Shiloh, TN 38376
Phone: (901) 689-5696

Hours: Daily

Giving birth to infamous names such as *The Hornet's Nest* and *The Sunken Road*, as well as to the famous, like Johnny Shiloh, The Battle of Shiloh (also known as Pittsburg Landing) was the first large-scale engagement of the Civil War. The two-day battle exacted a heavy toll on the Union and Confederate Armies, with casualties totaling over 23,000 killed, wounded, missing, and captured. The greatest loss was that of Confederate General Albert Sidney Johnston, who was struck in the right leg while leading his troops at the Peach Orchard. Johnston bled to death before the flow from his wounded leg could be stanched.

The Park, which encompasses 3,960 acres, contains 96% of the historic battlefield. A 9.5 mile driving/walking tour is available which allows visitors to explore the 151 monuments, 600 troop position markers, and over 200 Civil War cannon that make Shiloh National Military Park so memorable.

The visitors center houses a museum (featuring weapons, uniforms, and other military equipment), a bookstore, and the 25-minute film "Shiloh - Portrait of a Battle," which is shown every hour and a half. Audio tapes for the self-guided driving tour of the Battlefield are available at the bookstore. Shiloh National Cemetery is located nearby.

Shorter Mansion

340 N. Eufaula Avenue
Mail:
P.O. Box 486
Eufaula, AL 36027

Hours: Monday - Saturday, 9am - 4pm
         Sunday, 1pm - 4pm

Serving double-duty as the Eufaula Visitors Center, the Shorter Mansion, a 1906 Greek Revival mansion, contains a collection of Confederate relics, antiques, and memorabilia from six Alabama governors.

Admission charged.

Sidney Lanier Cottage

935 High Street
Macon, GA 31201
Mail:
P.O. Box 13358
Macon, GA 31208-3358
Phone: (912) 743-3851

Hours: Mon - Fri, 9am - 1pm, 2pm - 4pm
         Saturday, 9:30am - 12:30pm

Birthplace of the great Southern poet, Sidney Lanier, this cottage has been converted to a museum which is owned and operated by the Middle Georgia Historical Society. Lanier was a poet, musician, and scholar who was nationally known and particularly beloved in the South. He served in the Confederate Army until captured aboard a blockade runner and confined at Fort Lookout, Maryland. The museum displays Lanier memorabilia and the gift shop sells books on the Civil War, items on Lanier, and other related articles.

Membership in the Middle Georgia Historical Society is available. The organization uses the Sidney Lanier Cottage as its headquarters and publishes a quarterly newspaper.

Membership: $15 per year (individual)
                 $25 per year (family)

Siege Museum

15 W. Bank Street
Petersburg, VA 23803
Phone: (804) 733-2404

For 10 long months during the Civil War, Petersburg lay under the slowly tightening noose of a Union siege Their only hope was to last until the North tired of the war and sought piece. The comfortable, often lavish lifestyle of prewar Petersburg was now replaced by destitution and desperation. The Siege Museum tells the story of the town's suffering and struggle during these dark times, times when blackberry leaves substituted for tea, corn was brewed into an artificial "coffee," and a chicken cost $50.

Soldiers & Sailors Memorial Hall

4141 Fifth Avenue (at Bigelow)
Pittsburgh, PA 15213-3547
Phone: (412) 621-4253
Fax: (412) 683-9339

Hours: Mon - Fri, 9am - 4pm
         Sat - Sun, 1pm - 4pm

The impressive Soldiers & Sailors Memorial Hall was built between 1908 and 1910 to honor veterans of the "War for the Suppression of the Rebellion of the Southern Slaveholders," known today as the Civil War. Sixty-one plaques line the four corridors of the first

The imposing and impressive exterior of the Soldiers & Sailors Memorial Hall of Allegheny County

Photo Courtesy of Soldiers & Sailors Memorial Hall

157

floor. These plaques contain the names of 25,930 men from Allegheny County who served in the Civil War.

In 1963 the Soldiers & Sailors Memorial Hall was rededicated to the memory of all veterans of U.S. conflicts and wars, though the Hall maintains a strong Civil War flavor. The building is inspiring both inside and out and contains a beautiful 2400 seat auditorium, a banquet hall, and conference rooms (available for rent). The Museum features a comprehensive Civil War Library which is available for reference and genealogical research.

South Carolina State Museum

301 Gervais Street
P.O. Box 100107
Columbia, SC 29202
Phone: (803) 737-4921

Hours: Monday - Saturday, 10am - 5pm
Sunday, 1pm - 5pm

Photo Courtesy of the South Carolina State Museum

With four floors of exhibits in art, history, natural history, science and technology, the South Carolina State Museum is sure to please just about everyone. Long-term exhibits relating to the Civil War include "The Blockade," "Secession," "Civil War Arms," "Antebellum Life," and a full-scale model of the CSS Hunley, the first submarine to sink an enemy ship. The museum is working on an exhibit about Free Blacks and hopes to create an exhibit about Reconstruction.

"The Blockade" examines the Union naval blockade of Southern ports. Among the artifacts are weapons brought in by blockade runners and household objects recovered from the wreck of a blockade runner.

The "Secession" exhibit includes one of the original 200 lithographs of the South Carolina Ordinance of Secession, which was passed in Charleston on Dec. 20, 1860. This particular copy was removed from the South Carolina State House when Sherman was in Columbia at the end of the war.

The museum's "Civil War Arms" exhibit includes a cannon used to defend Columbia against Sherman's troops and a variety of guns and edged weapons, including some manufactured in South Carolina.

The "Antebellum Life" exhibit examines the life of slaves and whites in the years before the Civil War and includes some slave-made objects. Museum programs often feature groups such as the 20th South Carolina Volunteer Infantry, and the 54th Massachusetts, the unit immortalized in the movie *Glory.*

Membership in the *Friends of the South Carolina State Museum* is available. Benefits include: twelve months free admission; *Images,* the State Museum newsletter; guest passes; invitation to annual Friends meeting; discounts on programs and workshops; behind-the-scenes tour; discount at the Cotton Mill Exchange museum store; discount on tickets to the Koger Center's season performances; and admission to Riverbanks Zoo at the group rate.

Admission charged.

Staunton River Battlefield State Park

Rt. 1, Box 183
Randolph, VA 23962
Phone: (804) 454-4312
Internet: http://www.halifax.com/county/
staunt1.htmp

Hours: Daily, 8:30am - Dusk (Grounds)
        Mon - Sat, 9am - 4:30pm
        Sun, 1pm - 4:30pm (Visitor Ctr)
        (March - October)
        Wed - Sat, 9am - 4pm
        Sun, 1pm - 4pm
        (October - March)

Staunton River Battlefield State Park is the site of the June 25, 1864 battle for control of the rail bridge where 492 "Old men and Young Boys," and Confederate regulars held off over 5,000 Union soldiers. A visitors center exhibit focuses on Wilson's raid and home life in Southside Virginia during the war. A large relief map highlights battlefield features.

The primary 86-acre park includes well-preserved earthworks, a planked railroad bridge across the river, an artillery emplacement, a self-guided walking trail, and an interpreter duing the summer. An additional 200 acres of battlefield was acquired in 1996 (across the river).

The Historic Staunton River Foundation, a publicly supported nonprofit organization, aids in the staffing and operation of the park.

Stones River National Battlefield

3501 Old Nashville Highway
Murfreesboro, TN 37129
Phone: (615) 893-9501

Hours: Daily, 8am - 5pm

With U.S. and Confederate casualties totaling over 23,000, Stones River proved to be one of the bloodiest engagements of the war. The battles (on December 31, 1862 and January 2, 1863) saw Confederate forces under Bragg pitched against the Union Army of the Cumberland under Rosecrans. Both sides claimed victory, though in the end, it was Bragg who retreated to the south, solidifying the Union position in Tennessee.

The park features a visitors center, the headquarters of Generals Bragg and Rosecrans, and Fortress Rosecrans (built by Union troops after the battle as a supply base).

The Stonewall Jackson House

8 East Washington Street
Lexington, VA 24450
Phone: (540) 463-2552

Hours: Monday - Saturday, 9am - 5pm
        Sunday, 1pm - 5pm

Early in 1859, after living in Lexington for nearly a decade, Thomas "Stonewall" Jackson and his second wife, Mary Anna Morrison, moved into a modest brick town house built at the turn of the century. It was the only house ever owned by Stonewall Jackson, a home he shared with his wife for two short years, until he rode off to war on April 21, 1861. Restored in 1979 by the Historic Lexington Foundation, the home is furnished with many of Jackson's personal possessions. Other period pieces, chosen to match items listed on Jackson's 1863 estate inventory, fill the house.

Guided tours are available on the hour and half hour. In addition to tours of the site, the museum sponsors a variety of educational programs, including lectures, workshops, special events, occasional tours and summer fellowships for graduate students. A biennial scholarly Stonewall Jackson Symposium is offered on even years.

The museum's gift shop offers an excellent selection of books, prints, notecards, and other items relating to the house and its most famous occupant.

Admission charged.

Photo Courtesy of the Stonewall Jackson House

The only home ever owned by Stonewall Jackson

Stratford Hall Plantation
Stratford, VA 22558
Phone: (804) 493-8038

Hours: Daily, 9am - 4:30pm

Photo Courtesy of Stratford Hall Plantation

A striking example of Stratford Hall's elegance and charm.

Located on the Potomac River off Virginia Route 3 (forty-five miles east of Fredericksburg) Stratford Hall Plantation, the birthplace of Robert E. Lee, dates to the 1730s when Thomas Lee built the enormous brick house, a wharf, and a grist mill on the site. The estate was also the birthplace of Richard Henry and Francis Lightfoot Lee, the only brothers to sign the Declaration of Independence.

The plantation consists of 1,600 acres and includes Stratford Hall, the re-built mill on its original foundations, the (empty) Lee family burial vault, slave quarters, coach house and stables, spring houses, the Stetson Reception Center, and a number of other buildings.

The Stetson Reception Center will start your tour of properly with a 13-minute video about the Lee family and Stratford Hall Plantation. The Reception Center also offers a museum area with Lee family memorabilia, and archaeological and architectural exhibits.

Owned and operated by the Robert E. Lee Memorial Association since 1929, Stratford Hall offers a number of special exhibits and other programs throughout the

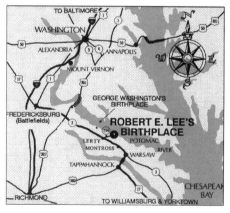

year. A visit will provide ample opportunity to view educational and interpretive events, or maybe an archaeological dig. Additionally, the Jessie Ball duPont Memorial Library offers a wealth of information on the Northern Neck and is available for research (by appointment).

Admission fee charged.

Surratt House Museum
9118 Brandywine Road
Clinton, MD 20735
Mail:
P.O. Box 427
Clinton, MD 20735
Phone: (301) 868-1121
Fax: (301) 868-8177

Hours: Thursday & Friday, 11am - 3pm
         Saturday & Sunday, Noon - 4pm
         (March 1 through mid-December)
         Group tours of ten or more
         by appointment

Built in 1852 as a farm house for the family of John and Mary Surratt, the historic Surratt House also saw duty as a tavern, hostelry, post office, and polling place. During the Civil War, the house served as a safehouse for Southern spies.

In the fall of 1864, John Wilkes Booth and a number of coconspirators, including the Surratts, formulated a daring plan to kidnap President Lincoln. When this kidnapping opportunity failed to materialize, and seeing the coming death of the Confederacy, Booth chose to assassinate Lincoln instead. On April 14, 1865, at Ford's Theater, he succeeded. Fleeing Washington after the deed, Booth stopped at the Surratt Tavern for weapons and supplies. From there he fled South only to be cornered in a barn on the Garrett farm and killed. On July 7, 1865, less than three months after Lincoln's death, Mary Surratt was executed with other conspirators for her part in the assassination, becoming the first woman to be put to death by the federal government

> *Membership in the Surratt Society is available*

Aside from guided museum tours (conducted by costumed docents), The Surratt House Museum offers a variety of programs and events which focus on the Lincoln assassination conspiracy. Of particular interest is the John Wilkes Booth Escape Route Tour, a twelve-hour bus excursion offered several times each year which takes visitors along many of the same roads and to many of the same buildings that Booth and David Herold traveled and visited during their 12-day flight in 1865.

Membership in the Surratt Society is available to those interested in the preservation and interpretation of historic Surratt House and Tavern. Members support the Surratt House either financially, or as volunteer guides (or both). Benefits include a membership card, free admission upon presentation of membership card, monthly newsletter, use of research library, reduced rates on tours sponsored by the Society.

Modest admission charged.
Membership: $5 General Membership

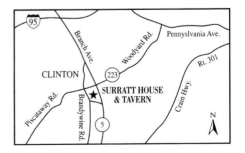

161

Sweetwater Creek State Conservation Park

Mt. Vernon Road

Mail:

P.O. Box 816

Lithia Springs, GA 30057

Phone: (770) 732-5871

Hours: Daily, 7am - 10pm

The ruins of the New Manchester Manufacturing Company, a Civil War era textile mill, is located on the grounds of the 1,986-acre park. Five miles of trails, picnic areas, a 215-acre lake, and educational programs are also available.

Tannehill Historical State Park

12632 Confederate Parkway

McCalla, AL 35111

Phone: (205) 477-5711

Fax: (205) 477-9400

Hours: Mon - Fri, 9am - 5pm (Museum)
          Sat & Sun, 10am - 5pm (Museum)

Located 12 miles southwest of Bessemer, off I-59, Tannehill Ironworks Historical State Park offers a look at the iron production efforts of the Confederacy. The

Iron and Steel Museum of Alabama is located at the site, providing an accurate depiction of how iron was made during the Civil War when fifteen different iron plants and six rolling mills made Alabama the arsenal of the Confederacy. When Lee surrendered at Appomattox, Alabama furnaces were producing over 70% of the Confederate iron supply.

The Park features over 200 improved campsites and craftsmen such as blacksmiths, weavers, potters, and a papermaker who still ply their traditional trades.

Photo Courtesy of Tannehill Historical State Park

When Lee surrendered at Appomattox, Alabama furnaces were producing over 70% of the Confederate iron supply.

Tennessee River Museum

507 Main Street
Savannah, TN
Phone: (901) 925-2363

Hours: Daily

As the invasion route for advancing Union troops, the Tennessee River saw its share of action. The Tennessee River Museum presents a number of Civil War displays, including "The War on the River," which examines the role of the river in the many battles for Tennessee. The exhibit begins with a one-half scale model of the bow of the U.S.S. Cairo, and contains artifacts from the doomed ironclad, as well as other gunboats. The "Army" exhibit presents artifacts, personal items, and weapons from the Battle of Shiloh, and the "Johnsonville" exhibit highlights General Nathan Bedford Forrest's cavalrymen.

Tennessee State Museum

5th and Deadrick Streets
Nashville, TN 37243-1120
Phone: (615) 741-2692

Hours: Tuesday - Saturday, 10am - 5pm
         Sunday, 1pm - 5pm

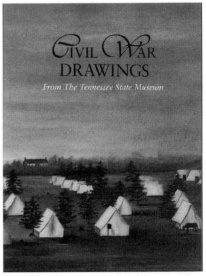

Civil War Drawings is one of the books offered by the Tennessee State Museum

The Tennessee State Museum is one of the largest state museums in the nation with more than 60,000-sq.-ft. of permanent exhibits and a 10,000-sq.-ft. changing exhibition hall. The museum's interpretive exhibits begin 15,000 years ago with prehistoric humans and continue through the early 1900s with special sections on Native American Indians, explorers, pioneers, the Antebellum age, the Civil War, and the beginning of a new century.

The Tennessee State Museum's Civil War holdings of uniforms, battle flags and weapons are among the finest in the nation, and represent the largest depository of Civil War artifacts from the western theater. Each of the major battles in Tennessee are commemorated with artifacts including the battles of Shiloh, Chattanooga and Franklin.

Artifacts of note include Sam Davis' boot (cut open to search for hidden papers when he was charged with spying); Nathan Bedford Forrest's favorite weapon, his 1851 model Navy Colt Revolver; Confederate Gen. Patrick Cleburne's hat; battle flags from several Tennessee units; hand-drawn map of Shiloh prepared for Confederate Gen. P.G.T. Beauregard; uniforms; and soldiers' personal items.

The museum store carries Civil War-related items, including the book, *Civil War Drawings from the Tennessee State Museum*, which contains 39 drawings or paintings done by soldiers or professional artists of military sites and battles in the state. Cost of the book is $10.

U.S. Army Military Police Corps Regimental Museum

Building 3182
Fort McClellan, AL 36205
Phone: (205) 848-3522
Fax: (205) 848-6139

Hours: Monday - Friday, 9am - 3pm

        Not specifically a Civil War museum, The U.S. Army Military Police Corps Regimental Museum, lets call it the MP Museum for short, offers displays which depict the role of Military Police during major U.S. conflicts, including the Civil War. The museum's collection includes firearms, uniforms, military vehicles, and Civil War photographs and artifacts.

Admission: FREE

US Army Quartermaster Museum

OQMG USA Quartermaster Center
1201 22nd Street
Fort Lee, VA 23801-1601
Phone: (804) 734-4203

Hours: Tuesday - Friday, 10am - 5pm
        Saturday & Sunday, 11am - 5pm

        Though this museum focuses on the Quartermaster Corps, not the Civil War, there are a number of items on display that will be of interest to Civil War enthusiasts, such as the saddle used by General Grant during the Civil War. The museum also contains a large collection of military uniforms, including Civil War.

Admission: FREE

General Grant's Saddle

Photo Courtesy of U.S. Army Quartermaster Museum

U.S. Naval Academy Museum

Preble Hall
118 Maryland Avenue
Annapolis, MD 21402-5034
Phone: (410) 293-2108
Phone: (410) 293-2109
Fax: (410) 293-5220

Hours: Monday - Saturday, 9am - 5pm
        Sunday, 11am - 5pm

        Situated in Preble Hall on the grounds of the U.S. Naval Academy, the four exhibition galleries at the U.S. Naval Academy Museum (totaling 12,000 square feet) are open to the public. The museum's holdings include ship models, paintings, prints, flags, uniforms, weapons, medals, sculptures, manuscripts, rare books, photographs, personal memorabilia, and ship equipment. The museum covers the entire naval history of the U.S. and not just the Civil War. Nevertheless, the museum is overflowing with history and tradition and offers an enjoyable way to spend a few hours. Before you leave the academy, stop by the chapel and visit the crypt of Revolutionary War hero John Paul Jones.

Admission: FREE

The Vanishing Glory

717 Clay Street
Vicksburg, MS 39180
Phone: (601) 634-1863

Hours: Daily, 9am - 5pm

This 30-minute show employs wide-screen production and quadraphonic sound. The Vanishing Glory is a historical dramatization of the Siege of Vicksburg, as told from the diaries and writings of the Vicksburg citizens and soldiers who lived through the campaign. Shows begin every hour on the hour with the last presentation beginning at 5 p.m. Groups of 40 or more may schedule times before or after regular hours.

Vicksburg Civil War Museum, Inc.

3327 Clay Street
Vicksburg, MS 39180
Phone: (601) 638-4759

Hours: Monday - Saturday, 8:30am - 5pm
Sunday, 1:30pm - 5pm
(Spring/Summer)
Mon - Sat, 8:30am - 4:30pm
Sun, 1:30pm - 4:30pm
(Fall/Winter)

Located only 75 yards from the entrance to the Vicksburg National Military Park, the Vicksburg Civil War Museum offers an impressive collection of artillery shells, bottles, and over 5,000 other items from the Civil War era.

Admission charged.

Vicksburg National Military Park

3201 Clay Street
Vicksburg, MS 39180
Phone: (601) 636-0583

Hours: Daily, 8am - 5pm (Visitors Center)
Daily, Dusk - Dawn (Park Grounds)

Vicksburg National Military Park offers a number of tour options, from cassette tape rentals for unescorted driving tours, to knowledgeable guides who ride along in your car, van, or bus. The complete driving tour is sixteen miles long and in-

The complete driving tour is sixteen miles long and includes the USS Cairo Museum (with over 1,000 maritime artifacts).

cludes the USS Cairo Museum (with over 1,000 maritime artifacts). Tours begin at the Visitors Center, where exhibits and artifacts from the Siege of Vicksburg are on display. An 18-minute film is shown every half-hour and provides a better understanding of the events surrounding the siege.

Admission charged.

Virginia Civil War Trails

Phone: 1-888-CIVIL WAR

Those interested in exploring the many Civil War sites located throughout Virginia can now do so using specially prepared maps which focus on particular campaigns or evolutions of the Civil War.

Virginia's Civil War sites are being packaged as "Virginia Civil War Trails," a project which includes the construction of pull-offs, placement of signs and preparation of maps, audio tapes and brochures. The project has four phases including, *Lee's Retreat, Lee vs. Grant: the 1864 Overland Campaign*, the *Shenandoah Valley Campaign* and the *Peninsula Campaign*. The *Shenandoah* and *Peninsula Campaigns* are still under development.

Call for additional information or maps.

Virginia Historical Society

428 North Boulevard
Mail:
P.O. Box 7311
Richmond, VA 23221-0311
Phone: (804) 358-4901

Hours: Monday - Saturday, 10am - 5pm
Sunday, 1pm - 5pm

Established by the Virginia Historical Society, the Museum of Virginia History offers seven museum galleries of art and artifacts from Virginia's colorful past. The museum is housed in a neoclassical building often referred to as Battle Abbey (the building was originally thought of as the "Battle Abbey of the South"). The original structure, which has been expanded, was built by the Confederate Memorial Association to honor the Confederate dead. The building also served (and continues to serve) as a repository for the records of the South's Lost Cause.

Long-term Civil War exhibits include *Four Seasons of the Confederacy: Murals by Charles Hoffbauer, Arming the Confederacy*, an impressive assortment of Confederate weaponry and accouterments from the Maryland-Steuart Collection, and *Making the Confederate Murals*, a look at the pastels, watercolors, oil and pencil sketches on paper and canvas, photographs, and clay models used by French artist Charles Hoffbauer during the creation of *Four Seasons of the Confederacy*. Hand-held electronic gallery guides (a great idea) allow you to decide how much information you want about each object, they also open drawers of "please touch" items.

Special events are sponsored by the museum and the Virginia Historical Society (VHS) throughout the year. Membership in the VHS is open to those interested in supporting the museum (see *Organizations*) and the Society's Library of Virginia History is available for research (see *Archives & Libraries*).

Admission fee charged.

The original structure, which has been expanded, was built by the Confederate Memorial Association to honor the Confederate dead.

Warren Rifles Confederate Museum

95 Chester Street
Front Royal, VA 22630

Hours: Monday - Friday, 9am - 4pm
         Sunday, Noon - 4pm
         April 15 - November 1
         by appointment rest of year

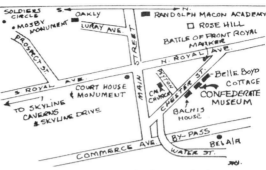

Owned and operated by the Warren Rifles Chapter, United Daughters of the Confederacy, the Warren Rifles Confederate Museum offers a collection of relics and records of the War between the States, including weapons, uniforms, flags, documents, pictures, and, of particular interest, memorabilia of Belle Boyd, Mosby's Rangers, Generals Jackson, Lee, Early, Longstreet, Ashby, and others. A book and gift shop is also available.

Washington Historical Museum

308 East Robert Toombs Avenue
Washington, GA 30673
Phone: (706) 678-1776

Hours: Tuesday - Saturday, 10am - 5pm
         Sunday, 2pm - 5pm

Owned by the City of Washington, the Washington Historical Museum is situated in a white frame, two-story house on land once owned by Micajah Williamson. The earliest section of the house was built circa 1835 by Albert Gallatin Semmes. Albert Semmes was the half-brother of Confederate General Paul Jones Semmes, and a cousin of Admiral Raphael Semmes, Confederate States Navy. Albert Semmes sold the house shortly after its completion and it was eventually enlarged to its present size by Samuel Barnett.

The second floor of the museum offers a collection of Civil War relics which were gathered over many years by the Last Cabinet Chapter of the United Daughters of the Confederacy. It is considered to be one of the finest collections in the South and includes Jefferson Davis' camp chest, General Robert Toombs' office chair, photographs, documents, Joe Brown's Pikes, and a collection of period guns on loan from the estate of the late Alexander Wright.

Photo Courtesy of the Washington Historical Museum

West Virginia Independence Hall

1528 Market Street
Wheeling, WV 26003
Phone: (304) 238-1300
Fax: (304) 238-1302

Hours: Daily, 10am - 4pm
(closed Sundays in Jan & Feb)

Considered the birthplace of the State of West Virginia, this National Historic Landmark saw the lively debates during the Civil War years which ultimately led to statehood in 1863. Originally built in 1859 to house the federal post office, custom house, and Federal court, the museum now offers tours, programs, and exhibits on state history.

Costumed guides portraying living history character Elizabeth Busbey give group tours of the building by reservation. The dialog of Ms. Busbey is based on descriptions of the Civil War years as published in the Wheeling papers. The historic courtroom serves as a unique background as she discusses the heated debates that took place over the issue of secession.

A 20-minute video entitled "For Liberty and Union" helps orient groups to the drama that played out at this historic site. The building is handicap accessible with elevator and ramp entrance.

Wilderness Road Regional Museum

P.O. Box 373
Newbern, VA 24126
Phone: (540) 674-4835/5094

The Wilderness Road Regional Museum offers an interesting display of Civil War items, including paper items which are shown at special times. The museum sponsors a number of events throughout the year, including at least two Civil War events. A selection of Civil War books is available.

Call for directions/additional information.

Williams-Brice House and Gardens

Sumter County Museum
122 North Washington Street
P.O. Box 1456
Sumter, SC 29151-1456
Phone: (803) 775-0908

Hours: Tuesday - Saturday, 10am - 5pm
Sunday, 2pm - 5pm

Witness to one of the last battles of the Civil War (the Battle of Dingle's Mill), Sumter offers a rich history. The Sumter County Museum documents America's military engagements in an exhibit that ranges from the Revolutionary War to Desert Storm.

Though not a Civil War museum, per se, the Sumter County Museum offers a peek at Southern life during that turbulent period. Guided and self-guided tours are available (group tours by reservation), as well as various programs, performances, and lectures offered by the museum. A gift shop is on site and the magnificent gardens can be rented for weddings, receptions, etc.

Winter Quarters State Commemorative Area

Route 1, Box 91
Newellton, LA 71357
Phone: (318) 467-9750

Located 3 miles southeast of Newellton on Louisiana Highway 608, Winter Quarters began as a small winter hunting lodge in 1803 and grew considerably as three separate additions added in the coming decades. The house was home to planter, inventor, physician, and Union sympathizer, Dr. Haller Nutt and his wife, Julia. Mrs. Nutt was left in charge of the plantation at the beginning of the Civil War and saved it from destruction by convincing General Grant to spare the home in exchange for feeding and quartering his troops.

Today, Winter Quarters houses artifacts and memorabilia of the Civil War, including uniforms, weapons, diaries, personal records, and period furnishings. A display dedicated to Dr. Nutt's medicinal and pharmaceutical contributions is also available.

Wisconsin Veterans Museum

30 West Mifflin Street
Madison, WI 53703
Phone: (608) 264-6086

Hours: Tue - Sat, 9:30am - 4:30pm
Sunday, Noon - 4pm
(April through September)

This 10,000-square-foot museum, dedicated to the citizen-soldiers of Wisconsin, contains two main galleries, a gift shop, and exhibit space for displays that change periodically. Seventeen detailed bronze figures adorn the front windows showcase, personifying Wisconsin citizens who served in U.S. conflicts, up to and including the Persian Gulf War. The centerpiece of the Civil War area is a diorama dramatizing the Battle of Antietam.

A unique service offered by the museum will be of interest to those with ancestors who were Wisconsin Civil War Veterans. For $6.25 plus tax and $2 shipping and handling, the

A unique service offered by the museum will be of interest to those with ancestors who were Wisconsin Civil War Veterans.

museum will ship a parchment-style document that details the history of your Civil War ancestor. The document appears as a handsome *Certificate of Service* and is suitable for framing. The information contained on each certificate is pulled from the museum's Civil War database. The records in this database were compiled from *Roster of Wisconsin Volunteers* (1866, The State of Wisconsin). Contact the museum for more information about this excellent service.

Photo Courtesy of the Wisconsin Veterans Museum

Other
Places of Interest

There were a number of Civil War "Places of Interest" that we didn't receive information from. Though we can't be certain the information presented here is correct, we've provided the name and address of these sites as a service to our readers.

The Atlanta Cyclorama
800-C Cherokee Ave., S.E.
Atlanta, GA 30315

Atlanta History Center
130 West Paces Ferry Rd., N.W.
Atlanta, GA 30305

Averasboro Battlefield
P.O. Box 1085
Dunn, NC 28334

Barbara Fritchie Replica House & Museum
154 W. Patrick Street
Frederick, MD 21701

Battle of Athens State Historic Site
Revere, MO 63465

Battle of Cynthiana
423 Mill Rd.
Midway, KY 40327

Battle of Munfordville
Hart County Historical Society
P.O. Box 606
Munfordville, KY 42765

Battle of Selma
212 Pine Needle Drive
Selma, AL 36701

Battle of Tebbs Bend
112 Kensington Way
Campbellsville, KY 42718

Beauvoir
2244 Beach Blvd
Biloxi, MS 39531

Behringer-Crawford Museum
1600 Montague Road
P.O. Box 67
Covington, KY 41012

Bennett Place State Historical Site
4409 Bennett Memorial Rd
Durham, NC 27705

Blue & Gray Museum
Municipal Bldg. (Old Depot)
P.O. Box 1285
Fitzgerald, GA 31750

Branson Civil War Museum
724 Jim Wright Fwy N.
Fort Worth, TX 76108-1222

Brices Cross Roads National Battlefield
NatchezTrace Parkway
Rural Route 1, NT-143
Tupelo, MS 38801

Buffalo National River Civil War Heritage Trail
P.O. Box 1173
Harrison, AR 72602

Bullock Hall
180 Bulloch Ave.
P.O. Box 1309
Roswell, GA 30077

Cape Fear Museum
814 Market Street
Wilmington, NC 28401

Carnifex Ferry Battlefield State Park
Route 2
P.O. Box 435
Summersville, WV 26651

Charleston Museum
360 Meeting Street
Charleston, SC 29403

Chatham
120 Chatham Lane
Falmouth, VA

Chickamauga & Chattanooga National Military Park
Point Lookout Visitor Center
Lookout Mountain, TN 37350

The Civil War Information Center
2 North Cameron Street
Winchester, VA 22601

The Civil War Soldiers' Museum
108 South Palafox Place
Pensacola, FL 32501

Clara Barton Museum
68 Clara Barton Road
North Oxford, MA 01537

Clara Barton National Historic Site
5801 Oxford Road
Glen Echo, MD 20812

Confederate Museum
929 Camp Street
New Orleans, LA 70130

Confederate Museum
34 Pitt Street
Charleston, SC 29401

Confederate State Capitol at Old Washington Historic State Park
P.O. Box 98
Washington, AR 71862

The Curlee House
705 Jackson Street
Corinth, MS 38834

Customs House
14th and Washington
Cairo, IL 62914-0724

Dover Hotel (Surrender House)
P.O. Box 434
Dover, TN 37058

Dr. Samuel A. Mudd House & Museum
P.O. Box 1046
LaPlata, MD 20646

Droop Mountain Battlefield State Park
HC 64
P.O. Box 189
Hillsboro, WV 24946

Fairfax Courthouse
4000 Chain Bridge Road
Fairfax, VA 22030

Fisher's Hill Battlefield Civil War Site
11 Public Square, Suite 200
Hagerstown, MD 21740

Fort Pickens
40 Gulf Island National Seashore
1801 Gulf Breeze Parkway
Gulf Breeze, FL 32561

Fort Branch
P.O. Box 355
Hamilton, NC 27840

Fort Delaware State Park
45 Clinton Street
P.O. Box 170
Delaware City, DE 19706

Fort Gibson Historic Site
P.O. Box 457
Fort Gibson, OK 74434-0457

Fort Granger
P.O. Box 305
Franklin, TN 37065

Fort Macon State Park
P.O. Box 127
Atlanta Beach, NC 28512

Fort Morris Historic Site
Fort Morris Road
Midway, GA 31320

Fort Pemberton
c/o Greenwood Convention &
Visitors Bureau
P.O. Drawer 739
Greenwood, MS 38935-0739

Fort Pike State Commemorative Area
Route 6, Box 194
New Orleans, LA 70129

Fort Pulaski National Monument
P.O. Box 30757
Savannah, GA 31410-0757

Fort Scott
National Historic Site
Old Fort Blvd.
Fort Scott, KS 66701

Fort Smith
National Historic Site
P.O. Box 1406
Corner of Third & Rogers
Fort Smith, AR 72902

Fort Stevens
Piney Branch Rd., N.W. (13th Street)
Washington, D.C.

General George Doles
Confederate Museum
c/o Georgia Division, SCV
P.O. Box 167
Milledgeville, GA 31061

George Armstrong Custer
Residence
c/o Urban Issues Program
University of Texas/Austin
Austin, TX 78712

Gettysburg National
Military Park
97 Taneytown Road
Gettysburg, PA 17325

Gilgal Church Battlefield
667 Kennesaw Due West Road
Kennesaw, GA 30152

Glorietta Battlefield
Pecos National Historical Park
P.O. Drawer 418
Pecos, NM 87552-0418

Harriet Beecher Stowe
House
2950 Gilbert Avenue
Cincinnati, OH 45206

Harriet Tubman Museum
340 Walnut Street
Macon, GA 31201

Helena Civil War Sites
Driving Tour
226 Perry Street
Helena, AR 72342

Historic Blakeley
State Park
33707 State Highway 225
Spanish Fort, AL 36527

Jacksonport State Park
P.O. Box 8
Jacksonport, AR 72075

J.E.B. Stuart Birthplace
Route 773
Ararat, VA 24053

Jefferson Barracks
Historic Site
533 Grant Street
St. Louis, MO 63125-4121

The Jefferson Davis
Memorial Museum
and Park
P.O. Box 422
Irwinville, GA 31760

Jenkins' Ferry State Park
1200 Catherine Park Road
Hot Springs, AR 71913

Jennie Wade House
Museum
548 Baltimore Street
Gettysburg, PA 17325

John A. Logan Museum
1613 Edith Street
Murphysboro, IL 62966

The Johnson House
6133 Germantown Avenue
Philadelphia, PA 19144

Kennesaw Mountain
National Battlefield Park
900 Kennesaw Mountain Drive
Kennesaw, GA 30144

Lincoln Tomb
Oak Ridge Cemetery
Springfield, IL 62702

Magnolia Springs
State Park
(aka Camp Lawton)
Route 5, Box 488
Millen, GA 30442

Manassas National
Battlefield Park
6511 Sudley Road
Manassas, VA 22110

Marietta National
Cemetery
500 Washington Avenue
Marietta, GA 30060

Mary Todd Lincoln House
578 West Main Street
P.O. Box 132
Lexington, KY 40501

Mill Springs Battlefield
Hwy. 235
P.O. Box 814
Somerset, KY 42502

Mine Creek Battlefield
State Historic Site
c/o Kansas State Histo rical Society
6425 SW Sixth
Topeka, KS 66615-1099

National Underground
Railroad Museum
115 East Third Street
Marysville, KY 41056

Newtonia Battlefield
P.O. Box 106
Newtonia, MO 64850

Oaklands Historic House Museum
900 N. Maney Ave.
Murfreesboro, TN 37130

Old Courthouse Museum
Eva W. Davis Memorial
1008 Cherry Street
Vicksburg, MS 39180

Olustee Battlefield State Historic Site
P.O. Box 2
Olustee, FL 32072

Palmito Ranch Battlefield
c/o Brownsville Convention & Visitors Bureau
650 Farm-to-Market 802
Brownsville, TX 78520

Parker's Crossroads Battlefield
273 N. Broad Street
Lexington, TN 38351

Perryville Battlefield State Historic Site
P.O. Box 296, Highway 1920
Perryville, KY 40468-9999

Point Lookout State Park
P.O. Box 48
Scotland, MD 20687

Poison Springs State Park
Hwy. 76
Bluff City, AR 71722

Port Republic Battlefield
11 Public Square, Suite 200
Hagerstown, MD 21740

Rich Mountain Battlefield Civil War Site
P.O. Box 227
Beverly, WV 26253

Road To Tara Museum
659 Peachtree Street, N.E.
Atlanta, GA 30308

Rock Island Arsenal Museum and Site
Attn: SIORI-CFM
Rock Island Arsenal
Rock Island, IL 61299-5000

Rosemont Plantation
Home of Jefferson Davis
P.O. Box 814
Highway 24 East
Woodville, MS 39669

Sabine Pass
State Historic Park
c/o Texas Parks & Wildlife Department
4200 Smith School Road
Austin, TX 78744

Salem Cemetery Battlefield
35 Cotton Grove Road
Jackson, TN 38301

Samuel Bell Maxey House
812 South Church Street
Paris, TX 75460

Savannah History Museum
303 Martin Luther King Jr. Blvd.
Savannah, GA 31401

Shenandoah Valley
Heritage Museum
382 High Street
Dayton, VA 22821

Smithsonian Institute
1000 Jefferson Drive, S.W. on the Mall
Washington, DC 20560

Spring Hill Battlefield
P.O. Box 1076
Columbia, TN 38402

The State Museum
of Pennsylvania
P.O. Box 1026
Harrisburg, PA 17108-1026

Stonewall Jackson's Grave
Stonewall Jackson Memorial Cemetery
South Main Street
Lexington, VA 22450

Stonewall Jackson's
Headquarters
415 N. Braddock Street
Winchester, VA 22601

Strasburg Museum
E. King Street
Strasburg, VA 22657

U.S. Grant Home
510 Bouthillier Street
Galena, IL 61036

U.S. Grant
National Historic Site
7400 Grant Road
St. Louis, MO 63123

War Memorial Museum
of Virginia
9285 Warwick Blvd.
Newport News, VA 23001

Wilson's Creek
National Battlefield
6424 West Farm Road 182
Republic, MO 65738

Places of Interest QuickFind Index

The following index identifies the Places of Interest (including Other Places of Interest) and breaks them down state by state. This will allow you to quickly identify those places of interest in your home state, a neighboring state, or at a location you plan to visit. To located a site by name, rather than by state, please refer to the Master Index at the end of the book.

Delaware

Delaware History Museum
Fort Delaware State Park

Florida

The Civil War Soldiers' Museum
Fort Clinch State Park
Fort Pickens
Fort Zachary Taylor State Historic Site
Museum of Southern History
Natural Bridge Battlefield State Historic Site
Olustee Battlefield State Historic Site

Georgia

A.H. Stephens State Historic Park
Andersonville National Historic Site
The Atlanta Cyclorama
Atlanta History Center
Augusta-Richmond County Museum
Blue & Gray Museum
Bullock Hall
Confederate Naval Museum
Fort James Jackson Historic Site
Fort McAllister State Historic Park
Fort Morris Historic Site
Fort Pulaski National Monument
General George Doles Confederate Museum
Gilgal Church Battlefield
Harriet Tubman Museum
The Jefferson Davis Memorial Museum and Park
Kennesaw Civil War Museum
Kennesaw Mountain National Battlefield Park
Magnolia Springs State Park
Marietta National Cemetery
Pickett's Mill State Historic Site
Rhodes Hall
Road To Tara Museum
Robert Toombs House State Historic Site
Savannah History Museum

Sidney Lanier Cottage
Sweetwater Creek State Conservation Park
Washington Historical Museum

Illinois

Customs House
The Galena-Jo Daviess County Historical Society & Museum
Grand Army of the Republic Memorial Museum
John A. Logan Museum
The Lincoln College Museum
Lincoln Tomb
Rock Island Arsenal Museum and Site
Rosehill Cemetery & Mausoleum
U.S. Grant Home

Indiana

The Lincoln Museum

Kansas

Fort Scott National Historic Site
Mine Creek Battlefield State Historic Site

Kentucky

Abraham Lincoln Birthplace National Historic Site
Abraham Lincoln's Boyhood Home
Battle of Cynthiana
Battle of Munfordville
Battle of Tebbs Bend
Behringer-Crawford Museum
Camp Nelson
Columbus-Belmont State Park
General Lloyd Tilghman House
The Lincoln Museum
Mary Todd Lincoln House
Mill Springs Battlefield
National Underground Railroad Museum
Perryville Battlefield State Historic Site

Louisiana

Beauregard-Keyes House
Camp Moore
Confederate Museum (New Orleans)
Fort Pike State Commemorative Area
Mansfield State Commemorative Area
Memorial Hall Confederate Museum
Port Hudson State Commemorative Area
Winter Quarters State Comm. Area

Maryland

Antietam National Battlefield
Barbara Fritchie Replica House & Museum
Boonsborough Museum of History
Clara Barton National Historic Site
Dr. Samuel A. Mudd House & Museum
Monocacy National Battlefield
National Museum of Civil War Medicine
Point Lookout State Park
Surratt House Museum
U.S. Naval Academy Museum

Massachusetts

Clara Barton Museum

Mississippi

Beauvoir
Brices Cross Roads National Battlefield
The Curlee House
Fort Pemberton
Gray & Blue Naval Museum
Longwood
Northeast Mississippi Museum
Old Courthouse Museum
Rosemont Plantation
The Vanishing Glory
Vicksburg Civil War Museum
Vicksburg National Military Park

Missouri

Battle of Athens State Historic Site
Battle of Lexington State Historic Site
The Confederate Memorial State Historic
    Site
Fort Davidson State Historic Site
General Sweeny's Civil War Museum
Jefferson Barracks Historic Site
Newtonia Battlefield
U.S. Grant National Historic Site
Wilson's Creek National Battlefield

New Hampshire

Saint-Gaudens National Historic Site

New Mexico

Glorietta Battlefield

North Carolina

Averasboro Battlefield
Bennett Place State Historical Site
Bentonville Battleground State Historic Site
Cape Fear Museum
CSS Neuse State Historic Site
Fort Branch
Fort Fisher Civil War Museum
Fort Macon State Park
New Bern Civil War Museum

Ohio

Fortification Hill
Gallia County Civil War Homecoming: A
    Federal Reunion
Harriet Beecher Stowe House
McCook House Museum
Our House Tavern State Memorial
Sherman House

Oklahoma

Fort Gibson Historic Site
Fort Towson Military Park

Pennsylvania

The Civil War Library and Museum
The Confederate States Armory & Museum
Farnsworth House Inn
The Gettysburg Headquarters of Robert E. Lee
Gettysburg National Military Park
Grand Army of the Republic Civil War Museum and Library
Jennie Wade House Museum
The Johnson House
LeMoyne House and the Military Museum of Southwestern Pennsylvania
The Lincoln Room Museum
National Civil War Wax Museum
Soldiers & Sailors Memorial Hall
The State Museum of Pennsylvania

South Carolina

Charleston Museum
Confederate Museum
South Carolina State Museum
Williams-Brice House and Gardens

Tennessee

The Abraham Lincoln Museum
The Battles for Chattanooga Museum
The "Battle of Carthage" Civil War Museum
Battle of Carthage State Historic Site
Britton Lane Battlefield
The Carter House
Chattanooga Regional History Museum
Chickamauga & Chattanooga National Military Park
Clarksville-Montgomery County Museum
Confederate Memorial Hall

Dickson-Williams Mansion
Dover Hotel (Surrender House)
Fort Donelson National Battlefield
Fort Granger
Fort Pillow State Historic Site
Hunt-Phelan Home
Johnsonville State Historic Area
Lotz House - War Between the States and Old West Museum
Mabry-Hazen House
Mississippi River Museum at Mud Island
Museum of East Tennessee History
Oaklands Historic House Museum
Parker's Crossroads Battlefield
Salem Cemetery Battlefield
Sam Davis Home
Shiloh National Military Park
Spring Hill Battlefield
Stones River National Battlefield
Tennessee River Museum
Tennessee State Museum

Texas

Branson Civil War Museum
The Confederate Museum
The Confederate Research Center and Museum
George Armstrong Custer Residence
Palmito Ranch Battlefield
Sabine Pass State Historic Park
Samuel Bell Maxey House

Virginia

Appomattox Courthouse National Historical Park
Arlington House
Belle Boyd Cottage
Belle Grove Plantation
Blandford Church and Cemetery
Boyhood Home of Robert E. Lee
Casemate Museum
Cavalry Museum
Cedar Creek Battlefield

Washington, DC

West Virginia

Wisconsin

Organizations

An alphabetical listing of Civil War Organizations, Associations, and Societies

American Battlefield Protection Program

National Park Service
P.O. Box 37127
Suite 250
Washington, DC 20013-7127
Phone: (202) 343-3941
Fax: (202) 343-1836
Internet: http://www.cr.nps.gov/abpp/abpp.html

The American Battlefield Protection Program (ABPP) is the only federal program wholly dedicated to the protection and preservation of historically significant battlefields on American soil. The ABPP accomplishes its mission by providing technical assistance and, through its Partnership Funding program, small amounts of seed money to public and private non-profit entities committed to battlefield preservation, protection, planning, interpretation, education, and tourism. Since its creation in 1990, the ABPP has helped protect and enhance more than 60 battlefields by cosponsoring more than 130 projects in 16 states and the District of Columbia.

The program's principal publications are the *Civil War Sites Advisory Commission Report on the Nation's Civil War Battlefields* and *Battlefield Update*, the ABPP's quarterly newsletter. Both are free.

American Civil War Association (ACWA)

P.O. Box 61075
Sunnyvale, CA 94088-1075
Email (CSA): AdjCSAACWA@aol.com
Email (Union): FedAdjACWA@aol.com
Internet: http://reenact.org/acwa/

The American Civil War Association (ACWA) is a reenactment association based in California which believes firmly in the concept that Living History is one of the most dynamic mediums available to those in pursuit of the past. In the name of living history, ACWA members don authentically reproduced uniforms and clothing, sleep in canvas tents, cook over an open fire, care for and fire period weapons, and live the life of a Civil War soldier or civilian.

The American Civil War Association has both a Union and a Confederate Brigade, plus a Civilian Corps. Union units include the 20th Maine Infantry, Company G, 79th New York State Volunteer Infantry, Company C, and Battery "D" Fifth U.S. Light Artillery. Additional Federal units being formed include the 69th New York Volunteer Infantry, Company B and the 2nd Wisconsin Volunteer Infantry. Confederate units include the 7th Virginia Infantry, 33rd Virginia Infantry, and the Richmond Fayette Artillery. Additional Confederate units being formed include the 9th Louisiana Volunteer Infantry and the 6th Alabama Volunteer Infantry.

I was particularly impressed with the Civil War-era currency printed by ACWA Paymaster, Major Arthur W. Henrick. The bills, offered as bounty for new recruits, are reproductions of U.S. and Confederate currency. Major Henrick goes to the trouble of individually signing some of these bills, as was the practice during the early years of the Civil War. This is one of the many ways in which the ACWA adds authenticity to its living history presentations. Those interested in joining one of the units in the American Civil War Association should contact the organization for a current list of Recruiting Officers.

American Civil War Historical Reenactment Society

1013 Logan Avenue
Toronto, Ontario
M4K 3E6
Email: andydesjardins@sympatico.ca

Representing the 50,000+ Canadians who served in the Union and Confederate Armies during the Civil War (including four Union Generals and twenty-nine Medal of Honor recipients), the American Civil War Historical Reenactment Society is a dedicated group interested in sharing their passion for this little-known part of Canada's history.

Armies of Tennessee, CSA & USA

P.O. Box 91
Rosedale, IN 47874
Phone: (317) 548-2594

Organized into the Confederate State Militia, Confederate Legion, and the Confederate Navy (including the Marines and Cadets), the Armies of Tennessee, CSA & USA, also has Union representation which mirrors that of the Confederate units. The organization has been and continues to be heavily involved in preservation efforts such as cemetery cleanups, monument restoration, and identifying soldiers buried as "unknowns."

Armies of Tennessee, CSA & USA also sponsors a Debutante Christmas Cotillion at the Fife Opera House in Palestine, Illinois, with proceeds going towards the restoration of the opera house.

Members must be 16 years old to field. In addition to the fighting units, a Nurse Corps is available, as are medical units. Battle Call is the organization's monthly newsletter. It includes news of battle reenactments, historical articles, and general member news.

Membership: $20 per year (individual)

Army of the Pacific

P.O. Box 1863
Santa Barbara, CA 93116

  Officially organized in February, 1994, the Army of the Pacific (AoP) is a living history organization for Federal Infantry in the Southwest and Pacific. With a membership primarily focused in California, Nevada, Utah, New Mexico, and Arizona, the AoP also has members in other states, including some on the East Coast. The AoP plans and/or participates in about 3 events per year, and attends Eastern reenactments about once every 18 months.

Association for the Preservation of Civil War Sites, Inc.

11 Public Square, Suite 200
Hagerstown, MD 21740
Phone: (301) 665-1400

  Incorporated in 1987, the Association for the Preservation of Civil War Sites (APCWS) has already made a significant and lasting contribution to battlefield preservation. The Association's philosophy is focused on ensuring perpetual preservation of sites, whether through acquisition of the land or other strategies. Their most recent victory was a signed contract for the purchase of 1543 acres at Brandy Station. The $6.2 million purchase came after an eight-year fight to save the land from development. The APCWS is now soliciting donations to help pay for the purchase. After one APCWS member donated $500,000 to this worthwhile cause, the Association issued a challenge to other members to match the amount via contributions of $50 and up. Individuals contributing $50 will receive a personalized certificate and 1 year free membership in the APCWS. This is a superb organization worthy of your support.

Association for the Preservation of Virginia Antiquities

Douglas Southall Freeman Branch
2109 Buckeye Drive
Richmond, VA 23228
Phone: (804) 648-1889

  The mission of the Douglas Southall Freeman Branch of the APVA is to identify and preserve Civil War battlefields and sites, carrying on the work begun by Dr. Freeman earlier this century. For many Civil War sites, particularly around Richmond, time has already run out. Earthworks have been bulldozed to make way for shopping centers and parking lots, the fields where men died by the hundreds and thousands are now covered with single- and multifamily homes. In fact, ninety-five percent of Richmond's defensive outer line is already gone. When you join the Douglas Southall Freeman Branch of the APVA, a portion of your dues will go directly to Civil War battlefield and site preservation, saving these national treasures for future generations. Membership includes free admission to organization properties which are open to the public, APVA newsletters, and invitations to special events.

Membership: $20 (individual)

Auxiliary to Sons of Union Veterans of the Civil War

1016 Gorman Street
Philadelphia, PA 19116
Phone: (215) 673-1688

With a history closely tied to the Grand Army of the Republic, the Auxiliary to Sons of Union Veterans of the Civil War has its roots in the many Ladies Aid Societies formed during the 1880s. From these societies of wives, widows, daughters, and other female descendants of Union veterans, a national organization was formed. On August 11, 1890, this organization, then known as the Sons of Union Veterans Auxiliary, was incorporated in the State of Ohio.

Today, the Auxiliary continues many of the fine traditions of its founders. Striving to keep the memory of their ancestors and the sacrifices they made alive for a new generation, the organization participates in ceremonies and programs to commemorate events and honor leaders and personalities of the Civil War period. Other notable contributions made by the Auxiliary include greeting new citizens at Naturalization Court, visiting hospitals and nursing homes, driving the elderly and disabled to church, doctors appointments, and food markets, presentation of certificates and monetary prizes at graduation ceremonies to students excelling in the study of American History, presenting talks and tours at the G.A.R. Civil War Museum and Library (see listing under *Places of Interest*), and many other community services.

Membership in the Auxiliary is available to female lineal or collateral descendants (at least 12 years old) of soldiers, sailors, or marines regularly mustered and honorably discharged from the Army, Navy, or Marine Corps of the United States during the War of the Rebellion, 1861-1865. Wives, mothers, widows, and legally adopted daughters of Sons of Union Veterans in good standing are also eligible. Women who do not qualify for hereditary membership may become Associates.

For more information about membership in this outstanding organization, contact the Auxiliary Recruiter at the address and phone number listed above.

Membership: $15 initiation fee
                $15 per year

Battle of Hartsville Preservation

c/o 105 E. Main Street
Hartsville, TN 37074
Phone: (615) 374-3222

The Battle of Hartsville Preservation is dedicated to preserving the sites associated with Colonel John Hunt Morgan's bold cavalry raid against a superior Union force at Hartsville, Tennessee. The organization publishes a driving tour brochure titled *The Battle of Hartsville, Tennessee*, which highlights significant locations of the raid. Those interested in helping with the preservation of the Battle of Hartsville can contact the association at the above address.

The Berkeley County Historical Society

126 East Race Street
Martinsburg, WV 25401
Phone: (304) 267-4713

The Belle Boyd House

Young, flamboyant Confederate spy Belle Boyd first gained fame and notoriety upon shooting and killing a Union soldier on July 4, 1861 when that soldier attempted to take down a Confederate flag. Belle, the daughter of a Martinsburg businessman, was soon gathering information on Union troop strengths and intentions and reporting her findings to Stonewall Jackson during his 1862 Valley Campaign

In early 1992 the owner of the Belle Boyd House in Martinsburg, West Virginia, then an apartment complex, wanted to raze the house to make room for—you guessed it—a parking lot. Thanks to the Berkeley County Historical Society this never happened. Organizing public opin-

ion against the demolition, they soon turned their attention to raising the necessary funds to purchase the house and begin its restoration. Today, the Belle Boyd House is home to the Berkeley County Museum, the Boyd Mason Civil War Museum, the Ben Boyd Store, the Berkeley County Historic Landmarks Commission, and a Berkeley County genealogy and archives section. The Berkeley County Historical Society also sponsors a number of events, including the annual Belle Boyd's Birthday Celebration.

The Bucks County Civil War Round Table

P.O. Box 1868
Doylestown, PA 18901

The purpose of the Bucks County Civil War Round Table is to promote and further stimulate interest in all aspects and phases of the Civil War period. Meetings are held at the Community Room of the Bucks County Courthouse at 7:00 p.m., the first Tuesday of each month. The Round Table has taken on the task of preserving and maintaining the monument to the 104th Regiment Pennsylvania Volunteer Infantry. The monument, erected in 1867-68, is one of the first Civil War monuments in the nation. It was cleaned and restored in 1993 by the 104th Regiment PVI Monument Committee, which was the predecessor organization to the Bucks County Civil War Round Table.

A quarterly newsletter, *The Swamp Angel*, is provided to members and descendants of soldiers in the 104th Regt. PVI. *The Swamp Angel Newsletter* is named after the famous battery which was constructed by the 104th and used in the bombardment of Charleston, South Carolina.

Membership: $15 per year (individual)
                $25 per year (family)

The Round Table has taken on the task of preserving and maintaining the monument to the 104th Regiment Pennsylvania Volunteer Infantry.

Camp Nelson Preservation & Restoration Foundation

P.O. Box 1170
Nicholasville, KY 40356

Directions: Located six miles south of Nicholasville, off U.S. 27 South

Founded in 1863 by Major General Ambrose Burnside, Camp Nelson once covered 4,000 acres with over 300 buildings and fortifications and served as a major Union supply depot. The site also served as a recruitment and training center for African American soldiers, providing 10,000 troops to the Union cause. It was no secret how President Lincoln felt about Kentucky and Union facilities like Camp Nelson, he summed it up when he said, "It would be good to have God on our side, but we must hold Kentucky!"

Now, determined to hold onto a piece of that Kentucky history, the Camp Nelson Preservation & Restoration Foundation has gathered together a small but determined group of individuals with the ultimate goal of establishing a museum and interpretive center (see *Places of Interest*). The Foundation has produced a video about the site and a print of the Officers' Quarters, both available at a reasonable cost (call 606-858-4360 for more information). The group has successfully sponsored a number of fund-raising events and is well on its way to achieving its goal, but they still need help. Membership is open to anyone with an interest in preserving this important Civil War landmark.

Membership: $25 per year

Camp Wildcat Preservation Foundation, Inc.

1986 Hazel Patch Road
East Bernstadt, KY 40729
Phone: (606) 843-2237
Fax: (606) 843-2237

Formed in 1993, the Camp Wildcat Preservation Foundation has erected three monuments, installed interpretive signs and Highway signs into the site in cooperation with the Laurel County Historical Society and the U.S. Forest Service, and, with the help of several organizations, purchased 290 acres of the battlefield site for preservation.

Camp Wildcat is located in the northern part of Laurel County, Kentucky, ten miles north of London, three miles from I-75 at exit 49, and two miles from U.S. 25. It is adjacent to Daniel Boones Trace on the north, and Scagg Trace on the south. In addition, the Sheltowee Trace National Recreation Trail, administered by the Daniel Boone National Forest, passes through the heart of the battlefield site on a section of the Wilderness Road.

Donations are accepted and appreciated. The foundation still owes approximately $40,000 of the $98,000 land purchase price and would like to retire the mortgage as soon as possible.

Membership: $25

. . . purchased 290 acres of the battlefield site for preservation.

190

Cedar Creek Battlefield Foundation, Inc.
Visitors' Center & Bookshop
P.O. Box 229
Middletown, VA 22645
Phone: (540) 869-2064
Fax: (540) 869-1438

Chartered in 1988, the Cedar Creek Battlefield Foundation soon purchased 158 acres of the battlefield of Cedar Creek—land that had already been designated as an industrial park. In 1996, after raising nearly a quarter-million dollars in principal and interest, the Foundation retired the debt on its initial land purchase and placed the land under a perpetual preservation easement to ensure that it can never be divided or developed. The Foundation then moved toward the realization of its other goals; the interpretation of the battlefield, the restoration of the Heater House on the battlefield, and the creation of a first class visitors and educational center.

In 1993, the Foundation opened a small visitors center and book shop on the battlefield. In 1996, the center was moved to a 5,000 square foot building on the heights overlooking the battlefield. A major interpretive center and museum dealing with the Battle of Cedar Creek and the Shenandoah Valley Campaign of 1864 is scheduled to open during the 1997 season.

Every October since 1990, on the weekend closest to the anniversary of the October 19 battle, the Cedar Creek Battlefield Foundation sponsors one of the premiere living history events in the country. Thousands of reenactors re-create the events of that dramatic autumn day in 1864, bringing to life the realities of the Civil War for the many spectators who gather to watch.

For those wishing to support the preservation of Cedar Creek Battlefield, the Foundation sponsors a program whereby honorary square feet of the battlefield can be "purchased" for $25 per square foot. "Property owners" receive a personalized certificate suitable for framing. A great gift idea for Civil War enthusiasts.

The Civil War Plymouth Pilgrims Descendants Society
c/o Scott W. Holmes, Secretary/Treasurer
4910 Grape Tree Lane
Roanoke, VA 24018

With membership open to anyone with an interest in the Union forces that played a role in the Battle of Plymouth, North Carolina, the Civil War Plymouth Pilgrims Descendants Society offers a forum for the exchange of information about this battle and its participants. Ten Union regiments and six naval vessels participated in the Battle of Plymouth, April 17, 1864. Outnumbered and surrounded, Union forces under General Henry Wessells were forced to surrender after several days of fighting. Close to 3,000 Union soldiers were taken prisoner and shipped south to Andersonville. On the way, they were given the nickname "Plymouth Pilgrims."

The Society participates in the annual Living History Weekend held in Plymouth, N.C. on the third weekend of April. Reenactments, a torchlight tour, and memorial services are all part of the weekend events. Members receive an informative quarterly newsletter and the opportunity to network with other members and with Regimental Historians who can assist in research.

Membership: $15 per year

Civil War Round Table Associates

P.O. Box 7388
Little Rock, AR 72217

Editor's Choice
SELECTION

Civil War Round Table Associates is a national "umbrella" organization which was formed in 1968 by Jerry Russell. The organization serves as an "informational clearing house" for Round Tables, individual Civil War buffs, and other related organizations. The basic idea is to provide better communications and cooperation between the various autonomous Round Tables, individuals, and organizations, particularly in the area of preservation.

CWRT Associates have won significant preservation battles at Manassas, Shiloh, Fredericksburg, Chickamauga-Chattanooga, Stones River, Gettysburg, Petersburg, Prairie Grove, Champion Hill, Antietam, Vicksburg, Kennesaw Mountain, and others.

Today, there are approximately 200 Civil War Round Tables throughout the country. Of these, nearly 50 were formed with the advice and assistance of CWRT Associates.

The prestigious Congress of Civil War Round Tables is held by CWRT Associates on an annual basis. The October 1997 Congress will include tours of "Civil War Washington," led by Edwin C. Bearss, retired Chief Historian of the National Park Service. The organization also sponsors Civil War study gatherings, including the Confederate Historical Institute annual conference in the spring, and the Society of Civil War Historians meeting in the fall. For those on the West Coast, there is a West Coast Civil War Conference every November.

Battlefield preservation is CWRT Associates most important function. In 1989, they formed a national lobbying group, known as HERITAGEPAC, which provides an effective vehicle for focusing preservation efforts on a national level.

The organization publishes a Round Tables and Preservation newsletter, *CWRT Digest*, which is provided to members.

Membership: $12.50 (regular)
 $20 (sustaining)
 $50 (contributing)
 $100 (life member)

Today, there are approximately 200 Civil War Round Tables throughout the country. Of these, nearly 50 were formed with the advice and assistance of CWRT Associates.

The first Civil War Round Table was formed in Chicago in 1940.

Civil War Round Table of Western Missouri
1209 Skyline Drive
Liberty, MO 64068

The Civil War Round Table of Western Missouri meets the second Wednesday of each month (except July, August, and December) at 7pm in the library at Truman High School (3301 South Noland Rd, Independence, MO). The Border Star is the official publication of the Round Table.

Membership: $15 per year (individual)
$22.50 per year (family)

Civil War Society
P.O. Box 770
Berryville, VA 22611
Phone: (540) 955-1176
Fax: (540) 955-2321
Membership: 1-800-247-6253

> *The (Civil War) magazine is the cornerstone of the Society*

After successfully launching *Civil War* Magazine in 1983, publisher Christopher Curran took his passion one step further by founding The Civil War Society in 1986. From its inception, the Society has placed a strong emphasis on historical education. They believe that history is not just an accumulation of events marked by time. Instead, history, in its truest form, is the study of mankind's strengths and weaknesses; humanity's glory and shame. By understanding the past, we can make a difference in ourselves and our future. All history, but American history in particular, offers great insights to who we are.

The Civil War Society achieves its educational goals through three basic means: *Civil War* Magazine, Seminars and Tours, and their Education and Preservation Activities. The magazine is the cornerstone of the Society and combines the latest research by the nation's leading Civil War historians with stunning paintings, rare period photographs, maps, and illustrations. Again, the intent is not just to explore the past, but to educate and derive vital lessons relevant to the present and future world peace.

Civil War takes a totally different approach to the Civil War, giving readers of all levels what they want. The articles are not fact-heavy dissertations for the specialist, but inviting, engaging stories for recent and casual students to the more seasoned student of the people and ideas behind the battles. Award-winning authors and recognized authorities teach and entertain while they tell the stories of America's costliest conflict. *Civil War* readers *understand* the campaigns by learning the reasons behind them. The Society seeks to illuminate lesser-known contributions by ethnic and other groups whose members may have forgotten that they share with all Americans a heritage rooted in our country's definitive experience.

Readers of *Civil War* will find original, full-color, hand-drawn, period-style maps by noted cartographer Terrence Haney; art-quality photographs of battlefields; leading historians talking about their latest research and newest books; new interpretations of events, people, and ideas behind the war; the most extensive Book and Video Review section of any history magazine; book advice from Dr. Gary Gallagher, one of America's leading Civil War scholars; travel pieces; and so much more.

Working in conjunction with individuals, local, state, and federal agencies, and private corporations, the Society collects and disburses contributions for preservation activities through its affiliated non-profit, tax exempt 501 (C) (3) Civil War Foundation. All management, marketing, and overhead fees are absorbed through the Society and *Civil War* Magazine, thereby enabling the Foundation to donate 100% of all contributions directly to education and preservation projects.

The unique combination of educational articles in *Civil War* and the Society's seminars and tours have enabled the Foundation to become a major benefactor in preservation and education through various donations and projects, including: Cedar Creek Battlefield Foundation in Virginia, the Conservation Fund's purchase of a threatened section of Shiloh battlefield in Tennessee, Beaver Dam Creek, Malvern Hill and Brandy Station. The Society's Civil War Foundation has also financed monuments at Hatcher's Run and Perryville and was the first to take a national stand against the proposed shopping center in Manassas and against Disney's plan to build a theme park at Haymarket.

As an educational society, the organization attempts to reach the youth of America by sponsoring and encouraging high school students to research and submit essays related to the Civil War. Cash prizes and financed seminar trips help to foster an interest in the program and, in turn, each year students from across the nation become more interested in American history.

In an effort to bring awareness to people of all ages, the Society also sponsors an annual Civil War Photography Contest. Ranging from monuments to battlefields, members discover pieces of history in their home towns and communities, bringing a greater awareness of how the Civil War touched their's and their neighbor's lives.

The Civil War Society says "Anyone can visit a battlefield - we bring it alive." Yes, it's a bold claim, but picture yourself in a canoe on the Antietam and you'll begin to understand what they mean. The Society conducts tours and seminars around the country. Rated as the country's best, they are lead by experts and attract participants from across the country and abroad.

Membership in The Civil War Society includes a subscription to the bi-monthly Civil War magazine, a society calendar, the Civil War Society newsletters, a personalized parchment membership certificate, the society's guide to tracing your Civil War ancestors, the opportunity to obtain a Civil War Society MasterCard (with a portion of every purchase going towards preservation), and the honor of claiming membership in an outstanding organization.

Membership:	$39 one year
	$68 two years
	$89 three years

> *The Civil War Society says "Anyone can visit a battlefield - we bring it alive." Yes, it's a bold claim, but picture yourself in a canoe on the Antietam and you'll begin to understand what they mean.*

The Civil War Trust

2101 Wilson Blvd.
Suite 1120
Arlington, VA 22201
Phone: (703) 516-4944
Fax: (703) 516-4947
Email: civilwar@ari.net
Information: 1-800-CWTRUST
Discovery Trail Guide: 1-888-CW-TRAIL

Editor's Choice
SELECTION

A simply outstanding organization, The Civil War Trust was begun in 1991 with the intent of leading a highly visible, national campaign to preserve American battlefield lands. The progress made by the Trust since then has been remarkable. Major victories include: securing $14.8 million to purchase land and conservation easements to protect 5600 acres at 24 historic sites in 13 states; growing the Trust's active membership to more than 24,000; developing the Civil War Discovery Trail which links more than 400 sites in 24 states; and the on-going development of the Civil War Discovery System, an interactive, multimedia computer database.

The Civil War Discovery Trail Official Guidebook features more than 200 pages that provide visitor information on more than 400 sites in 24 states. The book provides a description of each site, maps and information on admission fees, if any, hours and days of operation, visitor services, special events, and directions. The cost of the book is $11.95.

The Civil War Discovery System, an interactive, multimedia computer database being developed by The Civil War Trust in cooperation with the National Park Service, features photographs, maps, historic documents, video footage, music, and narration. The easy to use touch-screen Discovery System will initially be located at national and state park visitor centers, followed by museums and other historic sites on The Civil War Trust's Civil War Discovery Trial. Endorsed by the National Council for the Social Studies, the system will also be available for schools beginning in Fall, 1996. The Discovery System table of contents will include six main selections. These are: 1) The Big Picture - A brief introduction to the Civil War, 2) The Civil War World - An encyclopedic series of Civil War-related units ranging from cannons to card games, 3) On This Date - whereby the day-by-day events of the Civil War can be recalled, 4) Specific Site - a special section custom-designed for the site where the system is located, 5) Soldier Records - The name, rank, unit and - where available - personal papers of each soldier who fought during the Civil War, a powerful function that allows visitors to look up relatives, and 6) Preserving Battlefields - information on battlefield lands threatened by development and how to support preservation activities.

For membership information, contact the Trust at the above address or phone 1-800-CWTRUST.

Membership: $20

> *The Civil War Discovery System, an interactive, multimedia computer database being developed by The Civil War Trust in cooperation with the National Park Service, features photographs, maps, historic documents, video footage, music, and narration.*

Coastal Heritage Society
303 Martin Luther King, Jr., Blvd.
Savannah, GA 31401
Phone: (912) 238-1779

Operating three of Savannah's most important and exciting historic sites, the Coastal Heritage Society seeks to protect the cultural and natural heritage of the coastal area. The Society pursues this goal by promoting this valuable heritage through active public programming.

Sites owned and operated by the Society include Old Fort Jackson, the Savannah History Museum, and the Historic Railroad Shops (please see separate listings under *Places of Interest*). Family and Corporate memberships are available in the Coastal Heritage Society. For information on membership or any Society activity, call or write.

The Company of Fifers & Drummers, Inc.
P.O. Box 525
62 North Main Street
Ivoryton, CT 06442

Not specifically a Civil War organization, The Company of Fifers & Drummers is composed of some 120 traditional "Ancient" Fife & Drum Corps, with a thousand members in the U.S.A., Switzerland, Canada, and Ireland. It is the largest organization of drum corps in the Western world. The organization publishes a quarterly publication called *Ancient Times*, has a company store, and operates The Museum of Fife & Drum in Ivoryton, Connecticut (see entry under *Places of Interest*).

Membership: $15 (individual/U.S.)
                       $25 (family/U.S.)

Photo Courtesy of The Company of Fifers & Drummers

Ancient Times, the Company of Fifers & Drummers' quarterly publication.

Daughters of Union Veterans of the Civil War
National Headquarters
503 South Walnut
Springfield, IL 62704
Phone: (217) 544-0616

Daughters, granddaughters, and other direct descendants of honorably discharged soldiers, sailors, and marines who served in the Union Army or Navy during the Rebellion of 1861 - 1865, are eligible for membership in the Daughters of Union Veterans (DUV) of the Civil War. The DUV helps perpetuate the memory, deeds, and loyalty of Union veterans who fought and died to preserve one nation, under God.

Local groups of the DUV are referred to as Tents, and are named for Army Nurses who served in the Civil War and other loyal women of the Civil War era whose patriotic deeds were recorded. States with three or more tents have a State Department and may have Members-at-Large.

The DUV museum, co-located with the headquarters, houses books, mementos, and documented records of the Civil War era. The museum is open Monday through Friday, 9am to 4pm.

Five Forks Commemorative Committee

P.O. Box 3092
Petersburg, VA 23805
Phone: (804) 541-0667

Each year, the Five Forks Commemorative Committee works to put on a Civil War reenactment in Dinwiddie County, Virginia (just southwest of Petersburg, Va., close to the Five Forks National Battlefield)

the last weekend of March. The Battle of Five Forks is always reenacted, along with another local battle (the Battle of Hatcher's Run, for example). The committee tries to balance the event by having a Federal victory one day, and a Confederate victory the other. The ultimate goal of the committee is to purchase land for a permanent reenactment site for the Battle of Five Forks, and as a multipurpose park for Dinwiddie County.

Friends of Fort Taylor, Inc.

P.O. Box 58
Key West, FL 33041
Phone: (305) 292-6850

Friends of Fort Taylor, Inc., was established to support Fort Zachary Taylor State Historic Site (see Places of Interest) by sponsoring fund raising activities for the

maintenance, restoration, and improvement of Fort Zachary Taylor. The organization is also involved in educational and living history programs at the fort.

Membership: $15 per year (individual)
                 $25 per year (family)

The General Longstreet Memorial Fund

c/o The North Carolina Division
Sons of Confederate Veterans
P.O. Box 1896
Raleigh, NC 27601

With no memorial, monument, or plaque to honor the memory of Confederate General James Longstreet, Lee's "Old War Horse," The General Longstreet Memorial Fund was established to pay tribute to the long-forgotten Southern general and gentleman. In September, 1995, the Na-

In September, 1995, the National Park Service granted approval for placement of the monument at the Pitzer Woods Commemorative area, Gettysburg, Pennsylvania.

tional Park Service granted approval for placement of the monument at the Pitzer Woods Commemorative area, Gettysburg,

197

Pennsylvania. Noted sculptor, Mr. Gary Casteel, is designing the life-sized equestrian monument. The only major stumbling block in the way of this long-overdue monument is funding. To overcome this, the organization is sponsoring a number of fund-raisers. For more information on fund raisers, on the monument, on how you can help, or simply to make a donation (which will be well-received), contact the organization chairman, Robert C. Thomas, at the above address.

Keep up the good work Mr. Thomas.

The Georgia Historical Society

501 Whitaker Street
Savannah, GA 31499
Phone: (912) 651-2125

The Georgia Historical Society was formed in 1839 by a group of public-spirited Georgians and incorporated by act of the state legislature "to collect, preserve and share the history of the State of Georgia." Today, the vision of these distinguished Georgians has been realized as the Society plays a leading role in the preservation of Georgia's history. The organization strives to fulfill its mission through the operation of its Savannah-based library and archives, presentation of programs and activities for its members and the public, a publications program, and assistance to local and county historical societies through a statewide affiliate chapter network. For information on the Society's library, please refer to the *Archives & Libraries* section, under Georgia.

Membership: $20 (student)
                $35 (supporter)

Gettysburg Battlefield Preservation Association

P.O. Box 4087
Gettysburg, PA 17325
Phone: (717) 337-0031

The Gettysburg Battlefield Preservation Association (GBPA) is a nonprofit organization founded in 1959 to acquire threatened battlefield land, promote the larger goals of preservation of the Gettysburg Battlefield, and educate the public on issues relating to its preservation. Since its founding they have acquired and donated over 200 acres of land to Gettysburg National Military Park, donated thousands of dollars to other preservation projects, and have been a careful watchdog of National Park Service Cultural Resource Management initiatives. Most recently the organization called to the public's attention the destruction of 7 acres of historic Seminary Ridge by Gettysburg College following a land exchange between the College and the National Park Service. Their efforts led to a Congressional investigation and hearing in May 1994.

At present, the organization has about 400 members nationwide, and they encourage membership from anyone who shares a concern for the preservation and management of Gettysburg National Park and the larger Gettysburg Battlefield National Register Historic District. Membership is available for a minimum donation of $10 a year, for which the member receives the association's newsletter "Battle Lines" (published twice a year), an "Enlistment Certificate" signed by noted Civil War historian and GBPA board member William Frassanito, and announcements of GBPA-sponsored events (such as the annual Civil War Book Show in July).

Special thanks to Walter Powell, President of the GBPA, for the above information—and for his groups diligence in protecting one of our national treasures.

Membership: $10 (min.) year

Hart County Historical Society
P.O. Box 606
Munfordville, KY 42765
Phone: (502) 524-0101

This section of Kentucky saw much troop movement during the Civil War. Because of the Louisville & Nashville Railroad line running north and south through Hart County, its bridges were the targets of struggle throughout the war. In September, 1862, the Battle for the Bridge was fought at Munfordville between Bragg's Confederate troops and Wilder's Federal force for possession of what was then the longest iron bridge in the world.

The Hart County Historical Society is currently involved in an intensive campaign to preserve and develop the battlefield, which is remarkably unchanged from its original condition. Earthworks remain in place, and there has been very little commercial or residential development in the area of the battle. In addition to its preservation efforts, the Society maintains the Hart County Historical Museum, located on Main Street in Munfordville. This museum houses an extensive collection of artifacts pertaining to all aspects of life in Hart County.

Membership: $10 per year
                      $100 lifetime

The Historical Society of Delaware
505 Market Street
Wilmington, DE 19801
Phone: (302) 655-7161
Fax: (302) 655-7844

Membership in the Historical Society of Delaware helps support a number of worthwhile programs, including the Delaware History Museum, the Research Library, and the Read House and Gardens.

The Delaware History Museum, located at 504 Market Street in Wilmington, features major exhibits on Delaware in the Civil War. The Research Library, located at 505 Market Street, has holdings that include regimental records, diaries, photographs, maps, newspapers, and other Civil War-related material. The Society also publishes *Delaware History*, a semiannual scholarly journal about all aspects of Delaware history, available free with membership.

Membership: $25 (individual)

Heritage Foundation of Franklin & Williamson County
P.O. Box 723
510 Columbia Avenue
Franklin, TN 37065-0723

The 850 member Heritage Foundation purchased Roper's Knob (a Union signal post) and is seeking assistance to retire the debt. Original earthworks are at the site. Membership in Friends of Roper's Knob is available for $100, while Heritage Foundation membership is $35 per year.

Heritage Preservation Association

P.O. Box 98209
Atlanta, GA 30359-1909
Phone: (770) 928-2714
Fax: (770) 928-2719
Membership: 1-800-86 DIXIE
Email: HPA@america.net
BBS: (770) 928-2723 (modem speeds up to 14400 bps, 8, 1, none)

"Guarding Our Future By Preserving Our Past"

Established for the purpose of preserving Southern history, Southern symbols, and Southern culture against the many attacks which have been leveled against them, particularly in this era of "Political Correctness," the Heritage Preservation Association has quickly established itself as a growing political force. The groups lobbying and public education efforts have secured a number of successes, including the defeat of an anti-flag boycott in Georgia, the defeat of attempts to censor the movie "Gettysburg" in Virginia, and the defeat of an anti-flag compromise in South Carolina, among others. But their work is far from over. With so many individuals and groups in this country who have forgotten the concept of free expression—something our Founding Fathers bleed and died for—the HPA faces a long and difficult struggle.

Currently the Association publishes a quarterly newsletter entitled *The Front Line*, and plans are in the works for a new bimonthly newspaper entitled *The Statesman*. The only requirement for membership is an interest in preserving Southern heritage. The HPA does not discriminate based on race, creed, sex, religion, or national/regional origin. With members in 49 states and 6 countries, the Association is not just a "Southern" organization, but a historical preservation organization for all Americans.

Membership: $40 (individual)

Hood's Texas Brigade Association

c/o The Confederate Research Center
Hill College
P.O. Box 619
Hillsboro, TX 76645

Hood's Texas Brigade Association was originally established on May 14, 1872, by members of the immortal Confederate brigade. The Association met continuously for sixty-three years, ending with a final meeting June 26-27, 1933. With the death of John Roberts of Arcadia, Texas, the last known survivor of the Association, the original organization ceased to exist.

Reactivated in 1966, Hood's Texas Brigade Association holds a biennial reunion on even years and issues a newsletter twice a year. Membership is available to direct and collateral descendants of members of Hood's Texas Brigade. The Confederate Research Center has the service records of all the members of the Brigade on microfilm and will use this for verification. Members will receive an authentically reproduced certificate of membership like the one issued by the Association on June 27, 1889.

Annual Dues: $5 (due January 1)

Indiana Historical Society

315 W. Ohio Street
Indianapolis, IN 46202
Phone: (317) 232-1882
Fax: (317) 233-3109
Internet: http//www.ihs1830.org/

Hours: Monday - Friday, 8:30am - 4pm

Collecting, preserving, researching, and interpreting the history of Indiana since 1830, the Indiana Historical Society welcomes new members and offers them the opportunity to explore the struggles, triumphs, and failures of the men and women who helped forge the state.

Membership helps support the *William Henry Smith Memorial Library*, the *Indiana Junior Historical Society*, the *Talking Books* program, research grants and fellowships, and services for local historical organizations throughout Indiana. Members also receive the bimonthly newsletter, *The Bridge*, a copy of the IHS Annual Report, a copy of the annual Publications Catalog, and substantial prepublication discounts on new Society books, along with a 20 percent discount on the Society's previous publications and many publications from the Indiana University Press.

Membership: $30 per year (individual)
                $10 per year (under 25)

Irish Brigade Association

Fort Schuyler
Bronx, NY 10465
Mail:
P.O. Box 3495
Wayne, NJ 07474-3495
Phone: (201) 694-7792
Email: laverty@crusoe.com

The Irish Brigade Association is an Irish-American military and naval history society devoted to the study of the Irish under arms. The Association is affiliated with and based at the Maritime Museum at Fort Schuyler, where, in 1861, the 69th New York Volunteers and the Irish Brigade were organized. Though the primary focus of the organization is the "Fighting 69th"

and the American Civil War, their interests also include the Irish who helped win the Revolutionary War, and Irish-American fighting men in other wars, including World Wars I and II.

Membership is available to those who "possess sufficient imagination to share our passion for the Irish dimension of the military and naval experience across the world." This group is for those who want to share in the history and tradition of so many proud fighting Irishmen—the Civil War, in particular, is ripe with their heroics and glory. The Association publishes a newsletter for members entitled "The Irish Volunteer."

Membership: $25 (individual)

The Iron Brigade Association

Carroll College
Institute for Civil War Studies
100 North East Avenue
Waukesha, WI 53186

Open to anyone with an interest in the famous fighting unit, the Iron Brigade

Association was initially formed in 1880 by veterans of the 2nd, 6th, and 7th Wisconsin, 19th Indiana, 24th Michigan, and Battery B of the 4th U.S. Artillery. In 1990, two sons of Iron Brigade veterans, William Upham and James Sullivan, issued a call for a "Reunion of the Iron Brigade Association," and the association witnessed its first gathering in a half century. At the reunion, Upham and Sullivan granted authority to the Milwaukee Civil War Round Table to keep an official roster of Iron Brigade Association members and to hold Iron Brigade reunions. The next formal meeting has been set for October 3-5, 1997.

Membership:

$5	(lifetime membership, plus Iron Brigade cross lapel pin)
$15	(lifetime membership, plus Iron Brigade medal)

Joshua L. Chamberlain Civil War Round Table

P.O. Box 1046
Brunswick, ME 04011-1046

With more than 300 regular and associate (long-distance) members in 25 states, the Joshua L. Chamberlain Civil War Round Table continues to grow, offering a steady diet of interesting and important programs. Meetings are normally on the second Thursday of each month, September through June, at 7 p.m. in the cafeteria area of the Brunswick Junior High School. Meetings are often preceded at 6:30 p.m. by Civil War era music and conversation, and may be followed by the showing of videotapes and films. The organization publishes ten issues of *First Call*, the Round Table's newsletter, each year. Audiotapes of programs are available for a modest fee.

Membership:	$20 per year (individual)
	$30 per year (family)
	$10 per year (associate)

Kansas State Historical Society

6425 S.W. 6th Avenue
Topeka, KS 66615-1099
Phone: (913) 272-8681
Fax: (913) 272-8682
TTY: (913) 272-8683

The mission of the Kansas State Historical Society is to preserve and promote the history of Kansas and the Great Plains. The Society maintains a research facility with extensive resources, including those relating to the Civil War and the Grand Army of the Republic (see *Archives & Libraries*).

Kentucky Historical Society

P.O. Box 1792
Frankfort, KY 40602-1792
Phone: (502) 564-3016
Fax: (502) 564-4701

With extensive holdings related to the Civil War and Kentucky history in general, the Society's library is a prime source for Civil War research (see *Archives & Libraries* for additional information). Membership includes a one-year subscription to the Society's quarterly scholarly journal, *The Register*, invitations to Society events, and discounts on selected publications from the KHS and University Press of Kentucky. Higher levels of membership include additional benefits.

Membership:	$15 (Student)
	$25 (Basic)
	$35 (Contributing, Libraries, Institutions)
	$50 (Friends)

The Lee-Jackson Foundation

P.O. Box 8121
Charlottesville, VA 22906
Phone: (804) 977-1861

Established for the purpose of perpetuating the memory of General Robert E. Lee and General Thomas J. "Stonewall" Jackson, the foundation concentrated its early efforts in acquiring and preserving homes, battlefields, and personal possessions associated with either Lee or Jackson. Since then, however, the organization has turned over some assets to local groups. Jackson's home in Lexington, Virginia was transferred to the Lexington Historical Foundation, Jackson's winter headquarters in Winchester, Virginia, as turned over to the city of Winchester, and personal items were transferred to the Virginia Military Institute or to the Washington & Lee University, both located in Lexington, Virginia. The foundation continues to own two battlefields in the Shenandoah Valley associated with Jackson, and the Lee Boyhood Home, located in Alexandria, Virginia.

The main mission of the Lee-Jackson Foundation today is education. Financial assistance is provided to college students based upon a competitive essay writing contest with Lee or Jackson as the subject matter. Contributions are greatly appreciated. Individuals who contribute $100 are awarded an appointment as Sergeant in the Stonewall Jackson Brigade, while $250 earns a commission as Colonel in the Stonewall Jackson Brigade. Both certificates are impressive and make handsome gifts when suitably framed.

The Longstreet Society

P.O. Box 191
Gainesville, GA 30503

The purpose of the Longstreet Society is to celebrate the life of Lieutenant General James Longstreet, C.S.A., 1821-1904, with an emphasis on his postwar life. General Longstreet spent the last 29 years of his life in Gainesville, Georgia, where he owned and operated the Piedmont Hotel. Acquired by the Longstreet Society, the Piedmont Hotel is being restored and, when complete, will serve as a museum, library, and as the society headquarters.

The society has taken upon itself the task of maintaining General James Longstreet's gravesite, which was long neglected. In April, 1995, they erected an American flag at the gravesite and it has now become a major tourist attraction. The Society also maintains General Longstreet's home site.

Each year in April the Longstreet Society, in conjunction with Brenau University, hosts a Longstreet Day, beginning in the morning with a service at the General's grave. The day's festivities include speakers, reenactors, and tours of Longstreet sites around Gainesville.

A quarterly newsletter (*Confidential to the Corps*) is provided to members and Longstreet mementos are available (T-shirts, tote bags, stationery, coffee mugs, etc.).

Membership:	$10 year (student)
	$30 year (individual)
	$50 year (family)
	$125 year (corporate)

The Military Order of the Loyal Legion of the United States

1805 Pine Street
Philadelphia, PA 19103

On April 15, 1865, as word spread throughout the country of Abraham Lincoln's assassination, rumors of a conspiracy to destroy the Federal government surfaced. Three Union Army officer friends who had met to discuss the sad news of Lincoln's death, were alarmed at this rumored conspiracy and quickly called other officers and ex-officers together to form an organization designed to counter such threats to the national government. This was the genesis of the Military Order of the Loyal Legion of the Unites States, or MOLLUS, as it is commonly known. By 1899, the Loyal Legion had more than 8,000 Civil War officers on its rosters. Prominent officers who have been past members include Generals Ulysses S. Grant and William T. Sherman, Lt. Generals Sheridan, Miles, and Schofield, Major Generals Custer, Hancock, McClellan, Hayes, Gregg and Dodge, and Admiral Farragut.

Today, MOLLUS objectives include perpetuating the memory of those who fought to preserve the unity and indivisibility of the Republic, honoring the memory of President Lincoln, and promoting his ideals. To this end, the 1,000-member organization is actively involved in a number of important projects, such as erecting, restoring, and maintaining plaques and monuments, supporting efforts to preserve Civil War battlefields and sites, and supporting the Civil War Library and Museum (see *Places of Interest*) in Philadelphia, an outstanding facility which was established by the Loyal Legion and contains many unique and important artifacts. This site also serves as the organization's national headquarters.

Membership categories are:

Hereditary: Male who is 18 years of age or older who is a direct male descendants of a commissioned officer in the U.S. Army, Navy, or Marine Corps who served during the Civil War, or male descendants of a brother or sister of any such officer.
Junior: Same qualifications as Hereditary, but for males under 18.
Associates: Male persons of the age of 18 or more who are not eligible for Hereditary membership, but who subscribe to the Preamble, Principles, and Objects of the Order and who have demonstrated a serious interest in the War of the Rebellion.
Honorary: Bestowed by the Commandery-in-Chief and Commanderies under provisions of the Constitution and By-Laws.

The official publication of the Military Order of the Loyal Legion of the United States is the *Loyal Legion Historical Journal*.

Military Order of the Stars and Bars

P.O. Box 59
Columbia, TN 38401
Phone: (615) 380-1844

Founded in 1938, the Military Order of the Stars and Bars (MOSB) is affiliated with the Sons of Confederate Veterans. The organization is comprised of ancestors of commissioned Confederate officers and officials of the Confederate government.

Missouri Civil War Reenactors Association

P.O. Box 417
Fayette, MO 65248

The Missouri Civil War Reenactors Association (MCWRA) currently has over 1,400 members in numerous states. *The*

Western Campaigner is the official journal of the Missouri Civil War Reenactors Association and helps keep members abreast of current events, upcoming reenactments, and general organization news.

Membership: $8 per year (individual)
                $12 per year (family)

The Museum of the Confederacy

1201 East Clay St.
Richmond, VA 23219
Phone: (804) 649-1861
Fax: (804) 644-7150

The Museum of the Confederacy is a private, not-for-profit corporation. It maintains the nation's largest collection of Confederate artifacts and art; over 15,000 items, and owns the White House of the Confederacy (wartime home of Jefferson Davis). The museum also houses the Brockenbrough Library (20,000+ books).

Your support will help preserve the finest collection of Confederate artifacts and art in the world.

Membership benefits include:
— free, unlimited admission to the museum, White House of the Confederacy, and Brockenbrough Library.
— subscription to the museum's quarterly newsletter and calendar
— 10% discount at the museum store (The Haversack)
— 10% discount on purchases through the museum's gift catalog
— advance notice and reduced admission to Evening Series Lectures, travel, and other museum workshops
— personalized membership card and welcome packet

Membership: $20 (for individuals outside the Richmond metro area)

> *the nation's largest collection of Confederate artifacts and art; over 15,000 items*

The Nassau County Civil War Round Table

Excelsior Chapter
81 Broadmoor Lane
Westbury, NY 11590-4107

With an active membership exceeding 100, The Nassau County Civil War Round Table discussion group meets every third Wednesday of the month from September to June at Carle Place, NY High School, at 7:30 p.m. (call 516-334-1900 for directions). To join, contact them at the above address or attend one of their meetings.

Membership:	$12 per year (student)
	$25 per year (individual)
	$30 per year (family)

National Civil War Association

P.O. Box 70084
Sunnyvale, CA 94086
Phone: (408) 927-7651 (recording)
Email: info_request@ncwa.org
Internet: http://ncwa.org/

the NCWA maintains a Speaker's Bureau for schools and organization interested in presentations on the Civil War.

The National Civil War Association currently has a membership exceeding 1500. Participants are members of either the Union or Confederate battalions, of the Civilian Corps (for noncombatant ladies and gentlemen), or of the Cadet Corps, which has members ranging in age from 8 to 15 years old.

Union forces in the NCWA are represented by the 1st United States Sharpshooters, 2nd Massachusetts Cavalry, 3rd United States Artillery, 4th United States Colored Troops, 7th Michigan Cavalry, 14th Indiana Infantry, 69th New York Infantry, 71st Pennsylvania Infantry, 79th New York Infantry, and the United States Medical Service.

Confederate forces are represented by the 1st Company, Battalion of South Carolina Sharpshooters, 1st Virginia Cavalry, 1st Virginia Infantry, 5th Texas Infantry, 7th Virginia Infantry, 9th Virginia Cavalry, 14th Tennessee Infantry, James River Squadron, Norfolk Light Artillery Blues, Levi's Horse Artillery, and the 15th Alabama Regimental Hospital.

Aside from reenactments, the NCWA maintains a Speaker's Bureau for schools and organization interested in presentations on the Civil War. The NCWA estimates that its speakers address over 500 audiences each year, discussing a broad range of topics related to the Civil War period. Speakers include Union, Confederate, and Civilian aspects of the war.

Membership in the NCWA is open to anyone with an interest in Civil War reenacting. You needn't be a history expert or Civil War buff to fit in. Many join with little knowledge of the War, but, through the Association, they soon learn the ways of the soldier—and make some friends in the process.

Membership:	$35 (individual)
	$50 (family)

National Park Service
P.O. Box 37127
Washington, DC 20013-7127
Internet: http://www.cr.nps.gov

In an era of failed government programs and growing disillusion with government services, a few government "stars" still shine brightly. One such "star" is the National Park Service. Occupying highly visible and important positions at all National Battlefields and Military Parks, the knowledgeable Rangers of the National Park Service provide a valuable link to the past, guiding visitors on walks and talks which go a long way toward explaining the often confusing events of the Civil War. National Battlefields, Battlefield Parks, Historic Landmarks, Historic Sites, and Military Parks under the jurisdiction of the National Park Service include:

Fort Morgan National Historic Landmark
Pea Ridge National Military Park
Rock Creek Park
Chickamauga and Chattanooga NMP
Fort Pulaski National Monument
Kennesaw Mountain NBP
Fort Caroline National Memorial
Perryville National Historic Landmark
Fort Jackson National Historic Landmark
Fort St. Philip National Historic Landmark,
Port Hudson National Historic Landmark
Antietam NB and Cemetery
Monocacy National Battlefield
Brices Cross Road National Battlefield Site
Champion Hill National Historic Landmark
Corinth National Historic Landmark
Tupelo National Battlefield
Vicksburg National Military Park
Wilson's Creek National Battlefield
Pecos NHP (Glorieta Unit), New Mexico
Fort Fisher National Historic Landmark
Johnson's Island NH Landmark
Gettysburg National Military Park
Fort Sumter National Monument
Fort Donelson National Battlefield

Fort Pillow National Historic Landmark
Franklin National Historic Landmark
Shiloh National Military Park
Stones River National Battlefield
Appomattox Court House NHP
Balls Bluff National Historic Landmark
Cedar Creek and Belle Grove NH Landmark
Fredericksburg and Spotsylvania NMP
Manassas National Battlefield Park
Petersburg National Battlefield,
Richmond National Battlefield Park,
Sailor's Creek National Historic Landmark
Harpers Ferry National Historical Park

Living up to its role as one of the key battlefield preservation and interpretation organizations, the National Park Service initiated the American Battlefield Protection Program (a separate listing for the American Battlefield Protection Program, or ABPP, is available at the beginning of the *Organizations* section). The program "provides technical assistance and small amounts of partnership funding to national and state parks, state and local governments, and nonprofit groups working to save threatened battlefields on American soil." ABPP efforts are primarily focused on the fifty Civil War battlefields identified as high priorities by the Civil War Sites Advisory Commission (CWSAC). These fifty priority I sites were identified after and in-depth study of 384 battle sites. The *Battlefield Update* is the quarterly newsletter of the American Battlefield Protection Program.

In partnership with other organizations, the National Park Service is currently developing the Civil War Soldiers and Sailors System. This monumental effort will result in a number of important data bases, including the Names Index, a data base providing the names and basic information pulled from the 5.4 million soldiers' records at the National Archives.

The National Park Service has an outstanding web site for these who surf the Internet. This web site has links to museums, historic sites, parks, battlefields, and just about anything else related to the National Park Service. It's a fun site. Drop by, you'll like what you see.

One last note: Next time you're at a National Battlefield, Historic Site, or other National Park Service site and you like what you see, be sure to tell the Rangers what a great job they're doing. Most of them really enjoy what they do, but alas, they *do* work for the well-intentioned, though often unappreciative Federal government. A word of praise, or better yet, a letter of thanks to the Park Director will go a long way towards maintaining the enthusiasm and energy of these valuable public servants.

National Trust for Historic Preservation

1785 Massachusetts Avenue, N.W.
Washington, D.C. 20036
Phone: (202) 673-4000
Fax: (202) 673-4038
TTY: (202) 673-4200
Membership: 1-800-944-6847
Internet: http://www.nthp.org

Chartered in 1949, the National Trust for Historic Preservation is the leader of the national preservation movement. Dedicated to the preservation of historic sites in general, not just Civil War sites, the Trust still plays a pivotal role in Civil War battlefield and historic site preservation. With more than 250,000 members nationwide and seven regional offices, the Trust is committed to saving America's diverse historic environments. Through thousands of local community groups in all 50 states, the Trust pursues its mission by providing technical advice and financial assistance, sponsoring educational programs and workshops, publishing a number of periodicals, and through the operation of 18 historic house museums owned and operated by the organization.

National Trust members receive a number of benefits, such as a subscription to *Historic Preservation*, the Trust's monthly magazine, free admission to most National Trust properties, a members-only discount on books from the Preservation Press, discounts at most museum shops and on special services, including educational tours of historic places.

Membership: $20 (individual)
  $24 (family)

With more than 250,000 members nationwide and seven regional offices, the Trust is committed to saving America's diverse historic environments.

National Woman's Relief Corps
Auxiliary to the Grand Army of the Republic, Inc.
629 South Seventh Street
Springfield, IL 62703

Organized on July 25 and 26, 1883 in Denver, Colorado and incorporated by Act of the 87th Congress, September 7, 1962, the National Woman's Relief Corps is dedicated to perpetuating the memory of the Grand Army of the Republic. Endeavoring to teach patriotism and duties of citizenship, the true history of our country, and love and honor of our flag, the organization has supported or participates in a number of active programs, including: scholarships, patriotic education (wide distribution of flags, American Creed Cards, etc.), Americanization, Drug prevention and education, child welfare, Red Cross, hospital volunteer service, memorials, national defense, legislation, Junior Corps, Etiquette of the Flag, and National Holiday observances. In the past, the organization spent millions of dollars on these programs and providing relief to Union Veterans of the Civil War and their dependents, Memorial Day in the South, Civil War Army Nurses, Soldiers Homes, and for veterans of other American wars.

The Grand Army of the Republic Memorial Museum was established by and is co-located with the National Woman's Relief Corps. See listing under *Places of Interest*.

The Nevada Civil War Volunteers
P.O. Box 11033
Reno, NV 89510

The Nevada Civil War Volunteers (NCWV) was established to promote the study of the War between the States and works toward educating the general public through a number of programs. Members participate in encampments, school presentations, parades, holiday balls, and other Civil War living history demonstrations. The NCWV portrays the following groups:

Union:
12th Wisconsin Volunteer Infantry Regt.
Artillery with a Mountain Howitzer
Field Hospital and surgery

Confederate:
Sussex Light Dragoons
Norfolk Light Artillery with a 3-inch Parrott Rifled Cannon
1st Tennessee

Civilian:
Ladies Auxiliary
Alert Club (the childrens' group)

One interesting program offered by the NCWV is called "Soldier For An Hour," whereby non-reenactors can get a taste of reenacting by drilling in the infantry and artillery for a fee of $5.00. This program includes mustering in and out papers and a free "medical exam" from the surgeon.

Monthly meetings are held the first Thursday of the month at 7:30. Membership includes a subscription to "The Sentinel," the organization's monthly newsletter.

Membership: $15 per year (individual)
                        $25 per year (family)

The North-South Skirmish Association, Inc.

These guys just might be having too much fun.

501 N. Dixie Drive
Vandalia, OH 45377

The North-South Skirmish Association was founded in 1950, and they've been having fun ever since. Dedicated to preserving the marksmanship traditions of the Civil War, the organization sponsors skirmish shooting competitions using ammunition in original or certified reproduction firearms of the Civil War period. Essentially, uniformed Confederate and Union teams compete in timed, rapid-fire events. Targets are typically placed at 50 and 100 yards and consist of breakable items such as clay pigeons, ceramic tiles, and water-filled cans.

Lowest total time wins. Team carbine and artillery matches are also sponsored, as are individual matches using revolvers and magazine fed shoulder arms like the Henrys and Spencers. Members and their families also compete for trophies in Civil War dress competitions

The Association's home range is Fort Shenandoah, located on several hundred acres in the lower Shenandoah Valley, near Winchester, Virginia. Facilities include a rifle fire range, separate revolver range, and private camping.

The Northumberland County Historical Society

1150 North Front Street
Sunbury, PA 17801-1126
Phone: (717) 286-4083

The Northumberland County Historical Society administers the Hunter House/Fort Augusta Museum, which has an exhibit of uniform and drum belonging to John Bolton Young, plus changing exhibits pertaining to the Civil War period. The Society also administers the Charlotte Darrah Walter Genealogical and Historical Library, which contains local, county and some state material pertaining to those who served in the Civil War.

Ohio Civil War Association

106 Haig Street
Celina, OH 45822
Phone: (419) 586-5294
Fax: (419) 586-6763

Sponsoring special events, including an annual Civil War Conference, the Ohio Civil War Association has members (Civil War Round Tables and other organizations) throughout Ohio and other states.

Point Lookout POW Organization

3587 Windmill Drive
Virginia Beach, VA 23456-2122

The Point Lookout POW Organization (PLPOW) was organized in 1991 to pay homage to Confederate ancestors, military/civilian, men/women, black/white,

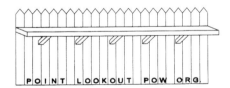

who were prisoners of war at Point Lookout, Maryland, from 1863 to 1865. The organization has members from 31 states and is still growing. A memorial service is held once a year on the prison grounds and the organization offers other programs throughout the year on Point Lookout and its POWs.

Membership includes six newsletters a year, discounts on Civil War books from special distributors, the opportunity to become a POW reenactor, and offers to purchase POW medals, pins, bumper stickers, T-shirts, POW dog-tags, and dice. For membership information, send a long self-addressed stamped envelope to the above address.

Membership: $20 per year

Reenactors of the American Civil War (RACW)

P.O. Box 1248
Magalia, CA 95954

The Reenactors of the American Civil War (RACW) was established in 1994. It currently organizes Civil War reenactments and encampments in Northern California, from Sacramento to the Oregon border. The organization is highly active in civic functions, parades, schools, and other public events.

Society for the Historical Preservation of the 26th Regiment NC Troops, Inc.

2139 Buffalo Shoals Road
Catawba, NC 28609
Phone: (704) 241-4483
Fax: (704) 327-3643
Email: SEACO@aol.com

The Society for the Historical Preservation of the 26th Regiment NC Troops is dedicated to perpetuating the history of the gallant 26th. At Gettysburg, the 26th North Carolina sustained more casualties than any other regiment, North or South, would sustain during the entire war. To this end, the Society sponsors the 26th Regiment NC Troops Reactivated (with over 275 members). Research into, and publication of manuscripts relating to North Carolina's role in the war is also of high interest and is encouraged by the organization. The Society collects and maintains various holdings of original manuscripts and photographic materials from North Carolina soldiers.

Perhaps most noteworthy is the Society's sponsorship of the North Carolina Confederate Burial Locator Project, whereby the location of over 15,000 graves of Confederate soldiers and veterans buried in North Carolina have been identified and, in 1996 alone, 394 military headstones were erected for soldiers who had previously lain in unmarked graves.

The Society publishes a quarterly magazine-style journal of North Carolina Confederate history, entitled *Company Front*, and a monthly newsletter called *Rebel Boast*. A subscription to *Company Front* is free with Society membership; a subscription to both publications is free with membership in the 26th Regiment NC Troops Reactivated.

Society Membership: $24 per year
26th NC Reenactment Unit Membership:
                             $26 per year

Society of Port Republic Preservationists, Inc.

P.O. Box 82
Port Republic, VA 24471

Sponsoring and participating in special events at Port Republic, Virginia, the Society of Port Republic Preservationists, Inc., works to preserve and interpret the town's history, including the Battle of Port Republic.

Membership: $5 per year

Sons of Confederate Veterans (SCV)

P.O. Box 59
Columbia, TN 38402-0059
Phone: 1-800-MY-SOUTH
Phone: 1-800-MY-DIXIE
Internet: http://www.scv.org

The oldest hereditary organization for male descendants of Confederate soldiers, the Sons of Confederate Veterans (SCV) is the direct heir of the United Confederate Veterans. Founded in 1896, the organization continues its role as historical, patriotic, nonpolitical force dedicated to the preservation of the true history and motivations of the Southern Cause.

Membership is available to direct or collateral male descendants of any veteran who served honorably in the Confederate armed forces. Proof of kinship can be provided in the form of a service record or pension record. If you lack the appropriate documentation, the SCV will assist you in tracing your ancestor's Confederate service via a network of genealogists.

State organizations of the SCV, known as Divisions, offer a variety of activities for members, while local units, called camps, sponsor events that range from preservation work and reenactments to scholarly pursuits and publications. Divisions typically publish a newsletter for members. Members also receive the bimonthly national magazine *The Confederate Veteran*, an excellent magazine with in-depth articles on the War Between the States, as well as news affecting Southern heritage.

Sons of Sherman's March to the Sea (S.S.M.S.)

1725 Farmer Avenue
Tempe, AZ 85281

Founded by Stan Schirmacher, the grandson of General Sherman's drummer boy, the Sons of Sherman's March to the Sea is open not only to direct descendants of those who participated in the march, but to anyone who wishes to honor General Sherman. Membership is so inexpensive it's almost free and there are no meetings to attend. The organization touts

> *open not only to direct descendants of those who participated in the march, but to anyone who wishes to honor General Sherman*

itself as a "show and tell" (others) outfit. They also have "Sons of Sherman's March to the Sea" tie-clasps and patches for sale.

Ancestor's records info: send three stamps
Lifetime Membership: $3 (open to all)

Sons of Union Veterans of the Civil War (SUVCW)

1200 S. Monroe Street
Arlington, VA 22204-4219
Email: webmaster@suvcw.org
Internet: http://suvcw.org/

The Sons of Veterans was formed by the Grand Army of the Republic in 1881 with the intention of having the organization carry on the G.A.R.'s proud tradition and memory. Membership was open to legitimate ancestors of G.A.R. members, as well as ancestors of men eligible for G.A.R. membership. In 1925, the Sons of Veterans changed its name to Sons of Union Veterans of the Civil War (SUVCW) and is the legally recognized heir to the Grand Army of the Republic.

The organization has 19 departments (each consisting of one or more states), 152 camps, and nearly 4,400 members. The SUVCW publishes *The Banner*, a quarterly newsletter for members.

Membership Eligibility:

Prospective members must be male descendants, fourteen years of age or older, and blood relatives (whether through lineal or collateral line) of a soldier, sailor, marine, or Revenue Cutter Service member. The ancestor must have served honorably, or received an honorable discharge, during the War of the Rebellion of 1861-1865.

Associate membership is available to men without the proper hereditary qualifications. These men must subscribe to the principles and objectives of the SUVCW. Associates may vote and hold any office except that of Commander-in-Chief.

South Carolina Historical Society

100 Meeting Street
Charleston, SC 29401
Phone: (803) 723-3225
Fax: (803) 723-8584
Internet: http://www.historic.com/schs/

The South Carolina Historical Society is the state's oldest and largest historical organization. The Society is a private, nonprofit organization which receives no governmental support for its activities. The objective of the organization is to collect, preserve, and publish the history of the state. This mission includes the operation of the Society's research library, which counts in its holdings over a million pages of manuscript material, an extensive photographic collection, and numerous other research items.

The Society also publishes two quarterlies, *The South Carolina Historical Magazine*, and *Carologue*. *The South Carolina Historical Magazine* serves as the voice of the scholarly historical community in the state, while *Carologue* is a general interest magazine which highlights the history and culture of South Carolina. Recently, the Society published *Broken Fortunes*, the most complete listing of men who died in the service of the state during the Civil War. Use of the library and subscriptions to the magazines are among the many benefits of membership in the Society.

For information on the Society's holdings, see their listing under *Archives & Libraries*.

South Carolina Battleground Preservation Trust, Inc.

P.O. Box 12441
James Island, SC 29422
Phone: (803) 762-3563

The South Carolina Battleground Preservation Trust exists for the purpose of preserving and protecting battlegrounds and related historic military sites in South Carolina through easement or title deed; the main focus being Civil War sites. The Trust also sponsors Living History events at some sites for public education purposes.

Sites currently protected by the Trust include Confederate Battery #5 at Seaside Plantation on James Island, Confederate Battery Cheves on James Island, Union Marsh Battery "Swamp Angel" behind Morris Island, and Fort Palmetto, or Confederate Battery #7, in front of Coles Island at the Stono Inlet.

Sites where preservation efforts are in progress include Fort Lamar and the surrounding Secessionville peninsula earthworks, the Star Battery, or Fort #2, the Union two-gun Battery on Long Island, Confederate Battery #1 and the three quarters of a mile of earthworks on James Island, Redoubts #1, #2, and #3 of the "Old East Lines" on James Island, and the New River Lines Confederate Earthworks in Jasper County.

Donations to the Trust will be used for maintenance of these sites, such as seeding, mowing and planting, purchase of signs, flags, flag poles, interpretation drawings, and living history programs. All gifts to the Battleground Trust are tax deductible. Membership in the Trust's *Provisional Preservation Army* is available at different ranks.

Membership: $15 (Private)
              $25 (Corporal)
              $35 (Sergeant)
              $50 (Lieutenant)

Turner Ashby Society

810 West 30th Street
Richmond, VA 23225
Phone: (804) 232-3406

The Turner Ashby Society is, at this printing, a new organization seeking new members and fresh ideas. A literary, research, and service organization, the society plans to publish a quarterly newsletter and hold seminars in conjunction with another Civil War group. Membership rates were not available at this printing. Please contact the society for more information.

United Daughters of the Confederacy

328 North Boulevard
Richmond, VA 23220-4057
Phone: (804) 355-1636
Fax: (804) 353-1396
Email: hqudc@aol.com

The United Daughters of the Confederacy have a long, distinguished history perpetuating the memory of Confederate veterans, and veterans from all other U.S.

wars. They have consistently sought ways to honor the Confederate men and women who died during the War Between the States and are responsible for innumerable charitable services and memorial efforts. Among their accomplishments is the Confederate Monument at Arlington National Cemetery which is over thirty-two feet tall, bronze, and contains thirty-two life-size figures. The monument was unveiled on June 4, 1914.

Annually, the Daughters place wreaths at the statues of General Robert E. Lee (on January 19th) and President Jefferson Davis (June 3rd) in Statuary Hall, United States Capitol; at the Jefferson Davis Monument, Monument Avenue, Richmond, Virginia for the Annual Massing of the Flags (June 3rd); at the Tomb of the Unknown Soldier, Arlington National Cemetery on Veteran's Day (November 11); and at the Confederate Monument, Arlington National Cemetery, on Memorial Day.

On the local, state, and national level, United Daughters of the Confederacy work with numerous civic organizations including homeless shelters, homes for battered women and children, hospital associations and food banks.

Membership is available to women no less than sixteen years of age who are blood descendants, lineal or collateral, of men and women who served honorably in the Army, Navy, or Civil Service of the Confederate States of America, or who gave Material Aid to the Cause.

Ulysses S. Grant Association
Morris Library
Southern Illinois University
Carbondale, IL 62901
Phone: (618) 453-2773
Email: jsimon@lib.siu.edu

Formed in 1962, the Ulysses S. Grant Association has collected copies of more than 200,000 Grant documents, allowing researchers the opportunity to better understand the life and career of U.S. Grant based on documentary evidence. Twenty volumes of The Papers of Ulysses S. Grant have since been published and are available to members at a 25% discount. Most importantly, membership in the Ulysses S. Grant Association helps support the study of Grant and the turbulent period of U.S. history in which he lived.

Membership: $100 (lifetime membership)

the Ulysses S. Grant Association has collected copies of more than 200,000 Grant documents

The U.S. Grant Network
W3547 Playbird Road
Sheboygan Falls, WI 53085
Email: USGlady@Excel.net
Email: grantnet2@aol.com

Publishing a quarterly newsletter devoted to the life and accomplishments of U.S. Grant, the U.S. Grant Network invites Grant supporters to join and share their passion for this truly great American.

Membership: $10 per year

The United States Civil War Center

Louisiana State University
Baton Rouge, LA 70803
Phone: (504) 388-3151
Fax: (504) 388-4876
Email: madden@cwc.lsu.edu
Internet: http://www.cwc.lsu.edu

Editor's Choice SELECTION

Superb and Outstanding may be descriptive words, but they do little to reflect how impressed I am with the Civil War Center (CWC). The brainchild of novelist David Madden, the United States Civil War Center was established with two missions in mind; 1) to create a database that includes information on all private and institutional holdings of Civil War materials throughout the nation, and 2) to promote the study of the Civil War from the perspectives of all academic disciplines, professions, and occupations. But perhaps more importantly, the Center was established because no organization existed which addressed *all* Civil War interests.

My first introduction to the CWC was on the Internet. If you're one of the many who have already ventured into cyberspace, chances are you have already come across the Civil War Center. They offer a—here we go again—superb, outstanding, and incredibly important web page that links Internet surfers to over 1200 Civil War-related sites. No matter what your Civil War interest might be, your best shot at getting information is via the CWC web page. I love it (just in case you have any doubts).

While there are many fine institutions taking the War Between the States to the Internet, the Civil War Center is *the* major force in this push to cyberspace. For this, researchers, novelists (myself included), reenactors, teachers, armchair historians, and everyone else with an interest in the Civil War should be grateful. This is one group whose work *must* continue. It's simply too important to ignore. Visit their web site and I'm sure you'll agree. If you don't have a computer, buy one (okay, borrow one if you must).

Membership is available in a number of categories, including General Membership, Student Membership, Benefactors Circle, Founders Circle, or a large and growing selection of other Civil War Circles, depending on your occupation or interest (e.g. Photographer Circle, Artist Circle, Writer Circle, Historian Circle, Physician Circle, etc.). Remember, one of the Center's missions is to explore the Civil War from the perspective of *all* disciplines, professions, and occupations.

Membership: $25 per year (General)
                $50+ per year (Circles)

The Internet address to remember
http://www.cwc.lsu.edu

Photo Courtesy of the U.S. Civil War Center

Virginia Historical Society
428 N. Boulevard
Mail:
P.O. Box 7311
Richmond, VA 23221-0311
Phone: (804) 358-4901
Fax: (804) 355-2399

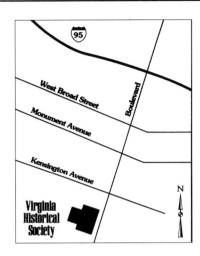

Founded in 1831, The Virginia Historical Society (VHS) is the oldest continuously operating cultural institution in the Commonwealth of Virginia. The Society owns and maintains the Museum of Virginia History, located at The Center for Virginia History, a neoclassical building often referred to as Battle Abbey. The museum offers seven museum galleries exhibiting rare Virginia treasures, including dramatic Civil War murals and a renowned collection of Confederate-made weapons (see *Places of Interest* for more information).

Long renowned for its research facilities, finding aids, and resources, the Society now serves the entire state with its Library of Virginia History. Other facilities include a paper conservation lab, an expanded and improved reading room, a 300-seat lecture hall, an education department, and climate controlled storage for the entire VHS collection (see *Archives & Libraries* for more information).

The Society sponsors a number of exhibits, events, lectures, conferences, and workshops throughout the year. With an emphasis on education, the subjects of these events range from Pocahontas to Virginia in the 1950s, with a variety that will appeal to just about everyone.

Members receive invitations to special openings and events, a 10% discount on purchases at the museum store, and free admission to all the galleries, the library, and the Virginia House in Windsor Farms. Also included with membership is a free subscription to the Society's renowned *Virginia Magazine of History and Biography*, now in its 103rd year of publication.

> *a renowned collection of Confederate-made weapons*

West Virginia Reenactors Association, Inc.
P.O. Box 2133
Buckhannon, WV 26201
Phone: (304) 472-5964

Dedicated to the commemoration and preservation of West Virginia's rich Civil War heritage. The WVRA is a family oriented, civic-minded organization over a 100 strong, which takes reenactment not just to the battlefield, but to schools, clubs, parades, and ceremonies.

Members portray their choice of *Infantry*: 1st West Virginia, Company A (USA), 25th Virginia, Company A (CSA); *Artillery*: 1st West Virginia Light (USA), Danville Light

(CSA); *Mounted Cavalry*: 7th West Virginia, Company H (USA), 11th Virginia, Company F (CSA); and/or Trans-Allegheny Soldiers Aid Society (CSA/USA)

The WVRA sponsors such events as "School of the Soldier," "Cheat Summit Living History, the Battle of Droop Mountain, the Battle of Rich Mountain, and the Spring Gala Ball (dance). The organization sanctions events such as Carnifex Ferry and Olgebay and attends-in-force such events as New Market, Sailor's Creek, and Gettysburg. Write or call for additional information.

EVERYTHING

Know of an organization, company, or place of interest that should *be in* Everything Civil War, *but isn't?*

Please, let us know.
Even though we sent out over 1000 requests for information, it's almost inevitable that we missed some companies and groups.

Please note that it is our policy to exclude companies and organizations which do not respond to our request for information. This is done in the interest of our readers, saving them time and frustration they might otherwise spend attempting to contact organizations which have ceased to exist.

Individual reenactment groups are not included in this book because information on such groups tends to change frequently. We do, however, list reenactment associations (umbrella organizations with multiple reenactment groups under them), such as the ACWA, NCWA, RACW, and others.

The next edition of *Everything Civil War* is planned for 1998.

Contact: Willow Creek Press of Washington at P.O. Box 3730, Silverdale, WA 98383-3730

Archives & Libraries

A state by state listing of Civil War resources

Note: Before sending search requests or fees to archives and libraries, contact them to determine the proper procedure for such requests. Most archives and libraries have special forms that must be used for search requests. Also, these forms will identify any special instructions regarding searches.

National Sources

Library of Congress

101 Independence Avenue, S.E.
Washington, DC 20540
Phone: (202) 707-9779
Internet: http://www.loc.gov

Hours: Mon, Wed, Thurs, 8:30am - 9:30pm
Tue, Fri, Sat, 8:30am - 5pm
These hours are for the Main Reading Room in the Jefferson Building. Other reading room times vary.

Located in the Jefferson Building, Madison Building, and Adams Building along Independence Avenue, SE, the Library of Congress maintains an extensive collection of Civil War documents, books, photographs, and other related items. Of particular interest is the Brady photographic collection now available through the Internet. The Library has made over 1,100 photographs available on line. A search engine quickly sorts through the collection for those looking for a particular personality or battlefield.

The Library of Congress holdings are too vast to list in detail, however, you'll want to explore the Jedediah Hotchkiss Collection. This 27,000-item collection (in the Manuscripts Division) includes diaries and letters from the Civil War, and business papers, research files, writings, lectures, and other material dating from after the Civil War.

Nice Web site.

National Archives and Records Administration

Washington, DC 20408
Phone: (202) 501-5400
and/or

National Archives and Records Administration

8601 Adelphi Road
College Park, MD 20740-6001
Phone: (301) 713-6800
Fax: (301) 713-6920
Fax-on-demand: (301) 713-6905
Internet: gopher://gopher.nara.gov
         http://www.nara.gov

Hours: Mon and Wed, 8:45am - 5pm
        Tues, Thurs, and Fri, 8:45am - 9pm
        Sat, 8:45am - 4:45pm

Anyone serious about Civil War research will sooner or later find themselves within the realm of the National Archives (NA). Those simply researching an ancestor will probably experience the Archives by mail only, while those pursuing more serious studies will likely find themselves in the research rooms of this valuable national treasure. Either way, the National Archives is one of the premier sources of Civil War information available. If you feel your research calls for a visit to the NA in Washington, D.C., check with your state archives first. Many have copies of the primary Civil War records held at the NA, especially those records relating to their state.

If you're researching an ancestor who fought in the Civil War you can request a copy of the veteran's service record or pension record by providing a minimal amount of information (name, branch, state, and Union or Confederate status). This information must be requested using NATF Form 80. If both service record and pension record is needed, a separate NATF Form 80 must be used for each. When the NA receives your NATF Form 80, a search for the requested record will be conducted. The NA will notify you of the success or failure of this search. If successful, the NA will request a $10 copy fee for the record, payable to the National Archives Trust Fund. There is no fee when a search fails.

For those interested in more detailed research, the NA offers a number of valuable reference books and pamphlets that will guide the experienced, as well as the inexperienced researcher. The three primary reference books—and most valuable—used by seasoned researchers are: *The Union, A Guide to Federal Archives Relating to the Civil War; The Confederacy, A Guide to the Archives of the Confederate States of America;* and *A Guide to Civil War Maps in the National Archives.* These books, along with a wide assortment of pamphlets, can be purchased from the National Archives at reasonable prices.

When planning a research trip to the NA, it's a good idea to write or phone before going to insure the type of records you're looking for are available. National Archives staffers can direct you to the right facility, helping you to avoid the frustration and wasted time of showing up at the wrong research room. Before using archival records, all researchers must obtain a researcher identification card. This will require picture identification, such as a driver's license, school card, or passport. Researcher status is available to anyone at least 16 years old. Persons under 16 may apply for special permission to use NA records as long as they are supervised by an adult researcher.

Although it is possible to register for research cards and use records in the evening and on Saturday, the records must usually be ordered before 3:00 P.M., Monday through Friday. Records ordered after 3:00 P.M. are retrieved the morning of the next business day and should be ready for use by mid-morning. Records are usually brought to the research room 1 hour after the scheduled pull time.

If you have a fax machine, several publications are available through the National Archives Fax-on-Demand System (301-713-6905). You must call from a fax machine to use this service. The NA charges no fee for Fax-on-Demand usage, though you may incur long-distance telephone charges. The NA also publishes the *Select List of Publications of the National Archives and Records Administration*, General Information Leaflet Number 3, which provides a list of finding aids which will help in your research. Civil War-related lists in this leaflet include Record Group (RG) 109 War Department Collection of Confederate Records; RG 110 Provost Marshal General's Bureau (Civil War); and RG 94 Adjutant General's Office, 1780's - 1917. These are some of the more blatant Civil War record groups. You'll also find record groups for the military academies, the Office of Naval Records and Library, Headquarters of the Army, and records from other agency that may offer insights into the Civil War.

Even if you're not planning a trip to the National Archives, I recommend reading an excellent series written by Michael P. Musick, a seasoned archivist at the NA. This extremely well-written three-part series was published in the summer, fall, and winter 1995 editions of the National Archives' quarterly magazine, . In this series, Mr. Musick shares his vast knowledge of Civil War records, knowledge gained over several decades of living and working with these historic documents. Mr. Musick has been described as *the* Civil War buff at the NA. Whether this is true or not, we can all learn from these three golden nuggets he has chosen to share with us.

Special thanks to Michael P. Musick for providing this information—and for his dedication to sharing the secrets of the National Archives.

National Park Service
P.O. Box 37127
Washington, D.C. 20013-7127
Internet: http://www.cr.nps.gov

A rich resource for Civil War researchers lies scattered throughout 300 parks and historic sites tended by the National Park Service. Covering all eras and aspects of America, from Native Americans and Colonialism to natural wonders, these parks contain over 28 million museum objects and specimen, and 14,000 linear feet of archives.

The National Park Service's excellent web site lists a sample of these artifacts, including John Wilkes Booth's derringer (Ford's Theatre National Historic Site), Lee's mess kit and field desk (Arlington House, The Robert E. Lee Memorial), Abraham Lincoln's saddle cover used at Gettysburg at the time of his Gettysburg Address (Gettysburg National Military Park), U.S. Garrison flag present during the opening shots of the Civil War (Fort Sumter National Monument), and George Armstrong Custer's Civil War Journal (Little Bighorn Battlefield National Monument). The National Park Service is filled with dedicated and knowledgeable historians (usually disguised as Park Rangers) who are eager to help you chart your course along the intertwined roads of history.

For more information on the National Park Service, see their listing in the *Organizations* section of this book.

State Sources

Alabama

State of Alabama Department of Archives and History

624 Washington Avenue
Montgomery, AL 36130-0100
Mail:
P.O. Box 300100
Phone: (334) 242-4435 (Reference Room)
Phone: (334) 242-4363 (Public Services)
Fax: (334) 240-3433

Hours: Tuesday - Friday, 8am - 5pm
          Saturday, 9am - 5pm

Since its founding in 1901, the Department of Archives and History has collected materials relating to Alabama's involvement in the Civil War. Holdings include manuscripts, photographs, maps, uniforms, weapons, and period flags. Virtually every facet of the Civil War as it relates to Alabama is represented in the department's extensive collection of Civil War material.

Arkansas

Arkansas History Commission

One Capitol Mall
Little Rock, AR 72201
Phone: (501) 682-6900

Hours: Monday - Saturday, 8am - 4:30pm

Civil War records available at the Arkansas History Commission on microfilm include:

Confederate

Index to compiled service records of Confederate soldiers who served in organizations from Arkansas
Index to Arkansas Confederate service records (Herndon's)
Confederate pension records, Arkansas
Ex-Confederate pension records, State Auditor's warrant books, AK

Unfiled papers of Confederate soldiers, all states
Index to Confederate soldiers in units raised directly by the Confederate Government
Service records of Confederate General & Staff Officers, etc
Confederate casualty lists & narrative battle reports, 1861-1865
Ex-Confederate amnesty papers, Arkansas
Confederate service records, Arkansas
History of Arkansas Confederate units
Confederate pension book index, Arkansas
Confederate miscellaneous pension records, Arkansas
1911 questionnaires, Confederate veterans
Consolidated index to compiled service records of Confederate soldiers
Inmates in the Arkansas Confederate Home

Service records: Confederate soldiers who raised directly by the Confederate Government
Records of Confederate Naval & Marine personnel, all states

Union
Index to compiled service records of volunteer Union soldiers who served in organizations from Arkansas
Index to U.S. Civil War pension records, Arkansas
Letters received by Sec. of Navy from squadron commanders, 1841-86, Mississippi Squadron, 1861-1865
History of Arkansas Union Civil War units 1-4th Cavalry & 1-4th Infantry (also Alabama & Arizona units)
Union service records, Arkansas
Index to Arkansas Union service records (Herndon's)
General index to U.S. military pensions, 1861-1934
Index to Black Civil War soldiers, U.S.C.T.
Service records of U.S. Colored Troops, Arkansas
1890 Special census schedules, Civil War Union veterans & their widows: Kentucky - Wyoming

The Arkansas History Commission also has more than 400 manuscript collections which include private and business papers of individuals, and records of religious, educational, business, patriotic, social, and civic organizations. The collection also includes state and federal papers, and the papers of Arkansas' governors.

The newspaper collection includes files of about 2500 titles published throughout Arkansas from 1819 to the present. In addition to papers featuring state and local news, there are also religious, professional, and special interest publications. The newspaper catalog lists publications by city, county and title for easy reference.

Other material available at the Arkansas History Commission includes extensive collections of photographs, county records, census records, military records, maps, church and cemetery records, and a collection of books and pamphlets.

Connecticut

Connecticut State Library
History and Genealogy Unit
231 Capitol Ave.
Hartford, CT 06106
Phone: (203) 566-3690 or 3692

Hours: Monday - Friday 9:30 am - 5 pm

The Connecticut State Library has extensive holdings of Civil War material. The major record groups (RG) relating to the Civil War era are listed here.

RG 2   *Records of the General Assembly.*
General Assembly papers and rejected bills for the years following the Civil War, including petitions and special acts relating to soldiers, sailors, and their families.

RG 5   *Records of the Governor.*
RG 5:9 includes applications for admission to military hospitals, 1873-1882, and miscellaneous Civil War papers, 1861-65.

RG 8   *Records of the Comptroller*
RG 8:67 contains material pertaining to Paymaster and Quartermaster Accounts, 1861-65. This is a miscellaneous collection of papers pertaining to the accounts for pay, expenses, supplies and equipment of Civil War military operations. Includes bank books, vouchers, pay rolls, inventories, clothing returns and correspondence.

RG 8:72 contains Records of Payments to Civil War Soldiers and Families, 1861-66. This is a two-volume compilation, arranged by town, of returns and payments from August, 1861 to August, 1866. The volumes contain the name of each serviceman, name of the wife, names and ages of children, regiment and company, rank, date of muster, terms of enlistment, changes in service, and payments made.

A list of dates on which various Connecticut regiments were mustered out appears at the beginning of volume two.

RG 12   *Records of the State Library*
Includes the records of the War Records Department. Item 9 contains lists, compiled from various sources, of Connecticut men and women who served in the Civil War. Item 44 includes some original discharge papers of Civil War soldiers admitted to Fitch's Home for the Soldiers (predecessor of the Veterans' Home and Hospital).

RG 13   *Records of the Military Department*
Military units in Connecticut came under the jurisdiction of the Adjutant General. During the war, that office was the central receiving point for information regarding enlistments, commissions, promotions, discharges, resignations, transfers of servicemen, operations, engagements, casualties of units, general orders, courts martial, pay, recruiting, bounties, pensions, deaths and wounds, substitutes, and several soldiers homes.

RG 69   *Manuscript Collection*
Manuscripts are available through the Manuscripts and Archives Catalog in the History Reading Room. For letters, journals, diaries, etc., relating to the Civil War, check the Manuscripts and Archives Catalog under the subject headings:
CONNECTICUT–HISTORY–CIVIL WAR
US HISTORY–CIVIL WAR
RG 69 also includes a number of manuscript collections not classified as "Catalogued Manuscripts."

RG 72   *Vital Records*
Item 4 within this record group is a list of veterans buried in Connecticut, ca. 1640–1934. The list contains the name, company, regiment, date of death, and age of each veteran.

RG 113   *Records of the Grand Army of the Republic, Connecticut Department.* Box 10 includes a list of members, obituary rolls, and a roster of Civil War veterans buried in Willimantic Cemetery.

RG 114   *Griffin A. Stedman, camp 6, Sons of Union Veterans of the Civil War. Connecticut Division, 1892-1936.*

RG 119   *The Army and Navy Club of Connecticut, 1892-1936.*
Formed Nov. 27, 1879, this club appears to have been limited to Civil War veterans. Records include biographical sketches, lists of members, obituary notices, etc.

Photograph Collections include:

PG 80   *Civil War Collection*
Includes 450 photos, prints, and glass negatives.

PG 85   *Brady Collection of Civil War Photographs, 1861-65*
        Includes about 7,500 photos and 134 lantern slides by Civil War photographer Matthew Brady.

PG 385   *Godard Collection*
        Includes Civil War lantern slides.

PG 570   *Connecticut Military Portraits, ca. 1860–1945*
        Includes individual and group portraits of Civil War soldiers and veterans of the Connecticut Volunteer Infantry.

PG 850   *Cartes de Visite, 1860–1885*
        Includes individual portraits of Civil War officers, group portraits of Civil War soldiers, and other Civil War portraits.

PG 860   *Daguerreotypes, Tintypes and Ambrotypes, ca. 1850–1882*
        Includes some portraits of Civil War soldiers.

The Connecticut State Library also has a substantial collection of Civil War reference books, regimental histories, prison data, and newspapers.

Special thanks to Richard C. Roberts, Unit Head, Connecticut State Library History and Genealogy Unit. This data was extracted from an excellent pamphlet prepared by Mr. Roberts.

Harriet Beecher Stowe Center
77 Forest Street
Hartford, CT 06105
Phone: (860) 522-9258
Fax: (860) 522-9259

Hours: By appointment

The Katharine S. Day House at the Harriet Beecher Stowe Center contains the Stowe-Day Library. This research library features a collection of 250,000 manuscripts and a photograph collection ranging from daguerreotypes to modern prints. The library's collection isn't specific to the Civil War, centering instead upon family history, social reform, women's studies, and the architecture and decorative arts of the 19th century. Researchers are welcome by appointment.

Delaware

Delaware Public Archives
Hall of Records
Dover, DE 19901
Phone: (302) 736-5318

The Delaware Public Archives is in the process of developing a publication which describes their Civil War holdings. I received a rough draft of this publication from the Delaware Public Archives and can tell you that it promises to be a thorough and informative publication. The following is a general overview of the sections contained in the 23-page Delaware Public Archives publication (minus the detailed descriptions you'll find in the original).

- Published "War of the Rebellion" records, Series I-IV

- Adjutant General Files

general, undated, 1861 (11 folders)
general, 1862 (13 folders)
enrollment books, 1862 (2 folders)
general, 1863 (2 boxes, 20 folders)
general, 1864 (18 folders)
Quartermaster reports, 1864
(7 folders)
general, 1865 (14 folders)
Quartermaster reports, 1865
(9 folders)
Muster-in rolls (3 boxes,
249 folders)
Miscellaneous rolls (72 folders)
Morning reports and Monthly
Returns (101 folders)
Muster-out rolls (6 boxes,
406 folders)
Miscellaneous oversized
(10 folders)
Papers of James E. Bailey
(7 folders)

- Civil War Records: Volumes
Service Records (16 volumes), including
1st Delaware, reorganized
1st Delaware Cavalry and Artillery
(Nield's Independent)
1st Delaware Cavalry
1st Delaware Cavalry, 3-months
service (volume blank)
1st Delaware Infantry
2nd Delaware Infantry
3rd Delaware Infantry, vols 1 and 2
4th Delaware Infantry, vols 1 and 2
5th Delaware Infantry, vols 1 and 2
6th Delaware Infantry, vols 1 and 2
1st Delaware Artillery
2nd Delaware Artillery

Clothing Books (14 volumes) including
1st Delaware Cavalry, Companies
B, D, E, and G
1st, 3rd, 4th, and 9th Delaware
Infantry (various companies)

Other Volumes (6 volumes)
Military Service Records Index
Adjutant General Card Index
Microfilm
Small Manuscripts
General Reference
(Roll of missing men #1, Delaware
Regiments, etc.)
Executive Papers
Reference Reels
(Such as *R31 - Pocket diary of Gen.
James Wilson*, or *R52 - Captain
Thomas Reynolds letters, 1862-1864.*)

Photographs
For example, Box 4 offers the following:

folder 5: Gen. Alfred T.A. Torbert, U.S.A.
folder 6: Cap't Townsend
folder 8: Sgt. Walsh
folder 10: Maj. Gen. James H. Wilson, Commanding Cavalry Corps, Military Division of the Mississippi, April 2, 1865.

Scrapbook
Contains newspaper and magazine clippings from 1863-65.

Other

Pamphlets
Newspaper Clippings
Prints and Engravings
Delaware Civil War Centennial
Commission
Direct Tax Refund Records (10
boxes) These are individual
claims for refunds of 1861 federal
taxes.
Books (located in the Research
Room) Such as Munden's *Guide
to Federal Archives Relating to the*

Civil War; Official Dispatches and Letters of Rear admiral DuPont, U.S.N. 1846-1848, and 1861-1863; Robertson's *The Civil War; The Campaign of 1864 in the Valley of Virginia and the Expedition to Lynchburg; History of Delaware, 1609-1888; Delaware in the Civil War;* and *History of the First Regiment Delaware Volunteers.*

Historical Society of Delaware Library

505 Market Street
Wilmington, DE 19801
Phone: (302) 655-7161

Hours: Monday, 1pm - 9pm
         Tuesday - Friday, 9am - 5pm

Collections include regimental records, diaries, correspondence, documents, photographs, maps, newspapers, and books from and about the Civil War era in Delaware. Holdings include the complete War of the Rebellion series. The Library also has rich genealogical holdings.

The Library staff will answer simple questions without charge by mail or telephone. For more extensive historical or genealogical research, staff will do an hour of research in the Library's collections for $20.00, prepaid. A publication, "Civil War Resources at the Historical Society of Delaware," is available for $4.00, postpaid.

Florida

Florida State Archives

Chief, Bureau of Archives and Records Management
R.A. Gray Building
500 South Bronough Street
Tallahassee, FL 32399-0250
Phone: (904) 487-2073

Hours: Monday - Friday, 8am - 5pm
         Saturday, 9am - 3pm

Located on the first floor of the R.A. Gray Building, the Florida State Archives houses 30,000 cubic feet of records documenting the activities of Florida's Territorial and State Government from 1821 to the present. The Archives also holds a small collection of local government records, a manuscript collection (records of individuals and organizations that have shaped and influenced the state), a photographic collection of 750,000 visual artifacts, and a genealogical collection that consists of an 8,000 volume library of source books (everything from family histories and cemetery records to genealogy journals and reference books).

Though it was a newer state with a relatively small population during the Civil War, Florida, once called the "Smallest Tadpole in the Dirty Pool of Secession," mustered over 15,000 troops for Confederate service, along with several thousand who chose to fight for the Union. Specific Civil War holdings at the State Archives include Confederate and Union Service Records and Pension Records, State records from the Civil War period, and significant manuscript collections of individuals and organizations, such as the J.T. Bernard Papers (he served on General Robert E. Lee's staff) and the organizational record book of the United Confederate Veterans, Florida Division.

Museum of Southern History

4304 Herschel Street
Jacksonville, FL 32210
Phone: (904) 388-3574

The Museum of Southern History offers a 3000-volume research library which includes genealogical research assistance free of charge. Contact them for additional information.

Hours: Tuesday - Saturday, 10am - 5pm

Georgia

Department of Archives and History

330 Capitol Ave., S.E.
Atlanta, GA 30334
Phone: (404) 656-2393

Hours: Monday - Friday, 8am - 4:15pm
          Saturday, 9:30am - 3:15pm

Charlotte Ray, Senior Archivist at the Georgia Department of Archives and History, has put together an informative pamphlet titled *Civil War Sources*, which identifies all Civil War holdings at the department. For starters, copies of the following National Archives microfilm publications are available for use by researchers:

1) Compiled Service Records of Confederate Soldiers in Organizations from the State of Georgia.
2) Compiled Service Records of Confederate Soldiers Who Served in Organizations Raised Directly by the Confederate Government.
3) Compiled Service Records of Confederate General and Staff Officers and Nonregimental Enlisted Men.
4) Combined Index (alphabetical listing of soldiers in 2 & 3 above).
5) Compiled Service Records of Union Soldiers in Organizations from the State of Georgia.
6) Confederate Marine and Naval Personnel.
7) Reference File Relating to Confederate Medical Officers.

Other records available at the Georgia Department of Archives and History include Confederate Pension Records; Records of the Governor and the Adjutant and Inspector General; Georgia Soldier Roster Commission; Confederate Soldiers' Home of Georgia Records; County Records (Superior Court minutes, tax digests, etc.); Nongovernmental Records (Civil War-related letters, diaries, memoirs, private collections); Cemetery Records; Photograph Collections; Newspapers, and books.

Book collections include the 19 volume *Confederate Military History Extended Edition*, *Units of the Confederate States Army*, *Military Bibliography of the Civil War* (4 volumes), *Official Records of the Union and Confederate Navies in the War of the Rebellion* (30 volumes), *The Official Atlas of the Civil War*, and *The War of the Rebellion: A Compilation of the Official Records of the Union and Confederate Armies* (128 volumes). The archives also holds copies of *Civil War Times Illustrated*, 1962 to date; *United Daughters of the Confederacy Magazine*, 1944 to date; *Confederate Veteran Magazine*, 1893-1932; and *Civil War History*, 1955 to date.

The pamphlet compiled by Charlotte Ray goes into much more detail and lists other holdings not mentioned here. Guidelines for requesting information are also provided, including copies of the information request form.

Georgia Historical Society Library

501 Whitaker Street
Savannah, GA 31499
Phone: (912) 651-2125
Phone: (912) 651-2128

Hours: Tuesday - Friday, 10am - 5pm
         Saturday, 9am - 3pm

The core of the collection housed at the Georgia Historical Society Library consists of manuscripts from the 18th, 19th, and 20th centuries, including family papers, colonial account books, diaries, papers of local military units, plantation records, papers of social and cultural organizations, and records of businesses such as the Central of Georgia Railway.

The extensive Civil War holdings include diaries, letters, photographs, artifacts, Confederate imprints, newspapers, and monographs. The primary sources include, but are not limited to, the Lafayette McLaws Collection, Confederate States Army Records (muster and pay records, unpublished after-action reports), and the Helen Dortch Longstreet Collection.

Illinois

Illinois State Archives Division

Archives Building
Capitol Complex
Springfield, IL 62756
Phone: (217) 782-4682

Indiana

Indiana Historical Society

315 W. Ohio Street
Indianapolis, IN 46202
Phone: (317) 232-1882
Fax: (317) 233-3109
Internet: http://www.ihs1830.org/

Hours: Mon - Fri, 8:30am - 4pm

Located on the third floor of the Indiana State Library and Historical Building, the Indiana Historical Society has worked to collect, preserve, research, and interpret the history and heritage of Indiana since 1830.

Indiana State Library

William Henry Smith Memorial Library
140 North Senate Drive
Indianapolis, IN 46204
Phone: (317) 232-3689

Iowa

State Historical Society of Iowa

600 East Locust
Capitol Complex
Des Moines, IA 50319
Phone: (515) 281-6200
and/or
402 Iowa Avenue
Iowa City, IA 52240
Phone: (319) 335-3916

Hours: Tuesday - Saturday, 9am - 4:30pm (archives, photograph, and manuscript collections closed Saturdays, unless arrangements are made in advance.)

The Library/Archives Bureau of the State Historical Society of Iowa houses an extensive collection of Iowa-related research material. Their holdings include a state archives collection, a census collection, a book and periodical collection, a newspaper collection, a manuscript collection, a photograph collection, a microfilm collection, a microfiche collection, a map collection, a reference collection, and various genealogical sources.

Resources specific to the Civil War include *Grand Army of the Republic (GAR) Post Minutes and Roster Books*, which contains minutes of post activities and rosters of members; *Persons Subject to Military Duty*, a listing by county and township of all men eligible for military service (series dates from 1861 to 1916); *Clothing Books*, which lists equipment and clothing issued to soldiers and how much was charged to their account; *Reports*, arranged by regiment and company, these reports identify when and where a company engaged in battle, who was injures or killed, and who was sick; *Correspondence*, arranged by regiment and company; and *Original Muster Rolls*, arranged by regiment and company (includes rolls for the Mexican War, Civil War, and the Spanish American War).

Civil War service record information on Iowa soldiers is also available from the archives in the form of a *Certificate of Service*. This certificate pulls information from records which normally contain general information such as name, nativity, residence, physical description, rank, when and where enlisted, by who enlisted, when and where mustered into service, date of termination of service, and other notations.

Kansas

Kansas State Historical Society

Library and Archives Division
6425 S.W. 6th Avenue
Topeka, KS 66615-1099
Phone: (913) 272-8681 ext. 117
Internet: http://history.cc.ukans.edu/
    heritage/kshs/kshs1.html

Hours: Monday - Saturday, 9am - 4:30pm

The Library and Archives Division of the Kansas State Historical Society collects and maintains historically significant research materials relating to Kansas, the Great Plains, and the West in general. Holdings include books, family histories, directories, county and town histories, personal papers, manuscripts, newspapers, photographs, government records (state & local), and maps. The Society also has an interlibrary loan program for its microfilm items. These microfilm items include newspapers, county plat books, manuscript collections, indexes to selected state archives records, federal census records for Kansas (1860 and 1870), and mid-decade state census (1865-1995).

More specifically, KSHS holdings include:

Newspapers. A nearly complete collection of all Kansas newspapers published from 1875 to the present is available on microfilm or in original form. A significant number of newspapers published prior to 1875 are also available and on microfilm. A finding aid to newspapers on microfilm can be found on the Internet through Kansas On-Line. Selected out-of-state newspapers are also held by the Society.

Biographies. This collection includes extensive printed biographies of both individuals and families.

County and Town Histories. Collection includes a large number of histories of Kansas and non-Kansas towns and counties. These histories often contain biographical information on residents. The "dead town list" is a compilation of more than 4,500 extinct or declining towns in Kansas.

Directories. This collection contains everything from farm and business directories to telephone books, 1859 to date. A selection of non-Kansas directories is also available.

Manuscripts. An assortment of diaries, company records, letters, personal &

business papers, governors papers, and others. Fiscal records and reunion registers for the Grand Army of the Republic (1879-1936), as well a GAR necrology list, post records, post charters, post ledgers, minute books, and quarterly reports are held. The collection also includes papers relating to railroad expansion in the state.

Photographs. Over 450,000 images are held dating from the 1850s to the present. Many images are available on microfiche in the research room (Microfiche may also be borrowed or purchased)

Maps and Architectural Drawings. Approximately 25,000 manuscript and printed maps, map reproductions, and architectural drawings are held by the Library and Archives Division. Many nineteenth-century state, county, and city maps, Indian land maps, military exploration, railroad development, and roads and trails maps are include in this collection. Of particular interest to Civil War researchers are the Kansas battle maps.

Miscellaneous library holdings include church histories and publications, cemetery records, school yearbooks, state publications, William P. Filby's *Passenger and Immigration Index*, and others. State records include rosters, descriptive rolls, muster rolls, quartermasters' records, morning reports, officers' commissions, and documentation about Kansas Civil War volunteer regiments from the Adjutant General's office are maintained. Muster rolls for Kansas volunteer regiments are on microfilm.

Membership in the Kansas State Historical Society is available and includes a subscription to *Kansas History* (the society's scholarly journal), and *Kansas Heritage* (their general-audience magazine). Benefits also include discounts at the museum store, at historic site stores, and on special programming. Members receive invitations to preview new and traveling exhibits.

If you have access to the Internet, the Kansas State Historical Society has a great web site.

Kentucky

Kentucky Department for Libraries & Archives

300 Coffee Tree Road
P.O. Box 537
Frankfort, Kentucky 40602-0537
Phone: (502) 875-7000

Hours: Tuesday - Saturday, 8am - 4pm

The Department for Libraries and Archives serves as the central repository for the Commonwealth's city, county, and state government records. Letters, diaries, photographs, and other private materials are collected by the department's sister agency, the Kentucky Historical Society, as well as the University of Kentucky and other academic libraries in the state.

Union Army Records held by the department include Compiled Service Records, The 1890 Census of Union Veterans and Widows, Report of the Adjutant General of the State of Kentucky, County Court Records, and Governor's Papers. The compiled service records held by the department consist of 515 rolls of microfilm, including two groups of supplemental records entitled "Misc. Card Abstracts" and "Personal Papers." This material was originally to be filed with the compiled service records. No index is available for this material, however the "Personal Papers" are arranged alphabetically by surname. The abstracts are arranged by unit, then by veteran's name.

Confederate Army Records held by the department include Compiled Service Records (136 rolls of microfilm), Louis-

ville Military Prison Registers, McLean Barracks Military Prison Records, Register of Confederate Prisoners who died in Federal Prisons, Amnesty Papers, Report of the Adjutant General, Confederate Pension Applications, The Kentucky Confederate Home, and miscellaneous sources. Records from Louisville Military Prison and McLean Barracks Military Prison dealing with civilian prisoners contains information on Kentuckians charged with engaging in guerrilla warfare, treason, or spying.

When researching Confederate soldiers, be sure to check the Compiled Service Records for Union volunteers. This may sound unusual, but in many cases, Southern sympathizers were drafted or otherwise forced into the Union Army against their will. These records frequently yield references to "desertion to the enemy," meaning the soldiers in question deserted and joined the Confederate Army at the first opportunity.

Special thanks to Archivist James M. Prichard.

Kentucky Historical Society

Old Capitol Annex
P.O. Box H
Frankfort, KY 40602-2108
Phone: (502) 564-3016
Fax: (502) 564-4701

Hours: Monday - Friday, 8am - 4pm
         Saturday, 9am - 4pm

The Library of the Kentucky Historical Society offers a wealth of Kentucky historical and genealogical information. Holdings include:

- Tax lists, by county, dating from the formation of the county (available on microfilm.
- U.S. Censuses: Kentucky 1810-1880, and 1900-1920 on microfilm
- Kentucky vital statistics on microfilm include births, marriages, deaths (1852-61). A card index is available.
- County court records (on microfilm), including wills and marriages, from the formation of the counties to 1900.
- Surname files which include various data arranged by family name.
- An extensive collection of Kentucky county and state histories.
- Newspapers (on microfilm).
- Indexed rosters of Kentucky soldiers in the War of 1812, Mexican War, Civil War, Spanish-American War, and World War I.

- Confederate pension records.
- Land records.
- Church records.
- Thousands of published genealogies.
- Maps.
- Rare books.
- Kentucky biographies and biographical histories.

A list of professional researchers is provided on request for a fee of $1.00 (please include a stamped, self-addressed envelope). A staff researcher is also available at an hourly rate. All visitors to the Society Library are free to use the library resources at no charge. The Society encourages you to visit in person.

Membership is available in the Kentucky Historical Society. See listing under *Organizations* for more information.

Military Records and Research Library

Department of Military Affairs
1121 Louisville Road
Pine Hill Plaza
Frankfort, KY 40601

Louisiana

Louisiana State Archives

3851 Essen Lane
Baton Rouge, LA 70809
Phone: (504) 922-1200
Phone: (504) 922-1209 - Research Library
Hours: Monday - Friday, 8am - 4:30pm

The Louisiana State Archives maintains census records, birth, death, and marriage certificates, military records, pension records, parish records, passenger lists and naturalization records, voter registration rolls, and tax assessment rolls. Military records for Confederate soldiers were often destroyed during the occupation of Louisiana by Union soldiers. Fortunately, in 1920 Andrew B. Booth compiled the available information and published *Records of Louisiana Confederate Soldiers and Commands*, which identifies over 75,000 names of soldiers enlisting in Confederate units raised in Louisiana. National Archives microfilm records include microfilm series #320, entitled, "*Compiled Service Records of Confederate Soldiers Who Served in Organizations From the State of Louisiana*, the compiled service records of 5,200 Louisianans who served in Union military units during the Civil War, and *Records of the Louisiana State Government, 1850-1888*.

Confederate Pension Records are indexed alphabetically and available for research use. Confederate pensions were granted in 1898 to soldiers—or their widows—who 1) served honorably from date of enlistment until discharge, or the end of the war, 2) were indigent and unable to earn a livelihood, and 3) applicant could not be a government employee. Union pension records for Louisianans are available only through the National Archives.

The Louisiana Heritage Center, located in the research library at the State Archives, is a computer data base containing the names of more than two million Louisianans. This data base is available to the general public, but appointments are required. The Archives also houses a Genealogy Library, modern laboratories for preserving and restoring fragile documents, and exhibit areas on the first floor.

Additional support of the State Archives, regarded as one of the more modern archival institutions in the country, is provided by the Louisiana Archives Foundation. Membership is available to those wishing to support the fine work of this organization. For more information, contact the foundation at P.O. Box 66989, Baton Rouge, LA 70896-6989, phone (504) 922-1206.

Louisiana State Library

760 Riverside Mall
Baton Rouge, LA 70821
Mail:
P.O. Box 131
Baton Rouge, LA 70821
Phone: (504) 342-4913

Maine

Maine State Archives
State House Station #84
Augusta, ME 04333
Phone: (207) 287-5795

Maryland

Maryland State Archives
Hall of Records Building
350 Rowe Boulevard
Annapolis, MD 21401
Phone: (410) 974-3914
Phone: (410) 974-3916

Massachusetts

Massachusetts Archives
220 Morrissey Blvd.
Boston, MA 02125
Phone: (617) 727-2816

Hours: Monday - Friday, 9am - 5pm
         Saturday, 9am - 3pm

The Massachusetts Archives' published collection *Massachusetts Soldiers, Sailors and Marines in the Civil War* is the most complete list of Massachusetts men serving in the Civil War and would be a good source to check before beginning your research in earnest. The Massachusetts Archives has an impressive list of holdings that runs for several pages. Groupings on this list include:

Index to Naval Correspondence, 1858-1916
Lists of Recruits Enrolled at Washington, DC, 1861-1865
Company Rolls of the Massachusetts Volunteer Militia, 1862
Lists of Mustering-outs, 1861-1865
Telegrams, 1864
Lists of Casualties and Hospitalizations, 1862-1866
Lists of Draft Substitutes by District, 1863-1865
Descriptive Rolls of Massachusetts Volunteers, 1861-1865
Index to Naval Bounty Payments, 1864
Descriptive Lists of Recruits from Southern States, 1864-1865

This is only a sample of what is available. You will also find records from the Surgeon General, Adjutant General, Paymaster General, Quartermaster, and Provost Marshal that cover recruitment, enlistment, muster rolls, descriptive rolls, pay, bounty, and clothing
Another significant collection for the Civil War period is the Executive De-

partment Letters, a series of incoming and outgoing correspondence to the Governor and Executive Office. The bulk of this collection pertains to the tenure of Civil War Governor John Andrew, and much of that to military matters.

Special thanks to J. Michael Comeau at the Massachusetts Archives.

Massachusetts Historical Society
1154 Boylston Street
Boston, MA 02215
Phone: (617) 536-1608

Michigan

State Archives of Michigan
Michigan Historical Center
Department of State
717 West Allegan
Lansing, MI 48918
Phone: (517) 373-1408
Email: archives@sos.state.mi.us

Hours: Monday - Friday, 10am - 4pm

The Civil War manuscripts held by the State Archives of Michigan include certificates, diaries, discharges, journals, letters, and miscellaneous documents of soldiers from Michigan units (primarily), Illinois, Indiana, Kansas, Massachusetts, New York, and Ohio units, and regular U.S. Army units. A complete list of individuals, states, regiments, companys, and the record groups (RG) containing the manuscripts is provided in State Archives Circular No. 20. Examples from the Michigan section of this list are listed in Table 1.

The State Archives of Michigan also maintains a fairly large photographic collection of Civil War soldiers and veterans. The individual portraits range from Civil War-era carte-de-visite (CDV) images to regular photographs, arranged alphabetically by name in the general Biography Index drawers. A separate index, in a special card catalog drawer, identifies the collection by unit first, then alphabetically by name. Both indexes are located in the Reference Room of the State Archives.

Unit	RG#	Name of Soldier	Record
1st Cavalry Regt., Co. D	76-134	Morris Dilts	Diary
1st Cavalry Regt., Co. D	70-101	James W. Howd	Diary
2nd Cavalry Regt., Co. D	67-111	John Vogel	Diary
3rd Cavalry Regt., Co. B	69-110	Phineas R. Freeman	Letters
3rd Cavalry Regt., Co. F	71-174	Stephens S. Delano	Diary
4th Cavalry Regt., Co. B-E-H	89-535	Henry Albert Potter	Diary
7th Infantry Regt., Surgeon	22	Cyrus Bacon	Diary

The State Archives publishes an excellent guide to military records, identified as *Finding Aid Number 1: Records of the Michigan Military Establishment 1838-1941.* Aside from serving as an excellent guide to military records held by the state, this guide provides a little history. For example, on page one we discover that "In 1859 the Legislature appropriated $3,000 annually for the support of the militia, composed of 38 companies, and required an annual four-day encampment. The State Military Board, a 5-member advisory board to the commander-in-chief, was also created by Act 169, MPA 1859." We also learn that Michigan provided over 92,000 men for federal service during the Civil War.

Minnesota

Minnesota Historical Society
Research Center
345 Kellog Boulevard West
Saint Paul, MN 55102
Phone: (612) 296-6980

Mississippi

Lauderdale County Dept. of Archives & History, Inc.
P.O. Box 5511
Meridian, MS 39302-5511
Physical Location:
Courthouse Annex, Second Floor
410 Constitution Ave
Phone: (601) 482-9752

Hours: Monday - Friday, 8am - 5pm

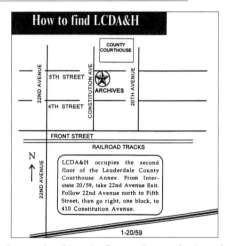

The Lauderdale County Department of Archives & History (LCDA&H) is a hybrid agency, both a department of the county government and a private, not-for-profit institution, staffed mainly by volunteers.

The LCDA&H offers a wide selection of publications based on extensive research of Mississippi archives (both in state and at the National Archives). Publications are available for Church Histories; Marriage Records; Census Records; Probate Court Records; Circuit Court Records; Land Records; Cemetery Records; Alabama Records; Clarke County, Mississippi, Records; Newspapers; Local Histories; Miscellaneous; Confederate Induction & Pension Records; Confederate Records – Deaths and Burials (14 volumes); and Confederate Burials (24 volumes). Most publications are under $12.

Membership: $10 a year (Individual)
             $15 a year (Family)

239

Mississippi Department of Archives and History

Charlotte Capers Building
100 South State Street
Jackson, MS 39205
Mail:
P.O. Box 571
Jackson, MS 39205-0571
Phone: (601) 359-6876
Fax: (601) 359-6964

Hours: Monday - Friday, 8am - 5pm
          Saturday, 8am - 1pm

The Mississippi Department of Archives and History maintains a Biographical Index of over 200,000 name entries for Mississippians, mostly from 19th century sources. Currently on computer output microfiche (COM) or card catalog, the index is being converted to electronic format for easier retrieval.

Primary department holdings include:

The Official Atlas of the Civil War
Cemetery and Bible Records (cemetery records for both Confederate and Union soldiers buried in Mississippi)
1890 Census of Union Soldiers and Widows living in Mississippi
Census Records
Regiment/Company Histories

Freedmen's Bureau (Index on microfilm and computer)
War of the Rebellion: Official Records of the Union and Confederate Armies
The Journal of Mississippi History
Publications of the Mississippi Historical Society
Confederate Service Records (available at a self-serve microfilm reader-printer)
Union Service Records (of Blacks who served from Mississippi)
Pension Records
Union and Confederate diaries and letters
State Records
Private Manuscripts
Photographs
Maps
Newspapers, 1803 to present
County Records
Surname Register (whereby addresses are provided by individuals having information on particular Mississippi families.

When researching pension records, keep in mind that a few pensions for Confederate service were paid in 1888-89, though most were paid after 1898-1900.

Special thanks to Military Records Librarian Sara S. Clark.

Missouri

Missouri State Archives

600 West Main Street
Mail:
P.O. Box 778
Jefferson City, MO 65102
(314) 751-3280

Hours: Mon - Wed, and Fri, 8am - 5pm
          Thurs, 8am - 9pm
          Sat, 8:30am - 3:30pm

Holdings include:
— individual service cards for both Union and Confederate soldiers
— morning reports
— clothing issue reports
— orders and letters
— descriptive rolls
— Confederate pension applications

The Archives also maintains a complete set of the *War of the Rebellion*, and the companion series *Supplement to the Official Records of the Union and Confederate Armies*, as well as the multi-volume set, *Confederate Military History*.

A quarterly newsletter is published by the Friends of the Missouri State Archives (P.O. Box 242, Jefferson City, Missouri 65102; individual membership is $10 a year)

Nebraska

State Archives Division
Nebraska State Historical Society
Division of Reference Services
1500 R Street
Mail:
P.O. Box 82554
Lincoln, NE 68501

New Hampshire

New Hampshire Division of Records Management and Department of State
71 South Fruit Street
Concord, NH 03301-2410
Phone: (603) 271-2236

New Jersey

Department of State Division of Archives and Records Management
Bureau of Archives and
Records Preservation
State Library Building
185 West State Street, CN 307
Trenton, NJ 08625-0307

New Mexico

New Mexico Records Center and Archives
404 Montezuma Street
Santa Fe, NM 87501
Phone: (505) 827-7332

New York

New York State Archives
New York Department of Education
Cultural Education Center #11D40
Albany, NY 12230
Phone: (518) 474-8955

New York State Historical Association
P.O. Box 800
Cooperstown, NY 13326
Phone: (607) 547-2509

North Carolina

Duke University Special Collections Library
Box 90185
Durham, NC 27708-0185
Phone: (919) 660-5822
Fax: (919) 684-2855

the papers of renowned Confederate spy Rose O'Neal Greenhow

Hours: Monday - Thursday, 9am - 9pm
Friday, 9am - 5pm
Saturday, 1pm - 5pm
(Abbreviated hours during academic vacations and the summer terms.)

The Special Collections Library at Duke University adjoins the William R. Perkins Library on the main quadrangle of the University's West Campus. Library holdings are available for use in the Dalton-Brand Research Room, named in honor of library patrons Harry L. and Mary K. Dalton and R. Alfred and Elizabeth D. Brand.

The archival collections at Duke University include on-line resources such as scanned pages and texts of writings, diaries, or journals of women during the Civil War. These resources include the 1864 diary of Alice Williamson, a 16-year old girl from Gallatin, Tennessee, and the papers of renowned Confederate spy Rose O'Neal Greenhow. The Special Collections Library also features an exhibit that examines the lives of American slaves from the late eighteenth century through the nineteenth century.

North Carolina Department of Cultural Resources

Division of Archives and History
109 East Jones Street
Raleigh, NC 27601-2807
Phone: (919) 733-3952

Hours: Tuesday - Friday, 8am - 5:30pm
         Saturday, 9am - 5pm

Printed material available at the North Carolina State Archives include:

North Carolina: The History of a Southern State
North Carolina History Told by Contemporaries
A Guide to the Study and Reading of North Carolina History
Histories of the Several Regiments and Battalions from North Carolina in the Great War 1861-'65; five large volumes (which became known as Clark's Regiments or as North Carolina Regiments)
A History of North Carolina in the War Between the States: Bethel to Sharpsburg;
The Civil War in North Carolina
Sherman's March Through the Carolinas
The War of the Rebellion: A Compilation of the Official Records of the Union and Confederate Armies (70 volumes, 128 books)
Official Records of the Union and Confederate Navies in the War of the Rebellion (30 volumes)
Atlas to Accompany the Official Records of the Union and Confederate Armies in the War of the Rebellion
Index to the Official Records
Roster of North Carolina Troops in the War Between the States (4 volumes which became known as Moore's Roster)
The Secession Movement in North Carolina
Reconstruction in North Carolina

State Archives Records include:

The Roll of Honor
On December 20, 1862, North Carolina's General Assembly passed a resolution calling for a Roll of Honor which would list the names of all North Carolina's Confederate troops. Nine volumes were compiled before the project faltered. Records for many units are fragmentary or nonexistent.

Pension Records
These records are arranged in two series: Applications for Pensions under the Act of 1885, and Applications for Pensions under the Act of 1901. Applications were normally completed at local courthouses and the information provided varied from county to county. Applications normally included: date of application, applicant's name (or husband's name), age, post office, company and regiment, date of enlistment, date and circumstances of wounds, nature and extent of disability, and an oath of eligibility. The state did not give pensions to Union veterans or widows.

The Civil War Collection
Public and private records in this collection include petitions for presidential pardon, bounty payrolls, Quartermaster Department records, muster rolls and pay records by regiment and unit, memoirs, essays, scrapbooks, and other miscellaneous records.

The North Carolina Division of Archives and History also offers a wide selection of reference books for sale through their Publications catalog. Titles include State

Troops and Volunteers: A Photographic Records of North Carolina's Civil War Soldiers; The Papers of Zebulon Baird Vance; Sherman's March Through North Carolina: A Chronology; and *North Carolina Troops, 1861-1865: A Roster.*

Special thanks to Assistant State Archivist Jesse R. Lankford Jr.

Ohio

Ohio Historical Society
1982 Velma Avenue
Columbus, OH 43211
Phone: (614) 297-2525

The State Library of Ohio
65 South Front Street
Columbus, OH 43266-0334
Phone: (614) 644-6966

Hours: Monday - Thursday, 8am - 5pm
        Friday, 9am - 5pm

The Genealogy Section of the State Library of Ohio is one of the specialized service areas dedicated to fulfilling the genealogical needs of researchers exploring their family roots. Service is provided through an open shelf collection of over 16,000 volumes, 5,600 microfilms, and 10,000 microfiche. Since Ohio is often called "The Gateway to the West," the Library's collection focuses on Ohio and the states that preceded it into statehood, with strong emphasis on the New England states of Virginia, West Virginia, and Kentucky. The collection is comprised of a broad spectrum of genealogical resources, including census microfilms, census indexes, family genealogies, county histories, vital records, county atlases, and military rosters.

The Library's collection is non-circulating. For those researchers unable to visit in person, policy allows the Library to check one family name in one Ohio county. Any information found in the indexed, printed sources will be sent to the requester for $1.00 (up to five pages, 20 cents for each additional page beyond five). A legal-size SASE is always appreciated.

Major Ohio Civil War holdings include:
- Ohio roster of the Soldiers of the Civil War with name index
- List of Ohio Civil War pensioners with index
- 1890 Ohio Special Census Schedule: Civil War Union veterans and their widows (on microfilm)
- Ohio Civil War regimental histories (on microfilm)
- Regimental publications and personal narratives of the Civil War: A Checklist, by C.E. Dornbusch, 1961
- Civil War literature of Ohio: A bibliography, by Daniel J. Ryan, 1911
- Sketches of War History, 1861-1865, papers read before the Ohio Commandery of the Military Order of the Loyal Legion of the U.S. (Five volumes)

- Ohio in the War, by Whitelaw Reid, two volumes, 1868
- Ohio handbook of the Civil War, by Robert S. Harper, 1961
- The Story of Camp Chase, by William H. Knauss, 1906

- A list of the Civil War and Spanish-American War regimental histories and Adjutant-General's reports in the stacks of the State Library of Ohio

Oklahoma

Oklahoma State Historical Society
Library Resources Division
Wiley Post Historical Building
2100 North Lincoln Boulevard
Oklahoma City, OK 73105

Pennsylvania

Grand Army of the Republic Civil War Museum & Library
4278 Griscom Street
Philadelphia, PA 19124-3954
Phone: (215) 289-6484

The G.A.R. Civil War Museum includes the Ruan House Library, which houses 2,000 archival volumes. This collection includes original *Harper's Weekly* and *Philadelphia Inquirer* newspapers for the entire war. Magazines, regimental and unit histories, the Official Record of the War of the Rebellion, and other Civil War volumes round out this collection.

Pennsylvania State Archives
Archives Building
Third & Forster Streets
Mail:
P.O. Box 1026
Harrisburg, PA 17108-1026
Phone: (717) 783-3281

Hours: Tuesday - Friday, 9am - 4pm
Saturday, 9am - Noon/1pm - 4pm
(microfilm use only)

The holdings of the Pennsylvania Archives include fifty-five thousand cubic feet of research material and over fifteen thousand reels of film covering the period from 1664 to the present. Archives are housed in a twenty-one story records building with temperature and humidity control. All records have been separated into sixty-nine Record Group (RG) collections, based on content. Manuscripts have been separated into over 400 Manuscript Groups (MGs).

Civil War records are found primarily in RG-2, RG-19, RG-25, and in Manuscript Group Six (MG-6), MG-7, MG-8, MG-11, MG-17, MG-60, MG-97, MG-98, MG-108, MG-147, MG-176, MG-211, MG-234, and other Manuscript Groups. Specifically, these Record and Manuscript Groups contain:

RG-2   Records of the Auditor General, including Civil War service and pension records and records relating to Civil War border claims.

RG-19   Records of the Department of Military Affairs. Contains Civil War veterans' card file of Pennsylvania soldiers (alphabetically listed), muster rolls, correspondence, regimental papers, records of drafted men and substitutes, substitutes' depositions, and conscientious objector depositions.

RG-25   Records of Special Commissions, including the Board of Commissioners on Gettysburg Monuments, Camp Curtin Commission, Commission to Supervise Flag Transfer, Fiftieth Anniversary of the Battle of Gettysburg Commission (including participants registers), General George G. Meade National Statue Commission, Pennsylvania Chickamauga-Chattanooga Battlefield Commission,

and the Pennsylvania at Cold Harbor Battlefield Memorial.

MG-6   Diaries and Journals Collection.
MG-7   Military Manuscripts Collection.
MG-8   Pennsylvania Collection.
MG-11   Map Collection.
MG-17   Samuel Penniman Bates Papers.
MG-60   Grand Army of the Republic Collection.
MG-97   Richard A. Oakford Papers.
MG-98   Orbison Family Papers - Philadelphia Ladies' Aid Society.
MG-108   Peter F. Rothermel Papers - Gettysburg.
MG-147   John Anderson Papers.
MG-176   General Richard Coulter Papers - 11th Regiment.
MG-211   Richmond (Mansfield) Ladies Soldiers Aid Society Papers.
MG-234   Bucktails (42nd Regiment) Collection.

A number of useful guides are available which will help one through the search process. These publications include a *Guide To The Genealogical Sources At The Pennsylvania State Archives, Guide To The Record Groups In The Pennsylvania State Archives, Guide To The Manuscript Groups In The Pennsylvania State Archives, Guide To The Published Archives Of Pennsylvania.*

U.S. Army
Military History Institute

Carlisle Barracks
Carlisle, PA 17013-5008
Phone: (717) 245-3103 (for books)
Phone: (717) 245-3434 (for photographs)
Phone: (717) 245-3601 (for manuscripts)
Internet: http://carlisle-www.army.mil/
    usamhi/

Hours: Monday - Friday, 8am - 4:30pm

The Military Historical Institute is the Army's central historical repository, with vast holdings on many aspects of military history. The Civil War is exceptionally well represented throughout the Institute's holdings. Among the 64,000 Civil War books are the War Department Collection of Civil War regimental histories, 16,000 strong. The 100,000 Civil War photographs include the famous Massachusetts Loyal Legion Collection. Unpublished letters, diaries, and memoirs are available for approximately 4500 Civil War soldiers, principally junior officers and enlisted men. Papers of prominent personages include: George L. Andrews (of Massachusetts), Luther P. Bradley, Henry S. Briggs, William T.H. Brooks, Eugene A. Carr, George Crook, Winfield Scott Hancock, Daniel Harvey Hill, Nelson A. Miles, Albert J. Myer, David S. Stanley, and John W. Turner. The papers, pictures, and publications cover regular, volunteer, and militia army forces raised by the two national governments and by the respective states and territories, both Federal and Confederate. A few holdings concern the Navy, Marine Corps, and Revenue Service. Some source material is also available for civilians in military relief work, in government offices, in war industry, in the path of war, and on the home front.

Finding aids include: THE ERA OF THE CIVIL WAR by Louise Arnold-Friend and MANUSCRIPT HOLDINGS OF THE MILITARY HISTORY RESEARCH COLLECTION (two volumes) by Richard J. Sommers. Both books are out of print but should be available in major research libraries. The Institute's Reference Branch will provide, upon request, a list of printed and manuscript holdings on any Civil War regiment or independent battalion or company. Those lists and other bibliographic citations and catalogues may be searched on the Internet (see Internet address below phone numbers).

Books printed (or reprinted) after 1940 may be borrowed through a town or university library on interlibrary loan. Rare books, photos, and manuscripts do not circulate but are available for study at the Institute. Thousands of Civil War authors, scholars, students, professors, buffs, reenactors, and genealogists use these holdings each year. The Institute is a public facility, which welcomes and encourages such usage.

The staff of the Institute includes four published Civil War authors: Louise Arnold-Friend, Randy W. Hackenburg, Richard J. Sommers, and Michael J. Winey. Visiting scholars in residence have included Russell F. Weigley, Charles P. Roland, Jay Luvaas, John Mahon, Edward M. Coffman, Stephen Ambrose, Joseph Glatthaar, Carol Reardon, and Harold W. Nelson. The Director of the Institute, Colonel William T. Vossler, serves on the Civil War artillery advisory committee of the Friends of the National Parks of Gettysburg.

Special thanks to the Military History Institute's Chief Archivist-Historian, Dr. Richard J. Sommers, for the above information.

Among the 64,000 Civil War books are the War Department Collection of Civil War regimental histories, 16,000 strong. The 100,000 Civil War photographs include the famous Massachusetts Loyal Legion Collection.

Rhode Island

Rhode Island State Archives
Room 43 State House
Providence, RI 02903

South Carolina

South Carolina Department of Archives and History
1430 Senate Street
P.O. Box 11669, Capitol Station
Columbia, SC 29211-1669
Phone: (803) 734-8577
Email: sox@history.scdah.sc.edu
Internet: http://www.scdah.sc.edu/homepage.htm

Hours: Tuesday - Friday, 9am - 9pm
Saturday, 9pm - 6pm
Sunday, 1pm - 6pm

The most efficient way for Civil War researchers to get a handle on the type and number of records held by the Department of Archives and History is to purchase *Guide to Civil War Records: A guide to the records in the South Carolina Department of Archives & History*, by Patrick J. McCawley. This 80-page indexed volume provides an in-depth description of those records relating to the Civil War and Confederate veterans. State and county records, National Archives microfilm, indexes from other state archives, private manuscripts, and other printed sources are all listed in this book, complete with a description regarding content and format. The books sells for $5 plus $1.75 postage and can be ordered from Carrie Bassett at the above address. For more information, contact Carrie at (803) 734-8590.

South Carolina Historical Society
100 Meeting Street
Charleston, SC 29401
Phone: (803) 723-3225
Fax: (803) 723-8584
Internet: http://www.historic.com/schs/

Hours: Tuesday - Friday, 9am - 4pm
Saturday, 9am - 2pm

The South Carolina Historical Society is the state's oldest and largest historical organization. The Society is a private, nonprofit organization which receives no governmental support for its activities. The objective of the organization is to collect, preserve, and publish the history of the state. This mission includes the operation of the Society's research library, which counts in its holdings over a million pages of manuscript material, an extensive photographic collection, and numerous other items. A highlight of the Society's holdings is the R.

Lockwood Tower Collection, which was one of the largest private collections of books concerning the War between the States in the nation before it was donated to the organization in 1990. Containing over 4,000 volumes, it forms the preeminent collection of books about the war within the state of South Carolina. Other related materials include the Charles V. Peery Confederate Imprint collection, which is one of the ten largest collections of Confederate printed material.

For more information on the Society, see their listing under *Organizations*.

Tennessee

The Tennessee State Library and Archives

403 Seventh Avenue, North
Nashville, TN 37243-0312
Phone: (615) 741-2764
Email: referenc@mail.state.tn.us

Hours: Monday - Saturday, 8am - 6pm

Research material at the Tennessee State Library and Archives (TSL&A) spans the state's history and includes military records from the Revolutionary War, Militia/Frontier records, War of 1812, Indian Wars, Mexican War, Civil War, Spanish American War, World War I, and World War II. Civil War resources at the Tennessee State Library and Archives include:

Tennesseans In The Civil War. Volume I provides brief histories of each Tennessee unit in the Civil War. Information about the place of residence of most soldiers in each company is available. This volume also includes a list of the units from each county. Volume II is an alphabetical list of soldiers, both Union and Confederate. Compiled from service records, muster rolls, newspapers published during the war, and other sources. Once a name and unit are identified, copies of an individual's service record can be located.

Military Service Records. The Library and Archives holds microfilm copies of service records for men in the state's Confederate and Union units. Place and date of enlistment, muster dates, promotions, captures, hospitalization, and death are usually noted. Copies are provided by mail to Tennessee residents (write for price quote); nonresidents should write to the National Archives for copies.

1890 Civil War Veterans Census - Tennessee. This census provides a list of Union veterans living in Tennessee in 1890, including their age, service history, and place of residence. A few Confederates are listed. This is a published abstract, original records are available on microfilm.

Index to Tennessee Confederate Pension Applications. Beginning in 1891, Tennessee residents who could prove Confederate service were eligible for pension payments from the state, even if their service was in another state. This volume has separate lists of soldiers, widows, and black soldiers who received pensions.

Tennessee Civil War Veterans Questionnaires. Detailed answers given by 1,600

Tennessee veterans (mostly Confederate) from 1915 to 1922. Published in five volumes with a full-name index.

Civil War Manuscripts Collection.
This collection includes military rosters, diaries, memoirs, letters, ledger books, and other records pertaining to the Civil War in Tennessee and elsewhere. The collection is contained in 29 boxes and numerous volumes, and it has been microfilmed. A guide is available which lists the contents of each box and folder. **The microfilm can be borrowed on interlibrary loan**.

The Library and Archives has a large selection of military records—from all U.S. wars—available on microfilm. Other resources include governors' papers, records of the Tennessee Supreme Court, diaries, Bible records, papers of prominent Tennesseans, Tennessee census schedules, county courthouse records, vital records (birth, death, etc.), Tennessee newspapers, periodicals, and land records.

Texas

Confederate Research Center

The Harold B. Simpson Hill College History Complex
Mail:
P.O. Box 619
Hillsboro, TX 76645
Phone: (817) 582-2555

The Confederate Research Center and Museum houses a collection of over 5,000 books, brochures, and pamphlets on the War Between the States, with an emphasis on Confederate Military History.

Resources include *The Official Records*, *Southern Historical Society Papers*, and the *Confederate Veteran & Confederate Military History*. Capsule histories of all 3,220 Confederate Regiments, Special Units, and Confederate Ships are available. Original letters, documents, maps, and photographs are also available.

> *Capsule histories of all 3,220 Confederate Regiments, Special Units, and Confederate Ships are available.*

The Center maintains a microfilm library which contains an index of each Confederate State, all service records of Hood's Texas Brigade, Texas newspapers published during the War, 1860 Census Reports of Texas counties, Post Returns of U.S. Forts in Texas (1848-1861), and an informational file on Texas soldiers who fought for the Confederacy.

The Confederate Research Center holds an annual Confederate History Symposium on the first Saturday of April (except Easter weekend), which features nationally known speakers, demonstrations of Confederate battle tactics and drill, and Confederate music. As this is a popular symposium, the Center recommends that you make reservations before March 1st.

Texas State Library

1201 Brazos Street
Box 12927, Capitol Station
Austin, TX 78711
Phone: (512) 463-5463

Vermont

Vermont Historical Society Library and Museum
Pavilion Building
109 State Street
Montpelier, VT 05602
Phone: (802) 828-2291

Virginia

The Mariners' Museum
100 Museum Drive
Newport News, VA 23606-3759
Phone: (804) 599-3122
Internet: http://www.mariner.org/mariner

Hours: Monday - Saturday, 9am - 5pm
(by appointment)

The Research Library and Archives of the Mariners' Museum features a collection of 75,000 volumes dealing with nauti-

> *The museum is home to the* **Monitor** *National Marine Sanctuary*

cal history. The museum is home to the *Monitor* National Marine Sanctuary, which include research material on the famous ironclad such as technical and historical reports, videotapes, photographs, slides, news articles, and information about the officers and crew. Information about the CSS *Virginia* (*Merrimack*) is also available.

Stratford Hall Plantation
Jessie Ball duPont Memorial Library
Stratford, VA 22558
Phone: (804) 493-8038

Hours: Monday - Friday, 9am - 5pm

On the grounds of Stratford Hall Plantation, birthplace of Robert E. Lee, is the Jessie Ball duPont Memorial Library. This library, available to "Friends of Stratford" at no cost (though an appointment is necessary), features a fine collection of over 10,000 manuscripts, periodicals, books, and other reference works dealing primarily with the Northern Neck of Virginia. Of particular interest are the Lee family letters and original surrender documents (not normally available to the public). The Library has expanded

> *Of particular interest are the Lee family letters and original surrender documents (not normally available to the public).*

its holdings on African-American history to provide resources for the Stratford Hall Plantation Seminar on Slavery. This includes works dealing with African-American genealogy.

Virginia Historical Society
Library of Virginia History

428 North Boulevard
Mail:
P.O. Box 7311
Richmond, VA 23221
Phone: (804) 358-4901
Fax: (804) 355-2399

The Virginia Historical Society's Library of Virginia History houses an exten-sive collection of personal, business, and legal papers representing several hundred years of Virginia's citizenry. Not specific to the Civil War, this collection features manu-scripts, letters, and other documents span-ning the years from the Colonial period to the 20th century.

Virginia Military Institute

Lexington, VA 24450
Phone: (540) 464-7566
Fax: (540) 464-7279
Internet: http://www.vmi.edu

> *more than 6,000 photographs and 400 manuscript collections*

Hours: Monday - Friday, 8am - 4:30pm

The Archives at the Virginia Mili-tary Institute contain an extensive collec-tion of 19th and 20th century holdings, in-cluding more than 6,000 photographs and 400 manuscript collections. The Archives web page (for those on the Internet) offers selected examples from the Institute's Civil War collection, including images and full text documents. The following examples were extracted from the VMI web site:

William J. Black Diary; Shoemaker's Co., Virginia Horse Artillery.
Henry H. Dedrick Papers; Private, 52nd Virginia Infantry.
John H. Ervine Letter; Sgt., 1st Virginia Cavalry.
John Garibaldi Papers; Sgt., 27th Virginia Infantry.
Andrew C.L. Gatewood Papers; VMI Cadet; 11th Virginia Cavalry.
Stonewall Jackson Papers; Prewar VMI Faculty; CSA General.
Jacob Kent Langhorne Papers; VMI Cadet; 2nd Virginia Cavalry.

Matthew Fontaine Maury Papers; Confederate Navy; postwar VMI faculty.
New Market Collection; Memoirs of battle veterans.
Thomas H. Williamson; My Service with Genl. Thos. J. Jackson.

Selected Special Topics include:

Death of Stonewall Jackson (May 1863).
Battle of New Market. (May 15, 1864).

The VMI Archives recommends that you call before visiting.

Special thanks to the VMI students and staff who maintain the VMI web site, which was the source of this information

> *Stonewall Jackson Papers; Prewar VMI Faculty; CSA General.*

Virginia State Libraries and Archives

11th Street at Capitol Square
Richmond, VA 23219-3419
Phone: (804) 786-2306

West Virginia

George Tyler Moore Center for the Study of the Civil War

Conrad Shindler House
Shepherdstown, WV 25443
Phone: (304) 876-5429

A division of the Community and Technical College at Shepherd College, the George Tyler Moore Center for the Study of the Civil War has the mission of developing educational programs on the Civil War

focusing on the development of a Civil War soldiers' personnel database.

era, specifically focusing on the development of a Civil War soldiers' personnel database. The Center is headquartered in the Conrad Shindler House, which was donated by Mary Tyler Moore, and houses the Center's offices, a research library, and the Civil War soldiers' database operation. The Center is named in honor of Ms. Moore's father, George Tyler, an ardent genealogist and longtime Civil War enthusiast.

West Virginia Division of Culture and History

Archives and History Section
1900 Kanawha Boulevard, East
Charleston, WV 25305-0300
Phone: (304) 558-0230 ext. 168
Fax: (304) 558-2779

Hours: Monday - Friday, 9am - 5pm
         Saturday, 1pm - 5pm

The West Virginia Division of Culture and History serves as the family and local history research library and as the West Virginia State Archives. The research library includes a complete original set of the *Official Records of the War of the Rebellion*, *Confederate Veteran* magazine, and numerous histories of regiments, battles, military encampments, and leaders of the Civil War. The collection includes works written in the years immediately following the war, as well as the latest scholarly works.

Microfilm holdings include the National Archives microfilm series of service records for both the Union West Virginia regiments and all the Confederate regiments of Virginia, including the counties which would separate in 1863 to form the new state of West Virginia. Some microfilm records are available showing locations of veterans' graves (these were compiled in the 1930s as part of the Works Progress Administration). Some newspapers from the period are also available on microfilm, including the *Wheeling Daily Intelligencer*, published daily at the site of what was then the state capital. A fairly complete run of *Harpers Weekly* for the war years and Frank Leslie's *Illustrated Weekly* are also available in the periodical collection.

253

The records of the State Archives include original muster and payrolls, orders, clothing books, correspondence and service cards for the Union West Virginia regiments. Many of the original documents are currently being arranged for eventual microfilming and are not easily accessed by researchers. There are also some muster rolls and cards for various county militia groups. The published reports of the Adjutant General for 1864 and 1865 include rosters and lists of the dead by regiment. The manuscript collections include an artificial collection of letters, diaries, and various documents from a variety of sources, compiled for easier access. In addition, numerous other collections contain materials of the Civil War period and are listed separately in the internal finding aid for manuscripts. The Boyd B. Stutler Collection in particular is rich in Civil War research materials, with an emphasis on John Brown and his raid on Harpers Ferry in 1859, long considered one of the major events leading to the war.

The Archives and History Section also publishes *West Virginia History*, an annual scholarly journal focusing on the history of the state. In addition to scholarly articles, it features listings of accessions to various repositories around the state and book reviews of recent works. Many issues include some materials dealing with the Civil War. Volume 55 of this publication (1996) has several articles concerning the war, as well as a roster of the First West Virginia Infantry. *West Virginia History* is available for $12.00 per annual issue, or $4.00 each for back issues in the quarterly format which ended in 1984.

In January, 1996, Archives and History published the *Explorer Timeline* CD-ROM. This IBM-compatible CD features over 12,000 events from West Virginia history, including over 500 relating to the Civil War. *Explorer* is a Windows-based program which requires a minimum of 66MHz or Pentium processor, 8MB RAM, and at least 3MB of hard disk space. It is available for $15.00, which includes shipping and handling. A Jefferson County, West Virginia CD-ROM, featuring numerous Civil War and John Brown materials, became available in 1996. Contact the Archives and History Section for further information on this second CD.

Special thanks to Archivist Debra Basham.

Wisconsin

Carroll College Institute for Civil War Studies

Lance J. Herdegen, Director
100 N. East Avenue
Waukesha, WI 53186
Phone: (414) 524-7198

The Institute for Civil War Studies was established at Carroll College in April, 1995, to call attention to the collection of the late W. Norman FitzGerald as a resource for students and scholars. The FitzGerald collection is housed in the Carroll College Library and includes 1,700 books, 400 pamphlets, and 75 maps. Also included are letters and other materials from noted Civil War authors such as Margaret Mitchell, Bruce Catton and Douglas Southall Freeman. The collection pays particular attention to Abraham Lincoln, the Confederate and Union navies, the Iron Brigade, and Wisconsin's role in the Civil War. The collection also includes the papers of such prominent individuals as Rufus King, who served as editor of *The Milwaukee Sentinel* and became the first commander of the Iron Brigade; his son, Charles King, a popular author and soldier; and Edward P. Adams, who served as quartermaster for a black regiment. The institute sponsors tours, speaker events, classes, and other events to attract Civil War experts and students. The Institute also offers a comprehensive Certificate of Civil War Studies educational and enrichment program (contact them for more information).

State Historical Society of Wisconsin

816 State Street
Madison, WI 53706
Phone: (608) 264-6400

Accommodations

A State by State listing of Bed & Breakfast Inns and Historic Hotels near Civil War Sites

Alabama

Grace Hall Bed & Breakfast
506 Lauderdale Street
Selma, AL 36701
Phone: (334) 875-5744
Fax: (334) 875-9967

Photo Courtesy of Grace Hall Bed & Breakfast

In April, 1865, Madison Jackson William, mayor of Selma, sent the Home Guard to fight the Battle of Selma from the porch of his home. After the battle, sixty percent of the city was burned by victorious Union forces. The mayor's home, now known as Grace Hall, was spared and survives to this day because Union officers occupied it after being received there by the mayor.

Offering six guest rooms, a beautiful entry hall, double parlors, and plenty of antiques, Grace Hall is now available for overnight accommodations, tours, parties, business and social breakfasts, luncheons, and dinners for 10 or more. Tours are by appointment.

Arkansas

Basin Park Hotel
12 Spring Street
Eureka Springs, AR 72632
Phone: (501) 253-7837
Reservations: 1-800-643-4972

Located near Pea Ridge National Military Park, the Basin Park Hotel offers 55 rooms and suites, some suites accommodating up to five guests. Amenities include phones, clock radios, and cable TV. Jacuzzi suites offer microwaves, VCRs, coffee makers, and refrigerators. The hotel also features the Balcony Restaurant & Bar, a dining room that seats 100 guests, a glass-roofed Atrium Room, and a ballroom on the top floor with a magnificent view of Eureka Springs.

Georgia

1810 West Inn

254 North Seymour Drive, N.W.
Thomson, GA 30824
Phone: (706) 595-3156
Reservations: 1-800-515-1810

Photo Courtesy of 1810 West Inn

The 1810 West Inn offers guest rooms (including a Honeymoon Suite) with private baths, central heat and air conditioning, antique furnishings, fireplaces, a screened veranda, complimentary social hour, and a Continental breakfast. The inn is situated on 12 landscaped acres, which includes nature trails. An informal conference room is available and small business groups are accommodated.

Beverly Hills Inn

65 Sheridan Drive, N.E.
Atlanta, GA 30305
Phone: (404) 233-8520

Located three minutes from the Atlanta Historical Society and the Governor's Mansion, Beverly Hills Inn offers eighteen spacious rooms, each with a kitchen, private bath, phone, color TV, balcony, and an eclectic collection of antiques throughout. You'll even find an authentic London taxicab parked in front. Enjoy a complimentary Continental breakfast before heading to the Cyclorama, only 15 minutes away, or Kennesaw Battlefield, only 30 minutes from the inn.

The Captain's Quarters

13 Barnhardt Circle
Fort Oglethorpe, GA 30742
Phone: (706) 858-0624
Fax: (706) 861-4053
Reservations: 1-800-710-6816

Step back into a more genteel era as you enter this beautifully renovated Classic Renaissance Revival home. Built in 1902 by the US Army for two captains and their families, the inn offers two suites and five rooms, all individually decorated and all with private baths. The spacious common rooms are decorated with family antiques and your hosts offer a three course breakfast each morning in the two dining rooms.

The Captain's Quarters makes the a great base for exploring the sites and history of the Chickamauga and Chattanooga campaigns. Located on the northern border of the Chickamauga National Military Park, the inn is less than 300 yards from the Visitors Center and Museum. Only twenty minutes away you'll find Lookout Mountain and downtown Chattanooga, or drive a little farther to numerous other historic, scenic, and recreational areas. A knowledgeable battlefield guide is available Sunday through Thursday by advanced arrangement.

The Gaslight Inn

1001 Saint Charles Avenue
Atlanta, GA 30306
Phone: (404) 875-1001
Fax: (404) 876-1001
Internet: http://www.gaslightinn.com

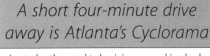

A short four-minute drive away is Atlanta's Cyclorama

The Gaslight Inn encompasses two restored homes, circa 1903 and 1913, near downtown Atlanta. The six-room inn offers a variety of accommodations ranging from affordable, elegant rooms to luxurious suites. Private, detached units are also available. All rooms have

Photo Courtesy of The Gaslight Inn

private baths and televisions, and include a continental breakfast.

From the inn you can walk to Copen Hill where General Sherman oversaw the burning of Atlanta in 1864. A short four-minute drive away is Atlanta's Cyclorama, a Civil War circular diorama depicting the Battle of Atlanta, and the Civil War museum. And Kennesaw Mountain National Park is a short twenty-five minute drive away.

Gordon-Lee Mansion

217 Cove Road
Chickamauga, GA 30707
Phone: (706) 375-4728
Reservations: 1-800-487-4728

Located just three miles from Chickamauga Battlefield and about ten miles from Lookout Mountain, the Gordon-Lee Mansion witnessed fierce action during the Civil War and is the only structure used during the Battle of Chickamauga which survived. It served as headquarters for General William Rosecrans, and afterwards as the main hospital treating the many casualties from the Battle of

Chickamauga (interestingly, Chickamauga means "River of Death," a prophetic name given by the Cherokee who once occupied the region). Six guest rooms are available, including a Honeymoon Suite and a two-room cabin near the mansion. All rooms come with private bathrooms, color cable TV (tastefully hidden in the armoires in the antebellum furnished rooms), and full breakfast. The mansion also contains an artifacts museum that is always open to guests for browsing.

The Holly Tree House Bed & Breakfast

217 W. Cuyler
Dalton, GA 30720
Phone: (706) 278-6620
Fax: (706) 278-1851

Located right on the line of the Blue and Gray Trail from Chattanooga to Atlanta, the Holly Tree House offers four spacious rooms with private baths, TV and VCR, and a full gourmet breakfast. An in-house video library is available, as well as a considerable amount of Civil War-related reading material. Dalton points of interest include the railway station (built in 1854) which was important during reconstruction, Dug Gap battlefield, and General Johnston's headquarters. Nearby points of interest include Tunnel Hill & Rocky Face Ridge (both part of the Atlanta campaign), Chickamauga Battlefield (20 minutes north), Kennesaw Battlefield and Railroad Museum (45 minutes south), Chattanooga—Battle of the Clouds (30 minutes north), and others.

Ivy Inn Bed & Breakfast

245 Fifth Avenue
Eton, GA 30724
Phone: (706) 517-0526
Fax: (706) 517-0526
Reservations: 1-800-201-5477

This Historic 1908 country Victorian home is located in Northwest Georgia, 25 minutes from the Battle of Dug Gap and Battle of Resaca. Chickamauga and Chattanooga are only 50 minutes away. The inn offers three guest rooms with private baths, TV and phone. Day trips to Atlanta or Ocoee River.

The Pathway Inn

501 South Lee Street
Americus, GA 31709
Phone: (912) 928-2078
Reservations: 1-800-889-1466

The Pathway Inn, a magnificent Victorian built in 1906, offers three bedrooms with private baths and whirlpool tubs. The home also features parlors, porches, down comforters, fireplaces, a sumptuous breakfast, afternoon tea, and an evening wine and cheese reception where guests can mingle and share the day's adventures.

The Pathway Inn is conveniently located eight miles from Andersonville Civil War Village. Near the village is the Andersonville National Historic Site, a notorious Civil War prison camp. The story of Andersonville was recently aired as a TNT movie, generating an increased interest in the site.

Pond View Inn

4200 Grady Street
Blackshear, GA 31516
Phone: (912) 449-3697
Reservations: 1-800-585-8659

Overlooking a pond and nestled on some 300 acres in Blackshear, Pond View Inn is the ideal location for a relaxing getaway. Guests can enjoy a hike through the fields and pastures, hayrides, fishing in one of the ponds, picnics, or just hanging out in one of the Inn's hammocks.

Four rooms and a suite are available, each with a private bath. A special Romance and Roses package is available that includes candlelight dinner, flowers, champagne, and breakfast in bed.

Pond View Inn will honor a $45 per night rate for any single Civil War buff traveler, plus $10 for each additional person.

Shellmont Bed & Breakfast Lodge

821 Piedmont Avenue, N.E.
Atlanta, GA 30308
Phone: (404) 872-9290

Three blocks from the site where Andrew's Raiders were hung, the Shellmont Bed & Breakfast offers guest suites with private baths in either the Main House or the Carriage House. Complimentary beverages, chocolates, and breakfast add to the southern hospitality, while Victorian archi- tecture, Tiffany windows, and authentic furnishings add ambiance. While the house is a post-Civil War structure, the land it sits on has yielded minie balls and other artifacts from the war.

Kentucky

Farley Place Bed & Breakfast

166 Farley Place
Paducah, KY 42001
Phone: (502) 442-2488

Authentically renovated to pre- serve its original charm, this mid-1800s Victorian offers period antiques, hardwood floors, a gracious foyer, spacious sitting room, and dining room. Rooms are available for either single or double occupancy, with or without a private sitting and dress- ing area, with either a private or a shared bath, and a choice of either a full or conti- nental breakfast.

Civil War enthusiasts should note that this is the former home of Emily Gant Jarrett, or "Aunt Em" as she was known lo- cally. She gained local fame on September 6, 1861, when Paducah was approached by Federal troops under General Grant. Cross- ing the Ohio River in gunboats, the Union forces spotted a large Confederate flag wav- ing from a pole in town and two of the gunboats began firing at the flag. Seeing their intent, Aunt Em raced to the flag pole and with the hesitant assistance of a young boy who worked for her, she rescued the flag and spirited it away. Despite an intense search of her home and General Grant's or- der that the flag be captured, it remained unmolested and hidden in Mrs. Jarrett's home for the remainder of the war. Twenty years later, it was laid in her casket, taking a place of honor next to the Southern patriot who risked so much to preserve the honor of the Confederacy.

Louisiana

Bed & Breakfast Inc.

1021 Moss Street
P.O. Box 52257
New Orleans, LA 70152-2257
Phone: (504) 488-4640

Fax: (504) 488-4639
Reservations: 1-800-729-4640

RESERVATION SERVICE

Bed & Breakfast Inc. offers a variety of historic accommodations in the New Orleans area. Romantic suites, intimate cottages, 19th century mansions, as well as turn-of-the-century family homes are available. Civil War buffs will want to stay in one of the 35 homes represented by B&B Inc. which are located within 2-4 miles of the Confederate Museum. With the distinction of being the oldest museum in Louisiana, the Confederate Museum houses the second-largest collection of Confederate memorabilia in the U.S., with over 100 battle flags, a collection of uniforms, rare Louisiana-made swords, and the personal effects of some of the South's greatest leaders. Reservations through Bed & Breakfast Inc. can be made by phone, fax, or mail and confirmation will be returned promptly. A free listing of homes is available upon request.

Maryland

Antrim 1844
30 Trevanion Road
Taneytown, MD 21787
Phone: (410) 756-6812
Reservations: 1-800-858-1844

If you're ready to spoil yourself—and you should—then check out the exquisite Antrim 1844. Located twelve miles from Gettysburg, the Antrim offers nine guest rooms within the mansion and five additional suites in out buildings (including one in The Ice House). Guest rooms feature antiques, fireplaces, canopy feather beds and marble baths or double jacuzzis. Activities include croquet, a target green, a tennis court, lawn bowling, horseshoes, badminton, a swimming pool with gazebo bar, or simply strolling about the twenty-three acre estate. But don't forget breakfast. The Antrim 1844 is renowned for its superb cuisine.

Inn At Antietam
220 East Main Street
P.O. Box 119
Sharpsburg, MD 21782
Phone: (301) 432-6601

Situated next door to the Antietam National Cemetery, and surrounded by the battlefield is a sanctuary called the Inn At Antietam.

From the porch you can look across the rolling farmland to the misty Blue Ridge Mountains. The Inn features four guest rooms with private baths, a solarium, parlor, dining room, wraparound porch with swings and rockers, and a patio.

Mississippi

The Generals' Quarters

924 Fillmore Street
Corinth, MS 38834
Phone: (601) 286-3325
Fax: (601) 287-8188

This 1872 Victorian Home is located in the downtown historic area of Corinth, a city rich in Civil War history. Fully restored, the Generals' Quarters offers rooms with private baths, cable TV, telephones, a full breakfast, an evening snack, and antique furnishings. A beautiful parlor and dining room on the first floor, a second floor lounge and veranda, and lovely gardens add to your enjoyment. The inn provides maps for a walking and a driving tour of the town, as well as directions to many historic and beautiful attractions close by.

Points of interest in the area include Battery Robinette, Curlee House (used by Confederate Generals Braxton Bragg and Earl Van Dorn, and later by Union General Henry Halleck), Corinth National Cemetery, Northeast Mississippi Museum, and Shiloh National Military Park (22 miles)

Highpoint

215 Linton Avenue
Natchez, MS 39120
Phone: (601) 442-6963
Reservations: 1-800-283-4099

Built on the grounds of the Clifton Plantation Home in 1890, the Victorian style Highpoint Bed & Breakfast is located in the historic district of Natchez, one block from the Mississippi River. The inn offers a choice of The King Room, Queen Room or Twin Room, each with modern or Victorian bath. Morning finds the inn filled with the

ca. 1890

aroma of custom-blended coffee and home baked muffins, which compliment the plantation breakfast.

Lincoln Limited Bed & Breakfast

Mississippi Reservation Service
P.O. Box 3479
Meridian, MS 39303
Phone: (601) 482-5483
Reservations: 1-800-633-MISS

RESERVATION SERVICE

Lincoln Limited Bed & Breakfast is a free reservation service that represents homes in various historical areas including Vicksburg and Natchez. Some homes still have Civil War memorabilia on display. A wide variety of homes, from Greek Revival mansions to Antebellum mansions are available. An extensive brochure of homes is available for $3.50.

The Mockingbird Inn

305 North Gloster
Tupelo, MS 38801
Phone: (601) 841-0286
Fax: (601) 840-4158

The seven guest rooms at The Mockingbird Inn feature international de-cor, private baths, private phones, cable TV, comfortable queen beds, and alarm clocks. Special services include Romance Packages, Sweetheart Gift Baskets, in-room massage therapy (by appointment), floral arrangements, and carriage rides on Friday and Saturday nights.

Robbins' Nest Bed & Breakfast

1523 Shiloh Road
Corinth, MS 38834
Phone: (601) 286-3109

This Southern Colonial Style home, circa 1870, sits on approximately 2 acres in the historic Civil War town of Corinth. The inn features three guest rooms on the second floor, complimentary afternoon tea and refreshments, and off street parking. Shiloh National Park is only a half hour drive from Corinth.

Missouri

Bellevue Bed & Breakfast

312 Bellevue
Cape Girardeau, MO 63701
Phone: (573) 335-3302
Reservations: 1-800-768-6822

Hunze Home

The truly unique Hunze Home, now Bellevue Bed & Breakfast, was designed and built in 1891 as a Victorian home with influences from several castles in Germany (Henry Hunze, the designer and first owner, remembered these castles from his native Germany). Fully restored by the present owners, much of the original grained woodwork and hardware remains. The home features four working pocket doors, four fireplaces, three bay windows, a beautiful staircase, and the original pull chain toilet in the downstairs bathroom. Amenities include air conditioning, private baths (one with a two-person whirlpool tub), off-street parking, family room with large screen TV, parlor with baby grand piano, full breakfast, and an available computer.

Local Civil War sites include Fort D (one of four forts built in a semicircle around the front of the village, known then as Camp Fremont), the Battle of Cape Girardeau Site (a marker was erected at the site near Broadway and Caruthers), Union Monument and Fountain, Confederate War Memorial, Common Pleas Courthouse, and Minton House, a Union smallpox hospital during the war.

Cedarcroft Farm
Bed & Breakfast
431 SE "Y" Hwy
Warrensburg, MO 64093
Phone: (816) 747-5728
Reservations: 1-800-368-4944
Email: bwayne@cedarcroft.com
Internet: http://www.cedarcroft.com

Built in 1887 by a Union army veteran, John A. Adams, Cedarcroft Farm Bed & Breakfast offers amenities such as central air conditioning, a more-than-you-can-eat country breakfast, a gas grill, a well-maintained horseshoe pit, 80 acres of woods, creeks, and meadows on a secluded farmstead where you might see deer, wild turkey, coyotes, hawks, or even a bobcat, and, for those just want to kick back, there's a collection of Civil War videos for the VCR.

Cedarcroft's web site offers Civil War links and the web pages for the 5th Missouri Infantry, CSA

Your host Bill Wayne can fill you in on the Civil War in Missouri and help you find important nearby battle sites such as Lexington and Lone Jack. Westport, Cole Camp, Warsaw, and Boonville are within easy driving distance, and Wilson's Creek is about two hours away.

Walnut Street Inn
900 E. Walnut
Springfield, MO 65806
Phone: (417) 864-6346
Fax: (417) 864-6184

Names as one of the "Top Twelve Inns in the Country" by Country Inns Magazine, the 14-room Walnut Street Inn is located in Springfield's historic district. Enjoy fireplaces, private baths (some with jacuzzis), private porches, and feather comforters. The Civil War Buff package includes tickets to General Sweeney's Museum, a perfectly packed picnic lunch to enjoy at Wilson's Creek National Battlefield, and an Innkeeper's Complimentary Gift Basket.

Woodstock Inn
1212 W. Lexington
Independence, MO 64050
Phone: (816) 833-2233

Located seven blocks west of Independence square, Woodstock Inn Bed & Breakfast features eleven guest rooms with private baths, separate heating and air conditioning, and a full breakfast. The inn sits approximately 500 yards north of the trench lines used during battles between the forces of Confederate General Sterling Price and Union General Thomas Ewing. The Harry Truman Home and Library is nearby, as well as numerous other historic sties.

North Carolina

The Curran House

312 South Third Street
Wilmington, NC 28401
Phone: (910) 763-6603
Reservations: 1-800-763-6603

Built in 1837 and located in Wilmington's Historic downtown, The Curran House Bed & Breakfast was originally known as The Mckay-Green House. The exterior architecture blends Queen Anne and Victorian Italianate.

Three uniquely furnished guest rooms are available at the inn, each with private bath, king or queen size bed, central air conditioning, and ceiling fans. Cable TV/VCR's are available upon request with no extra charge. A selection of books, magazines, and games are available in the living room, which serves as a gathering place for many of the inn's travelers.

A short walk will take you to the many shops, museums, galleries, restaurants, and waterfront attractions Wilmington has to offer.

The Inn at St. Thomas Court

101 South Second Street
Wilmington, NC 28401
Phone: (910) 343-1800
Fax: (910) 251-1149
Reservations: 1-800-525-0909

in the heart of Wilmington's historic downtown

Spacious one and two-bedroom suites await you at the exquisite Inn at St. Thomas Court. Some rooms are equipped with modern kitchenettes and washer/dryers. Microwaves, wet bars, whirlpool tubs, and VCRs are available. Each suite has its own private entrance, telephone, and TV. A breakfast basket and daily newspaper are delivered to your suite each morning. While nestled in the heart of Wilmington's historic downtown, take advantage of the local attractions, such as a horse-drawn carriage ride or a cruise aboard a 19th-century paddle wheel steamer. Golf and tennis facilities are also nearby.

James Place Bed & Breakfast

Nine South Fourth Street
Wilmington, NC 28401
Phone: (910) 251-0999
Reservations: 1-800-303-9444

The three uniquely decorated guest rooms at the James Place B&B are equipped with central air conditioning and ceiling fans to assure guest comfort. If you want to unwind, take a long soak in the hot tub on the private brick courtyard, or rock yourself stress-free in the wicker rocker on the front porch.

A large selection of attractions are within easy walking distance from the inn, including the Cape Fear Museum, horse-drawn carriage tours, Bellamy Mansion, Cotton Exchange Shops & Restaurants, a micro brewery, and antique shops. Further away you'll find Fort Fisher Battleground and Civil War Museum (20 minutes drive), Poplar Grove Plantation (15 minutes), Orton Plantation (25 minutes), and Historic Southport Antique Center (35 minutes).

Magnolia House Bed & Breakfast

315 George Street
New Bern, NC 28562
Phone: (919) 633-9488
Reservations: 1-800-601-9488

Located two doors from Tryon Palace, once home to the Royal Governor of North Carolina, and one block from the Civil War Museum, you will find Magnolia House centrally positioned in the heart of the historic district. Fine restaurants, quaint shops, museums, and antique shopping are within walking distance.

Magnolia House is furnished with local estate antiques and family pieces. Take a peek at owner John Trudo's collection of local Civil War artifacts and his assortment of books on local and North Carolina Civil War history. The inn offers three uniquely decorated guest rooms, each with a private bath. A full breakfast is served at your convenience. You may choose to have it in the charming dining room, on the front porch, or under the magnolia tree for which the inn was named. Honeymoon and anniversary packages are the house specialty and gift certificates are available.

Taylor House Inn

14 North Seventh Street
Wilmington, NC 28401
Phone: (910) 763-7581
Reservations: 1-800-382-9982

Five guest rooms are available at the Taylor House Inn, each with private bath, beds of brass, wicker, pine, or mahogany, antique chests, armoires, desks, fine linens, central air conditioning, and ceiling fans.

Breakfast by candlelight in the formal dining room offers up such culinary delights as bread pudding, cheese souffle, fresh fruit topped with yogurt, muffins, sweet potato pie, banana bread, gourmet coffee, tea, and blended juices.

Pennsylvania

Baladerry Inn

40 Hospital Road
Gettysburg, PA 17325
Phone: (717) 337-1342

Many private homes became informal field hospitals during the Civil War, such was the case with present-day Baladerry Inn. It once was a simple country home, but in July of 1863, it became caught up in the furious Battle of Gettysburg and served as a place of healing.

Today, the Baladerry Inn offers amenities such as spacious grounds, flower gardens, a tennis court, dining terrace, majestic Great Room, private baths, and a full country breakfast.

Battlefield Bed & Breakfast Inn

2264 Emmitsburg Road
Gettysburg, PA 17325
Phone: (717) 334-8804
Fax: (717) 334-7330

Nestled on 46 acres just off Emmitsburg Road, Battlefield Bed & Breakfast Inn is truly unique. A relaxing carriage ride over the historic grounds is included with every stay (except during Winter, or inclement weather). You'll also have the opportunity to participate in one of the daily Civil War historical demonstrations put on by the Inn, enjoy authentic Civil War music, take a leisurely stroll around the grounds, and partake of a breakfast of historic proportions.

The four Union and four Confederate guest quarters at the Battlefield Bed & Breakfast have a theme dedicated to the units which fought on the South Cavalry Battlefield; rooms such a General Merritt's Headquarters Suite, Reilly's North Carolina Battery, and the 2nd U.S. Dragoons.

Beechmont

315 Broadway
Hanover, PA 17331
Phone: (717) 632-3013
Reservations: 1-800-553-7009

Built thirty years before the Civil War, the Beechmont has seen its share of history, including the Battle of Hanover as it erupted just outside the Beechmont's front door. Available rooms include the Diller Suite, Hershey Suite, Custer Room, Farnsworth Room, Kilpatrick Room, Stuart Room, and Hampton Suite.

The Brafferton Inn

44 York Street
Gettysburg, PA 17325
Phone: (717) 337-3423

A sculpture of Colonel Brafferton directs guests safely to the front door of the Brafferton Inn where they are warmly greeted by new hosts, Jane and Sam Back. Having purchased the inn in February 1993, the Backs have renovated it to include ten guest rooms, each with a private bath and individual air conditioning, while retaining all of the convincingly historic charm of this antebellum Bed and Breakfast. In fact, in one of the upstairs guest rooms (aptly called the Bullet Room) curious visitors will discover a Union bullet lodged in the mantel of the fireplace where it has remained since the Battle of Gettysburg, July 1863.

All of the rooms are handsomely furnished and decorated with a large collection of 18th and 19th century antiques. Guests will enjoy relaxing in the atrium with its skylight roof and exposed brick walls, or behind the house on the patio amidst the herb and flower garden.

Country Escape Bed & Breakfast

275 Old Rt. 30
P.O. Box 195
McKnightstown, PA 17343-0195
Phone: (717) 338-0611
Fax: (717) 334-5227
Reservations: 1-800-484-3244 code 4371

Located six miles from Gettysburg on the same road the Confederates took to the Battle of Gettysburg, Country Escape Bed & Breakfast welcomes families and children. Enjoy a full breakfast after a restful night's sleep on one of their queen size beds. Amenities include individual air conditioning and heat in each guest room, a hot tub under the stars, children's play area, cable TV, and a wide range of video tapes available.

Dobbin House Tavern

Gettystown Inn
89 Steinwehr Avenue
Gettysburg, PA 17325
Phone: (717) 334-2100

The Gettystown Inn, located adjacent to the Dobbin House Tavern, offers five rooms with private baths, air conditioning, antiques, and a full country breakfast (served in the Historic 1776 Dobbin House Tavern). A cozy common room features cable TV, a VCR, and a large variety of Civil War tapes.

The Abigail Adams Ballroom, which holds up to 130 guests, is available for private parties, rehearsal dinners, wedding receptions, business meetings, and bus groups. Call or write for information on their banquet planning kit.

The Doubleday Inn

104 Doubleday Avenue
Gettysburg, PA 17325
Phone: (717) 334-9119

Situated directly on the Gettysburg National Military Park battlefield, The Doubleday Inn is a beautifully restored Colonial country inn which enjoys splendid views of historic Gettysburg and the battlefield. Guests enjoy the atmosphere from either the lovely grounds and guest patios or from the air-conditioned comfort inside.

The nine guest room inn is filled with cozy antiques and Civil War accents, including a small library about the battle. A full candlelight country breakfast is served daily along with tea or cool refreshments in the afternoon. On selected evenings, guests are treated to interesting discussions with knowledgeable battlefield historians. If you'd like to surprise someone with a romantic getaway, gift certificates are available.

Farnsworth House Inn

401 Baltimore St.
Gettysburg, PA 17325
Phone: (717) 334-8838
Fax: (717) 334-5862

Located in the heart of Gettysburg, the Farnsworth House Inn offers five air-conditioned rooms in mid-Victorian style, each with a private bath. While there, check out the Farnsworth House art gallery, bookshop, military relic shop (all wars), and nightly Gettysburg ghost stories (in-season).

Gettysburg Hotel

One Lincoln Square
Gettysburg, PA 17325
Phone: (717) 337-2000

Photo Courtesy of the Gettysburg Hotel

Experience the gracious hospitality of the newly reconstructed Gettysburg Hotel. Offering fine dining and a variety of charming guest rooms, including inside jacuzzi suites. Established in 1797, the hotel has a long list of distinguished guests, including President and Mrs. Eisenhower, Carl Sandburg, Henry Ford, General Ulysses S. Grant, and Daniel Webster. Three tastefully decorated meeting rooms are available and can accommodate up to 125 people. Civil War Romantic Escape Packages and Family Packages are also available.

Keystone Inn Bed & Breakfast

231 Hanover Street
Gettysburg, PA 17325
Phone: (717) 337-3888

This large brick, late Victorian style home was built in 1913 and features four guest rooms, each with a reading nook. Two rooms offer private baths, the other two have a shared bath. A full breakfast is served, with selections such as cinnamon-apple or blueberry pancakes, waffles, eggs, fresh fruit, and other dishes.

The Old Appleford Inn

218 Carlisle Street
Gettysburg, PA 17325
Phone: (717) 337-1711
Fax: (717) 334-6228
Reservations: 1-800-275-3373

Adjacent to Gettysburg College and only two blocks from Lincoln Square, The Old Appleford Inn offers 11 charming bedrooms with private baths and air conditioning. Individually decorated and furnished with antiques, some rooms feature canopy beds, working fireplaces, stained glass windows, or claw-foot tubs. Other amenities include a library with fireplace, spacious parlor with grand piano, and a plant-filled sunroom. Enjoy a breakfast of fresh fruit, homemade cakes and breads, and superb main dishes served in the Victorian candle-lit dining room.

The Old Barn Bed/ Breakfast & Country Inn

One Main Trail
Carroll Valley, PA 17320
Phone: (717) 642-5711

Photo Courtesy of Old Barn Bed/Breakfast & Country Inn

Only minutes from Gettysburg is the Old Barn Bed/Breakfast & Country Inn. Once a Confederate Army Field Hospital, the inn now offers fourteen guest rooms on four acres, including an in-ground swimming pool. Murder Mystery and special weekends are available in January & February. The inn is also available for family reunions, group seminars/workshops, VIP conferences, or other special events.

The Tannery Bed & Breakfast

449 Baltimore Street
Gettysburg, PA 17325
Phone: (717) 334-2454
Email: tannery@cvn.net

The Tannery offers lodging and a continental breakfast to Gettysburg visitors on the site of John Rupp's steam tannery. The house, which was built in 1868, has seven private guest rooms, each with a private bath. There is also a two-bedroom suite. Guests have access to the family living quarters, though most choose to gather on the front porch and enjoy a tall glass of lemonade instead. Located four blocks south of the town center, The Tannery is within easy walking distance of most Gettysburg museums, antique shops, restaurants, and other places of interest.

South Carolina

1837 Bed & Breakfast/Tea Room

126 Wentworth Street
Charleston, SC 29401
Phone: (803) 723-7166

Formerly a wealthy cotton planter's home with a brick carriage house, the 1837 Bed & Breakfast/Tea Room offers intimate accommodations in Charleston's Historic District. Enjoy walking to historic sites, restaurants, and antique shops. Rooms are individually decorated and furnished with canopied beds, antiques, period pieces, artwork, and other carefully chosen furnishings. Room amenities include private entrance and bath, air conditioning, refrigerators, color TV, full breakfast, and a complimentary pot of tea or coffee. Afternoon tea is served every day from 3-5 p.m.

The Battery Carriage House Inn

20 South Battery
Charleston, SC 29401
Phone: (803) 727-3100
Fax: (803) 727-3130
Reservations: 1-800-775-5575

One of Charleston's most gracious antebellum homes, The Battery Carriage House Inn offers all the elegance one would expect from a home used in the filming of "North and South" and "Queen." Eleven quiet

Photo Courtesy of The Battery Carriage House Inn

garden rooms feature such modern luxuries as Cable TV with HBO, private steam baths or whirlpool tubs, robes, newspaper, and a silver tray continental breakfast.

Just beyond the gates of the estate lies White Point Gardens, the Battery, and Charleston Harbor—while across the water lies Fort Sumter.

The Capers-Motte House
69 Church Street
Charleston, SC 29401
Phone: (803) 722-2263

The pre-revolutionary 20-room, three-story mansion on Church Street, known as The Capers-Motte House, was built around 1735 and stands as one of Charleston's historic gems. Faithfully restored and furnished in Georgian style, the inn is rich in history, including an indentation thought to be from a Union shell during the Civil War.

Located only one block from the Charleston waterfront where Ft. Sumter is plainly visible, the inn has its own private view of the historic fort from one of the third-floor bedrooms—a quiet peek at the place where it all began in April 1861.

East Bay Bed & Breakfast
301 East Bay Street
Charleston, SC 29401
Phone: (803) 722-4186

Birthplace and home of Phoebe Pember, who was one of twenty people and events chosen for the 1995 special edition of Civil War stamps. Call or write for current room rates and availability.

Historic Charleston Bed & Breakfast
57 Broad Street
Charleston, SC 29401
Phone: (803) 722-6606
Fax: (803) 722-9589
Information: 1-800-743-3583

RESERVATION SERVICE

Representing more than 50 Bed & Breakfast locations in Charleston, Historic Charleston Bed & Breakfast offers a one-stop resource for lodging in this historic city. Office hours are Monday through Friday, 9:00 a.m. to 5:00 p.m.

Twenty-Seven State Street Bed & Breakfast
27 State Street
Charleston, SC 29401
Phone: (803) 722-4243

Built as a private residence circa 1800, Twenty-Seven State Street is located in the French Quarter of the original walled city. The inn's carriage house suites are furnished in antiques and reproductions and include a spacious bedroom/living room, private bath, kitchenette, and private entrance. Other amenities include a morning paper, fresh fruit and flowers, cable TV, private phone, central heat and air, bicycles, and parking.

As a bonus, the inn is only two blocks from Charleston Harbor and its rich, inviting history.

Tennessee

Bed & Breakfast About Tennessee

P.O. Box 110227
Nashville, TN 37222-0227
Phone: (615) 331-5244
Email: FDodom71282@aol.com

RESERVATION SERVICE

This service offers thoroughly screened hosts and a questionnaire placement system whereby a compatible host is carefully selected to insure a pleasant experience. A full travel service is also provided, including car rentals, sight-seeing and VIP tours, special events tickets, airline, cruise line, railroad, and steamship tickets. Accommodations available in:

Nashville	Memphis	Knoxville
Murfreesboro		Clarksville
Andersonville		Monteagle
Gatlinburg		Cookeville
Chattanooga		Greenville
Shelbyville		Columbia
Jonesboro		Franklin
Buchanan		Smithville
Crossville		Tullahoma
Sewanee		Lynchburg
Jackson		Altamont

Bluff View Inn

412 East Second Street
Chattanooga, TN 37403
Phone: (615) 265-5033

Fine art and antiques can be found throughout this 1928 Colonial Revival mansion. Spacious rooms and suites with private baths are offered, decorated with heirloom furnishings and stately fireplaces. The inn recently purchased the T.C. Thompson House, located nearby, which features four guest rooms on the main floor and two suites upstairs. The suites provide fully-equipped kitchens, sitting rooms, private bedrooms, and spacious bathrooms with large jetted tub/showers. A full gourmet breakfast is served between 7-9 a.m. in the Renaissance Commons.

Photo Courtesy of Bluff View Inn

suites provide fully-equipped kitchens, sitting rooms, private bedrooms, and spacious bathrooms with large jetted tub/showers

English Manor

6304 Murray Lane
Brentwood, TN 37027-6210
Phone: (615) 373-4627
Phone: (615) 373-4640
Reservations: 1-800-332-4640

Seven guest rooms are available at English Manor, covering a spectrum from the modest to the luxurious. All rooms include phones, TVs, air conditioning, tables & chairs, ceiling fans, and a full breakfast. A 50-inch TV with VCR is available in the lounging area. The English Manor also offers catering for almost any occasion.

Virginia

Berryville Bed & Breakfast

100 Taylor Street
Berryville, VA 22611
Phone: (540) 955-2200

The Berryville Bed & Breakfast offers three comfortable rooms, each with private bath, and one suite with two bedrooms sharing one bath. The house, built in 1915, is in the English country style and offers an acre of grounds for enjoyment. The master suite features a fireplace. Civil War enthusiasts will enjoy the Shenandoah Room which features artifacts and prints of the war.

The inn is located only ten miles from Winchester—which changed sides 72 times during the war—and twenty miles from Harpers Ferry. Museums and battlefields abound, many within a half hour drive. Nearby battle sites include Bolivar Heights, Cedar Creek, Cool Spring, and Kernstown. Antietam, Manassas, and New Market are an hour's drive and Gettysburg can be reached in less than two hours. The Berryville Bed & Breakfast houses a number of books and magazines on the Civil War. Owners Don and Jan Riviere will be happy to help you plan a memorable visit to the beautiful Shenandoah Valley.

Chester House

43 Chester Street
Front Royal, VA 22630
Phone: (540) 635-3937
Fax: (540) 636-8695
Reservations: 1-800-621-0441

The stately Chester House mansion offers six spacious rooms, plus The Carriage House (a private hideaway for two). Three sitting rooms and nine fireplaces add to the ambiance. Minutes away you'll find Warren Rifles Confederate Museum, Belle Boyd Cottage, caverns, battlefields, great restaurants, wineries, horseback riding, golf, tennis, fishing, and canoeing on the Shenandoah River.

Cross Roads Inn

9222 John Sevier Road
New Market, VA 22844
Phone: (540) 740-4157

The Cross Roads Inn features bedrooms with private baths, four-poster and canopy beds with down comforters, a gourmet breakfast, and afternoon coffee/tea with Mary-Lloyd's famous strudel. Antiquing, museums, caverns, and, of course, Civil War sites are located nearby.

Edgewood Plantation

4800 John Tyler Memorial Highway
Charles City, VA 23030
Phone: (804) 829-2962

Built in 1849, Edgewood Plantation has a colorful history that includes links to Benjamin Harrison and U.S. President William Henry Harrison. During the Civil War, Edgewood's third floor was used by Confederate generals to spy on McClellan's troops as the camped at nearby Berkeley Plantation. On June 15, 1862, J.E.B. Stuart stopped at Edgewood on his way to warn General Lee of the Union Army's strength. The tragedy of the Civil War is etched in one of the window panes at Edgewood, where Elizabeth "Lizzie" Rowland, scratched her name as she waited in vain for her lover to return from the war. He never did and Lizzie died of a broken heart. Some say she still waits, watching for her lover from her upstairs window.

Edgewood offers eight opulent rooms, furnished with antiques, lavish canopy beds, and lace and damask window treatments. Spend the night in the elegance of Scarlett's Room, Jeb Stuart's Room, or Prissy's Quarters. Six room are located in the main house and two are in the former slave's quarters. All rooms are air conditioned. Other amenities include gazebos, a swimming pool, formal gardens, and a full Plantation candlelight breakfast in the dining room.

Edgewood specializes in Victorian High Teas, personalized weddings, corporate meetings, banquets, and special holiday tea parties and luncheons at a time when the home is adorned with 17 Christmas trees.

The Emmanuel Hutzler House

2036 Monument Avenue
Richmond, VA 23220
Phone: (804) 353-6900

Located in the center of the 1.3 mile Monument Avenue historic district,

three miles from the White House and Museum of the Confederacy, and four miles from the Richmond Battlefield Park, The Emmanuel Hutzler House is a great jumping off point for Civil War sightseers. Take an evening stroll down Monument Avenue and see towering statues of Confederate heroes, Lee, Stuart, Maury, and President Jefferson Davis.

The spacious rooms at The Emmanuel Hutzler House are furnished in antiques and reproductions, with premium bedding, linens, carpeting, and queen-size beds. Some baths have jacuzzi tubs. All rooms offer telephones, cable television, and central air. Lighted, off-street parking is another amenity.

Federal Crest Inn

1101 Federal Street
Lynchburg, VA 24504
Phone: (804) 845-6155
Fax: (804) 845-1445
Reservations: 1-800-818-6155

The Federal Crest Inn, a Georgian Revival Mansion, circa 1909, is located a short twenty minutes away from historic Appomattox. The home features magnificent woodwork and architectural details, with amenities such as queen canopy beds, whirlpool tub, bedroom fireplaces, air conditioning, a full country breakfast, and a gift shop. Convenient to the Confederate Cemetery, Fort Early, Pest House/Medical Museum, Appomattox, golf, vineyards, antiquing, and all area colleges.

Fort Early Bed & Breakfast

3629 Fort Avenue
Lynchburg, VA 24501
Phone: (804) 846-3628

Located in historic Lynchburg, Fort Early Bed & Breakfast offers rooms with queen size beds and private baths. Local Civil War attractions include Fort Early, only two blocks away from the bed & breakfast, and Appomattox. Other attractions include Poplar Forest, Thomas Jefferson's summer retreat, Red Hill, last home and burial place of Patrick Henry, and the Blue Ridge Parkway.

Killahevlin

1401 N. Royal Avenue
Front Royal, VA 22630
Phone: (540) 636-7335
Fax: (540) 636-8694
Reservations: 1-800-847-6132

This historic Edwardian mansion is situated on a Civil War encampment site and is reputed to be the location where two of Mosby's Rangers were hanged. The owners recommend you bring your metal detectors.

The inn offers 6 rooms/suites with private bathrooms and amenities that include whirlpool tubs, working fireplaces, interesting antiques, a wonderful view of the Blue Ridge Mountains, a spacious screened veranda, porches, gazebos, and an ornamental koi fish pond with waterfall. Enjoy complimentary wine and Irish draft beer on tap at Killahevlin's private Irish Pub. Breakfast includes such delights as freshly ground Kona coffee or gourmet teas, fresh fruits and juices, specialty cereals, homemade goodies, preserves, Belgian waffles, country sausage, french toast, crispy bacon, or a scrumptious omelette made to order.

Civil War attractions in the area include the Confederate Museum, the Belle Boyd Cottage, Belle Grove Plantation, Cedar Creek Battlegrounds, and New Market Battlefield.

La Vista Plantation

4420 Guinea Station Road
Fredericksburg, VA 22408-8850
Phone: (540) 898-8444
Reservations: 1-800-529-2823

From 1865-1900, Stonewall Jackson's death bed was stored at La Vista Plantation. Now on display at the Stonewall Jackson Shrine, the bed and its famous occupant have attached themselves forever to the history of La Vista. Located at the heart of some of the fiercest fighting of the Civil War, La Vista now offers a peace- ful and relaxing setting. The ten-acre grounds present a balance of pastures, woods, gardens, and a pond stocked with bass and sunfish.

Rooms include premium bedding, private baths, air conditioning, color TV, radio, refrigerator, alarm clock, and phone. The English basement apartment is approximately 1200 square feet, has two bedrooms and a sitting room, and a fully equipped plantation kitchen. Perfect for groups of 3 or more.

Linden Row Inn

100 East Franklin Street
Richmond, VA 23219
Phone: (804) 783-7000
Fax: (804) 648-7504
Reservations: 1-800-348-7424

Built in 1847, the 71-room Linden Row Inn offers a taste of Southern hospitality, to include Southern cuisine, a complimentary continental breakfast, and an evening wine and cheese reception in the

Parlor. Edgar Allan Poe fans will be delighted to know that Linden Row's garden was the author's childhood playground. The brick-walled garden and patio now serve as the courtyard of the Inn.

Photo Courtesy of Linden Row Inn

Rooms at the Linden Row Inn are individually climate controlled, furnished in period antiques, and include cable TV and AM/FM radio. The inn is also within walking distance of the Valentine Museum, White House and Museum of the Confederacy, and other attractions. The Inn's Board Room and Parlor Suites are available for conferences and small meetings.

The Madison House Bed & Breakfast
413 Madison Street
Lynchburg, VA 24504
Phone: (804) 528-1503
Reservations: 1-800-828-MHBB

Featuring a private collection of antiques in the parlors, a library of books, some dating back to the late 1700s and 1800s, as well as numerous books on the Civil War, a full breakfast, and an afternoon tea, your stay at the Madison House Bed & Breakfast will be one you won't soon forget.

Each bed chamber offers a full, private bath, air conditioning, cable TV, telephone, working fireplace, 100% cotton sheets, convenience items such as toothpaste, shampoo, aspirin, hair dryers, soft bathrobes, and oversized bath towels. Centrally located off Business Route 29 in downtown Lynchburg, the Madison House is close to shopping, colleges, historic points of interest, antiques, ships, restaurants, and Civil War sites.

The inn is available for special events such as business meetings, bridal or baby showers, rehearsal dinners, holiday parties, weddings, and receptions.

Mr. Patrick Henry's Inn
2300-02 East Broad Street
Richmond, VA 23223
Phone: (804) 644-1322

This pre-Civil War inn, cast in Greek Revival architecture, offers a choice of four Colonial suites, each with a fireplace, private bath, and kitchenette. The inn also features a gourmet restaurant, an English pub, and a garden patio.

Accommodations can be arranged for private parties, business functions, rehearsal dinners, and receptions.

North Bend Plantation Bed & Breakfast
12200 Weyanoke Road
Charles City, VA 23030
Phone: (804) 829-5176

Built in 1819 for the sister of William Henry Harrison, the ninth president of the United States, North Bend Plantation is rich in Civil War history. In 1864, Union troops under General Sheridan occupied the area, during which time they dug trenches from Kittewan, across North Bend to Weyanoke and the James River. Gen-

eral Sheridan used North Bend as his headquarters while his corps built a pontoon bridge across the James River. When the bridge was complete, Sheridan and his men proceeded on to Petersburg. Today, Civil War breastworks survive at the eastern edge of North Bend, and The Sheridan Room houses the desk used by General Sheridan during his occupation, an artifact which is now a treasured family heirloom.

Five guest rooms are available at the North Bend Plantation, all with private baths. A full country breakfast is served, including dishes such as waffles, omelets, biscuits, bacon, sausage, fruit, and juice. A fine collection of old and rare books is available, including volumes of *Harpers Pictoral History of the Civil War*, *The Official Records of the War Between the States*, *Confederate History of the Charles City County*, and *A Confederate Youths Primer*. Lawn games and a pool are also available.

The Page House Inn
323 Fairfax Avenue
Norfolk, VA 23507
Phone: (804) 625-5033
Fax: (804) 623-9451
Reservations: 1-800-599-7659
Email: PageBnB@aol.com

Your stay at the Page House Inn includes room amenities such as private baths, telephones, TV and clock radios, luxurious linens, cotton towels, robes, fine furnishings and antiques, a full candy dish at all times, reading material, and insulated walls and floors for sound attenuation. Some rooms have fireplaces and whirlpool tubs.

The inn is within walking distance of a number of attractions, including the Harrison Opera House, antique shops, historic walking tours, MacArthur Memorial, river cruises, and Hampton Roads Naval Museum (where you can see a display and artifacts of the U.S.S. Monitor).

The William Catlin House
2304 East Broad Street
Richmond, VA 23223
Phone: (804) 780-3746

Located in the Historic Church Hill District of Richmond, The William Catlin House was built in 1845 and is now furnished with a variety of antiques, family heirlooms, period furniture, canopied four-poster beds, large armoires, oriental rugs, crystal chandeliers, and, well, hospitality.

Working fireplaces in the bedrooms, goose down pillows, and sherry and mints only add to the luxury.

Nearby attractions include the Valentine Museum, the White House and Museum of the Confederacy, battlefield parks, and plantations. Non-Civil War attractions include St. John's Church (site of Patrick Henry's famous "Liberty or Death" speech), the Edgar Allan Poe Museum, King's Dominion, and other historic and entertainment-related attractions.

West Virginia

Boydville

601 South Queen Street
Martinsburg, WV 25401
Phone: (304) 263-1448

Photo Courtesy of Boydville

This 1812 Manor House sits on ten acres in historic Martinsburg, ten miles from Antietam and twenty miles from Harpers Ferry. The Inn has a rich Civil War history that includes many visits by Stonewall Jackson, the spying career of Belle Boyd, and the direct intervention of President Lincoln to save the manor house from being burned by Union troops.

Six guest rooms are available, four with private baths and two that share a bath. Rooms are furnished in American and English antiques and the Inn offers original artwork that includes a mural painted in France in the 1830s and foyer wallpaper hand painted in England especially for Boydville in 1812. An expanded Continental Breakfast is included.

Harpers Ferry Guest House

P.O. Box 1079
800 Washington Street
Harpers Ferry, WV 25425
Phone: (304) 535-6955

The Harpers Ferry Guest House offers large, bright, air-conditioned rooms, modern baths, queen size four-poster beds, full breakfast, and off-street parking. Harpers Ferry National Historical Park is minutes away and Antietam Battlefield is within easy driving distance.

McMechen House Inn

109 North Main Street
Moorefield, WV 26836
Phone: (304) 538-7173
Reservations: 1-800-2WVA INN

The McMechen House Inn offers seven guest rooms, three private meeting rooms, an outdoor deck, and a top-notch restaurant. During the Civil War the house

served as headquarters to both Union and Confederate forces. Breakfast and afternoon tea are included with each room. Amenities include phone, Fax machine, TV/VCR, and an antique/book/gift shop on the premises. The inn is also available for weddings, corporate receptions, holiday parties, and other special occasions.

Special events dealing with the Civil War are occasionally offered at the inn, such a one-man show titled "The Story of W.H. Maloney" which tells the story of how a visit to McMechen House affected the outcome of the Battle of Moorefield. The inn is also an active participant in The Battle of Moorefield Commemorative Weekend, held in August.

Ranson - Armory House

690 Washington Street
Harpers Ferry, WV 25425
Phone: (304) 535-2142

From John Brown to Stonewall Jackson, Harpers Ferry certainly saw its share of action before and during the Civil War. A silent witness to these events was the home at 690 Washington Street. Built in 1830, this home, the Ranson-Armory House, sat quietly through the conflict.

Rooms at the Ranson - Armory House offer private baths, mountain views, and a wealth of history just outside your door waiting to be explored. Antietam National Battlefield is also within driving distance.

Thomas Shepherd Inn

Corner of German & Duke Street
P.O. Box 1162
Shepherdstown, WV 25443
Phone: (304) 876-3715
Fax: (304) 876-1386
Email: Mrg@intrepid.net
Internet: http://www.intrepid.net/
    thomas_shepherd

Located on part of the 222-acre site granted to Thomas Shepherd (the town's namesake) in 1734, Thomas Shepherd Inn was built in the mid-19th century as the Lutheran Church's parsonage. Today it features seven spacious, air conditioned rooms with private bath. The living room, two formal dining rooms, library, and porch add to the ambiance. A full breakfast and complimentary beverages are also included.

Antietam National Battlefield and Harpers Ferry are nearby, as well as other historic and entertainment attractions.

Master Index

Democracy and the Constitution

Democracy and the Constitution

Essays by Walter Berns

The AEI Press

Publisher for the American Enterprise Institute

WASHINGTON, D.C.

To Robert Goldwin
treasured adviser and friend

Distributed to the Trade by National Book Network, 15200 NBN Way, Blue Ridge Summit, PA 17214. To order call toll free 1-800-462-6420 or 1-717-794-3800. For all other inquiries please contact the AEI Press, 1150 Seventeenth Street, N.W., Washington, D.C. 20036 or call 1-800-862-5801.

Library of Congress Cataloging-in-Publication Data

Berns, Walter, 1919-
Democracy and the constitution : essays / by Walter Berns.
     p. cm.
   Includes index.
   ISBN-10 0-8447-4239-2 (pbk : alk. paper)
   ISBN-13 978-0-8447-4239-7
   1. Constitutional law—United States. 2. Democracy. I. Title.

KF4550.B389 2006
342.73—dc22

                                                               2006019283

   11 10 09 08 07 06   1 2 3 4 5 6

Printed in the United States of America

Contents

Introduction

One of the distinctive things about America is that its Founders were political theorists as well as practitioners. Consider, as the most telling example, the Declaration of Independence. It was drafted by Thomas Jefferson, John Adams, and Benjamin Franklin, men who had distinguished political careers, but who also wrote books and scientific papers and founded universities (Jefferson the University of Virginia and Franklin the Philadelphia Academy, which became the University of Pennsylvania). Franklin was also one of the founders of our first so-called learned society (the American Philosophical Society), and Jefferson served as one of its first presidents. As for James Madison, Alexander Hamilton, and John Jay, they combined under the pseudonym of Publius to write *The Federalist* (or *Federalist Papers*), which has been described in our own time as "the most important work in political science that has ever been written, or is likely ever to be written, in the United States."[1]

Not only were they all political theorists, but they were completely confident of the theory they espoused. "We hold these truths to be self-evident," they declared in 1776, that all men are equally endowed with certain unalienable rights, and that government is instituted "to secure these rights." They believed it important that students, specifically university students, receive instruction in these matters. Accordingly, when designing the curriculum for his University of Virginia, Jefferson proposed that students be thoroughly schooled in "the general principles of liberty and the rights of man, in nature and in society." To this end, he recommended, among the books to be read, John Locke's treatises of government, and, of course, the Declaration of Independence, *The Federalist*, and the Constitution. Who better to assign this reading than professors of political science? At any rate, I thought it appropriate to devote a good portion of my time in the classroom to expounding and defending the principles of liberal democracy and the institutions embodying it here in the United States.

First among these institutions is the Constitution, which, alas, is not always taken seriously by judges, even Supreme Court justices. They tend to treat their judicial commissions as letters of marque authorizing them to keep the Constitution in tune with the times, as the saying goes, which in practice means *their* view of the times and what *they* think the times require. For example, in the University of Michigan Law School case of 2003,[2] the Court held—presumably because the "times" required them to hold—that a race-conscious admissions policy was not unconstitutional at the time, but would become so in twenty-five years' time; which is to say, the policy was obviously unconstitutional, but we are not yet prepared to say so.[3]

What is true of the Constitution is also true of the Declaration of Independence. We have it on the authority of James Madison (see *Federalist* 39) that the Constitution is "reconcilable with the fundamental principles of the Revolution," but courses on those principles are hard to find in our universities. For example, the history department at Harvard, our oldest and most distinguished university, apparently does not have a course on the American Revolution or on the Founding of the United States. Yet, the subject would seem to be of considerable importance. Did God have something to do with the Founding? Can we do without him now? Was the Revolution really a revolution? On the same subject, what is the provenance of our unalienable rights, and which of them, if any, do we retain after government is instituted?

These are enduring questions, and their importance justifies the publication, in most cases the republication, of these essays, beginning with those on constitutionalism. What is more, the United States happens now to be engaged in the effort to export democracy—meaning, I trust, constitutional democracy—to countries that have never known it, an effort in which I have personally been involved. As I wrote in the preface of my book, *Making Patriots*:

> In 1987, the bicentenary of our Constitution, I was in Brazil, where the people had recently overthrown a military dictatorship and had begun the process of writing a democratic constitution. I had been invited to lecture on constitutionalism. At one place, a university in Recife, after I had finished my prepared remarks, someone got up and denounced, not me, but the local

official who had sponsored my appearance. "Why," he shouted, "did you invite an American? What can they tell us about constitutions? They've had only one. Why didn't you invite a Bolivian? They've had a hundred."[4]

There was, of course, good reason to invite an American to address this subject. Who else? Who is better suited to do it? What other country can match our experience of constitutional government? Besides, there is nothing peculiarly American about our principles. On the contrary, they are abstract and universal principles of political right, a product of political philosophy; any people might subscribe to them, and Jefferson expected that, in the course of time—and with a little help?—every other people would do so. Speaking of the Declaration of Independence on the eve of its fiftieth anniversary, he said,

> May it be to the world, what I hope it will be, (to some parts sooner, to others later, but finally to all,) the signal of arousing men to burst the chains [that bind them], and to assume the blessings and security of self-government. . . . All eyes are opened, or opening, to the rights of man.[5]

As always, I am grateful for the support given me over the years by the American Enterprise Institute and especially its president, Christopher DeMuth, who encouraged me to publish this volume of essays, and by Morgan Goatley, who, quite literally, put them all together. My greatest debt is to my daughter, Elizabeth Fradkin, who, at a time when I was incapacitated, stepped in, read and corrected the proofs. For this, and for her devotion generally, I am very grateful.

With the exception of "Under God" and "Remembering Herbert Storing," all of these essays were published earlier, the earliest in 1987. I have made modest revisions to some of them for this publication, but others I have been content to leave as they were. In one way or another, they all address the subject of constitutional democracy, which, as we know from experience, is never out of date.

Washington, D.C.
May 2006

Part I

Constitutionalism

Preface

Tocqueville does not use the word, but he was speaking of constitutional- ism when he said that men living in democratic centuries "do not readily comprehend the utility of forms." Indeed, he contends that they "scorn" them, even "hate" them, because they get in their way. By "forms" he means the ways, especially the proper ways, of doing things; in our case, they prescribe the powers of government (legislative, executive, judicial), by whom the powers are to be exercised, and, of greatest importance, *how* they are to be exercised.

Forms are not designed to be efficient, and they can be cumbersome or, as Tocqueville puts it, inconvenient. But, he says, this "inconvenience" is precisely what renders them so useful to freedom, their principal merit being to serve as a barrier between the strong and the weak, he who governs and he who is governed, to slow down the one and to give the other the time to recollect himself. He concludes by saying that "democratic peoples naturally have more need of forms than other peoples, and they naturally respect them less."[1]

If so, this makes the American achievement all the more remarkable, and the judgment of its people commendable. In 1787, their appointed leaders devised a very formal Constitution, one that imposed a variety of limits on popular rule, and, in 1789, by ratifying it, they themselves agreed to live under and within it. And so they have now for more than two hundred years.

1

Ancients and Moderns: The Emergence of Modern Constitutionalism

The idea of constitutionalism, or limited government, is as old as political science, but there were constitutions before there was constitutionalism or political science. The ancient Greek cities had constitutions; fragments of more than a hundred of them have been preserved in the works of ancient grammarians and lexicographers. But Aristotle's *Constitution of Athens* is the only one to have survived more or less intact and recognizable for what it is, and what it is not.

The *Constitution of Athens* is not a document (or part of a document) in any way similar to the Constitution of the United States; which is to say, it is not a written constitution. It is, instead, a history of a constitution, but unlike the British it does not begin with, or take its bearings from, anything similar to Magna Carta. It is a history of changing constitutions (or "constitutional orders")—monarchy, oligarchy, democracy, anarchy, tyranny—but not a history of constitutional change. Ruler followed ruler, time and again and for years on end, but none could claim a legal or constitutional right to rule, not even the legendary Solon, to say nothing of his successors.

Solon (Plutarch devotes a chapter to him in his *Lives*) first came to public notice by pretending to be mad, and, even so, with the city at war with itself—the people at war with the wealthy—he was chosen to be archon and lawgiver, "the rich consenting because he was wealthy, the poor because he was honest."[1] A famous lawgiver, he said he wrote laws "for a hundred years," but the people "began to quarrel" during his absence in Egypt and Cyprus, and after his return Pisistratus seized power. Then, having established a tyranny, Pisistratus was driven into exile by the parties of Megacles and Lycurgus.[2] So goes this history, and it is clearly not a history of constitutional government or constitutionalism.

4

According to its editors and translators, the *Constitution of Athens* "cannot have been intended for publication," and they go on to suggest that Aristotle (and his students) must have written it before he wrote the *Politics*.[3] This is almost surely the case. The former is an account of what is, the latter an attempt to provide knowledge of what might be; and this, according to Aristotle's own principles, cannot be done without knowing what is. Which is to say, theory depends (in part) on practice. Moreover, in the beginning—and Aristotle was at the beginning—political philosophy was the study of politics unmediated by, or without reference to, any previous philosophic study of politics.

So it was that—unlike Machiavelli, who had to contend with Plato and Aristotle (and silently with the Bible), or Locke with Filmer, Rousseau with Hobbes and Locke, Marx with Hegel, Nietzsche with Socrates, and Heidegger with everybody—Aristotle could proceed directly to the study of the fundamental political questions: What is the *polis* (city) and the citizen, and what is the best form of government, or constitution? The whole of book 4 of the *Politics* is devoted to answering (or, at least, discussing) the latter question; but since the best constitution is ideal (and therefore unattainable), the question becomes, which is the best practicable constitution?

Many factors enter into the decision, such as a city's size, location, wealth, and whether its people are capable of living and willing to live under the rule of law. After weighing the many factors, Aristotle decides in favor of what has come to be called a "mixed regime," which he describes in one place as a "mixture of oligarchy and democracy." From this mixture comes a middle class, and it is clear, he says, that the "political community administered by the middle class is the best."[4] It alone "is free from factions," and for that reason is likely to be stable and its rule moderate. He gives it the name "polity"; it is his version of constitutional government.

The modern case for constitutional government was best stated by the reputed Father of the American Constitution, James Madison. "In framing a government which is to be administered by men over men," he said in *Federalist* 51,

> the greatest difficulty lies in this: you must first enable the government to control the governed; and in the next place oblige it to control itself. A dependence on the people is, no doubt, the

primary control on government; but experience has taught mankind the necessity of auxiliary precautions.

What he proposed as a precaution, and what the Americans adopted, was a separation of powers, a system different (but not altogether different) from the first mixed constitution to be adopted, that of republican Rome.

Designed so as to avoid the defects inherent in each of the simple forms of government—monarchy, aristocracy, and democracy—Rome's mixed constitution did not separate powers, but it guarded against an undue concentration of power by a system of checks and balances. Rome's political philosopher (Cicero) favored it because it provided all that could be hoped for from a constitution: "an even balance of rights, duties, and functions, so that the magistrates have enough power, the counsels of the eminent citizens enough influence, and the people enough liberty."[5]

The Greek historian Polybius (205–123 BC) said that this mixture was so successful "that it was impossible even for a native to pronounce with certainty whether the whole system was aristocratic, democratic, or monarchical."[6] In fact, however, any native with his wits about him could have seen that the aristocracy played the decisive role in this government. Cicero was candid about this. He said that the success of this system depended on the aristocracy, which must be "free from dishonor [and] a model for the rest of the citizens."[7] The English constitutionalists, Bolingbroke, Burke, Bagehot, and even John Stuart Mill, could appreciate this. In fact, could it not be said that England's success depended on the aristocratic element in its own constitution?

But what is meant by success? Montesquieu, writing in the mid-eighteenth century, denied that the Roman constitution was a success. Polybius—Montesquieu referred to him as the "judicious Polybius"—declared it one, but his account was theoretical and idealized, unsupported by evidence. Montesquieu looked at its history, and found, instead of a stable, institutionalized balance of factions, a slow but steady evolution toward mob rule. He wondered whether there might not be a way of improving on the Roman system, and, with this in mind, he examined the English constitution.

He did this in a chapter entitled, "Of the Constitution of England," but his account of the English constitution was as much idealized as

Polybius's account of the Roman.[8] And deliberately so. The English figures in his account only because it bore some resemblance to the form of government under which political liberty was best secured. This proved to be one in which the three powers of government—the executive, legislative, and judicial—were divided, and in which the legislative was also divided, one house representing the body of the people, the other representing the nobles, those distinguished by birth, wealth, or honors. The executive, in turn, should be a monarch, and possess the veto power, and the judiciary was to be independent of the other branches because its task—like that of the judiciary under the American Constitution—was to protect civil liberties, property rights, and the rule of law.

But the English differed from Montesquieu's model constitution in important respects. The House of Commons could not, at that time, be said to represent the body of the English people. Its franchise was limited to a few propertied men, and its leading figures—Walpole, Stanhope, Pitt— were anything but common. Nor could a judge refuse to enforce, or overturn, an Act of Parliament. Sir Edward Coke claimed this power in Dr. Bonham's case, saying that "when an Act of Parliament is against common right and reason, or repugnant, or impossible to be performed, the common law will control it, and adjudge such act to be void."[9] The king responded by dismissing him from office.

It was not until the Act of Settlement of 1701 that the tenure of judges was made independent of the king, but by that time the constitutional issue had been resolved against the Crown—in fact, if not in theory—and in favor of Parliament. So it was that the last monarch to veto an Act of Parliament was Queen Anne in 1708. Singular at the time, it would not be repeated by her successors, especially the first of them, George I. Not only was he a German, and spoke only German, but he came to the throne not by divine right or rule of descent, but by Act of Parliament. Champions of Parliament, the Whig party would have imposed this requirement on all future claimants for the throne, whereas the Tory party believed fervently in the divine right of kings.

Implicit in this disagreement was the larger and constitutional question of who was to rule, Parliament or king; the Whigs favored the one, the Tories the other. Interestingly enough, Montesquieu made no mention of the Whigs and Tories. Such parties (Tocqueville was later to call them "great" parties) were not supposed to exist in his system. By his time, however, and thanks largely to the Whigs, the principle of parliamentary supremacy was firmly established in the English constitution.[10]

This constitution was obviously not based on the new idea of separated powers. Nor did it conform to Thomas Paine's still newer idea of a constitution as an act of the people antecedent to government and defining the authority committed to government.[11] It was, even then, an old constitution. Bolingbroke said as much in his *Dissertation upon Parties* in 1733:

> By constitution we mean, whenever we speak with propriety and exactness, that assemblage of laws, institutions, and customs, derived from certain fixed principles of reason, directed to certain fixed objects of the public good, that compose the general system, according to which the community hath agreed to be governed.[12]

By laws, Bolingbroke probably had in mind, first of all, Magna Carta. Originally merely an agreement between King John and the barons of the realm, it was made a statute in 1297. He also would have been thinking of the Toleration Act of 1689, guaranteeing religious liberty (except for Roman Catholics); the Bill of Rights of 1689, guaranteeing, among other things, free parliamentary elections and the right to petition for redress of grievances, and forbidding cruel and unusual punishments; the Act of Settlement of 1701, which defined the conditions upon which the Crown should be held and provided that the judges would serve during good behavior (*Quam diu se bene Gesserint*); and the Triennial Act of 1694, which limited the life of a parliament to three years. Bolingbroke was thinking of the Triennial Act when he said the Septennial Act of 1716 was a "monstrous" violation of the principles of the Revolution of 1688. Paine looked at the Septennial Act and drew the conclusion that England had no constitution.

He would have been closer to the truth if he had said that England had no constitution in his sense, meaning a constitution whose provisions could be enforced. In this case, the Septennial Act would be declared unconstitutional or *ultra vires*, thus unenforceable. Under the English constitution, however, Bolingbroke could say only that the government enacting it was not a good government, with the hope that it might be replaced at the next election. As Lord John Russell was to say some years later, "the only appeal is to the people at large."[13] Paine would have thought this fruitless. But this, surely, was a mistake; over the years, the English proved to be a good constitution—indeed, "the envy of less happier lands"[14] and its governments better than most.

The English constitution was to find its greatest champion fifty or sixty years after Bolingbroke in the person of Edmund Burke, a member of the House of Commons for almost thirty years and a staunch defender, as well as a reformer, of the British Empire. The French Revolution was to turn him into a political theorist of sorts, an antitheory theorist, a constitutional theorist, in order to protect England from the theory responsible for the "extraordinary convulsion" in France. The French Revolution, a "revolution in sentiments, manners and moral opinions," was something new, and something alarming, especially because its principles appeared to be readily exportable. Its declaration of the rights of man would appeal to men everywhere—Rousseau (after Hobbes and Locke) was not writing only for the French—and it threatened to reduce not only the French but the peoples of all Europe to "one homogeneous mass." Burke called it a "barbarous philosophy," giving rise to a selfish politics of self-interest. Burke spared no words in denouncing it.[15]

The new French constitution was, he said, "the very reverse of [the British] in its principle." Self-interest was no part of the latter; British society rested on a contract, but not a contract that could be dissolved and renewed at the pleasure of any generation. It was, instead, a contract—Burke referred to it as a partnership—"between those who are living, those who are dead, and those who are to be born."[16] Unlike the French, who had "made a philosophy and religion of their hostility to such institutions," the British were "resolved to keep an established church, an established monarchy, an established aristocracy, and an established democracy, each in the degree it exists, and in no greater."[17] Landed property was also established, because with it came the rule of gentlemen.

These institutions are "established," not recently made or designed; as Burke puts it, king, lords, juries, "grand and little"—all are prescriptive. Prescription, in Roman law, gave title to landed property by possession or long-continued use and without a deed; Burke transforms this rule of private law into a rule of public law. "Prescription is the most solid of all titles," he says, "not only to property, but, which is to secure that property, to government."[18] The British constitution rests on these prescriptive establishments; indeed, Burke calls it a "prescriptive constitution . . . whose sole authority is, that it has existed time out of mind."[19] Prescription, he says, is the "great fundamental part of natural law."[20]

But what *is* the natural law, of which prescription is the fundamental part? Except in name, it differs widely from that of Hobbes or Aquinas. For Hobbes, the fundamental law of nature, which derives from the right of nature, is "*to seek peace, and follow it*"; for Aquinas, the natural law, grounded on the eternal law (God himself), prescribes the ends, and the order of ends, to which man is by nature inclined. But Burke says nothing about the substance of his natural law; nor, unlike Aquinas, does he say that a human law that disagrees with natural law does not have the force of law.

But if prescription is the fundamental part of that law, it prescribes the means rather than the ends to be pursued by government, or better, it describes the manner in which the constitution has grown over time. From Magna Carta to the Declaration of Rights, Burke says, "It has been the uniform policy of our constitution to claim and assert our liberties, as an *entailed inheritance* derived to us from our forefathers, and to be transmitted to our posterity [as] an estate specially belonging to the people of this kingdom." This policy, he adds, "appears to me to be the result of profound reflection; or rather the happy effect of following nature, which is wisdom without reflection, and above it."[21]

But, even in this sense, the natural law is a law beyond and above human legislation. The importance of this should not be minimized. Burke did for the British constitution what Bolingbroke and others never attempted to do; they spoke of the laws making up the constitution, but Burke provided it with a law of laws, or, as he puts it, a "superior law."[22] By giving the constitution a natural-law foundation, he enhanced its status in France and, of greater importance, its authority in England, especially among those charged with governing there.

But who are they? Not the people. It is the role of government to provide for human *wants*, by which Burke means not food and lodging but a "sufficient restraint upon their passions." This is missing "out of civil society"—or as Hobbes and Locke put it, in the state of nature—and is a requirement in, indeed, a condition of, civil society. Thus, it is required of government that the "inclinations of men be thwarted, their will [be] controlled, and their passions brought into subjection." Burke goes so far as to say that "the restraints on men, as well as their liberties, are to be reckoned among their rights."[23] To secure this right, the majority of men must be guided by the few who are superior in virtue and honors (*"virtute et honore majoroes"*), or a "true natural aristocracy."[24]

Thus, what Aristotle, Polybius, and Montesquieu proposed to do with their various versions of a mixed constitution and James Madison with his "auxiliary precautions," Burke proposed to do with his natural aristocracy: to impose a check on the popular will.

But, beginning in 1832, and continuing in 1867 and 1884, the British voting franchise was expanded to include, first, the middle class and manufacturers, then the workingmen in towns and cities, and, finally, the householders and lodgers in all counties and boroughs throughout the United Kingdom. In effect, England became a democracy of householders, and still later, especially after the House of Lords lost its place as an equal second chamber, a democracy simply. Yet, socially speaking, many of the political leaders chosen under a democratic franchise in the early years of the twentieth century—Balfour, Baldwin, Asquith, Austen, and Neville Chamberlain, to say nothing of Churchill—did not much differ from the Victorians Palmerston, Gladstone, Disraeli, Joseph Chamberlain, and Randolph Churchill or, for that matter, the "natural aristocrats" of Burke's time, Pitt, Fox, Grenville, and Townshend. Democracy came into its own with the election of the first Labour government in 1945, but I doubt that even Burke would say that this marked the end, or the beginning of the end, of constitutional government in Britain.

Now, fifty-plus years later, Ralf Dahrendorf (the one-time head of the London School of Economics and now a member of the House of Lords) wonders whether European democracy can survive globalization.[25] For the same reasons, I wonder whether British constitutionalism can survive membership in the European Union.

Britain has yet to agree to the common currency, but, except for that, the European die is cast. The Queen's subjects are now citizens of the Union, with its parliament in Strasbourg and its vast and ever vaster bureaucracy in Brussels. Under the treaties, dutifully signed by the British (Douglas Hurd and Francis Maude at Maastricht, Robin Cook at Nice), the Union promises to "strengthen the protection of the rights and interests of the nationals of its Member States," as well as their "fundamental rights, as guaranteed by the European Convention on Human Rights signed in Rome 4 November 1950,"[26] and, finally, to protect their fundamental rights from being violated by their own governments. This is to be done by the European Council, which "can declare the existence of a serious and persistent breach of fundamental rights [and to enforce this provision] it may suspend certain rights of the country concerned."[27] (To protect what remains of her sovereignty, Britain would have 78 of 732 seats in the European Parliament, 29 of 345 votes in the council, and one member each in the Court of First Instance and in the Court of Justice.) Whether its structure is such as to guarantee a government of limited powers remains to be seen.

I don't know if the British are serious about this, but the Germans surely are. As they see it, the Europe of nation states was a Europe of wars, and they intend to do away with wars by doing away with nation states. Do the British understand this? The new Europe under the now-rejected constitution would have a common foreign policy. All well and good, perhaps, except that constitutional government, to the extent that it has existed anywhere, has existed only in a nation state, and then, as the Framers of the American Constitution knew very well, only under certain conditions.[28] For this reason, they would have thought it preposterous to yield any part of their sovereignty to a super or supranational body. I think Burke would have agreed.

Burke is famous among Americans for his support of their revolution. He pointed out, correctly, that "the people of the colonies [were] descendants of Englishmen"; and that England was a nation that respected her freedom; and that the colonists emigrated from England "when this part of [English] character was most predominant; and [that] they took this bias and direction the moment they parted from [English] hands."[29] And he was mostly correct when he said the colonists were devoted to liberty according to English ideas and on English principles. Indeed, it was the practice of the aggrieved colonists to speak of their rights as Englishmen. Yet, like the French, they made a revolution by invoking the rights of man, not their rights as Englishmen, and, more precisely, their natural rights to life, liberty, and the pursuit of happiness.

The fact is, the American Revolution was closer to the French than Burke was willing to recognize. Admittedly, it was not a revolution in "sentiments, manners, and moral opinions"; nor did the Americans abolish a church, seize its property, and kill its priests and prelates; nor, by way of demonstrating a determination to rid themselves of every vestige of their Christian (indeed, their religious) inheritance, did they replace the Gregorian calendar with one devoid of any ecclesiastical connections. Nevertheless, they did claim that America was a new order of the ages (a *novus ordo seclorum*), and they meant this claim to be taken seriously.

Certainly, theirs was a new kind of constitution. It was based on a new principle, derived from the new idea of democracy which, in turn, was the product of the new political philosophy of Thomas Hobbes and, especially, John Locke ("America's philosopher," as he came to be called). It was Locke who (greatly to simplify) demonstrated that all men are created equal insofar as they are equally endowed with certain unalienable rights. Following him, Americans said government is instituted "to secure these rights," and when any form of government fails to do this, "it is the Right of the People to alter or to abolish it, and to institute new Government, laying its foundation on such principles and organizing its powers in such form, as to them shall seem most likely to effect their Safety and Happiness." This means that the people are the source of legitimate government. The name for this is popular sovereignty, and popular sovereignty is the salient feature of modern constitutionalism.[30]

It is not, however, the only feature. Since all men are created free and equal, it follows that no man may govern another without his consent. This consent is originally given in a constitution, and, since the constitution states the terms under which men agree to be governed, the constitution has to be written. Men insist on this, and not only Americans. Thus, every country in the world—except Britain, New Zealand, Israel, Saudi Arabia, Oman, and Libya—now has a written constitution. Now, the modern world is, as Alexis de Tocqueville was the first to point out, irreversibly democratic; this, he said, is a "providential fact."[31] What this means is that limited or constitutional government can no longer (if it ever could) be achieved by mixing democracy with oligarchy or aristocracy, and it goes without saying that the day is long past when someone can claim to rule by the grace of God. Limited or constitutional government is possible in this democratic world only if the people are willing to impose limits on themselves. The American people did just this in 1788 when they ratified the Constitution.

Its Framers made no effort to conceal the fact that they intended to put limits on democratic majorities; they said as much. The Constitution, they said, would exclude the people *"in their collective capacity"* [italics in original] from any share in the government.[32] They took pride in the fact that their government was not a democracy, but a republic that put some distance between the people and the levers of power. The Constitution did this by providing

- a president chosen not by the people but by electors who, having made their choice, would immediately disband;

- a Senate chosen not by the people but by the various state legislatures, each state, regardless of the size of its population, being entitled to choose two;

- a House of Representatives chosen not by a majority of the whole people (*"the people in their collective capacity"*) but by majorities within each of the districts into which each state would be divided;

- and, finally, a Supreme Court, with the power to veto popular legislation and whose members would, in effect, serve for life.

Generally, the Constitution provides a system of majority government, but the governing majority is assembled not from among the people directly but from among the representatives of the people. Because they represent different interests, and because the legislative branch is separated from the executive, and because the legislative is itself divided into House and Senate, assembling this majority is no simple matter. It was not supposed to be. Even so, as I said, this majority is subject to a Supreme Court veto.

The people were left in no doubt about the essential features of this Constitution. Every aspect of it was subjected to intense scrutiny during the ratification debates, which were carried on in town meetings, state conventions, and the popular press. Among the opponents were famous men, leading figures in the Revolution—Patrick Henry, for example. He led the opposition in Virginia, saying the Constitution had "an awful squinting; it squints toward monarchy."[33] Yet Virginia (albeit by a narrow margin) voted in favor of ratification, as did every other state. Under the circumstances, this was truly remarkable.

Equally remarkable is the fact that the Constitution has endured for more than two hundred years. Of course, it has been amended, and, aside from the original ten comprising the Bill of Rights, almost every one of the amendments has been democratic in character—putting an end to slavery, for example, expanding the voting franchise, providing for the popular election of senators, and permitting the Congress to levy a progressive tax on incomes. But this does not, I think, fully explain the abiding popularity of the Constitution.

Thomas Jefferson was of the opinion that a constitution could endure only if it were frequently submitted to the people for amendments, but Madison objected. He objected because

> every appeal to the people would carry an implication of some defect in the government, and frequent appeals would, in great measure, deprive the government of that veneration which time bestows on everything, and without which perhaps the wisest and freest governments would not possess the requisite stability. [34]

Rather than submit constitutional questions to the people, Madison preferred that they be submitted to the courts, ultimately the Supreme Court; and the manner in which the courts consider and dispose of them has much to do with the continued popularity of the Constitution. One jurist saw this even though he refused to acknowledge what it was that he saw. The Supreme Court, he said, is preoccupied "with the constitutionality of legislation," and this, in turn, causes the people to be preoccupied "with a false value." The tendency of focusing attention on the constitutionality of legislation, he said, "is to make constitutionality synonymous with wisdom."[35] Exactly, and this goes far to explaining the continuing popularity of the Constitution.

It has survived so long not because it is written in stone (so to speak) but because the people have become accustomed to it. More than that, they have come to esteem it and the men who framed it. Madison hoped it would somehow acquire "that veneration which time bestows on everything"; and so it has. Burke would appreciate this. He spoke of the British constitution as a "prescriptive constitution . . . whose sole authority is, that it has existed time out of mind." Something like this might also be said of the American.

2

The Illegitimacy of Appeals to Natural Law in Constitutional Interpretation

I

I begin by stating the obvious: Federal judges are not in the habit of invoking natural law to support their constitutional decisions. Rather, they invoke one or another—and sometimes a handful—of specific constitutional provisions. This is not an accident. Their authority is limited to deciding cases and controversies—for my purposes here, cases arising "under the Constitution" or "the laws of the United States"—which they weigh in the balance with the relevant constitutional provision. And most of these provisions—or, at least, those most frequently cited—have to do with rights, which, again, is not by accident since, as we are taught by the Declaration of Independence, the purpose of government is the securing of rights.

True, there once were occasions when Supreme Court justices appealed to something at least formally akin to natural law. For example, in the very early *Calder v. Bull*, Justice Samuel Chase grounded his decision on "the first principles of the social compact" (which led the dissenting James Iredell to protest that a court was not entitled to hold a legislative act void on the ground that it was contrary to "natural justice"),[1] and a few years later, Justice William Johnson, in a concurring opinion, joined in the invalidation of a state law by invoking "the reason and nature of things: a principle which will impose laws even on the Deity."[2]

But these extraconstitutional excursions have long since fallen into disrepute, at least nominally. The modern Chase or Johnson eschews reliance on "natural justice" or the "reason and nature of things" in favor of some constitutional text that, as he reads it, makes such excursions unnecessary.

As sometimes read, these texts prove to be more capacious or commodious than earlier justices could have imagined. Thus, in the Connecticut birth control case, Justice William O. Douglas referred to various guarantees in the Bill of Rights and found in them "penumbras, formed by emanations," which, in turn, contained "a right of marital privacy." Three of his concurring colleagues found that right in the Ninth Amendment.[3]

This sort of jurisprudence found no favor with Justice Hugo L. Black. He denounced it as the "natural law due process [or 'whatever'] philosophy," and, in case after case, denied that the Court had any such jurisdiction. "If these formulas based on 'natural justice,' or others which mean the same thing, are to prevail, they require judges to determine what is or is not constitutional on the basis of their own appraisal of what laws are unwise or unnecessary."[4] Although Black may have been right about the purpose for which they are employed, these "formulas"—natural law or justice and reserved rights—do not in fact mean the same thing. In fact, they mean different things.

But Black was not alone in failing to distinguish them; so, too, did the venerable Roscoe Pound. Hoping to breathe some life into the "forgotten" Ninth Amendment, Pound seized upon the possibility that, with their reference to the "[rights] retained by the people," the Framers of the Constitution had in mind natural rights or—like Black, he tended to confuse them—natural law. But he was not willing to accept the understanding of these rights, or this law, current at the time of the Founding. In the fashion of those jurists and scholars who promote the cause of a "living constitution," he came up instead with the idea of mutable law and rights—mutable but, *mirabile dictu*, still natural. "Unlike the law of nature of the eighteenth century," he said, "the revived natural law is not a fixed system of precisely formulated rules to stand fast forever." The same is true of natural rights: "From this standpoint," he said, "the Ninth Amendment is a solemn declaration that natural rights are not a fixed category of reasonable human expectations in civilized society laid down once for all in the several sections of the Constitution."[5]

Except as a term used to lend dignity or authority to a judge's idiosyncratic policy preferences, the idea of nature simply disappears from Pound's jurisprudential musings. What is *natural* about a right or a law that has no fixed definition? How can *nature* provide the standard by which we measure our laws and policies if, like them, the idea of nature changes with the times? Yet clearly, although they may have defined it differently, those who first employed the term "nature," whether in connection with law (Cicero and Thomas Aquinas) *or* rights (Thomas Hobbes and Thomas Jefferson), intended that it provide such a standard and understood its meaning as fixed.[6] It is, of course, the idea of a fixed meaning, not the idea or need of a standard, that is unacceptable to so many modern judges and constitutional lawyers. But, as I have argued in another place, you cannot have the one without the other.[7]

II

I have made the point that natural law and natural rights are not interchangeable terms. This is readily illustrated, if not demonstrated, in the work of the Court. Justice Black may denounce his colleagues for employing what he calls the "natural law due process [or 'whatever'] philosophy," or, as he put it in another case, the "natural-law-due-process formula,"[8] but the natural law, strictly speaking, played no role whatever in these cases, particularly in the most notorious among them, *Griswold v. Connecticut, Roe v. Wade*, and *Bowers v. Hardwick* (the 1986 case that upheld Georgia's antisodomy laws).[9] There the justices (in *Bowers*, the four of them in the minority) relied not on the natural law but on a right, specifically a right of privacy: for contraception, abortion, and sodomy, all practices specifically condemned by natural law as properly, or at least traditionally, understood.[10]

What, then, do we mean by moral philosophy and what is its role in constitutional interpretation? Here is John Quincy Adams writing in 1839 on the occasion of the Constitution's fiftieth anniversary:

> [The Constitution's] VIRTUES, its republican character, consisted in its conformity to the principles proclaimed in the Declaration of Independence, and its administration must necessarily be always pliable to the fluctuating varieties of public opinion; its stability and duration by a like overruling and irresistible necessity, was to depend on the stability and duration in the hearts and minds of the people of that *virtue*, or in other words,

of those principles proclaimed in the Declaration of Independence and embodied in the Constitution of the United States of America.[11]

The Declaration begins by invoking both "the Laws of Nature and of Nature's God" and, in the following paragraph, the self-evident truth that government is instituted to secure the "unalienable rights" with which all men are equally endowed by their "Creator." It identifies the most important of those rights—to life, liberty, and the pursuit of happiness—but it says nothing further about those laws, nothing to aid us in identifying them or their relationship to the unalienable rights. Both the laws and the rights derive from, or are the gift of, the Creator, "Nature's God." But who is he?

According to John Courtney Murray, the well-known Catholic theologian, he is the God who revealed himself in the Bible. The Declaration of Independence, he writes, recognizes the sovereignty of this biblical God. The rights of which it speaks are the rights of Englishmen and the product of "Christian history," and these rights, even in the form they take in the Bill of Rights, are "tributary to the tradition of natural law, to the idea that man has certain original responsibilities precisely as man." That is to say, the rights of man are derived from his responsibilities (or duties). Responsibilities are primary, and rights secondary or derivative.[12] Here Murray might have quoted Matthew 22:37–40: "You shall love the Lord your God with all your heart, and with all your soul, and with all your mind. This is the great and first commandment. And the second is like unto it, you shall love your neighbor as yourself." Whatever rights we have are, presumably, dependent on our obedience to this law. John Locke, of course, had it otherwise. He said the state of nature has a law of nature to govern it, which law obliges everyone "as much as he can, to preserve the rest of mankind," but to do this only "when his own preservation comes not in competition."[13]

Now it is obvious that the Declaration does not speak of the rights of Englishmen; it speaks of "certain unalienable rights" which, on the face of it, would seem to suggest that rights are primary, as Locke said they were. One of these is the right to pursue happiness, presumably—although this will require argument—a happiness that each of us defines for himself. Was this a right enjoyed by Englishmen? The basis of it would seem to be freedom of conscience. Did English law, modeled, as Murray says, on the natural law, recognize freedom of conscience? Freedom of conscience would find expression in a separation of church and state. Did England separate church and state? Be that as it may, does Roman Catholicism recognize freedom of conscience? Murray's answer to this is emphatic: Catholicism, he says, rejects "the absolute primacy of conscience," and his account of the provenance of the Bill of Rights requires him to conclude that freedom of conscience is not embodied in the First Amendment.[14] This amounts to saying that the principles of the First Amendment are not those of John Locke who, in his "Letter Concerning Toleration," said that "the care of . . . everyman's soul belongs unto himself, and is to be left unto himself," or of Thomas Jefferson, who said that "the operations of the mind [unlike] the acts of the body, are [not] subject to the coercion of the laws [and that] our rulers can have no authority over such natural rights, only as we have submitted to them [but the] rights of conscience we never submitted, we could not submit."[15]

Murray's question, and ours, comes to this: To understand the "Laws of Nature and of Nature's God" do we turn to Thomas Aquinas or John Locke?

Murray acknowledges the difference between Thomas's "natural law" (or, as he sometimes writes, "law of nature"), and Locke's law of nature; the last chapter of his book is devoted to explaining it. Locke's law of nature, he says, was the creature of the Enlightenment, and it was "as fragile, time-conditioned, and transitory a phenomenon as the Enlightenment itself."[16] So, too, with the "theory of natural rights," whose philosophical scaffolding he dismisses as "philosophical nonsense."[17] Locke's ideas of the law of nature, the rights of man, and the origins of society, he says, "are not derived from what is 'real,' from the concrete totality of man's nature as it really is."[18] Apparently, Locke did not see that, as a rational being, man can know the good toward which he is by nature inclined (which is the foundation or, better, the condition of the natural law as Thomas expounded it); indeed, although Murray does not point this out, Locke expressly denied that "the Law of Nature [is] inscribed in the minds of men" and that "the Law of Nature [can] be known from the natural inclination of mankind."[19]

According to Murray, quoting Thomas, men can know the natural law that forbids killing, or more precisely, murder. But according to Locke's law of nature, men may "destroy noxious things," which means, as Locke subsequently makes clear, the law of nature allows men to kill other human beings. His position here is similar to that of Hobbes, who baldly states that a justly condemned murderer has a right to murder his jailers in order to save his own life.[20]

I could go on to make a list of the ways in which Locke's law of nature differs from the traditional natural law—contrasting their views on the basis of human sociality, on legitimate government, on the conscience, on happiness, on the care of children and on the honor due parents by children, and so on—but this work has already been done.[21] The question is, what does this have to do with America?

Murray's answer is nothing, or nothing much. Locke's ideas were picked up by "the French enthusiasts," he says, but not by the commonsensical British or, as he would have it, by the Americans. Whatever its vitality today, America was conceived in "the tradition of natural law," not, he argues, Locke's law of nature.[22]

But if Murray is mistaken about this, if we have a constitutional right to worship as we please or not to worship at all, and if this constitutional right derives from our natural right of conscience, or, in Jefferson's words, from our natural right to worship twenty gods or no god,[23] or from our unalienable right to define happiness as we see fit because, as Locke puts it, there can be no definitive understanding of happiness;[24] and if that natural right of conscience derives from the providential fact that the care of each man's soul belongs to himself alone, which means that, contrary to the Bible as read by Catholic, Protestant, and Jew alike, as well as to the Koran, God has not provided for the care of souls; if, in a word, the provenance of the Declaration of Independence and the Constitution is in the thought of John Locke, then what follows for John Courtney Murray and, to bring this home to us, the proponents of a natural law–based judicial review?

But the great body of evidence shows that Murray was wrong. It is undeniable that the Declaration adopts the language of Locke ("pursuit of happiness," "long train of abuses," mankind "are more disposed to suffer").[25] Undeniable that Jefferson, who drafted the Declaration, spoke of Locke as one of the three greatest men ever to live (the others being, interesting enough, Bacon and Newton). Undeniable that James Wilson, one of its principal Framers, spoke of the Constitution as founded on "the revolutionary principle [of] Mr. Locke"; this new Constitution, he said, would establish the first government in history grounded unambiguously on the true principles of natural right, and "the great and penetrating mind of Locke seems to be the only one that pointed towards even the theory of this great truth."[26] Undeniable that the Founders spoke repeatedly of natural right and the state of nature—which has no place in Thomas's classic natural law—and undeniable that this was, as Jefferson said, the common language spoken by Americans at the time, Federalists and Anti-Federalists alike, including the simple citizens of the various towns north of Boston.[27] Undeniable that, in his explication of the Constitution, Publius (James Madison in this case) spoke of "the Social Compact" and, like Jefferson in the Declaration, of "the transcendent law of nature and of nature's God."[28] Undeniable, I think, that it was Locke's and Montesquieu's view of man's nature that lies behind Madison's famous statement in *Federalist* 10 that the "latent causes of faction are . . . sown in the nature of man." And it is undeniable, finally, that Madison, having said that justice is "the end of government [and] civil society," proceeds to define justice by referring to "a state of nature" and in terms made familiar by Hobbes and Locke.[29]

Again, I could go on, but I think enough has been said to prove that what Murray calls the American proposition is, contrary to what he says, Lockean in origin, not Thomistic. For Thomas, as well as his English counterpart, Richard Hooker, the natural law is grounded on the eternal law—which is to say, on God himself, or on his providence or governance—and derives its strength ultimately from the threat of divine punishment but immediately (and necessarily) from the more evident threat of civil punishment. The reason for this derives from the fact that while the first principles of the natural law are (or are said to be) promulgated and known to all men, insofar as they are rational, those principles alone are not sufficient guides for human action. This means that the natural law has to be supplemented by civil law, which, modeled on the natural law, provides a surer guide to virtuous action. The existence of such a natural law rests on certain presuppositions, generally an understanding of human nature bound up with a teleological view of the universe.[30]

I shall not—indeed, I am not qualified to—enter into a discussion of whether natural law is possible without those presuppositions. Nor shall I enter into a discussion of the political consequences—most importantly, the possibility of constitutionalism—if, as is widely assumed, modern science has made it impossible to believe in a teleological universe or, stated otherwise, if Nietzsche was right about the death of God—"Nature's God," as well as the God of Revelation.

My objective is to consider whether judges are justified in declaring laws unconstitutional because they conflict with the natural law. I take this to mean the premodern natural law which, I have implied, was rejected by the Framers of the Constitution in favor of the laws of nature as defined by Thomas Hobbes and John Locke. The natural law they rejected directs men's action, by means of commands and prohibitions, toward a variety of ends which possess a natural order, "ascend[ing] from self-preservation and procreation via life in society toward knowledge of God."[31] According to this premodern natural law, self-preservation is a duty (which means suicide is forbidden), but according to Hobbes and Locke, it is a right (which, as I indicated above, means one may murder his executioner). These new laws of nature (mere deductions from the fundamental right of nature to preserve ourselves) simply direct us to seek peace by entering into a contract with others, according to which we enter into civil society and agree to surrender our natural rights or powers in exchange for the civil rights or liberties which are to be secured or protected by government.[32] Thus, our natural rights to life and liberty are exchanged for the civil rights—or, in our case, the constitutional rights—not to be deprived of them without due process of law.

But, as Jefferson said, and the religious provisions of the First Amendment imply, our natural right of conscience is not surrendered; we cannot surrender it. This, more than any other principle or provision of the Constitution, characterizes the American system of self-government: The laws may deprive us of life and liberty but not of the right to pursue the happiness we define for ourselves. In this respect, which can rightly be said to be the decisive respect, we are governed by ourselves, not by the law. In a word, rather than taking its bearings from a natural law that prescribes the means to the various ends given by nature—a law that tells us how to live our lives—the government of the United States is obliged to leave us alone.

But if, under the Constitution, the Congress is forbidden to take cognizance of the natural law when it legislates, does it not follow that the judiciary is forbidden to take such cognizance when it adjudicates? And given the fact that the traditional natural law rests on presuppositions that no contemporary judge—or, at least, none known to me—would accept, is it not likely that any judicial reference to such a law is, as Justice Black said it was, simply a cloak for what the judge thinks governmental policy ought to be?

III

The Ninth Amendment speaks not of natural law but, instead, of the rights "retained by the people." In line with this, nowhere in his forty-nine-page introduction to the volume he edited on the Ninth Amendment does Randy E. Barnett make any reference to natural law; so far as I know, he does not even employ the term.[33] Instead, and quite properly in my judgment, Barnett addresses the two questions that arise from the Ninth Amendment: What are these unenumerated rights, and are they justiciable?

The Bill of Rights was intended to impose restrictions only on the federal government. This means that it was only the federal government that was forbidden "to deny or disparage [the other rights] retained by the people." However, beginning in 1925, the Supreme Court incorporated most of the provisions of the Bill of Rights, including, presumably, the Ninth Amendment, into the due process clause of the Fourteenth Amendment, thereby making them applicable as restrictions on the states as well as on the federal government.

I note that, to the extent the Ninth Amendment has been invoked by the Supreme Court, this has been done only in state cases, never, to my knowledge, in a case involving federal legislation. I am impelled to ask, why not? Is it that Congress has never enacted a law that can be said to have deprived a person of an unenumerated right? That, to coin John Marshall's phrase, "is too extravagant to be maintained." Is it, then, that the justices do not dare to invoke an unenumerated right to strike down a provision adopted by both houses of Congress and signed into law by the president of the United States, in short, a law enacted by a national constitutional majority?

Writing in *Federalist* 78, Alexander Hamilton said that "it would require an uncommon portion of fortitude in the judges to do their duty as faithful guardians of the [written] Constitution, where legislative invasions of it had been instigated by the major voice of the community." I suggest that more than fortitude would be required of the judges to invalidate such legislation by invoking a right nowhere specified in the Constitution.

It seems to me that any Ninth Amendment argument worth its salt must address the question of whether the Framers intended the judiciary to exercise such an extraordinary power. Such consideration might begin by noting what the Framers did *not* do—for example, they did not *expressly* authorize any kind of judicial review, and they repeatedly rejected Madison's call for a council of revision with the authority to "examine every act of the National Legislature before it shall operate"—and what they *did* do. For example, they contrived to have the country governed by carefully structured constitutional majorities, and authorized these majorities to "make all Laws which shall be necessary and proper for carrying into Execution the [previously delineated] Powers, and all other Powers vested by this Constitution in the Government of the United States, or in any Department or Officer thereof." Did they also authorize the judiciary to override these laws by substituting a definition of necessity and propriety found in a right "retained by the people" or, as Professor Barnett's critics would have it, in the "bottomless well" or the "Pandora's box" of the Ninth Amendment?

If, to quote Marshall again, this "is too extravagant to be maintained," what was the purpose of the Ninth Amendment? I am obliged to address this question, if only briefly.

In the course of shepherding the Bill of Rights through the House of Representatives in the First Congress, Madison asked whether it could not fairly be said that the amendments proposed by the House committee (on which he served) were not, with exceptions he noted, the amendments demanded by the various state ratifying conventions.[34] What he neglected to mention was an amendment proposed by New York, Massachusetts, North Carolina, Rhode Island, and, especially, his own state of Virginia. This was an amendment acknowledging a right that without question everybody at the time understood to be fundamental: the right to reserve rights, or, stated differently, the right of the people to decide *whether, how,* and *where* or *by whom* they shall be governed; in short, the right exercised by the people in 1776.

During the Virginia ratification debates, Patrick Henry, the most prominent of the Anti-Federalists, said, "There are certain political maxims, which no free people ought ever to abandon. . . . That all men are by nature free and independent, and have certain inherent rights, of which, when they enter into society, they cannot by any compact deprive or divest their posterity."[35] His colleague, Edmund Randolph, made the same point: What was needed in a bill of rights was a "perpetual standard . . . around which the people might rally" if or when the legislature should violate the limits of its powers. In other words, the Constitution should remind the people of their ultimate sovereignty, or their right "to alter or abolish" a government that, in their judgment, had violated the trust bestowed on it, or, as still another Virginian put it, to renew or give it a "fresh spring at stated periods." A statement of this sort was put at the head of the Virginian constitution, so why not, he asked, at the head of this constitution of the "general confederation"?

Madison, and the Federalists generally, did not disagree with the principle, but, as Herbert Storing has demonstrated in his definitive study of the origins of the Bill of Rights, Madison especially was determined that a statement of that principle not be given a prominent place in the Constitution. "Recurrence to first principles," Storing writes,

> does not substitute for well-constituted and effective government. In some cases, it may interfere. Does a constant emphasis on unalienable natural rights foster good government or a sense of community? Does a constant emphasis on popular sovereignty foster responsible government? Does a constant emphasis on a right to abolish government foster the kind of popular support that any government needs? The Federalists did not doubt that these first principles are true, that they may be resorted to, that they provide the ultimate source and justification of government. The problem is that these principles, while true, can also endanger government. Even rational and well-constituted governments need and deserve a presumption of legitimacy and permanence. A bill of rights that presses these first principles to the fore tends to deprive government of that presumption.[36]

If my reading is correct, that "perpetual standard," or that statement of first principles, was not pressed "to the fore"; it was not, as in the case of Virginia, placed at the head of the Constitution; rather, it was consigned to the Ninth Amendment. There, but in a much less conspicuous place, and in language much more sober than Patrick Henry's, it serves as a reminder to the people that they are the source of the powers exercised by government.

It is of some interest to note that the people of Virginia claimed to be exercising this right in 1861 when they adopted an ordinance repealing the ordinance of June 25, 1788, ratifying the Constitution—in a word, when Virginia pretended to secede from the Union. The right to consent to government, they said, implies the right to withhold that consent and to withdraw that consent. Such a right, they said, was expressly recognized in the Ninth Amendment.[37]

The fact that the Ninth Amendment was cited in the secession debates, and that the debates in all the seceding states were filled with statements to the effect that the right to withdraw consent is *the* fundamental right retained by the people, does not *prove* that my reading of the amendment is correct; but what was said in those debates does bear an uncanny resemblance to what was said in 1788 by Patrick Henry, Samuel Adams, and the other Anti-Federalists in their call for a bill of rights.[38] If this, then, is what they meant by a right "retained by the people," it is a right that was adjudicated not in any court, state or federal; it was adjudicated (so to speak) on the battlefield.

3

Preserving a Living Constitution

That federal judges might do what is now claimed they have a right to do was foreseen by some of the Anti-Federalists, particularly "Brutus," who gave it as one of the reasons why the Constitution should not be ratified. The Court, he said,

> will be authorised to decide upon the meaning of the constitution, and that, not only according to the natural and ob[vious] meaning of the words, but also according to the spirit and intention of it. [The judiciary will] be exalted above all other power in the government, and subject to no controul.[1]

Alexander Hamilton, writing in *Federalist* 81, did his best to dispel this fear. There is not, he said, "a syllable in the plan under consideration which *directly* empowers the national courts to construe the laws according to the spirit of the Constitution, or which gives them any greater latitude in this respect than may be claimed by the courts of every State." Within a decade, however, Brutus's fears proved justified.

First Invocation of Extraconstitutional Principles

The first invocation of extraconstitutional principles came in *Calder v. Bull* (1798), where the Court held that an act of the Connecticut legislature setting aside a probate court decree was not an ex post facto law and, therefore, not void under article 1, section 10, of the Constitution. Having delivered that judgment, Justice Samuel Chase, in what can only be described as *dicta*, went on to say that state authority is limited not only by express

constitutional prohibitions but by the "first principles of the social compact."[2] While agreeing with the Court's judgment in the case, Justice James
Iredell took strong exception to this statement of judicial power. "It is true,"
he said, "that some speculative jurists have held, that a legislative act against
natural justice must, in itself, be void; but I cannot think that, under such
a government, any court of Justice would possess a power to declare it so."
Both the state and the federal constitutions, he pointed out, have defined
with precision the objects of the legislative power and have restrained its
exercise "within marked and settled boundaries." He continued,

> If any act of Congress, or of a Legislature of a state, violates those
> constitutional provisions, it is unquestionably void; though, I
> admit, that as the authority to declare it void is of a delicate and
> awful nature, the Court will never resort to that authority, but in
> a clear and urgent case. If, on the other hand, the Legislature of
> any member of the Union, shall pass a law, within the general
> scope of their constitutional power, the Court cannot pronounce
> it to be void, merely because it is, in their judgment, contrary to
> the principles of natural justice. The ideas of natural justice are
> regulated by no fixed standard: the ablest and the purest men
> have differed upon the subject.[3]

There is little question but that on this point Iredell was expressing
the view of the Framers, and that they held this view largely for the reasons
he gave, reasons as compelling—indeed, as I argue, more compelling—
now as then.

True, on one occasion, even John Marshall seemingly acknowledged the
right of the Supreme Court to appeal to something akin to "natural justice"
when declaring a statute unconstitutional. Announcing the judgment of the
Court in the politically explosive case of *Fletcher v. Peck*, he said, "The state
of Georgia was restrained [from passing the law in question] either by general principles, which are common to our free institutions, or by the particular provisions of the constitution of the United States"; this, he said,
was the "unanimous opinion of the court."[4] But Marshall cannot fairly be
cited by the proponents of what we have come to call an "activist" court. In
his opinion, Marshall himself relied solely on an express provision of

the Constitution; the Georgia law, he argued, was one "impairing the Obligations of Contracts" in violation of article 1, section 10.

It was Justice William Johnson, alone among the seven justices who sat on the case, who had recourse to the idea of natural justice. "I do not hesitate to declare," he said in a concurring opinion, "that the state does not possess the power of revoking its own grants," but, he added, "I do it on a general principle, on the reason and nature of things: a principle which will impose laws even on the Deity."[5] It would appear that Marshall felt compelled by the political situation to announce an opinion that had the support of a "unanimous" Court, and that it was this necessity that led him to refer to "general principles" in addition to an explicit provision of the Constitution.

Beyond *Calder v. Bull* and *Fletcher v. Peck*, there were even occasions—and long before the advent of contemporary "activism"—when the Court struck down state laws without any reference whatever to the Constitution. Prominent among these is a Kansas municipal bond case, *Savings and Loan Association v. Topeka*. Kansas law permitted municipalities to issue bonds and use the proceeds to attract industry to the cities. Speaking for the Court, Justice Samuel F. Miller held the law to be a form of "robbery," a taking of private money (in the form of taxes) to use not for a public purpose, but to bestow it instead on "favored [private] individuals." This, he said, "is not legislation [but rather] a decree under legislative forms."[6] This led Justice Nathan Clifford to protest that "Courts cannot nullify an Act of the State Legislature on the vague ground that they think it opposed to a general latent spirit supposed to pervade or underlie the Constitution, where neither the terms nor the implications of the instruments disclose any such restriction."[7]

"Natural Justice"

Put simply, the idea that judges are entitled to rest their decisions on the principles of "natural justice"—or any of its modern synonyms—is incompatible with the Framers' idea of a written constitution. With a written text, they held, comes certainty, and with certainty comes legitimacy; and both certainty and legitimacy are put in jeopardy by rules of constitutional construction that, in effect, permit the judges to do as they will. James Madison even found reason to complain (albeit mildly) of Marshall's opinion in *McCulloch v. Maryland*:

> It was anticipated I believe by few if any of the friends of the Constitution, that a rule of construction would be introduced as broad & as pliant as what has occurred. And those who recollect, and still more those who shared in what passed in the State Conventions, thro' which the people ratified the Constitution . . . cannot easily be persuaded that the avowal of such a rule would not have prevented its ratification. . . .
>
> There is certainly a reasonable medium between expounding the Constitution with the strictness of a penal law, or other ordinary statute, and expounding it with a laxity which may vary its essential character, and encroach on the local sovereignties with which it was meant to be reconcilable.[8]

If, as he said in a subsequent letter, the judges are not guided by the sense of the people who ratified the Constitution, "there can be no security for a consistent and stable, more than for a *faithful* exercise of its powers" (emphasis added).[9] The legitimacy of government depends on adherence to the written text, the text that the people ratified or to which they gave their consent; so, too, does the possibility of limited or constitutional government.

The classic statement of these propositions can be found in Marshall's opinion for the Court in *Marbury v. Madison*: The "whole American fabric has been erected," he wrote, on the principle that government derives from and is dependent on the will of the people. "This original and supreme will organizes the government, and assigns to different departments their respective powers." In the American case, it also assigns limits to those powers, and "that those limits may not be mistaken or forgotten, the constitution is written." It was for this reason that he (and, he suggested, all Americans) deemed a written constitution to be "the greatest improvement on political institutions."[10] Thomas Jefferson made the same point when he said that "the possession of a written Constitution [was America's] peculiar security."[11] As for the judiciary, its duty was to serve as its "faithful guardians."[12]

Statements of this sort abound in the literature of the time:

- "In a government which is emphatically stiled a government of laws, the least possible range ought to be left for the discretion of the judges."[13]

- "If the constitution is to be expounded, not by its written text, but by the opinions of the rulers for the time being, whose opinions are to prevail, the first or the last? [And if the last] what certainty can there be in those powers [which it assigns and limits]?"[14]

- "Would it not make the constitution an instrument of flexible and changeable interpretation, and not a settled form of government with fixed limitations? Would it not become, instead of a supreme law for ourselves and our posterity, a mere oracle of the powers of the rulers of the day, to which implicit homage is to be paid, and speaking at different times the most opposite commands, and the most ambiguous voices?" As Marshall put it in *Marbury*, the Constitution is to be fixed, made "unchangeable by ordinary means."[15]

These various statements derive from a clear understanding of the principles informing the Constitution. No one governs by the grace of God; God (or "Nature's God") endowed men with the rights of life, liberty, and the pursuit of happiness, but he did not provide them with an effective means by which these rights might be secured. Their security required men to institute government, and, precisely because men are naturally all free and equal, the government derives its just powers from the consent of the governed. Or, to state it otherwise, because men are by nature free and equal, no one may govern another without his consent. In our case, that consent was rendered with and in the Constitution, which was ordained and established by us, "the people of the United States." By doing so, we agreed to exchange the natural right to govern ourselves for the civil right to be governed by laws to which we give our consent. As someone put it, consent is the needle's eye through which natural rights must pass in order to become the civil rights that government is empowered to secure; thus, what is secured by government is not so much the natural rights to life, liberty, and property, but the civil or constitutional right not to be deprived of them "without due process of law."

The Constitution, then, is a fundamental law and was so described in *Federalist* 78, but it is not a "higher law" in the traditional sense of that term. As Robert Kraynak puts it, "Unlike divine or natural law [the Constitution] does not exist independently of the human will; it is created by the will of the people and may be altered or amended by the people according to preestablished rules."[16] Or, to return to *Federalist* 78, "Until the people have, by some solemn and authoritative act, annulled or changed the established form, it is binding on themselves collectively, as well as individually; and no presumption, or even knowledge of their sentiments, can warrant their representatives in a departure from it prior to such an act."

The Authority of Judges

But the authority denied to the legislature, and denied even to the people (except when they act in the prescribed "solemn and authoritative" manner), is now claimed by our judges. According to Justice William Brennan, popularly said to be the greatest of these, "The genius of the Constitution rests not in any static meaning it might have had in a world that is dead and gone, but in the adaptability of its great principles to cope with current problems and current needs."[17] And, as he demonstrated in case after case, it was he and his fellow judges who were charged with adapting it.

The temptation to adapt it, to keep it up to date, so to speak, seems to be irresistible, for "conservatives" like Rufus W. Peckham,[18] as well as for liberals like Brennan and William O. Douglas.[19] Indeed, I suspect it would prove to be irresistible even for the most insistent critics of the practice, among whom I include myself. My first published article in the field had to do with *Buck v. Bell*, where the Court upheld a compulsory eugenical sterilization statute.[20] Surely, one would like to think, the Constitution does not permit surgical operations to be performed on unwilling patients. In support of its holding, the Court referred to an earlier case where it had upheld a statute requiring children to be vaccinated, but is there not a difference between that and a statute requiring adult women to undergo salpingectomies?[21] (As I put it thirty-odd years ago, no smallpox in the one case and no children in the other.) The state program was outrageous. A little investigation would have revealed that *Buck v. Bell* was a "friendly suit" and, therefore, not a case or controversy in the sense of article 3. The Court might have denied jurisdiction, but this would have had the effect of affirming the state court decision upholding the statute. On what ground might the Supreme Court have declared the statute unconstitutional? That it rested on "facts" that could not withstand scrutiny? They surely could not; the state's sterilization program rested on an already discredited Mendelian "recessive gene" theory. But such considerations are relevant in the legislative setting, not (we used to be told) in the judicial.

A little investigation would also have disclosed that some of the advocates of the program were admirers of Adolf Hitler, who, they said, deserved praise for adopting "many eugenic measures, including the sterilization law and other measures to eliminate the non-Aryan element from Germany."[22] But of what constitutional relevance is that? Besides, not all the advocates of sterilization were admirers of Hitler. Then, what about the fact that the law applied only to the (alleged) mental defectives in state institutions and not to the "multitudes outside"? But by reaching all those "similarly situated," the law satisfied what were then understood to be the requirements of equal protection. In the event, the Court dismissed the complaint in a few paragraphs. "Three generations of imbeciles are enough," said Justice Oliver Wendell Holmes for the nearly unanimous Court, and that was that.

Justice Pierce Butler dissented, but without opinion. Rumor has it that, as the only Roman Catholic on the Court, he feared that anything he said would be misunderstood. On what could he have grounded his dissent? A few years later (in 1930), Pope Pius XI issued an encyclical (*Casti Conubii*) declaring sexual sterilization to be contrary to the natural law, and Butler might have been tempted to cite it if the encyclical had existed then. The Constitution, however, does not "enact" the natural law as expounded by the pope or, for that matter, by Thomas Aquinas, any more than the "Fourteenth Amendment [enacts] Mr. Herbert Spencer's Social Statics."[23] What, then, was left to Butler and those of us who opposed the statute, other than some version of emanations radiating from those penumbras cast by the First, Fourth, Fifth, Ninth, and Fourteenth amendments? As I said, the temptation to go beyond the text of the Constitution appears to be irresistible. It may even be inevitable.

Was it not the great chief justice himself who enjoined us never to forget that it was a constitution we were expounding, "a Constitution intended to endure for ages to come, and consequently, to be adapted to the various crises of human affairs"?[24] And what is this but to say that its vitality or viability depends on its adaptability?

The Failure of Congress

In fact, however, as I have pointed out before, Marshall did not say that the Constitution may be adapted to the "various crises of human affairs"; he said that the legislative powers granted by the Constitution are adaptable to meet these crises.[25] And much of what we regard as the inevitability of judicial activism is the result of Congress's failure to use its powers, specifically its powers under section five of the Fourteenth Amendment. Its failure to do so—for example, its failure in the course of time to declare that one of the privileges or immunities of American citizenship is to attend a nonsegregated public school—not only opened the door for the Court but made it *necessary* for the Court to assume a political role; and, as we say, the rest is history.

It is a history of employing constitutional clauses—equal protection and due process especially—in tasks for which they were not intended and are illsuited, tasks for which the legislative power was intended and is well-suited. To invalidate poll taxes, for example, legislatures, unlike courts, have no need to invoke a principle that, of necessity, they must find either in the text or the interstices of the Constitution; nor do they have to say, as the Court did say, that "the Equal Protection Clause is not shackled to the political theory of a particular era [or] due process to a fixed catalogue of what was at a given time deemed to be the limits of fundamental rights."[26] They have only to decide that, under modern conditions, these taxes serve no useful and legitimate purpose. As Justice Hugo L. Black said in dissent, however, the Court had to invoke the familiar "natural-law-due-process formula," which, he suggested, is simply a "cloak for what it thinks governmental policy should be."[27]

And so it is, and so it necessarily is, except that no one on the Court actually speaks of the natural law, natural justice, or "the first principles of the social compact"—not in our day. Whatever might have been Justice Butler's inclinations when he dissented in *Buck v. Bell,* the traditional natural law rests on presuppositions that no contemporary judge or constitutional lawyer—or, at least, none known to me—would accept.[28] Their education forbids it. What about natural rights, or natural law as understood in the Declaration of Independence?

To justify our independence, we invoked "the Laws of Nature and of Nature's God," but our habit today is not to take that seriously. Even Carl Becker, the author of the one book devoted exclusively to explicating this first of our Founding documents, does not take it seriously. As he would have it, Jefferson and his colleagues appealed to the laws of nature only because they had to appeal to something, and it is pointless to ask whether they were serious in their claims: "To ask whether the natural rights philosophy of the Declaration of Independence is true or false," he says, "is essentially a meaningless question."[29]

Others take it seriously but, in the process, demonstrate their unfamiliarity with the subject—the venerable Roscoe Pound, for example. Hoping to breathe some life into the "forgotten" Ninth Amendment, Pound seizes upon the possibility that, with their reference to the "[rights] retained by the people," the Framers had in mind natural rights or—he tends to confuse them—natural laws.[30] But, an early opponent of the idea of original intent, he is not willing to accept the understanding of these rights or these laws current at the time of the Founding. Instead, he comes up with the idea of mutable rights and laws, mutable but—*mirabile dictu*—still natural. "From this standpoint," he says, "the Ninth Amendment is a solemn declaration that natural rights are not a fixed category of reasonable human expectations in civilized society laid down once and for all in the several sections of the Constitution." And "unlike the law of nature of the eighteenth century," he says, "the revived natural law is not a fixed system of precisely formulated rules to stand fast forever."[31]

As I said, we began in 1776 with an appeal to the self-evident truth that all men are endowed by their creator with certain unalienable rights. It is altogether reasonable to assume that, in 1787–88, when we gave our consent to the Constitution, we understood it to embody, or to be informed by, the principles of that Declaration, and that we further assumed that occasions would arise when, to decide a case or controversy, it would be necessary *and* appropriate for the Court to invoke them. Which is to say, as it is in the *United States Code* (as well as other official compilations of our laws), we once understood the Declaration to be the first of our "organic laws."[32] Leo Strauss made this point in 1953 when he wrote that "about a generation ago, an American diplomat could say that 'the natural and divine foundation of the rights of man' is self-evident to all Americans."[33] But Strauss went on to cast doubt whether that could still be said in his time. He referred to Germany, where the idea of natural right had been abandoned—where the term itself had become almost "incomprehensible"—and he suggested that this would happen in America. Indeed, if Sanford Levinson is right, that has now happened.

About a hundred years ago, Friedrich Nietzsche, the most influential of German thinkers, pronounced the death of God—"Nature's God," the God of the Declaration of Independence, as well as the God of the Bible—and we are indebted to Levinson, a leading American professor of constitutional law, for his candor when pointing to the consequences of this. "The death of constitutionalism," he declares, "may be the central event of our time, just as the death of God was that of the past century (and for much the same reason)."[34] Nature's God endowed us with rights, and the Founders provided us with a Constitution that, to secure these rights, put constraints on the popular will. With his death, those constraints are deprived of all moral authority. In Levinson's words, "Law is stripped of any moral anchoring," with the consequence that there is nothing "to which the will [is] bound to submit"[35]—no moral order, no moral laws, and, as Nietzsche said, no reason to be burdened by guilt. Levinson claims—and who would contest him?—that his view of our situation is the one "emphasized today at most major law schools"—and not only in the law schools.

The Death of Constitutionalism

We now live in a postmodernist world, and it is important to understand what that implies: constitutionalism is dead. The thought that made it possible is no longer believed. Rationalism is dead. The idea of nature gave way to history and historicism, then radical historicism, and in our case to "post-modernist" legal thought. And this, as Levinson accurately portrays it and as Thomas L. Pangle pointed out in his review of Levinson's book, "is inspired by the brooding, anti-rationalist, quasi-religious and proto-fascist philoso-phies of Nietzsche and Heidegger, supplemented by their more recent French and American 'deconstructionist' epigones, Derrida, Foucault, Barthes, de Man and Richard Rorty."[36] There are, I would emphasize, no constitutional-ists in this group, and, if Levinson is right, our law teachers, and ultimately our judges, will not be able to escape their influence.

But if constitutionalism is dead, so is the prospect for judicial review. If, as Levinson puts it with commendable candor, "there is nothing that is unsayable in the language of the Constitution,"[37] why should the people and their elected representatives defer to judgments rendered by an unelected judiciary? Levinson can think of no reason why they should, but Michael Perry (in some ways the most thoughtful of the proponents of a "living" con-stitution) says the judges speak for the people by appealing to their aspira-tions. The judges, he says, should be guided by the "beliefs or aspirations as to how the community's life, the life in common, should be lived." But he has to acknowledge that "different persons will have different views as to what an aspiration requires," and, this being so, he concludes that "the judge should rely on *her own beliefs* as to what the aspiration requires." How does she form those beliefs? By testing them "in the crucible of dialogic encounter with the wisdom of the past, of the tradition, including original beliefs, precedent, and anything else relevant and helpful."[38] The difference between this and a reliance on personal preferences is not readily discernible, and why the peo-ple and their elected representatives should defer to the judges' preferences is not at all evident. Why should they?

But Perry turns the question around. He asks, why are today's public officials "morally obligated to defer to the beliefs . . . of the long-dead and mostly WASP men who ratified the second Constitution—the Civil War amendments"? He says that they are not so obliged, that it is "counterintu-itive" to suppose that they are.[39]

Although Perry is a Roman Catholic and I am a latter-day WASP, it is not for that reason that I think this is a matter not to be decided by intuition. Would he think otherwise if the constitutional provision involved was of recent provenance—if, for example, it had been proposed last year by a convention called by the Congress on the application of two-thirds of the states and consisting of large numbers of non-WASPs? Perhaps, but, assuming the later provision is not intended to repeal the earlier, what is it that gives the provision a greater claim to obedience? On what basis could Perry say that the later convention—acting, let it be noticed, under the authority of a provision adopted by the earlier—enjoys a status denied to the earlier?

Legitimacy and Authority

But let the matter be decided by intuition—the public's intuition—and ask which judge has a greater claim to obedience, the one who points to those five provisions indicating, in one way or another, that the Constitution permits the imposition of the death penalty[40] and, on the basis of this constitutional evidence and despite his own beliefs on the matter, concludes that death is not a cruel or unusual punishment, or the one (Justice Brennan) who, having discerned what he regards as our true "aspirations," decides that the death penalty is unconstitutional? Or, again, which judge has a greater claim to obedience, Justice Antonin Scalia, who concludes that Title VII of the 1964 Civil Rights Act means what it says when it forbids sexual preferences in hiring, or Justice Sandra Day O'Connor, who admits that Title VII has been interpreted, and is being interpreted, "to permit what its language read literally would prohibit," and who goes so far as to say that Justice Scalia had proved this "with excruciating clarity," but, nevertheless, after engaging in some of that Perry moral discourse, concludes that the statute must be read to permit what it literally forbids?[41]

But this is a matter of legitimacy, which cannot be determined by intuition. Whether we can expect legislatures to defer to courts depends ultimately on the right of the people to adopt a constitution for themselves *and* for their posterity, a constitution binding upon themselves and, until "annulled or changed" in the prescribed manner, binding upon their posterity. That, in the words of *Federalist* 78, is the "fundamental principle of republican government." Judges may claim the obedience of other public officials because, and only because, they represent the people in their constituting capacity. Unlike elected officials, their constituents are those "long-dead and mostly WASP men" and, when acting in a "solemn and authoritative" manner, their living descendants. (Thanks to a series of constitutional amendments, these descendants are not necessarily either WASPs or men.)

The judges must acknowledge this. Even Justice Brennan claims to derive his authority from the Constitution, which, in this one respect at least, retains the meaning it had at the beginning. His decisions may derive from a *living* Constitution, but his authority to render them derives from that good old (in this one respect) "static" Constitution. The question is whether the people will continue to recognize that authority when the judges are no longer willing to limit themselves to enforcing the Constitution as written or, to quote Madison again, if the judges are not guided by the sense of the people who ratified it. I know of no one who has put this better than Fred Baumann:

> The problem created by the doctrine of the living Constitution for the legitimacy of the Constitution is obvious. It is that the Constitution then preserves only a formal existence, that it becomes a kind of moral capital on which the Supreme Court ceaselessly draws but that it can never replenish. As that capital is drawn down, it becomes ever clearer that it is not the Constitution that lives but only its name; consequently neither the Constitution nor the Court deriving its justification from the Constitution can enjoy further legitimacy.[42]

We obviously have not reached that point yet. The idea of constitutionality—and its converse, unconstitutionality—is still accepted by the American people but only, I suspect, because, in their commendable innocence, they continue to believe that it is the Constitution whose provisions the Court is enforcing. One has to wonder what will happen when they come to understand, as Joseph Rauh, a prominent lay proponent of the "living Constitution," wants them to understand, that the "Supreme Court is part of our nation's political process." He says that "the sooner this is accepted as inevitable the better."[43] I doubt that. I think they think that political decisions should be made democratically, by their political representatives whom, under the Constitution, they elect to office and whom they can remove from office. If so, and if the Court were to proceed along the lines traced by Brennan and retraced by Perry, Rauh, and the others, the "living Constitution" is not calculated to enjoy a long life.

4

The Demise of the Constitution

On January 20, 1989, George H. W. Bush took the following oath of office, an oath prescribed in the Constitution itself and, because of that, taken on each of the fifty-nine occasions since George Washington first took it in 1789: "I do solemnly swear . . . that I will faithfully execute the Office of President of the United States, and will to the best of my Ability, preserve, protect and defend the Constitution of the United States."

What does it mean to preserve, protect and defend—to say nothing of celebrating—the Constitution? Or, to put the question in a manner that suggests more clearly what is to follow, what is it that the president is sworn to preserve, protect, and defend? And why is it important to do so? President Bush did not say. Indeed, in the inaugural address that he then proceeded to deliver, he made no reference to the Constitution; neither, as it turns out, did most of his immediate predecessors or his immediate successors.

It was otherwise in the nineteenth century; only Lincoln and Grant, each in his second inaugural, failed specifically to refer to or speak of the Constitution. In 1825, John Quincy Adams devoted a major part of his inaugural address to it and, in the process, provided us with an understanding of what a president swears to preserve, protect, and defend, and why it deserves to be preserved, protected, and defended. "We now receive it," he said by way of summary,

> as a precious inheritance from those to whom we are indebted
> for its establishment, doubly bound by the examples which they
> have left us and by the blessings which we have enjoyed as the
> fruits of their labors to transmit the same unimpaired to the
> succeeding generation.[1]

Thanks to him and others—and, of course, especially to Lincoln—the Constitution, with its blessings, has been transmitted to generations even into the twentieth-first century. Thanks to the fact that it speaks only of "persons" and "Indians not taxed"—rather than of black and white, Christian and Jew, European, Asian, and African, noble and plebian, male and female, the Founders' Constitution has made this country a haven "for all sorts and conditions of men."[2] It has, from the beginning, defined a private realm, a realm in which we are free to pursue happiness as we understand it, or, as someone put it, "a realm in which we can tend to the salvation of our [own] souls," one whose existence "makes corruption voluntary to an appreciable degree." This is a Constitution that allows us to choose a government and, within broad limits, to prescribe its business, a government of, by, and for the people. This is a Constitution that is the product of profound *thought* about the failure of earlier republics, about the weaknesses of the first national constitution (the Articles of Confederation), about the conditions of the country, about the people of the United States, about the *thoughtful* objections raised by those who opposed its ratification, and most of all, *thought* about the nature of man and the purpose of government.

The product of that thought has now endured for more than two hundred years, among written constitutions by far the oldest. Consider: at last count—or, at least, at my last count—there were 164 countries in the world, 158 of them with written constitutions, but over half of them written since 1974, a statistic that provides some measure of the problems of constitutional government—and of our good fortune.

For all these reasons, and especially as the country prepared to celebrate, first, its sesqui- and then its bicentennial, one might have thought that presidents would have had something to say about the Constitution when taking the oath of office. But after McKinley, references to it became the exception rather than the rule. Theodore Roosevelt made no mention of it; Taft had something to say about the three post–Civil War amendments, but Woodrow Wilson (who elsewhere suggested that it be abandoned) did not utter the word "Constitution" in either of his inaugural addresses, nor did Harding or Hoover. Coolidge acknowledged it in passing, but Franklin Roosevelt, after a perfunctory reference to it in his third inaugural, spoke of it only in his fourth, and then only to complain of its imperfections. Truman ignored it altogether, as did Eisenhower, Kennedy, Johnson, Nixon (in 1969), and

Reagan (in 1985). As one might expect, considering the conditions surrounding his assumption of office, Gerald Ford referred to the Constitution in 1974, but from Jimmy Carter came not a word about it. Instead, he appealed to the Bible, quoting this passage in Micah 6:8: "He hath shown thee, O man, what is good; . . . and what doth the Lord require of thee, but to do justly, and to love mercy, and to walk *humbly* with thy God." That said, Carter proceeded to walk *proudly* down Pennsylvania Avenue with his wife.

It might appear that the Constitution has gone out of favor, and, sad to say, in some circles it has. In the law schools and, alas, also in the political science departments, the Constitution as written and authoritative text has certainly gone out of favor. This was made manifest by the reaction to the nomination of Robert Bork for a seat on the Supreme Court in 1987. To say nothing of my colleagues in political science, whose views were similar but not formally publicized, some 1,925 law professors—surely a good proportion of the total—publicly opposed his appointment, and took the trouble of communicating their opposition to the Senate Judiciary Committee. Bork, they said in one way or another, was out of the academy's "mainstream," as surely he was, and is.

Bork counsels fidelity to the Constitution as written and ratified by the people; which is to say, he sees the Constitution as *law*, "a superior paramount law, unchangeable by ordinary means," as the great Chief Justice John Marshall put it, law binding judge as well as legislator and executive.[3] But according to today's "mainstream" lawyers, the Constitution is a mere "epiphenomenon," and no one can be bound by an epiphenomenon. As one of them said, rather than carry any precise meaning that judges are bound by oath to recognize and obey, the most important constitutional provisions "do *not* rule out any answer a majority of the Court is likely to want to give."[4] Social, historical, and economic conditions—as seen by the judges—take precedence over the Constitution's written text, and they may dictate any outcome. Thus, as we are told by another "mainstream" academic lawyer, "There is nothing that is unsayable in the language of the Constitution." Nothing in it, not even the precise language of the Fifth Amendment, stands in the way of a statute taking "private property without [just] compensation," or compensation of any sort; none of its provisions forbids even "the establishment of a proletarian dictatorship" that would deny political rights to all but "proletarians and/or party members."[5]

Some "mainstream" lawyers go further. Rather than toy with the Constitution's text, they see it as lacking moral principles, and would consign it to the scrap heap. Whereas Bork has said the sole task of the judge "is to translate the [Framers'] . . . morality into a rule to govern unforeseen circumstances,"[6] they accuse the Framers as being, at best, morally indifferent. This is the view popularized by Ronald Dworkin, one of Bork's principal opponents. What is required, Dworkin has said, is a "fusion of constitutional law and moral theory, a connection that, incredibly, has yet to take place."[7]

One might protest that a Constitution that secures the rights of man—the *equal* rights of man—is not lacking in moral principle. But consider Madison's statement in *Federalist* 10, to the effect that the first object of government is the protection of different and unequal faculties, including the different and unequal faculty of acquiring property. Protecting the equal rights of unequally endowed men can only lead to inequality, not of Madisonian rights, but of wealth, position, rank. Is this not unjust? Manifestly so, by contemporary academic standards. Securing these rights leads to distributive injustice, to coin a phrase. Madison did not take rights seriously; he was not a genuine egalitarian; he made no provision against the Rockefellers of this world, to say nothing of the Donald Trumps.

Taking rights seriously—which is the title of Dworkin's book—leads to an egalitarian constitution under which there would be no Donald Trumps but, to adopt Dworkin's term, there would be trumps, of the sort known to bridge players. These would be dealt by the government to those who, for whatever reason, do not do well in the game of life, including the less talented, who deserve a better hand than nature dealt them. They have a right to some form of redistribution, he insists, and to "equal concern and respect," which, in his scheme, is the foundation of all rights.[8]

Dworkin calls them natural rights, thereby endowing them with a stature in addition to that gained by association with his name, but, on the face of it, they seem to be designed to work against nature or to remedy what he regards as the injustices of nature. Their source is in John Rawls's "original position," not in John Locke's state of nature; and unlike Locke and his predecessor Thomas Hobbes, Dworkin makes no attempt to demonstrate that they are intrinsic to man as man. He simply adopts the term because it's a convenient "assumption," a convenient foundation for his "conception of fairness." These rights depend on a hypothesis—his word—that "the protection of certain individual choices [is] fundamental." Thus, the refashioned constitution would be built on rights coming from a hypothesis, not on "unalienable rights" coming from "Nature's God," which Dworkin dismisses as a "preposterous notion."

But what is to be said of a natural right contrived in defiance of nature? Dworkin may dismiss the Founders' idea of human nature as "preposterous," but he cannot deny that nature distributes talents or faculties unequally; such differences were evident to James Madison and the other Framers, and, like it or not, they are evident to Dworkin—evident but, as he would have it, "morally irrelevant." But are they, these natural differences, *politically* irrelevant? Can they be ignored when framing a government?

What does Dworkin propose to do with the exceptionally talented? He denies them any knowledge of their talents. He asks, what sort of society would reasonable men choose to live in? To answer this question, and following John Rawls, he puts them—the naturally talented and the others—behind an imaginary "veil of ignorance."[9] There, eager to possess a great deal of what society has to offer—rank, esteem, or wealth, for example—but ignorant of what nature has bestowed on them by way of talents and, therefore, of what society is likely to give them by way of rank, esteem, and wealth, they would, being reasonable, choose a society that distributes these goods more or less equally. They would do so out of the fear that, if they had to compete for them, they would end up with less. In this way, nature would be thwarted.

Still, one must wonder whether it would, in practice, work out this way. Are there not likely to be a few men, even behind that "veil of ignorance," who would be willing to take a chance—especially since the alternative offered by Rawls and Dworkin might appear unspeakably dreary to them? So why not opt for equality of opportunity? Why not opt for the American way?

Even so, when the veil has been lifted, as it would be once the society is in being, would those who prove to be naturally talented not be tempted to rebel against Dworkin's dispensation? Dworkin may say that it is naturally right for them to be content with an equal share—after all, they would have voted for it—but the naturally talented are not likely to be satisfied. They would be inclined to say that a contract made in ignorance is not a legal or binding contract. And since they would not yet have been deprived of their passions, they would be very likely to rebel, especially since

Dworkin endows them, and everybody else, with a constitutional right to disobey the law.

Much the same can be said of the constitution favored by still another "mainstream" lawyer, Bruce Ackerman of the Yale Law School. Although he is critical of Rawls (and by implication, Dworkin), Ackerman manages to reconstruct the Constitution and come up with a liberal state that is, on the whole, similar to the one favored by them, even though he claims his is the first to be based on a purely relativistic principle. On it he builds his egalitarian state. Justice for him is treating everyone alike. He demonstrates this by means of a series of dialogues which, in a way, serve the same purpose as Rawls's and Dworkin's "veil of ignorance." Just as they deprive persons of any knowledge of their talents when they constitute society, he excludes the arguments of the talented from inclusion in his dialogues; each of his participants must acknowledge the principle, "I'm at least as good as you are." From this "constrained conversation," as he puts it, he arrives at a liberal state that refuses to treat any "lifestyle" as superior to others because all are arbitrary. For Ackerman, authority means authoritarian and "coercive," so he's against it, even (except during the earliest years of a child's life) the authority of parents and, of course, the authority of teachers and school boards. "As the child gains increasing familiarity with the range of cultural models open to him in a liberal society," he writes, "the choice of his curriculum should increasingly become his responsibility, rather than that of his educators."[10]

Let a thousand flowers bloom. But will they? And will what blooms be flowers? Tocqueville, for one, would have doubted it. Aiming at no place in particular, this liberal society will, and will willy-nilly, get someplace, and, if Tocqueville's—and, for that matter, the Founders'—vision was true, there is no reason to be complacent about the kind of place it will be. The society that thinks pushpin is as good as poetry (to borrow Clifford Orwin's phrase) will end up with a lot of mediocre pushpin and a little mediocre poetry. From the Founders' perspective, that would be a very dreary prospect indeed.

But never mind about the Founders; they're dead and gone—and discredited. What about their likes today? Would they be willing to accept this dispensation? The talented presented no problem for Ackerman when he designed his brave new world—he simply deprived them of a voice in his constituting dialogues—but what would he have to do to get them to live in it? Unlike Dworkin, he can't even say they voted for it and are, therefore, obliged to accept it. To put the question generally, how does Ackerman propose—in practice—to rectify what he sees as the injustices of nature? And nature, I repeat, discriminates; not with respect to rights, with which we are equally endowed, but with respect to mental faculties and physical attributes. With respect to these we are not equal—a fact that might be ignored in our books, but not in our politics.

Here, like Allan Bloom on a similar occasion, I think of Herodotus's account of a Babylonian law by which all the marriageable girls were auctioned off; the beautiful ones brought high prices from the rich and voluptuous men, and the city used the money so acquired to provide dowries for the ugly girls. In this way, the naturally unattractive were made attractive. But thanks to modern science, we can do better than that. By means of genetic engineering, we can make everyone look alike.

Of course, such means cannot be adopted by our government as presently constituted; but constitutional government—indeed, the very idea of constitutionalism as we have understood it since 1776—is now said to be dead. Its death is announced by Sanford Levinson. "The death of 'constitutionalism,'" Levinson writes, "may be the central event of our time, just as the death of God was that of the past century (and for much the same reason)."[11] Indeed, constitutionalism is dead precisely because God, even "nature's God," the god of the Declaration of Independence, is dead. Nature's God endowed us with rights and, through the agency of the Founders, provided us with a Constitution that, in order to secure those rights, put constraints on the popular will, which they understood to be the egalitarian will. With his death, those constraints are deprived of all moral authority—in Levinson's words, "Law is stripped of any moral anchoring"—and we are left with nothing but will. Nothing is left to guide the will; no "constraints of a common moral order to which the will [is] bound to submit."[12]

This leads me to my conclusion. The task assigned by the Framers to the Supreme Court was not an easy one. The judges were to be the "faithful guardians of the Constitution," and this would require of them "an uncommon portion of fortitude." It would, of course, require of them more than that. According to the same Framers, "A constitution is, in fact, and must be regarded by the judges as, a fundamental law [and] it therefore belongs to them to ascertain its meaning."[13]

Thus, care of the Constitution was put in their hands, but nothing was done, or could have been done, to ensure that when interpreting it, they remained persuaded of the truth of its principles. Resting on, derived from, political theory, the Constitution was vulnerable to changes in the world of theory. In the last letter he is known to have written, Thomas Jefferson could say that "all eyes are opened, or opening, to the rights of man"; but there was no guarantee that they would stay open, or, even if open, that they would remain fixed on the rights of man. Felix Frankfurter, himself a famous Supreme Court justice, and before that a famous Harvard law professor, praised Oliver Wendell Holmes for bringing philosophy to the Court and, therefore, to the Constitution, but Holmes's "philosophy" was not that of the Framers; and in the fifty-odd years since he left the bench, we have moved some distance along the path he marked out, and some further distance from the world of the Framers.

Yet, in form at least, we still live under the Framers' Constitution, and I suppose that every four years—and sometimes more frequently—presidents will continue to take the oath to "preserve, protect, and defend" it. But its substance is, to a large extent, in the hands of the justices and, ultimately, in the hands of the schools where they learn their law, or their jurisprudence—and, alas, I have to confess, their political science, for what I said about the law schools could also be said of the political science—and, indeed, the history—departments. Thus, the Constitution presidents will be under oath to defend may turn out to be a Constitution not worth defending.

5

Solving the Problem of Democracy

What is government itself but the greatest of all reflections on human nature? If men were angels, no government would be necessary. If angels were to govern men, neither external nor internal controls on government would be necessary. In framing a government which is to be administered by men over men, the great difficulty lies in this: you must first enable the government to control the governed; and in the next place oblige it to control itself.

—*Federalist 51*

Some years ago, before an audience of federal judges and law professors, I said that there probably was not a law school in the United States that did not offer a course in constitutional law, or many that did not make it a part of the required curriculum, but that, so far as I knew, none had a course on the Constitution itself. With a few conspicuous exceptions, the same was true of political science departments. There, as in the law schools, professors focused on the decisions handed down by the courts, mainly by the Supreme Court of the United States, differing from their law school colleagues only in their reasons for doing so.

The law professors were in the business of training practitioners who would need to know how to advise their clients (including, perhaps, government officials) and to try cases. Their emphasis, therefore, was on the law of those cases. The political scientists were interested in the factors that led, or might have led, to the decisions; as "scientists," they wanted to be able to predict the outcome of future cases. Their emphasis, therefore, was on judicial behavior, which they attempted to explain by quantifying the factors that, they thought, might enter into it.

50

Lost in all this was any interest in constitutionalism. Those who ought to have been professionally concerned with it seemed to have taken it for granted. (After all, the United States had lived under the Constitution for more than two hundred years. So what was the problem?) Pressed to define constitutionalism, they would have been nonplussed; few made the effort, and fewer still studied it.

This indifference may have been inevitable; Tocqueville seems to have thought so. What is constitutionalism but formal government? And, as he points out, democrats—and American professors are surely democrats—are distrustful of forms and do not comprehend their utility. They aspire to easy and present gratifications, he says, and are exasperated by anything that stands in their way:

> Yet this objection which the men of democracies make to forms is the very thing which renders forms so useful to freedom; for their chief merit is to serve as a barrier between the strong and the weak, the ruler and the people, to retard the one and to give the other time to look about him. Forms become more necessary in proportion as the government becomes more active and more powerful. . . . Thus democratic nations naturally stand more in need of forms than other nations, and they naturally respect them less.

This, he concludes, "deserves most serious attention."[1] That it received such attention at the beginning of the United States should be evident to anyone who takes the trouble to study the records of the convention that framed the Constitution and the debates (which were vigorous and extensive) surrounding its ratification. My task here is to explain the product of those deliberations and the problems it was intended to solve, in the opinion (an opinion emphatically confirmed by South Africa's experience in drafting a new constitution in the 1990s) that those problems were not, and are not, unique to America.

America's Good Fortune

Beginning in the autumn of 1787, Americans were asked to deliberate on, with a view to ratifying, a new constitution for the United States. "The subject speaks its own importance," we read in *Federalist 1*,

> comprehending in its consequences nothing less than the existence of the UNION, the safety and welfare of the parts of which it is composed, the fate of an empire in many respects the most interesting in the world.

Nor would these consequences be confined to America; not, at least, according to the authors of *The Federalist*:

> It has been frequently remarked that it seems to have been reserved to the people of this country, by their conduct and example, to decide the important question, whether societies of men are really capable or not of establishing good government from reflection and choice, or whether they are forever destined to depend for their political constitutions on accident and force.[2]

Now, some two centuries years later, we can say that America did set an example, and that many, indeed most, countries have followed it. How many have profited from it is, however, another question. By my last reckoning (undertaken before the breakup of the Soviet Union and Yugoslavia), there were 164 countries in the world, all but 6 of them with written constitutions—the exceptions were Britain, New Zealand, Israel, Saudi Arabia, Oman, and Libya—but of those 158 written constitutions, over half had been written since 1974; and in the period when America has had one constitution, France has had five. (And, as the old joke has the Paris taxi driver saying, "*Il y aura une sixième* [There will be a sixth].")

Although some may question how much the world has learned or, to be fair, can learn from the American example, without question Americans stand to learn much from the experience of other peoples. They can, for example, learn to appreciate their Constitution, and, incidentally, how much its success is the product of the favorable circumstances that attended its birth.

This fact was acknowledged by Publius, the pseudonymous author of *The Federalist*. The country was geographically united, he said, bound by navigable waters that facilitated communication and commerce, and blessed with a variety of soils and productions watered "with innumerable streams for the delight and accommodation of its inhabitants."[3] This passage comes to mind when we read of drought and its attendant starvation in places like Somalia.

Publius then points out that, in addition to its material blessings,

> Providence [had] been pleased to give this one connected country to one united people—a people descended from the same ancestors, speaking the same language, professing the same religion, attached to the same principles of government, very similar in their manners and customs, and who, by their joint counsels, arms, and efforts, fighting side by side throughout a long and bloody war, have nobly established their general liberty and independence.[4]

I recall this passage whenever I read of events in what was once Yugoslavia, where the Christian Serbs seem determined to annihilate the Muslims in Bosnia-Herzegovina; in Iraq where the government waged war on its own Kurds and Shiites; in what was once Czechoslovakia; in Nagorno-Karabakh and Georgia, and other parts of the once mighty Soviet Union; or, for a final example, in strife-ridden Cambodia.

Indeed, I have had occasion to recall this passage whenever I have, in one way or another, participated in discussions of constitutional matters in other countries:

- In Cyprus, for example, where in 1979 Professor Daniel Elazar and I were in Nicosia to discuss federalism in a country where Greeks and Turks were (and still are) separated by a line drawn across the breadth of the country, a line that was (and still is) being patrolled by a United Nations peacekeeping force.

- In Brazil where, in 1987, after listening to what I had to say on the subject of constitution-making, a member of the audience denounced the organizer of the program for inviting an American to speak on that subject. "What," he asked, "can we learn from America? In two hundred years they've had only one constitution. Why not a Bolivian? They've had a hundred."

(No doubt many factors have contributed to the longevity of our Constitution—not the least of them, lest we forget, being the Union victory in our Civil War—but the good luck that attended its birth is surely one of them.)

And, most recently, in South Africa, where the discussion of a new constitution necessarily involved the role (almost surely disruptive) of political parties. In this respect, also, America was fortunate. As Publius says, the convention that drafted the Constitution of the United States "must have enjoyed, in a very singular degree, an exemption from the pestilential influence of party animosities—the disease most incident to deliberative bodies and most apt to contaminate their proceedings."[5]

Indeed, unlike every other country that has attempted to write a constitution since America set the example in 1787, the question of who was to participate in the convention charged with writing it simply did not arise in the United States; it was not an issue. It could not be an issue. Contrary to the objection raised by that angry Brazilian, America has had two constitutions, and under the first of them—the so-called Articles of Confederation and Perpetual Union—the United States then consisted of thirteen quasi-sovereign states. There was, therefore, no question but that the convention of 1787, if it were to meet, would be, and could only be, a meeting of those states, each choosing its own representatives (and in whatever number it chose), and each state casting one vote. The importance of this should not be minimized. All the preliminary issues that have plagued the constitution-making process in other countries—who would be represented, and in what numbers, and with what authority, and where the convention should meet, and for how long, and in what language (or languages) the deliberations should take place, to say nothing of the question of whether they should be secret, closed to the press—were absent in the United States in 1787.

America was especially lucky—and again the comparison with South Africa in drafting its 1996 constitution is telling—in that its people were one people. They were one not only because they spoke the same language, professed the same religion, were attached to the same principles of government,

and were very similar in their manners and customs, but, as Publius emphasizes, they were united by a common enemy defeated in "a long and bloody
war"—not just a common, but a foreign, enemy. Abraham Lincoln was to
make much of this fact in the first of his major speeches. Speaking of the
period immediately after the American Revolution, he pointed out that

> the deep rooted principles of *hate*, and the powerful motive
> of *revenge*, instead of being turned against each other, were
> directed exclusively against the British nation. And thus, from
> the force of circumstances, the basest principles of our nature
> were either made to lie dormant, or to become the active agents
> in the advancement of the noblest of cause [sic]—that of estab-
> lishing and maintaining civil and religious liberty.[6]

Americans should bear all this in mind (and be humbled by it) whenever they address the subject of constitution-making in other countries, for
no other country is now blessed as America was blessed at its beginning. In
fact, it is no exaggeration to say that, among all the countries that have
attempted to constitute (or, in the typical case, reconstitute) themselves,
only the United States was given the opportunity to make a truly new
beginning. Unlike France, for example, it did not continue to find itself
with a sullen nobility, dispossessed by the revolution of its property and
its privileges but not of its hopes for their recovery under a restoration of
un ancien régime. Tocqueville acknowledged one aspect of this when he
said that the "great advantage of the Americans is that they arrived at a state
of democracy without having to endure a democratic revolution, and that
they [were] born equal instead of becoming so."[7]

Nor was the United States faced with what Karl Marx would later call a
proletariat nursing its legitimate grievances and thirsting for revenge. As
Tocqueville said, there was no proletariat in America.[8] There was, of course,
a large number of Africans enslaved under the laws of the states (almost
exclusively the southern states), but unlike the Xhosas, Zulus, and certain
other inhabitants of South Africa today who have some political power, they
had neither political power nor, for well into the nineteenth century, a political voice.[9] As for the Indian tribes native to the North American continent,
their presence, unlike that of the slaves, was noted in the Constitution, but

only as an alien people with whom the government might enter into treaties.[10] (These treaties had to be written and rewritten as the Indians were pushed ever farther westward, even as the Xhosas were pushed back first beyond the Great Fish and then the Keiskamma and Great Kei rivers.) Still, while America may owe the relatively easy adoption of the Constitution to those circumstances, it owes its subsequent prosperity, security, and stability to that Constitution—and to the handful of men who drafted it and secured its ratification. As I once wrote,

> Some were unknown (and remained so), but most of them came not as strangers to each other. The more distinguished among them especially had worked together in the Congress or army and, even when that was not the case, knew each other by reputation. They were a remarkably learned and talented group of men. Even Richard Henry Lee, who did his best to prevent the ratification of the Constitution, acknowledged that "America would probably never see an assembly of men of like number more respectable."[11]

They included James Madison, James Wilson, Benjamin Franklin, Alexander Hamilton, Gouverneur Morris, John Rutledge, Oliver Ellsworth, and, presiding over their deliberations, George Washington. (Thomas Jefferson, in Paris at the time, referred to the convention as "an assembly of demigods.")[12]

Perhaps the most important consideration—and here again the contrast with South Africa is significant—was that they not only knew each other but, with very few exceptions, and despite the sharp divisions engendered especially by the slavery issue, they trusted each other and had reason to do so. They understood the problems they faced and designed a government capable of dealing with them. These problems were not unique to the United States; indeed, they were similar to those faced by South Africa in drafting its new constitution.

Principles of Government

The Framers of the Constitution had no illusions that their task was an easy one. The country's geographical isolation would not, by itself, protect it from foreign enemies; the Constitution would have to make provision for its defense. Thus, Congress was given the power "to declare war, grant Letters of Marque and Reprisal, and make Rules concerning Captures on Land and Water"; "to raise and support Armies"; "to provide and maintain a Navy"; "to provide for calling forth the Militia to execute the Laws of the United States, suppress Insurrections and repel Invasions"; and the president was made "Commander in Chief of the Army and Navy . . . and of the Militia of the several States, when called into the actual service of the United States."

In the event, these provisions proved to be adequate. Although sorely tested on occasion, especially during the Civil War, they allowed for the defense of the nation without—or only once—jeopardizing the liberties of the people.[13]

Then, although it was true that almost all Americans professed Christianity, the Framers knew that this was no guarantee that America would be free of sectarian warfare. To guard against it, they consigned religion to the private sphere by separating church and state. They did this by providing that "no religious Test shall ever be required as a Qualification to any Office or public Trust under the United States," and by forbidding Congress "to make any law respecting an establishment of religion, or prohibiting the free exercise thereof." In this way, they hoped to take religion out of politics.

What is true respecting the problem of national defense is equally true respecting the religious problem. Compared with other times and places, America, during the entire course of its history under the Constitution, has been remarkably free of religious strife—without (if the public opinion polls are to be believed) the people becoming irreligious.

The problem of most concern to the Framers, and the one whose resolution required their greatest attention, had to do with the principles of government. In fact, even at the beginning there were sharper differences respecting these principles than Publius would have us believe. He conveniently neglected to mention that at the time of the Revolution, about 20 percent of the population—or approximately five hundred thousand persons—were Tories, who for one reason or another neither fought for independence nor were attached to its principles. Some were officeholders under the Crown, or soldiers, or Anglican clergy; others, and the politically more interesting, were "throne and altar Tories," dedicated monarchists loyal to the king as head of the church and head of state. Most of them remained silent during the revolutionary struggle, but many chose to become political exiles. Some returned to England, and some thirty-five to forty thousand of them went to Nova Scotia where, in 1784, they persuaded the British government to partition this "New Scotland," thereby establishing for them another colony, New Brunswick, which later became (along with Nova Scotia) one of the ten Canadian provinces. Only the departure of the Tories made it possible for Publius to say that the Americans were attached to the same principles of government.

Those principles were set down in the Declaration of Independence of 1776, when Americans declared themselves to be a "new order of the ages," the first nation in all of history to build itself on the self-evident truth that all men are created equal insofar as they are all endowed by Nature's God with the unalienable rights of life, liberty, and pursuit of happiness. The purpose of government, they then said, was to secure these rights. This was to be done—because, given their principles, it had to be done—only with the consent of the governed. With the Tories gone or silenced, there was no disagreement on this score.

But it was understood by the Framers that, while Americans were attached to the idea of rights, they would not always agree on the definition of rights, or on how rights were to be secured, or on whose rights deserved to be secured, or preferred. In fact, the Framers expected the people to have sharply differing views on these matters. Thus, the "one people" that declared its independence in 1776, and the "we, the people" that constituted a government in 1787–88 in order to "secure these rights," would, as a matter of course, be divided into factions thereafter, and, unless steps were taken to avoid it, warring factions. According to Publius (in number ten, the most frequently quoted and celebrated of the *Federalist Papers*), "The latent causes of faction are . . . sown in the nature of man," and by definition these factions have interests "adverse to the rights of other citizens, or to the permanent and aggregate interests of the community." As the Framers saw it, this was the principal problem the Constitution had to deal with.

What is more, nature, so equitable in its endowment of rights, was by no means equitable in its endowment or distribution of talents or faculties, particularly, as Publius put it, the "faculties of acquiring property." Some men are naturally more intelligent, more enterprising, or more energetic, as well as healthier, stronger, or handsomer than others. Thus, by securing the equal rights of *un*equally endowed human beings, the society would be divided between "those who hold and those who are without property," or between the wealthy and the poor, or between the relatively wealthy and the relatively poor. Still, Publius did not hesitate to say that protecting these "different and unequal faculties"—naturally different and naturally unequal—was "the first object of government."

Accomplishment of this object was made especially difficult because those without property, or with less property, would constitute a majority, and under a republican government the majority would rule. The task facing the Framers was to design a Constitution making it less likely that this majority would misrule.

A Republican Government

There was no question but that the government would have to be republican in form. As Publius said in *Federalist* 39, "No other form would be reconcilable with the genius of the people of America; with that honorable determination which animates every votary of freedom to rest all our political experiments on the capacity of mankind for self-government." Unfortunately, while there had been republics, none could serve as a model for America. For this reason, the Framers of the Constitution had to devise a new form of republican government. As Harvey C. Mansfield Jr. explains, there are important differences between the new republicanism and the old:

> [The new] republic is based on the presumption that *the* problem of popular government comes from within the regime—from factions and tyrannical majorities. So it provides a constitution through which the people chooses to limit itself not by preventing the majority from ruling as in oligarchy, or by retaining a privileged class to rule with the majority as in "mixed government," but [rather] by constructing a majority so that it will not be factious or tyrannical. This new kind of republic is contrasted [*Federalist* 9, 10, and 14] to the old kind found in the republican tradition, which is given the pejorative label *democracy*. In democracy, the presumption is that the danger comes from outside the regime—from monarchy and oligarchy. So the popular spirit must

be aroused and kept in a state of vigilance against its enemies; and instead of a constitution providing self-chosen limited government, the main requirement is to cultivate this vigilant spirit in republican virtue. Republican virtue, in turn, requires a homogeneous people and a small territory so that citizens can know and trust one another.[14]

Publius's description of the earlier, classical republics—he mentioned specifically the "petty republics of Greece and Italy"—was harsh indeed. They provided no barriers "against domestic faction and insurrection," he said; they were regularly overwhelmed by "tempestuous waves of sedition and party rage"; rather than serving as models for America, they were nothing so much as "the wretched nurseries of unceasing discord, and the miserable objects of universal pity or contempt."[15] Indeed, had it not been possible to devise models of a more perfect structure, "the enlightened friends to liberty would have been obliged to abandon the cause of [republicanism] as indefensible."

Fortunately, the science of politics had "devised models of a more perfect structure . . . which were either not known at all, or imperfectly known to the ancients": the regular distribution of power into distinct departments; the introduction of legislative balances and checks; the institution of courts composed of judges holding their offices during good behavior; and the representation of the people in the legislature by deputies of their own election. These are "means, and powerful means, by which the excellencies of republican government may be retained and its imperfections lessened or avoided."[16] This "more perfect structure" provided the forms that, in Tocqueville's words, "serve as a barrier between the strong and the weak," and in so doing serve as the means by which democracy is constitutionalized.

The Model of John Locke

Chief among the political scientists to whom the Framers were indebted for this new model of republicanism was John Locke. Like that of Thomas Hobbes before him, Locke's political science begins with an analysis of the nonpolitical state of nature. Whereas, according to Hobbes, the state of nature was indistinguishable from the state of war, wherein the life of man was "solitary, poor, nasty, brutish and short," Locke speaks rather of the "inconveniences of that condition."[17] But these "inconveniences" are such that, at a certain point, war becomes inevitable. Thus, "to avoid this state of war," as Locke puts it, "is one great reason of men's putting themselves into society and quitting the state of nature."[18] They do this by entering into a compact by which every man agrees to divest himself of "his natural liberty and puts on the bonds of civil society."

Hobbes, again, required men to yield their natural rights, or liberty, to a Leviathan, but Locke finds this objectionable. Men are not so foolish, he says, to take care to avoid the mischiefs that may be done them in the state of nature by "polecats or foxes," only to be "devoured by lions," which is to say, by Leviathans, whose every act is to be considered law.[19] To prevent this, he requires men to hand over their natural rights, not to a Leviathan but, rather, to the community, with the understanding that the community be governed by laws made by a legislative body:

> The great end of men's entering into society being the enjoyment of their properties in peace and safety, and the great instrument and means of that being the laws established in that society, the first and fundamental positive law [which is to say, constitutional law] is the establishing of the legislative power.[20]

It is not by chance that article 1 of the Constitution of the United States establishes the legislative power. There is safety when the supreme power is exercised by the legislative, rather than by the Leviathan. As Locke says, the legislative rules not by "extemporary, arbitrary decrees" but by "promulgated, standing laws." In a well-ordered commonwealth,

> the legislative power is put into the hands of diverse persons who, duly assembled, have by themselves, or jointly with others, a power to make laws; which when they have done, being separated again, they are themselves subject to the laws they have made, which is a new and near tie upon them to take care that they make them for the public good.[21]

There is safety, too, in the fact that the legislature will not be in constant session, which requires that there be another power to "see to the execution of the laws."[22]

With this, Locke lays the foundation for a separation of powers, one of the features of the "more perfect structure" that Publius speaks of in *Federalist* 9. And not merely one of the features, but the central feature, because it serves both "to control the governed" and to oblige the government "to control itself."

The obligation of the government to control itself should require little demonstration; it is certainly familiar to all students of American government. As Publius says (in *Federalist* 47), "The accumulation of all powers, legislative, executive, and judiciary, in the same hands, whether of one, a few, or many, and whether hereditary, self-appointed, or elective, may justly be pronounced the very definition of tyranny." The separation of powers, combined with the innovation the Framers learned from Montesquieu— namely, bicameralism—is one of the defining characteristics of the more perfectly structured republic.

It remains to describe how the separation of powers serves to control the governed. Traditionally, republicans were animated by a distrust of the executive, which in most cases meant the monarch. Thus, having declared their independence from George III, Americans proceeded to establish governments which, in the case of the first national constitution (the Articles of Confederation and Perpetual Union), deliberately neglected to provide for an executive or, in the case of the early state constitutions, contained provisions "for reducing the executive to a position of complete subordination [to the legislature]." The Virginia constitution of 1776 was typical in this respect:

> [The governor] shall, with the advice of a Council of State, exercise the executive powers of the government, according to the laws of this Commonwealth; and shall not, under any pretense, exercise any power or prerogative, by virtue of any law, statute or custom of England.[23]

The experience gained from this practice proved to be bitter, and the Framers of the Constitution of 1787 were determined that it not be repeated. Too frequently the laws had gone unenforced, taxes uncollected, and the common defense neglected. With this in mind, they separated the executive and legislative powers and endowed the executive with powers derived from the Constitution itself.

Article 2 of the Constitution begins with this terse statement: "The executive Power shall be vested in a President of the United States of America." This executive was charged with the duty of executing the laws— as the Constitution puts it, "he shall take Care that the Laws be faithfully executed"—but also with responsibilities having little or nothing to do with the literal meaning of the word "execute."

It is Locke, again, who first makes the republican case for an independent executive. An executive is needed to execute the laws, and in this capacity he is subordinate to (even if not controlled by) the legislative power ("the supreme power of the commonwealth"). But Locke goes on to indicate that the well-being or, to be more precise, the safety of the commonwealth cannot be assured by laws alone.

There is, in the first place, the problem of foreign affairs, which, he suggests, cannot be directed by "antecedent, standing, positive Laws." Foreign affairs belong to the "federative power," which Locke likens to the natural power every man had in the state of nature. Since the exercise of this power—the power of "war and peace, leagues and alliances, and all the transactions with all persons and communities [outside] the commonwealth"—requires prudence, Locke puts it into the hands of the independent executive.[24]

In addition to foreign affairs, however, the good of the society may require that some domestic matters "be left in the hands of him that has the executive power." There will be "cases where the municipal law has given no direction," or where "a strict and rigid observation of the laws may do harm," or where it will be proper "to mitigate the severity of the law" by pardoning those who offend against it. Such cases require "prerogative," which Locke defines as the "power to act according to discretion for the public good, without the prescription of the law and sometimes even against it."[25]

One of the abiding questions of American constitutional law is whether "the executive power" vested in the president of the United States includes something like the prerogative as Locke defines it. Congress is inclined to deny that it does, but presidents, including the best of them, have ever claimed it.[26] And, if we accept the authority of *The Federalist*, the Framers of the Constitution intended him to have it. The following passage from *Federalist* 28 might have been written by Locke:

> That there may happen cases in which the national government may be necessitated to resort to force cannot be denied. Our own experience has corroborated the lessons taught by the examples of other nations; that emergencies of this sort will sometimes exist in all societies, however constituted; that seditions and insurrections are, unhappily, maladies as inseparable from the body politic as tumors and eruptions from the natural body; that the idea of governing at all times by the simple force of law (which we have been told is the only admissible principle of republican government) has no place but in the reveries of those political doctors whose sagacity disdains the admonitions of experimental instruction.

As Locke says, emergencies cannot be dealt with by "antecedent, standing law"; they require the exercise of prerogative which, to repeat, he defines as the power to act according to discretion for the public good, without the prescription of the law "and sometimes even against it." Locke's prerogative, then, is an extralegal power, extralegal because it exists by necessity, not by virtue of a constitution. But, according to Publius, this power to deal with emergencies is given a place in the Constitution; it is part of the executive power vested in the president of the United States. When exercising it, therefore, the president is not acting extralegally. For, according to *Federalist* 31,

> a government ought to contain in itself every power requisite to the full accomplishment of the objects committed to its care, and to the complete execution of the trusts for which it is responsible, free from every other control but a regard to the public good and to the sense of the people.[27]

Among the objects committed to its care is "the preservation of the public peace" (*Federalist* 23), and, as Publius makes clear, there will be times when this can best be done, in fact can only be done, by the president exercising powers coming directly from the Constitution and "free from every other control but a regard to the public good and to the sense of the people."

Because he is not chosen by the legislature, and because he holds powers independently of the legislature, he can act without its consent. Because, unlike the numerous legislature, he is one, not many, he can act with dispatch. And because he is one, not many, it is easy to fix responsibility for what he does.[28]

To summarize: The separation of powers is a means of obliging the government to control itself; in this respect, it serves to limit government, which, in the American case, means the government of the democracy. It is also a means of controlling the governed by authorizing the president not only to enforce the law directly on the people but, if necessary—for example, in times of "domestic insurrection" (*Federalist* 26)—to employ the extraordinary powers of his office. In this respect the separation of powers serves to ensure an effective government, a government as strong as necessary. President Lincoln, who was faced with a massive insurrection, was to prove just how strong and effective this government could be.

The Role of the Judiciary

It is widely assumed, abroad as well as in the United States, that the most effective means of limiting government is the power exercised by the independent judiciary, the power of judicial review. With this power the courts, ultimately the Supreme Court of the United States, may nullify the actions of legislature and executive alike by declaring them unconstitutional. Indeed, it was with this in mind that Publius (in *Federalist* 9) speaks of the independence of the judiciary as one of the elements of the "more perfect structure" that made republican government possible. And there is no question about that independence: once appointed (by the president with the advice and consent of the Senate), federal judges serve during good behavior, which in most cases means until they die or retire. (In fact, no Supreme Court justice has left the bench in any other manner.) In the more than two centuries of its existence, the Court has declared over a thousand legislative enactments and executive actions unconstitutional.

Judicial review is thought to be especially important as a means of protecting those individual rights specified in the first ten amendments to the Constitution, popularly known as the Bill of Rights. It is sometimes said, for example, that Americans owe their freedom of speech, press, and religion primarily to judicial enforcement of the First Amendment (which forbids Congress to make any law "respecting an establishment of religion, or prohibiting the free exercise thereof; or abridging the freedom of speech, or of the press"). But this is only partly true, and the way in which it is not true should concern those who would rely on a judiciary for protection of their rights.

I have discussed this issue in great detail elsewhere.[29] Here it is enough to point out that it was not until 1965 (and only once or twice since) that the Court declared an act of Congress a violation of the First Amendment. The record is much the same with respect to the other provisions of the Bill of Rights. The Supreme Court has never declared a punishment imposed under federal law to be "cruel and unusual" in violation of the Eighth Amendment.

The judiciary has made a difference, however, in those cases where the states and localities have abridged rights. Literally hundreds of state statutes and local ordinances, as well as acts committed by local police, have been declared unconstitutional by the Supreme Court. That is, the courts have played their protective role as part of the federal system, or, to state the reason for their success here, when they have been opposed by local (or, at most, regional) rather than national majorities. The local authorities are inclined to obey court orders, and, on those infrequent occasions when they refuse to do so, the courts can usually depend on the president to see to it that they do. After all, the Constitution requires him to see to it that the laws are faithfully executed. (Thus, when the city of Little Rock, Arkansas, backed by the governor of the state, refused to obey a court order requiring the racial integration of a local high school, President Eisenhower sent in elements of an airborne division; and that, as the saying goes, was that.) But enforcing an order against the president or Congress of the United States, while technically no different, is another matter, and sometimes proves to be impossible. (As legend has it, President Andrew Jackson once said, "John Marshall [the chief justice at the time] has issued his order, now let him enforce it.") A few examples will serve to illustrate the point:

- In 1857, the Supreme Court declared unconstitutional an act of Congress prohibiting slavery in the northern section of a federal territory. That decision was a major cause of the Civil War, and, the war having been won by the Union, it was reversed by a constitutional amendment in 1868.

- In 1870, the Court, by a vote of four to three, struck down a Civil War statute making non–interest-bearing notes ("greenbacks") legal tender in payment of "all debts, public and private." Having been authorized by Congress to do so, the president proceeded to appoint two additional justices and, the following year, the enlarged Court—by a vote of five to four—reversed the earlier decision.

- In 1895, the Court struck down a federal statute imposing a tax on incomes. Congress responded by proposing an amendment to the Constitution (the sixteenth) which, when ratified in 1913, gave it the power "to lay and collect taxes on incomes, from whatever source derived, without apportionment among the several States, and without regard to any census or enumeration."

- Following a number of decisions striking down New Deal economic or commercial legislation, President Franklin D. Roosevelt proposed that Congress enlarge the Court from nine to (potentially) as many as fifteen members. The Court, in its famous (or infamous) "switch in time that saved nine," reversed itself— indeed, not only reversed itself but, in effect, announced that it would no longer question Congress's power to regulate interstate commerce.[30]

There are, of course, cases where judgments of unconstitutionality have been accepted by the Congress. In 1990, for a recent example, the Court struck down a federal statute prohibiting the burning of the American flag. Burning the flag, the Court said, is (or in this case was) a form of symbolic expression protected by the free speech provision of the First Amendment. But this was hardly a case where the Court succeeded in imposing its judgment on an obstinate Congress. That statute was enacted, or, at least, it was supported, by its principal sponsors in the House and Senate, precisely in order to give the Court the opportunity to declare it unconstitutional. Declaring it unconstitutional was, to say the least, politically easy. When, however, during World War II, President Roosevelt issued an executive order (subsequently ratified and confirmed by an act of Congress) empowering the secretary of war to round up thousands of Japanese-Americans and ship them off to detention centers, the Court acquiesced—not without a struggle, and not unanimously, but nevertheless, acquiesce it did.[31] The decision was greeted with dismay or disgust by many in the legal fraternity, but they ought not to have been surprised. As Publius said even in the beginning (in *Federalist* 78), "It would require an uncommon portion of fortitude in the judges to do their duty as faithful guardians of the Constitution, where legislative invasions of it had been instigated by the major voice of the community."

Fortunately, so far as the national legislature is concerned, such invasions are the exception, not the rule; in fact, they are rare—so rare that judicial action to protect rights is only rarely required—and they are rare largely because the Constitution, by devising a "more perfect" republican structure, makes it difficult for the "major voice of the community" to be expressed. As Publius says (and the emphasis is his), "*the people in their collective capacity*" are excluded from any share in the government.[32]

A Republican Constitution

The remarkable thing is that the Framers were able to persuade the people to ratify this republican Constitution. Plainly, the Framers made no effort to conceal the fact that they intended to put limits on democratic majorities; they said as much. They said that they intended the Constitution to exclude the people in their collective capacity from any share in the government; they said that the chief object of the government was to protect the diverse faculties of men, especially their "different and unequal faculties of acquiring property"; they took pride in the fact that their government was not a democracy but, rather, a republic that put some distance between the people and the levers of power:

- Their Constitution provided a president chosen not by the people but by electors who, having made their choice, would immediately disband.

- It provided a Senate chosen not by the people but by the state legislatures, each state, regardless of the size of its population, being entitled to choose two.

- It provided a House of Representatives chosen not by a majority of the whole people ("the people in their collective capacity") but by majorities within each of the districts into which each state would be divided.

- It provided a Supreme Court with the power to veto popular legislation and whose members would, in effect, serve for life.

Generally, the Constitution provided a system of divided power and checks and balances, and it was understood that what was most in need of being checked were popular majorities. Yet, these popular majorities gave it their consent.

The people were left in no doubt about the essential characteristics of the Constitution. Every aspect of it was subjected to intense scrutiny during the ratification debates. These debates, pitting Federalists (who favored ratification) against Anti-Federalists (who opposed it), were carried on in town meetings, state conventions, and in the popular press; and for every Federalist paper there was an Anti-Federalist paper, for every Publius a Cato, for every Cassius a Brutus or Agrippa or Centinel or Hampden. The Anti-Federalists complained of the six-year terms for senators, of the reeligibility of the president, of the provision for a standing army (which they saw as a weapon to be used against the people), and, generally, of what they called the "aristocratic tendency of the Constitution." Patrick Henry, for example, who led the opposition in Virginia, said the Constitution "has an awful squinting; it squints towards monarchy."[33] Yet Virginia, like every other state, voted narrowly in favor of ratification. Under the circumstances this was truly remarkable.

Publius recognized this, and argued strenuously against Jefferson's suggestion that, in effect, the ratification process be repeated from time to time.[34] What Publius believed to be true then—namely, that given another chance, the people would be likely to reject the Constitution because of the restrictions it imposed on popular majorities—would almost surely be true today. This judgment is strengthened by the changes that have been made since the Constitution was first adopted. Senators are now chosen by popular vote of the people in the states,[35] and the right to vote, in state as well as federal elections, has been extended not only to blacks and women, but to persons "eighteen years of age or older," and cannot be denied to persons by reason of their "failure to pay any poll tax or other tax."[36] Then, too, the early appearance of political parties had the effect of taking the choice of the president from the nominally independent electors and putting it in the hands of the people; and the day will surely come when the electoral college itself will be abolished and replaced by a system of direct popular election.[37] (This did not happen in 2000, however, even though the presidential candidate who won a majority of the popular votes, Al Gore, failed to win an electoral college majority.)

A Model Constitution

These changes in the direction of more democracy may satisfy the people, at least for the time being. They clearly do not satisfy many political scientists who, because of the positions they occupy, are capable of exerting an influence out of proportion to their numbers. The more radical among them (mostly Marxists) teach their students—and, thanks to a policy of open admissions and generous government subsidies, something approaching fifty percent of the people are, or have been, students—that the Constitution is an "elitist document" providing "democracy for the few."[38] Others, including a handful of the most illustrious, complain that, while not necessarily elitist, it still fails to provide government sufficiently (by which they mean immediately) responsive to the wishes of the people.

Of course, it was not intended to do this. By providing for the representation of the great variety of interests within the "extensive territory" of the United States, the Constitution was intended to prevent the formation of a majority with a common interest "adverse to the rights of other citizens, or to the permanent and aggregate interests of the community."[39] In the United States, governing majorities are assembled not from among the people directly (not even when they are organized in or by political parties) but from among the representatives of the people. Because they represent different interests, and because the legislative branch is separated from the executive, and because the legislative branch is itself divided into House and Senate, assembling this majority is not a simple matter.

The political scientists find this exasperating; they write books complaining of the deadlock of democracy and propose to end that deadlock by instituting something like the British system. In a word, they want party government, in which party serves as the means by which majority opinion is readily translated into public policy.[40] For them, popular government means giving the people what they want (or what they say they want) as soon as they want it, which means a government unable to do anything unpopular.

Woodrow Wilson, a president of the American Political Science Association (APSA) as well as of the United States, was one of the earliest proponents of party government in the United States. Writing in 1885, he complained that the Congress was too strong and the executive too weak, and the consequence of this was irresponsible government. How, he asked, can we identify whom to praise and whom to blame for what is done under this system? Indeed, who can be said to govern when power is divided between the executive and the Congress, and, within the Congress, dispersed among the various standing committees?

The cure for this was government by majority party. "The British system is perfected party government," Wilson wrote, and among the features that make it perfect is that no effort is made in the House of Commons "to give the minority a share in law-making."[41] Nowhere does he express any concern that a majority so organized and led might fit Publius's description of a faction.[42] Whereas the Constitution was intended to make democracy safe for the United States, Wilson's policy, which he embodied in a demagogic slogan, was to make the world safe for democracy. (Historians can decide whether, or to what extent, the world he helped to create provided the degree of safety he envisioned.)

Wilson's complaint and prescription were echoed in 1950 by an official committee of APSA, and in 1963 by James MacGregor Burns, another president of the association.[43] Indeed, there seems to be something about political scientists that leads them to favor efficient majority-rule government and to be oblivious to the forms (in Tocqueville's sense) that make it safe.

Writing from the Marxist perspective, still another president of APSA saw the Constitution as the product of a conspiracy among the holders of public securities, or of personal as opposed to real property.[44] Other scholars have demonstrated that he was wrong about the conspiracy,[45] but there is no denying that the Framers intended to lay the foundation for a commercial society:

By multiplying the means of gratification, by promoting the introduction and circulation of the precious metals, those darling objects of human avarice and enterprise, it serves to vivify and invigorate all the channels of industry and to make them flow with greater activity and copiousness.[46]

And there is no denying Madison's assertion that the protection of the diverse faculties of men, especially the "different and unequal faculties of acquiring property," was the "first object of government."[47]

Yet what is this but the principle underlying the free market? And is not the free market the cause of the country's material prosperity? And is not that prosperity widely shared? And is this not—as it was intended to be—one of the means of mitigating democratic envy and, therefore, of solving the problem of democracy? Those who complain of the free market are not, even now, the people. (What Tocqueville said 160 years ago remains true today: "As everyone has property of his own to defend, everyone recognizes the principle upon which he holds it.")[48] They are, instead, those who, without warrant and holding no public office, claim to speak in the name of the people: the Marxists and a handful of political scientists, to say nothing of those who have gone to school with Friedrich Nietzsche, Martin Heidegger, and their postmodernist epigoni.[49]

These dissenters were not on the scene in 1787–88, and their absence must be counted among those circumstances that favored the adoption of the Constitution. Without them, the Framers were able to persuade the people to ratify a constitution that establishes a government of the people and for the people, but not immediately by the people. As Publius says, it is a government that derives all its powers directly or indirectly from the great body of the people and is administered by persons holding their offices during pleasure, or during good behavior, but from which "the people in their collective capacity" are excluded.[50] By any fair reckoning, however, the people have not been excluded from its benefits.

6

Constitutionalism and Multiculturalism

Hath not a Jew eyes? hath not a Jew hands, organs, dementions, sences, affections, passions, fed with the same foode, hurt with the same weapons, subject to the same diseases, healed by the same meanes, warmed and cooled by the same Winter and Sommer as a Christian is; if you pricke us doe we not bleede? if you tickle us, doe we not laugh? if you poison us doe we not die? and if you wrong us shall we not revenge? if we are like you in the rest, we will resemble you in that.

— Shakespeare, *The Merchant of Venice*, act 3, scene 1

Alexis de Tocqueville, writing in the 1830s, very much feared that liberty and equality would be at war with each other; today there is a tendency among some intellectuals to think that peace between them can be achieved by combining them under the label "cultural pluralism." Cultural pluralism implies equality, we are told, and equality implies freedom for the various elements (mainly religious opinions and ethnic groups) being combined. It also implies—indeed, it is said to require—a "nonideological state," or an ideologically neutral state; and it is only a short step from this to say that such a state is obliged to promote "multiculturalism" by making it a part—in fact, the organizing principle—of the public school curriculum, for example. In such a curriculum all "cultures" are to be treated as equal, or as equally deserving of respect. But there is a question as to whether multiculturalism is compatible with the principles of the Constitution and, therefore, capable of providing a foundation for what is said to be the cultural pluralism we have long enjoyed in this country. Whether it is compatible depends on what is meant by culture.

Although not the first to use the term in its modern sense, Thomas Carlyle (in the 1860s) spoke of culture as the body of arts and learning separate from the "work" of society. This definition has the merit of reflecting (and that very clearly) the problem that gave rise to the idea of culture and the attempt to define it in the early nineteenth century. Carlyle was preceded by Coleridge, Keats, Shelley, and Wordsworth, who, in his role as poet, saw himself as an "upholder of culture" in a world that disdained it, and by John Stuart Mill, for whom culture meant the qualities and faculties that characterize our humanity, or those aspects of humanity that he foresaw would be missing in a utilitarian society. He was followed by Matthew Arnold, for whom culture meant not only literary pursuits but—in a sentence that became familiar if not famous—the pursuit of "the best which has been thought and said in the world."[1]

What these critics had in common was a concern for the sublime (or the aesthetic), and a complaint against the modern democratic and commercial society in which it had no firm place. The founders of this modern society—say, John Locke and Adam Smith—promised to provide for the needs of the body (and in this they surely succeeded); culture was intended to provide for the needs of the soul—Coleridge, for example, made this the business of his "clerisy." As Allan Bloom put it, "Only when the true ends of society have nothing to do with the sublime does 'culture' become necessary as a veneer to cover the void."[2]

The proponents of multiculturalism have something different in mind when they speak of culture. Introducing Charles Taylor's essay on the subject, political scientist Amy Gutmann says that public institutions, "including government agencies, schools, and liberal arts colleges and universities, have come under severe criticism these days for failing to recognize or respect the particular cultural identities of citizens." She mentions specifically African-Americans, Asian-Americans, Native Americans, and women.[3] Culture here seems to mean not Matthew Arnold's formulation of it, which, as such, might serve (as Shakespeare's plays and poems have served) to civilize and, in some way, even to unify peoples; rather, culture here seems to mean the different customs, ways, mores, or morals/manners—*moeurs,* as Tocqueville called them—of peoples, groups, and (if we are to believe Amy Gutmann) even the sexes. Thus, in the body of his essay, Taylor refers specifically to the French Canadians, whose *moeurs* are not those of the English Canadians, and for which the former demand recognition—demand it and apparently deserve it, not because their culture is superior in Matthew Arnold's sense to that of the English Canadians, but simply because it is theirs.

No country has done more to recognize the diversity of morals/manners than Canada; it even has a (federal) Department of Multiculturalism and Citizenship and provides generous subsidies for "ethnic" music, painting, dance, drama, and museums. Initiated in the 1970s by Prime Minister Pierre Elliott Trudeau, its purpose was "to add to the cultural richness of Canadian life by assisting the smaller ethnic groups [that is, groups other than the English and French Canadians] to maintain certain of their traditional cultural forms and a distinct sense of identity, if such was their desire."[4] These diverse groups were to form the Canadian "mosaic." But it is one thing to provide subsidies for folk dancing groups and ethnic cooking and quite another to allow these groups, without exception, to retain their "cultural identities." The feasibility of the latter program would surely depend on what it is in their culture that they want to retain. After all, to the extent that the Canadians allow some groups to retain their cultural identities, they will inherit some nasty ethnic rivalries.

Nevertheless, Canadians speak of multiculturalism as a form of Canadian nationalism "that will convert ethnic rivalries from one of the problems or weaknesses of a society into one of its strengths."[5] But success here will depend, to some extent at least, on a strengthening of national identity and a corresponding weakening of ethnic identity, a subject I'll have more to say about in due course. But how does a government intend to go about converting its Serbs and Croats, for example, into Canadians? Not, surely, by policies designed to refurbish and strengthen their memories or otherwise preserve their traditions. Better that they forget their history lest they be led to repeat it in Canada.[6] And they can be led to forget it only by being taught that Canada is something more than the sum of its diverse parts and something better than any of its parts. This, of course, is what the United States set out to do in 1787, except that its "parts" were understood to be individuals with rights, not groups making up a "mosaic."

The Framers of our Constitution never spoke of multiculturalism, cultural pluralism, or, for that matter, even of pluralism. Such terms were not part of their political vocabulary.[7] Nor were they sanguine about the possibility of combining cultures. Instead, as the following passage from

Federalist 2 indicates, they were sanguine about our prospects only because we were (or were said to be) united in all essential respects:

> Providence has been pleased to give this one connected country to one united people—a people descended from the same ancestors, speaking the same language, professing the same religion, attached to the same principles of government, very similar in their manners and customs, and who, by their joint counsels, arms, and efforts, fighting side by side throughout a long and bloody war, have nobly established their general liberty and independence.

The same concern for unity, or a similarity of manners, customs, and, above all, opinion concerning the principles of government, is reflected in the early statements and congressional debates having to do with immigration and naturalization. These debates took place in 1790 and 1794, and everyone who addressed the issue favored population growth and, to that end, a liberal immigration policy; but, at the same time, everyone recognized the importance of excluding the immigrant who, in Madison's words, could not readily "incorporate himself into our society," or, as Theodore Sedgwick put it, would not "mingle [here] in social affection with each other, or with us," or, finally, "would not be attached to the principles of the government of the United States."[8]

As Jefferson said, "Every species of government has its specific principles [and] ours perhaps are more peculiar than those of any other in the universe." He, of course, knew nothing of those who would be of concern to later generations of politicians, the fascists and communists. He was concerned with monarchists and even the immigrants who had been ruled by monarchs. He was afraid that they would bring with them "the principles of the governments they leave, imbibed in their early youth; or, if able to throw them off, it [would] be in exchange for an unbounded licentiousness, passing, as is usual, from one extreme to another." Those principles, he continued, they might transmit to their children. "In proportion to their numbers, they will share with us the legislation [and] will infuse into it their spirit, warp and bias its direction, and render it a heterogeneous, incoherent, distracted mass."[9]

Thus, rather than seeing advantages of diversity, the Framers wanted immigrants to be assimilated, incorporated into "our society," with a view to maintaining a population whose members would be attached to the same principles of government. (As Jefferson put it, a "homogeneous" society would be "more peaceful [and] more durable.")[10] They had no idea of accommodating a variety of disparate "cultures." From the available evidence, it appears they would have thought that impossible.

What we see as cultural differences, they saw as religious differences. Indeed, they probably would have agreed with one of his critics that Horace Kallen (who was the first to use the term cultural pluralism) did not take culture seriously precisely because he did not appreciate its religious foundations:

> If we think of culture not superficially in terms of graphic arts, music or literature, but as the firm cradle of custom in which the baby is laid and which inevitably forms his emotional life, his food habits, his language, his thoughts, his skills, his sexual life, his work, and his moral values, the envisioned fluid "cultural mobility" becomes rather incredible. One cannot be brought up in all languages, all family patterns, all religions.[11]

Since our constitutional principles are most evident in those provisions dealing with religion, for our purposes here, cultural pluralism, at least initially, will mean religious pluralism. What, besides language (and political memories), distinguishes the French from the English Canadians save religion? Is it possible that the culture in multiculturalism—especially when it is taken seriously—means religion, or at least has its ultimate source in religion? After all, as Shakespeare's Shylock indicates (see the epigraph above), we are *one* with respect to the body and its passions, but *many* only with respect to our memories and our manners/morals, whose source is in our political and religious (or irreligious) beliefs. Understanding the conditions of our religious pluralism will shed some light on the possibility—or better, the impossibility—of multiculturalism.

In 1776, we declared ourselves a "new order of the ages," the first nation in all of history to build itself on the self-evident truth that all men are created equal insofar as they are equally endowed by nature's God with the unalienable rights to life, liberty, and the pursuit of happiness. The purpose of government, we then said, was "to secure these rights." This was to be done—because, given our principles, it had to be done—only with the consent of the governed.

But it was understood by the Framers of the Constitution that the governed would not always agree on the definition of rights, nor on how rights were to be secured, nor on whose rights deserved to be secured or, in the event of a conflict, preferred; in fact, the Framers expected the people to have sharply differing views on these matters. Thus, the "one people" that declared its independence in 1776 and the "we, the people" that constituted a government in 1787–88 in order to secure those rights, would, as a matter of course, be divided into factions thereafter, and, unless steps were taken to avoid it, warring factions. According to James Madison (writing in number 10, the most frequently quoted and celebrated of the *Federalist Papers*), "The latent causes of faction are . . . sown in the nature of man," and by definition these factions have interests "adverse to the rights of other citizens, or to the permanent and aggregate interests of the community."

Given these conditions, the securing of equal rights would not be an easy matter; it would be especially difficult because nature, so equitable in its endowment of rights, was by no means equitable in its endowment or distribution of talents or faculties, particularly, as Madison put it, the "faculties of acquiring property." Still, he did not hesitate to say that protecting these "different and unequal faculties"—naturally different and naturally unequal—was "the first object of government." The consequence of securing the equal rights of unequally endowed human beings would be a society divided between "those who hold and those who are without property." It followed for him that the regulation of these property factions—creditors, debtors, and landed, manufacturing, mercantile, moneyed, and "many lesser interests"—would be the "principal task of modern legislation." Unlike the others—such as religious factions—these property factions could be regulated (and accommodated) because, although divided one from another, they shared a common interest in economic growth, and to promote this growth would be the task of modern legislation. America's business would be (as Calvin Coolidge many years later said it was) business.

Madison proved to be a poor prophet with respect to the "business" that occupied the country during the first half of the nineteenth century. From 1819, when Congress began to debate the Missouri question, through the years of the Mexican War (and the Wilmot Provision it provoked), the compromise of 1850, the Kansas-Nebraska Act of 1854 (and the "Bloody Kansas" it provoked), the *Dred Scott* decision of 1857, the Civil War and Reconstruction, Congress, and indeed the entire country, was principally concerned with an issue that Madison neglected to mention in *Federalist* 10: namely, the slavery issue and the factions it aroused.

To judge from what he wrote in *Federalist* 56, Madison expected (or hoped) that time would resolve this issue. "At present," he wrote, some of the states, and especially the southern states, were "little more than societies of husbandmen. Few of them," he went on, "have made much progress in those branches of industry which give a variety and complexity to the affairs of a nation." But he expected this would change in time; with time would come a diversification of the state economies, which, if true, would relieve the southern states of their dependence on slave labor, with the result that slavery would cease to be, or would not become, an issue in national politics. In fact, of course, it became *the* issue in national politics, and the Madisonian system proved incapable of resolving it. Had he foreseen this, Madison might have said in 1788 what Abraham Lincoln said in 1858, namely, that "a house divided against itself cannot stand," which, until proven otherwise, can stand as our definitive statement on the possibility of multiculturalism.

The question then arises as to why Madison was so confident that the other sorts of factions he identified, particularly religious factions, would not require legislative "regulation." Or, to speak more plainly, why did he think this modern "civilized" nation would be able to avoid the religious problem? That had not been true in the past, especially in the Britain whose history he knew so well, and it is not true everywhere now. In the Britain he knew, religion had given rise not only to factions but to civil war and revolution. Why was he confident that this would not be the case in America?

The answer is that the Constitution took religion out of politics, thereby making legislative regulation unnecessary. By separating church and state—specifically, by guaranteeing the free exercise of every religion while favoring none—the Constitution guarantees a proliferation of religious sects, a plurality or "multiplicity of sects," as Madison puts it in *Federalist* 51, none of them capable of constituting a legislative majority. The various sects will have to live with each other; more to the point, as merely one among many, each sect will be required to forgo any attempt to impose its views on the others. The government itself will be neutral in religious matters, and this makes it possible to say that almost anybody, of any religious persuasion—or, at least, nominally of any religious persuasion—can become an American. All we require is a pledge of allegiance "to the flag of the United States" and "to the republic for which it stands," implying (especially nowadays) that anybody can make the promise, and that no one will have difficulty keeping it.

In saying this, however, we tend to forget the restrictions we used to impose—on Chinese immigration, for example—or the limits we in fact used to enforce. Until recently, that pledge of allegiance was understood to imply a renunciation even of certain political opinions—for example, the advocacy of the overthrow of government by force or violence. It was only in 1974 that the Supreme Court held that members of the Communist Party could not be kept off the ballot for refusing to take an oath renouncing such advocacy.[12] Nor was our record much different with respect to religious opinion, and this despite the First Amendment. For example, our toleration did not extend so far as to embrace the Mormons and their practice of plural marriages. "To call [the advocacy of bigamy and polygamy] a tenet of religion is to offend the common sense of mankind," the Supreme Court said in 1890.[13] When, a few years earlier, Abraham Lincoln was asked what he would do about the Mormons, he replied that he proposed "to let them alone"; but his Democratic adversary, Senator Stephen A. Douglas, campaigned to keep them out—by keeping Utah out—of our union.

But all this is history, a history that many of us would prefer to forget; today no one has reason to be concerned about the Communists, and no one publicly advocates polygamy (to say nothing of slavery). It is, of course, true that the Constitution is not *altogether* neutral respecting religion. It counts the years in a Christian manner (see article 7), and it recognizes, at least for one purpose, Sunday as the Sabbath (see article 1, section 7); but the non-Christians have learned to live with this. Speaking for a Supreme Court majority, Justice George Sutherland once said, "We are a Christian people," but that was in 1931, and no one—at least, no one in an official capacity—would say that today.[14] Instead, we are inclined to speak of "our Judeo-Christian tradition"; and if there were to be, as there has been in Britain, a great increase in the number of Muslims among us, I have no doubt that our multiculturalists would happily adapt this to read "our Judeo-Islamic-Christian tradition."

The situation in Britain is worth describing because, while interesting in itself, it also serves to remind us of the persistence of the religious issue and the difficulties facing a multicultural society. Britain has a religious problem today, and not simply because, unlike us, they do not separate church and state. By law, the Church of England remains the established church: its archbishop of Canterbury retains his precedence, even over the prime minister, and only its doctrines are protected by the law of blasphemy. Despite this, the British might claim to be a pluralist society, in practice if not in principle. They began in 1689 by tolerating most Protestants, including the Quakers, and over the course of the years—which, in the event, proved to be centuries—extended this privilege to Roman Catholics, Jews, and every variety of Protestant. In theory, there remains, as there was in 1689, a majority church, but only 2.3 percent of the population now attend its services on any given Sunday. The Queen, an Anglican in England and a Presbyterian in Scotland, might attend "chapel" services in Wales, a Roman Catholic Mass in Liverpool, or Jewish services in a synagogue without arousing public comment.

Under the 1944 Education Act, religious minorities in Britain were permitted to invoke the "conscience clause" in order to exclude their children from participating in certain acts of worship or religious instruction programs in the state schools; more than that, Roman Catholics and Jews were entitled to public funding for their own denominational schools. For all these reasons, Britain might have thought that it had become, in the words of the Anglican *Book of Common Prayer*, a haven for "all sorts and conditions of men." Instead, as I said, it finds itself with a religious or cultural problem. And, faced with a similar situation, so might we.

The problem arose from the fact that there are now one and a half million Muslims in England alone, a total exceeding the number of Roman Catholics and Jews combined; and Muslims especially do not believe, because they cannot believe, in the separation of church and state. Bernard Lewis explained why this is so. "Muhammed," he said, "was not only a prophet and a teacher, like the founders of other religions; he was also the head of a polity and of a community, a ruler and a soldier."[15] It was this (and "a thousand other reasons") that led Tocqueville to say that Islam and democracy could not readily coexist.[16] The Salman Rushdie affair made the British very much aware of this; they learned, as we might come to learn, that Muslims do not believe in freedom of speech, for example.

Freedom of speech is not the only problem for Muslims (to the extent they remain committed Muslims). The other is secularism, and Britain, having embarked on the path of toleration in 1689, has reached the point where it has become a secular society. In response to complaints made by various minority groups—not, we are told, only the Muslims—the British government decided to "celebrate diversity" by instituting a program of multicultural religious instruction in the state schools. Under the new program, all religions were, nominally at least, to be "taught"; in fact, however, each was to be taught as a "possible system of meaning and value," or, in the words of the Swann Report recommending the program, taught insofar as its doctrines were not in conflict with "rationally shared values."[17]

Reasonably enough, the Muslims objected to the program (as well as to other elements of the curriculum: anthropomorphic art, sensual music, "progressive" sex education, and the Darwinian theory of evolution). They continue to cling to their "cultural identity" by taking their religion seriously, unlike the British majority. Because they do, they prefer the old system, under which the state schools taught Christian doctrine (or a watered-down version of Christian doctrine) but allowed them to remove their children from the program by invoking the "conscience clause" on their behalf. As they see it, better a "benign uniformity," as one commentator put it, than a "compulsory 'diversity.'" At least under the old system, they were not compelled to subscribe to opinions contrary to their articles of religion.

As one writer suggested, the problem might be resolved by providing public funding of denominational schools without exception:

> British Muslims, and for that matter British Hindus, Sikhs, and even its conservative Protestants, continue to be denied the denominational status that their numbers and popularity demand. They resent this. They point out, correctly enough, that they pay taxes like everyone else, and should accordingly be granted the same privilege as any other religious minority. They conclude, reasonably enough, that they are denied those privileges because the central authorities fear that, if granted them,

they might actually use them for something other than the pursuit of "rationally-shared values."[18]

Rather than accommodating its Muslims, Hindus, and Sikhs by providing public funding of denominational schools without exception, the British majority insists on imposing its policy of not taking religion seriously on minorities that do take it seriously. As a result, Britain has a serious cultural problem.

Unlike the British, we confine religion to the private sphere, and there is much to be said for that policy. Moreover, we protect it there. Thus, in 1925, the Supreme Court held that no state may compel students to attend public, rather than private or parochial, schools.[19] As Jefferson once said, "Our civil rights have no dependence on our religious opinions, any more than our opinions in physics or geometry."[20] Still, contrary to Madison's expectations, the religious problem abides. Try as we might, there are certain to be times in the life of a nation, even a nation devoted to business and its regulation, when men's religious opinions will carry more political weight than their opinions in physics or geometry—or, as the abortion issue should remind us, than their opinions in genetics, ontology, sociology, or whatever. Of course, Madison would have said that abortion did not belong on the national political agenda, and that it was only because of the Supreme Court's improper intervention that it was put there. On the whole, however, our policy of separating church and state has served us well, which is why it is important to understand what it requires of us.

Separation of society and state; separation of the private and the public; separation of church and state; these distinctions are major stones in the foundation on which American constitutionalism is built, and all of them rest on the constitutional distinction between soul and body. If not the first to make these distinctions, John Locke was the first to persuade Americans of their necessity in politics and, in his (Virginia) Bill for Religious Freedom, Jefferson was the first to propose that the last of them be embodied in legislation. He had made a careful study of Locke's "Letter Concerning Toleration" and, in so many words, repeated Locke's statements concerning the care of body and soul respectively. According to Locke, the commonwealth is "a society of men constituted only for the procuring, preserving, and advancing . . . [of] life, liberty, health, and indolency of body; and the possession of outward things, such as money, lands, houses, furniture, and the like"; whereas the care "of each man's soul belongs to himself."[21] Or, in Jefferson's words, "The operations of the mind, [as opposed to] the acts of the body, are [not] subject to the coercion of the laws."[22] Accordingly, the Framers of the Constitution separated church and state, thereby making religion a wholly private matter.

Keeping it private is another matter. As I have pointed out in another place, because the biblical religions especially—Judaism, Christianity, and Islam alike—teach that souls belong to God and that, whether through the agency of Moses, Jesus, or the Archangel Gabriel (or Jibral), God has revealed His will or His law respecting the care of souls, there is always the possibility (if not a clear and present danger) that someone not attached to our constitutional principles will claim to know God's will and try to enforce it on his neighbors.[23] Indeed, as we are reminded almost daily by events in Iran and Iraq, there are people who, when given the chance, will do just that. Such people prefer to fight religious wars rather than accept cultural pluralism; as such, they cannot be "attached to the principles of the government of the United States," and, to recall Madison's words, they cannot readily be incorporated "into our society."

We cannot tolerate *them* (at least, not in any numbers) because *they* are not tolerant; more precisely, we must insist that they disclaim the authority on the basis of which one might *be* intolerant. This means that, in their capacity as citizens, they must recognize the right of liberty of conscience. For example, just as the Constitution expects us to forget that we are no longer English (Irish, German, or whatever), it expects Episcopalians, for instance, to forget the eighteenth of their thirty-nine Articles of Religion, which reads: "They also are to be [held] accursed that presume to say, that every man shall be saved by the Law or Sect which he professeth, [so long as] he be diligent to frame his life according to that Law, and the light of Nature." In their capacity as citizens, however, Episcopalians are required to be guided by that light of nature. They are expected to follow the example of a Reverend Mr. Shute in the Massachusetts Ratifying Convention of January 30, 1788, who said,

> Far from limiting my charity and confidence to men of my own denomination in religion, I suppose, sir, that there are worthy

characters among men of every denomination—among the Quakers, the Baptists, the Church of England; and even among those who have no other guide, in the way to virtue and heaven, than the dictates of natural religion.[24]

In the light of nature (and according to the Constitution), nobody is "accursed." On the contrary, everybody is endowed with the unalienable right to pursue happiness as he (and not his neighbor or the government) defines it. As Locke put it, liberty of conscience is "every man's natural right," a principle echoed by Jefferson in the (Virginia) Bill for Religious Freedom, where we read that "the rights [of conscience] hereby asserted are of the natural rights of mankind." That principle is embodied in the Constitution—in fact, our constitutionalism rests on it—and we are all expected to acknowledge it when we act politically. The Constitution speaks not of Christian, Jew, or Muslim, but consistently only of undifferentiated "persons" (and, in one place, of "Indians, not taxed"). By so speaking, it seeks to discourage religious (and antireligious) parties in favor of secular political parties. It expects us—whatever our religion, and whatever our cultural "identity"—to be able to come together in those parties. But it is not easy to form a governing political majority with those whom, by their failure to subscribe to our particular articles of religion, we hold to be "accursed."

Thus, contrary to the multiculturalists, the Constitution is not ideologically neutral. If it were, all political issues would be properly resolved, one way or the other, by popular vote of the people or their elected representatives. Among these issues is, or was, the one that engaged Senator Stephen A. Douglas and Abraham Lincoln in the 1850s: the issue of slavery in the territories. Douglas called his slavery policy "popular sovereignty" and, thus dignified, made it the principle of his Kansas-Nebraska Act. But Lincoln insisted that the Act was un-American precisely because it took no stand—which is to say, because it was neutral—on the question of whether slavery was good or bad. The Act's moral neutrality contradicted the self-evident truth that all men are created equal.

So, too, with respect to religious issues. Of course, the Constitution is neutral with respect to religion, neutral insofar as it forbids any government policy favoring one religion over another; but this means that religious issues, like that of slavery in the territories, are not properly resolved by popular vote of the people or their elected representatives. Were it otherwise, no constitutional principle would stand in the way of a self-styled "moral majority" determined to impose its ways on those it regards as immoral minorities. Our religious pluralism depends not on ideological neutrality but on the continued vitality of the principles we held to be self-evident in 1776 and embodied in the Constitution in 1787–88, and prominent among these truths is that the care of each man's soul belongs to himself alone. Not every "culture" recognizes these truths; those that do not cannot be regarded as equal to ours. Which is to say, in the light of the Constitution, all men are created equal, but not all "cultures."

As Amy Gutmann points out (as if it needed pointing out), we encounter problems with multiculturalism "once we look into the *content* of the various valued cultures." She wonders whether we can afford to respect, or "recognize," illiberal cultures or, as she puts it, "those cultures whose attitudes of ethnic or racial superiority . . . are antagonistic to other cultures."[25] She would surely agree that we cannot allow the successors to the Ayatollah Khomeini to send their agents among us to assassinate our "blasphemous" Salman Rushdies. Unlike Iranian law, under our Constitution there is no such thing as blasphemous speech. If, nevertheless, such assassins do appear among us and commence their vocation, and we apprehend them, are they entitled to be tried by a jury prepared to help a group preserve its cultural identity? There are those who say so.

The Sixth Amendment to the Constitution provides that in "all criminal prosecutions, the accused shall enjoy the right to a speedy and public trial, by an impartial jury of the State and district wherein the crime shall have been committed." In recent years black Americans, whether on trial themselves or as the victims of alleged crimes committed by others, have insisted that juries cannot be impartial unless they are representative. In response, several state legislatures, including Florida's, proposed laws guaranteeing racially balanced juries. This may be in violation of the Sixth Amendment, which, the Supreme Court said recently, requires "impartial" juries, but does not require, and may even forbid, "representative" juries.[26]

This jury issue is not new; in fact, it is at least nine hundred years old. In 1255, King Henry III ordered the arrest of some ninety-two Jews on charges of ritual murder. On being indicted and sent to London for trial, eighteen of them, "regarding conviction as a foregone conclusion unless they were allowed a mixed jury, refused to put themselves upon the country." This was construed as a confession of guilt, and the eighteen were summarily executed.

The privilege of being tried by a mixed jury—or, in the official language of the time, by a panel *de medietate*, which, in this case, meant half Jewish, half Christian—was sometimes denied, and, upon Edward I's accession to the throne in 1272, was revoked for a time; but when honored, it served as some protection for this particular "cultural" community. That protection came to an end on—and surely not by chance—All Saints Day, November 1, 1290, when Edward "issued a decree consigning the Jewry of England to perpetual banishment."[27] And with the banishment ended this early experiment in multiculturalism.

Then there is the more recent British practice, the one adopted to deal with the multicultural situation in Northern Ireland. (To paraphrase W.S. Gilbert, Northern Ireland is the very model of a modern multiculturalism.) The current problem is a variation of the one the British faced earlier when they governed the whole of Ireland. Not surprisingly, at that time, trial by jury did not function in Ireland as it did in England. Too often, Irish juries simply refused to convict the guilty; even so, we are told, "that most hallowed right of English law, trial by common jury, was preserved even in Ireland" for most of the nineteenth century.[28] Not so in Northern Ireland today. Faced with unacceptable differences in the way Protestant and Catholic defendants were treated, the British Parliament, in 1973, abolished trial by jury for defendants accused of violent crimes.[29] So much, then, for that "most hallowed right of English law, trial by common jury."

Banishment is one way to deal with a multicultural problem, and abolishing trial by jury is another, but neither is permitted to any government of the United States; our Constitution based on the rights of man forbids it. Do we, then, adopt different rules of justice for our different groups? Amy Gutmann says that "recognizing and treating members of some groups as equals now seems to require public institutions to acknowledge rather than ignore cultural peculiarities, at least for those people whose self-understanding depends on the vitality of their culture."[30] But instead of recognizing their "cultural peculiarities," especially their peculiar or different rules of justice, do we not owe it to ourselves to persuade them of the superiority of ours: trial by impartial jury and the other elements making up due process of law; government by the consent of the governed;

freedom of speech, press, and conscience—in other words, government designed to secure the unalienable rights not of groups or "cultures," but of man? Indeed, does not our system of constitutional government itself presuppose *one* people, in the words of *Federalist* 2, a people "attached to the same principles of government"? To pose the jury question bluntly, does not the criminal justice system presuppose that African-, Hispanic-, Asian-, and Jewish-American defendants can receive a fair trial by "impartial" juries and judges? And that it will be a sorry day for this country if they cannot?

The jury problem pales almost to insignificance when weighed with the problem facing many liberal democracies today, especially those of Western Europe, that of accommodating refugees from the east and south. The problem is new, but its seeds were sown in religious conflicts five hundred and more years ago. In 1993, political scientist Samuel P. Huntington wrote that "the most significant dividing line in Europe may well be the eastern boundary of Western Christianity in the year 1500":

> The peoples to the north and west of this line are Protestant or Catholic; they shared the common experiences of European history; they are generally economically better off than the peoples to the east . . . The peoples to the east and south of this line are Orthodox or Muslim; they historically belonged to the Ottoman or tsarist empires; they were only lightly touched by the events shaping the rest of Europe. ...Conflict along the fault line between Western and Islamic civilizations has been going on for 1,300 years.[31]

The movement of peoples today—sometimes almost entire populations—illustrates not only the enduring strength of these religious and ethnic hatreds but the extent of the problem facing liberal regimes today. It is sufficient to mention Germany, where the influx of refugees from Eastern Europe has given rise to a resurgence of nationalist sentiments of the nastiest kind; or Italy, which turned back entire shiploads of people fleeing Albania; or France and its treatment of Muslims, most of them North Africans.

In this situation, it is easy to sympathize with Prime Minister Trudeau's multicultural policy; generous, tolerant, and seemingly liberal, it was supposed to provide an example to a world sorely in need of what it had to offer. It was to make Canada "a special place, and a stronger place," stronger than the United States, a multicultural "mosaic" rather than a "melting pot," "a brilliant prototype for the moulding of tomorrow's civilization."[32]

At Trudeau's urging, Canada officially became a bilingual country. In order to become the master of its own fate, it arranged to have the British North American Act of 1867 converted into the Canadian constitution, or, in the word at the time, it "patriated" its constitution from Britain. To guarantee the rights of all its people, in whatever province they might reside, in 1982 it attached to that "patriated" constitution a Charter of Rights and Freedoms. Since then the country has been engaged in what might be described as a perpetual and itinerant constitutional debate, moving from Ottawa, to Meech Lake, to Charlottetown, with frequent stops in all the provincial capitals, most frequently and persistently Quebec. At issue was (and is) Canadian unity.

The first Ottawa round—commentators adopted the parlance of prize-fighting to describe the debate—ended when Trudeau's nation-building effort, with its emphasis on the equal rights of Canadian citizens at the expense of the powers of the provinces, went down to defeat at the hands of the Quebecois. In round two, the western provinces, reacting to Trudeau's language and energy policies, began to demand a restructuring of the senate in order to check the power of populous Ontario and Quebec. This was followed by the election of a separatist government, under René Lévesque, in Quebec.

Round three began in 1980 with Trudeau's effort to bypass the provincial governments by appealing to the people directly, but, failing in this, he was forced to make the concessions demanded by the provincial governments in order to get the constitution "patriated"; even so, Quebec refused to go along. Round four engaged the aboriginal peoples, who, dissatisfied with a constitutional provision guaranteeing their "existing rights," renewed their demand for self-government; at the same time, Ottawa (now represented by Brian Mulroney) and Quebec (now represented by Robert Bourassa) began a series of negotiations with the various provincial premiers leading to the Meech Lake Accord of April 30, 1987. Under this agreement, all the provinces would gain the powers demanded by Quebec, although Quebec was to be recognized as a "distinct society." Under its terms, the accord had to be ratified by the federal parliament and all ten provincial legislatures. This requirement proved to be its undoing because, by involving the legislatures it involved the people, if only indirectly, and, as the public opinion polls indicated, a majority of the people were strongly opposed to it. Round five came to an end in October 1992, when a majority of Canadians, in a majority of the provinces, rejected the Charlottetown Accord in a national referendum. It was rejected largely because, in order to win equal representation in the Senate, the polygenetic western provinces had to agree to allow largely French Quebec, regardless of the size of its population, to have 25 percent of the seats in the House of Commons. One commentator described the process as "a deal-maker but a referendum-breaker."[33] Then, in October 1995, a proposal to make Quebec a sovereign nation was defeated 49.4 to 50.6 percent in a popular referendum. The leader of the separatist *Bloc Québecois*, Lucien Bouchard, said that "the next time will be the right time, and the next time may come sooner than people think."[34]

From this brief account it is possible to draw several conclusions bearing on multiculturalism: The effort to accord recognition and its attendant privileges to one group, cultural or otherwise, will provoke either similar demands from other groups or, especially when the people are brought into the process, a stubborn refusal to make the accommodation. The "Ukrainians" of Manitoba are less likely than their political leaders (at least those at Meech Lake) to indulge the "French" of Quebec. Like other "peoples," especially in a regime that recognizes "peoples," they have pride too. Thus, although the Meech Lake politicians saw the proposed constitutional recognition of Quebec's "distinct society" as merely symbolic and understood that what really mattered was the extent of the powers granted to the provinces, the "people" stamped their feet and said no.

Comparisons with the United States are surely unfair to Canadians; but, if we would avoid its problems, comparisons with Canada can be useful to us. Canada began as two societies and remained two largely separated societies for the better part of its history; and its efforts to build one multicultural society have ended, for the time at least, with a country more divided than ever. Whereas, if (but only for the time being) we put aside the black-white division (which was resolved, to the extent that it was resolved, only by a civil war), America began as one people; and its policy of assimilating, rather than accommodating, its immigrants has allowed it (for the time, at least) to remain one. It was able to assimilate them because it was able to persuade them that its ways, its rules of justice, and its religious principles were superior to those they may have brought with them.

"All eyes are open, or opening, to the rights of man. The general spread of the light of science has already laid open to every view the palpable truth, that the mass of mankind has not been born with saddles on their backs, nor a favored few booted and spurred, ready to ride them legitimately, by the grace of God." So wrote Jefferson in the last of his many letters.[35] But too many eyes are closed, or closing, today. Today that abstract or palpable truth is too often seen as mere opinion, one opinion among many, and all of them equal, and if our multiculturalists have their way—and if all cultures are equal, why should they not have their way?—all of them to be taught in the public schools. The idea of the rights of man will occupy no special place in such a curriculum. As one of many ideas, its authority is almost certain to be weakened, and with its weakening will come a weakening of the foundation on which we have built the pluralism—and the liberty—we have enjoyed from the beginning.

It is especially likely to be weakened when the loudest voices we hear today are contemptuous of the world built by Jefferson and his colleagues. His invocation of "the light of science" is seen by some as part of a plot, a way of justifying the continued hegemony of his kind, namely, white European males and their white American male coconspirators.

This contempt for things American—at its base a self-contempt—was nowhere better expressed than in the 1993 Bienniel Exhibition of American Art at New York's Whitney Museum. Intended to portray the "victims" of American civilization, the show (described in the catalogue as a "multicultural" exhibition) featured videos and photographs of black gang members, Mexican hookers, battered women, transvestites, female self-portraits with dildos and prosthetic breasts; "installations" displaying a splat of simulated vomit; and, at the end, in cut-out letters two feet high, the statement "In the rich man's house the only place to spit is in his face." As evidence of their having paid the admissions fee, and by order of the museum's director (rich, white David Ross), visitors were required to display a button bearing the words "I can't imagine ever wanting to be white."[36]

Leo Strauss had something like this Whitney exhibition in mind when, in 1968, he wrote that every such accusation presupposes a law—in this case (so severe were the Whitney accusations) something like a holy law—against which political life is to be measured.[37] One might think that life in the United States could be heaven, or was supposed to be heaven; but the Founders promised no such thing. What they promised was liberty, including the liberty to tend to the salvation of our own souls, and the country they established was the first in all of history to make, and to keep, that promise. By keeping it—here I quote Werner J. Dannhauser—they made "corruption voluntary to an appreciable degree."[38]

The proponents of multiculturalism fail to appreciate what has been accomplished in and by the United States, and their project, when taken seriously, would have the effect—and, in the case of the Whitney people, the intended effect—of undermining its foundation. The future of constitutionalism depends, in part, on our ability to understand this.

Part II

Constitutional and Political Matters

Preface

It was in the context of accounting for the extraordinary role of lawyers in America that Tocqueville pointed out that "there is almost no political question in the United States that is not resolved sooner or later into a judicial question,"[1] or, as he might have meant (and surely could have said), into a constitutional question. It is a fact that, in this country, much of the ordinary business of government—taxing, spending, judging, fighting, punishing—ends up in the courts, ultimately in the Supreme Court. In addition to these, there are constitutional questions as such—that is, questions about the Constitution itself. These are the sort of questions featured in the essays below. For example:

What is the proper relation between the states and the Union? What is required of a territory to become a state? How is a president elected, and what are the rules governing the conduct of the office? What do we mean by rights? Specifically, what do we mean by the establishment of religion, and what is freedom of speech?

These last are First Amendment questions, and most of the essays are devoted to them. Not that it matters much, but I disagree with the Court's "mainstream" and typically liberal answers to them, especially those having to do with speech. I do not expect to change this opinion, but isn't there something to be said for persistence? John Milton must have thought so. As he famously said in his *Areopagitica*, "Let [truth] and falsehood grapple, who ever knew Truth put to the worse in a free and open encounter?"[2]

7

States' Rights and the Union

Forrest McDonald is a reputable scholar. Early American historians especially are indebted to him, not only for his important study of the formation of the republic and his celebrated biography of Alexander Hamilton, but because, in his book *We the People*, he convincingly discredited Charles Beard's quasi-Marxist interpretation of the Constitution and, by so doing, removed the shadow Beard had cast over the reputations of its Framers. Thanks largely to McDonald, we now know what we always believed, that the Constitution is not the product of selfish men wanting to feather their own nests.

But the present volume—*States' Rights and the Union: Imperium in Imperio, 1776–1876*—is something else again; indeed, one might well ask why he bothered to write it.[1] McDonald says it is the first "book-length study" of the states' rights controversy.[2] True enough; yet he knows very well—in effect he says—that anyone familiar with the history of the United States during its first hundred years will find nothing new in this book. But how many are they? For the others (and we may have reached the point where this means almost everybody), the book provides an instructive account of this controversy, of the disagreements concerning the nature of the Union and the line to be drawn between the authority of the general government and that of the several states. He says the country was preoccupied with this issue, or with the "tensions" arising out of it, beginning in the days of Hamilton and Jefferson and continuing through the better part of the nineteenth century. Indeed, as he would have it, "the tensions continued to be felt as the twentieth century came to an end."[3]

But "tensions" is hardly the word to describe our situation today, in part because we no longer argue about the nature of the Union; for most of us, at least, that issue was settled in the Civil War. We continue to have our disagreements, of course, and some of them have something to do with states' rights. For example, we disagree over whether Congress may forbid the carrying of handguns in state and local schoolyards, or require state courts to hear federal claims against state governments; but these disagreements are readily resolved, and everyone agrees that they ought to be resolved, by the Supreme Court. This is a far cry from the days when the champions of states' rights talked of interposition, nullification, and, finally, secession.

Each of these principles—McDonald calls them concepts or doctrines— derives from the basic states' rights proposition that the Constitution is a compact entered into by the states, and, therefore, that the states are entitled to define its terms. Thus, when Congress (in 1798) enacted the notorious Alien and Sedition Acts, Virginia and Kentucky, in resolutions written, respectively, by Madison and Jefferson, declared them to be breaches of the constitutional compact. The powers of Congress are strictly limited, Madison said, and in the case

> of a deliberate, palpable, and dangerous exercise of other powers, not granted by the said compact, the states, who are parties thereto, have the right, and are in duty bound, to interpose, for arresting the progress of the evil, and for maintaining, within their respective limits, the authorities, rights and liberties, appertaining to them.[4]

Unable to gain support for the resolutions from the other states, Madison and Jefferson set about the task of organizing a political party, and Jefferson, having been elected president in 1800, proceeded to pardon all those who had been convicted under the Sedition Act which, under its own terms, expired in 1801.

After interposition came nullification, a principle associated with the great name of John C. Calhoun. Here the offending act of Congress was the tariff of 1828, known in South Carolina as the Tariff of Abominations. South Carolina responded by adopting an "Exposition," secretly drafted by Calhoun, calling for a state convention authorized to decide whether the law was constitutional. In the meantime, Congress revised the tariff, but only slightly, and in 1832 the convention called by South Carolina adopted the Ordinance of Nullification, declaring the tariffs of 1828 and 1832 unconstitutional and forbidding the collection in the state of the duties levied by them. What followed was a major constitutional crisis involving (among others) Calhoun, Daniel Webster, and President Andrew Jackson, who threatened to send in the army. It was resolved only when Congress adopted a compromise tariff proposed by Henry Clay.

McDonald devotes an entire chapter to the secession crisis, and many prior pages to the issue that provoked it, slavery. What is of interest here is that he thinks the champions of states' rights—principally Jefferson, Calhoun, and ultimately Jefferson Davis—had the better of the argument about the nature of the Union. (Calhoun, he says, "decisively demonstrated the soundness" of their view in the Senate debates over nullification.) They claimed that there was no United States prior to the ratification of the Constitution in 1787–88, that it came into being with the Constitution, which was the work of "sovereign" states. The Confederates took this to mean that the states, having formed the Union, were entitled not only to "nullify" what they saw as infractions of it, but to secede from it.

Lincoln, of course, disagreed; he insisted that the Union was formed when we, as "one people," declared our independence in 1776, but McDonald says this view is "untenable." As it happens, Lincoln was right, and can be proved right by the Constitution itself. There, specifically in article 7, we read that it was written (and sent to the Continental Congress, which, in turn, was to send it out for ratification) on "the Seventeenth Day of September in the Year of our Lord one thousand seven hundred and Eighty seven and of the Independence *of the United States of America the Twelfth*" (emphasis added). As Lincoln said, and said again in the first line of his Gettysburg Address, the United States was born in 1776.

This is not an unimportant matter. For if Lincoln was wrong, the Confederates were right, and if they were right about the Union, they were right about secession and their stand in the war that followed it. The war, then, was Lincoln's doing and, as the unreconstructed Confederates insist even today, he was wrong to fight it. Does McDonald agree with this?

He does not say, but, for some reason having nothing to do with the states' rights controversy, he criticizes Lincoln severely for the way he fought the war. Lincoln, he says, violated the Constitution time and again. Unlike the "moderate" Jefferson Davis, he "rode roughshod" over those who opposed him, repressing the disloyal "with a vengeance," and he used "coercion" to keep the border states in line and the army to control elections.[5] McDonald goes so far as to say Lincoln's Emancipation Proclamation "actually freed no slaves," but that "it served its purpose, for Britain and France ultimately abandoned the idea of intervening" in the war.[6]

This would have been a better book had McDonald confined himself to the facts. His judgments are not only unnecessary but mistaken and offensive.

8

Talkers

Our presidents have become big talkers; Bill Clinton, for example, was forever on the radio or running around the country making speeches, pounding the lectern, and asking the public to support his legislative programs. Rather than object, the people think it altogether appropriate that the president should address them directly and on radio and television. Everyone else does, everyone with something to sell, so why shouldn't the president? Still, there was a time when presidents were supposed to confine their talking to written communications addressed to the Congress.

In 1868, Andrew Johnson was impeached and put on trial before the Senate, in part, at least, because of his practice of making public political speeches; presidents were not supposed to do this. Accordingly, the tenth of the impeachment articles against him reads, in part, as follows:

> That said Andrew Johnson, President of the United States, unmindful of the high duties of his office and the dignity and proprieties thereof, and of the harmony and courtesies which ought to exist and be maintained between the executive and legislative branches of the Government of the United States [did] openly and publicly, and before divers assemblages of the citizens of the United States convened in divers parts thereof, make and deliver in a loud voice certain intemperate, inflammatory, and scandalous harangues, and did therein utter loud threats and bitter menaces as well against Congress as the laws of the United States duly enacted thereby, amid the cries, jeers, and laughter of the multitudes then assembled and within hearing.[1]

As we know, he was acquitted—but only by the margin of one vote—although the Senate never got around to voting on this particular charge.

The first president to be formally charged with high crimes and misdemeanors, Johnson was not, however, the first to be criticized for taking his case directly to the people. That dubious distinction belongs to Martin Van Buren who, during the last year of his term, made a tour of his home state of New York and turned it into a campaign for reelection and, interestingly enough, was rebuked for it. Received by a huge crowd in New York City, he began his remarks by saying, "I am cheerfully and gratefully affected by this cordial reception by my Democratic fellow citizens of New York City and county of New York." As Jeffrey Tulis reports in the best book on this subject, *The Rhetorical Presidency*, "This was the extent of his partisanship, but it provoked a storm of protest."[2] Whig politicians on the governing councils of three of the towns Van Buren later visited managed to pass resolutions declining to receive him—the president of the United States!—because of what was thought at the time to be the impropriety of that remark. An outdated notion? Not entirely. In 1994, Texas representative Richard Armey was severely criticized when, by way of responding to the charge that Republicans were blocking legislation simply to deny Clinton a legislative victory, he said, "*your* president is just not that important to us."[3] In one important respect at least, a president is supposed to be nonpartisan, the president of all the people and not merely of those who voted for him.

It was not so much his partisanship, however, but the mere fact of appealing directly to the people that led to Andrew Johnson's impeachment. His trial was unprecedented, but his alleged offense was one the Founders warned against. "Of those men who have overturned the liberties of republics," we read in the first of the *Federalist Papers*, "the greatest number have begun their career by paying obsequious court to the people, commencing demagogues and ending tyrants." In that preelectronic age, popular appeals were thought to violate constitutional principles, particularly those prescribing the legislative process.

The argument went as follows: The legislative power, the first in the constitutional order, belongs to Congress; the president's legislative role, as stated in article 2, section 3 of the Constitution, is limited to providing "Information on the State of the Union" and recommending "such Measures as he shall judge necessary and expedient." But, as the Constitution makes clear, this information and these recommendations were to be delivered to the Congress, not to the people, and the practice throughout most of the nineteenth century was to deliver them in the form of written communications. (Thomas Jefferson initiated this practice and Woodrow Wilson, who wrote a book arguing that the Constitution's legislative process was outmoded, began the modern practice of delivering State of the Union messages orally.) Presidents probably expected the public to read them, but the fact that they were written, and formally addressed to the Congress, guaranteed the absence of anything resembling a demagogic appeal.

Aside from issuing proclamations, or responding to addresses or "serenades," presidents spoke directly to the people mostly on special occasions: on assuming office (and, in George Washington's case, on leaving it), or to dedicate the opening of the Erie Canal and, for the most famous example, the cemetery at Gettysburg. Before the coming of radio and television, even presidential candidates kept aloof from the public, issuing no statements on their own behalf and making no speeches. When running for the Senate in 1858, Abraham Lincoln crossed the state of Illinois, debating his opponent, Stephen A. Douglas, before huge crowds, but in 1860 he stayed at home and kept his mouth shut; the presidency was thought to be different.

Things began to change with Theodore Roosevelt, who spoke of the office as a "bully pulpit," and the change was institutionalized by Woodrow Wilson. This is not the place to discuss the changes Wilson made and why he made them—Tulis devotes a chapter to the subject—but, generally, Wilson sought to refashion the constitutional order along the lines of the British model: government by majority party, with the president as party (and popular) leader. Modern technology rendered this easier. The consequences, not all of them intended by Wilson, are familiar to us.

The Constitution, praised in *Federalist* 63 for excluding the people "*in their collective capacity*" from any share in the government, has been popularized. As Jimmy Carter put it—and I don't recall anyone finding it inappropriate—we want "a government as good as the people,"[4] and not, as the Founders intended, a government ultimately dependent on but better than the people.

To an ever-increasing extent, the president takes his case directly to the people, as if his authority to act comes from them rather than from the Constitution. Thus, to justify his Haitian policy, President Clinton went on television, not to the Congress, and in his speech said nothing about the Constitution. All this talking requires him to employ a corps of speech-writers, who, along with the press secretaries, play an essential role in the governing process.

The role of the press itself has been enhanced. First invited to the White House by Theodore Roosevelt, the press now occupies extensive quarters in it and has become a fourth—and as tribune of the people, not the least—branch of government.

Political pollsters, beginning with Pat Cadell under Jimmy Carter, now have White House passes, giving them ready access to the presidents, who, in turn, are provided with accurate assessments of their popularity with the people. It's no wonder that Bill Clinton, for example, found it necessary to talk so much; so did one of his immediate predecessors who, in some circles at least, was praised as a "great communicator." We have come to expect our presidents to be popular leaders, populists in effect, and, given our enhanced electronic "networking" capacities, there is little reason to think we have seen the end of the process. Ross Perot, an expert in "playing obsequious court to the people," may have been the herald of our future. Our biggest talker yet, he promised, if elected, to institute an "electronic town hall," or a government by call-in show. The people, under no obligation to think before they talk, would tell him what they wanted, and he promised to oblige them. He further promised to resign if he failed to oblige them. If he had succeeded, we would have had a popular government incapable of doing anything unpopular, which, inevitably, would mean unpopular with a majority determinable by plebiscite. The Founders called this—see *Federalist* 47—one of the forms of tyranny.

9

Why a Vice President

Why should anyone want to be vice president? One of the men who held the post spoke of it as "the most insignificant office" ever contrived by the wit of man, and the men who wittingly contrived it—I mean, of course, the Framers of the Constitution—may have been of the same opinion.[1] At least, they said nothing whatever about the qualifications of those who were to hold the office; unlike presidents and members of the House and Senate, vice presidents, so far as the Constitution is concerned, may be of any age or even any nationality.

But the vice presidency is taken more seriously today than it apparently was by the Framers of the Constitution. The reason for this has nothing to do with the office itself—after all, its powers are almost nonexistent—and much to do with a presidential candidate's chances of winning election. Interestingly enough, the reason the Framers created the office in the first place had something to do with—in fact, had *only* to do with—the election of the president.

The Framers had a hard time settling on the method by which the president was to be chosen. It was proposed, successively, that the president be chosen by the national legislature, by a part of the legislature, by state governors, by popular vote of the people, by electors appointed by the state legislatures or the national legislature, chosen in districts within the states, or by the people directly.

But there were objections to each of these methods. A chief executive chosen by the Congress would make him its agent, which would be a violation of the principle of the separation of powers. If chosen by state governors, "the executive . . . will not be likely to defend with becoming vigilance & firmness the National rights against State encroachments."[2] By popular vote of the people? But George Mason of Virginia "conceived it would be as unnatural to refer the choice of a proper character for chief Magistrate to the people, as it would, to refer a trial of colours to a blind man."[3] Besides, said Hugh Williamson of North Carolina, "The people will be sure to vote for some man in their own State, and the largest State will be sure to succeed."[4] By electors appointed by the state legislatures? This proposal engendered no discussion whatever; put to the vote, only Maryland and Delaware favored it. "We seem," said Elbridge Gerry of Massachusetts on July 24, "to be entirely at a loss on this head." Indeed they were. As James Madison said the next day, "There are objections against every mode that has been, or perhaps can be proposed."[5]

What is of interest here is that during the entire course of the debate, which began in May when Edmund Randolph introduced the so-called Virginia Plan for the Constitution and continued for over three months, no mention was made of a vice president.

This was not the result of oversight. The convention was aware of the necessity to provide for the case of the president's removal, death, or resignation. Thus, in its report of August 6, the Committee on Detail recommended that, in such an event, "the powers and duties of his office" be exercised by the president of the Senate. The office of vice president did not make its appearance until September 4 when, in its report, the Committee on Unfinished Parts recommended the establishment of the electoral college.

As adopted in the Constitution, the report provided that the electors were to vote for two persons, "of whom one at least shall not be an Inhabitant of the same State with themselves," and "the Person having the greatest Number of Votes shall be the President, if such Number be a Majority of the whole Number of Electors appointed. In every case, after the Choice of the President, the Person having the greatest Number of Votes of the Electors shall be vice president."[6]

A careful consideration of this provision reveals why we have a vice president. Each elector was given two votes, both to be cast for president (it was not until the adoption of the Twelfth Amendment in 1804 that electors were required to cast one vote for president and the other for vice president). Why two votes? Because, if each elector had one vote, and if he cast it for "an Inhabitant of the same State with [himself]," no one would win an electoral college majority, and the choice of the president would devolve upon the Senate (subsequently changed to the House of Representatives). But give the electors two votes each and the result would likely be the same because, without a second office to fill, they would have reason to "throw away" their second votes.

Consider the situation that would have attended the selection of the first president had George Washington (everyone's first choice) *not* been a candidate. There were sixty-nine electors casting a total of one hundred thirty-eight votes for president. The number required for election was thirty-five ("a Majority of the whole Number of Electors appointed," not a majority of the ballots cast). If, as the Framers assumed, most electors were to cast their first votes for a favorite son, no one would win a majority, and the issue would turn on the second votes. How would they be cast? Would the Virginians, for example, having cast their first votes for Thomas Jefferson, cast their second for John Adams? Not likely. To do so might give Adams (Massachusetts's favorite son) the thirty-five votes needed for election. They would be more likely to cast them for, say, Daniel of St. Thomas Jenifer of Maryland, or (except that he had been killed in a duel) Button Gwinnett of Georgia—someone for whom no other elector was likely to cast a second vote. In a word, to enhance the chances of their first choice, electors would be inclined to "throw away" their second votes.

The vice presidency was created to make it less likely that electors would do this. With two offices to fill, and knowing that the vice president would succeed to the office in the event of the president's death or removal, they would have reason to cast their second votes for the best man from some other state rather than for a nonentity. "Such an officer as vice-president was not wanted," said Hugh Williamson on September 7. "He was introduced only for the sake of a valuable mode of election which required two to be chosen at the same time."[7] Exactly.

The vice president's only constitutional duty is to preside over the Senate (and cast a vote only in the event it "be equally divided"), and he was given that assignment only because, as Roger Sherman put it, "he would [otherwise] be without employment."[8] With little to do—Dick Cheney is an exception to this—most vice presidents have spent their time in office doing little, and the republic is none the worse off for the little they did; but nine of them succeeded to the presidency—a fact that political parties would do well to remember when choosing a president's running mate.

10

Two-and-a-Half Cheers for the Electoral College

Andy Warhol once said that everyone has fifteen minutes of fame during a lifetime—or, at least, is entitled to fifteen minutes of fame. His began when he painted his picture of a box of Brillo, or of a can of Campbell's tomato soup, and it lasted for the rest of his life. Mine (such as it was) began on November 8, 2000, the day after the election, and lasted for six weeks. During that period, I had at least a hundred telephone calls from reporters—mostly American, but a number of them foreign—with questions, generally "what if" questions, concerning the electoral college.

For example, what if Florida is unable to appoint its 25 electors by December 18, the day electors meet in their various state capitals to cast their votes for president and vice president? Implicit in this question was another: Would Al Gore then be president? The answer is yes. The Constitution (first in article 2, section 2, and then in the Twelfth Amendment) says, "The person having the greatest number of votes for President, shall be the President, if such Number be a Majority of the whole Number of Electors appointed"—not the whole number of electors (538) but the whole number of electors *appointed* (513, or 538 minus 25). Leaving aside Florida, Gore had 268 electors, more than the required 257, a majority of the 513. (As it happens, the Framers of the Constitution anticipated the failure of a state to act, and added the word "appointed" to meet that situation. See the convention debates for September 5, 1787.)[1]

For another example, what if the choice of the president goes to the House of Representatives? Will it be the old or the new House that makes the choice? The answer is, the new House. According to the Twentieth Amendment, the terms of House members end at noon on January 3, and, under the relevant federal statute, electoral votes are counted on January 6. But what about the choice of a vice president? Under the Constitution, that decision is made by the Senate, the Senate seated on January 3, which, as it happens, will consist of fifty Democrats and fifty Republicans in 2001. Will Al Gore, as president of the Senate, be able to break the tie and vote for himself? Again, the answer is yes, because, under the Twentieth Amendment, the terms of president and vice president do not end until noon on January 20. But suppose the House cannot agree on a president, and the Senate on a vice president, what happens then? The answer is—see section 19 of the federal statute—the Speaker of the House of Representatives becomes acting president, provided he resigns as speaker and his seat in the House. But suppose—as is altogether likely, since his term as acting president will end as soon as a president or vice president is chosen—he refuses to resign? Well, then, the president pro tempore of the Senate shall, "upon his resignation as President pro tempore and as Senator, act as President." But suppose—and again it is altogether likely— *he* refuses to resign? Well, under the presidential succession act, the secretary of state shall act as president. But the secretary of state, Madeleine Albright, is not eligible because she is not a natural-born citizen. Well, then, the job will go to the next in line, the secretary of the treasury, Larry Summers, and, if necessary, down the list of cabinet members until we reach the secretary of veterans affairs. It is only after him that we would have a problem, and this is a problem that is not likely to arise.

I was asked these and other questions because, as the editor of a book entitled, *After the People Vote, A Guide to the Electoral College*, it was assumed that I knew the answers. What is important here is not that *I* knew the answers but, rather, that there *were* answers. This is important because succession to office, particularly the highest offices, should not be left to chance—for example, whether the wife of a monarch is able to produce an heir, or a male heir—or to the dictates of force; rather, it should be governed by rules, as in our case, by constitutional, statutory, and parliamentary rules, providing for almost every conceivable contingency. And this we have done. Thus, in my judgment, no one—at least, no friend of constitutional government—has reason to complain of the method by which this country chooses its presidents, not so long as these rules are followed.

But is it a rule that electors actually vote as they are expected, or in some cases, as they are pledged to vote? Constitutionally, they may vote as they please; indeed, the electoral college was adopted with this in mind. Unlike the typical citizen in the late eighteenth century, who, it was assumed, would be likely to vote for someone from home, so to speak—someone from his own state—it was expected that the electors would be persons active in public affairs, and, therefore, would know the qualifications of persons from other states, and would vote accordingly.

But the situation quickly changed with the advent of political parties which, by nominating presidential candidates, took the original decision out of the hands of citizens and electors alike; and it was only after that that we began to speak of "faithless electors." The term itself has no place in the Constitution as written; to speak of an elector as "faithless" suggests that the constitutional rule has been superseded by custom, or, more likely, by state law or political party rule—for example, laws or rules pledging an elector to vote for the candidate of his party. Hence, the question, a constitutional question: May electors be punished if they violate their pledges? In 1952, a divided Supreme Court of the United States upheld the legality of a pledge required by a political party from *candidates* for the office of presidential elector; but the Court did not address the issue of whether a pledge required of an *elector* was legal and could be enforced.[2] This, then, is a question for which, as yet, there is no answer.

But the issue arose as early as 1912 when, in Kansas, eight of the ten electors who were pledged to vote for the Republican candidate William Howard Taft, announced that, if elected, they intended to vote instead for Theodore Roosevelt. As one might expect, the Taft supporters went to court, and, after losing in the Kansas courts, petitioned the Supreme Court for a writ of error. The petition was considered by two of the justices—and never reached the Court as a whole; therefore, there is no record of the case, *Marks v. Davis*, in the Court's official reports—and, after argument, they issued the writ. By doing so, they indicated that, in their judgment, the Court had jurisdiction in the case, which is to say, they decided that there was a *federal* question involved in it, that it was not solely a matter of state law. This is of some interest today because, in November 2000, the Supreme Court took jurisdiction in the case of *Bush v. Gore*, and rendered a judgment that put an end to the Florida dispute.

But, to return to Kansas, what about the issue of whether electors might vote as they please?

The two justices (Van Devanter and Pitney) had no reason to answer that question because, at the last moment, and I mean literally at the last moment, the Taft people succeeded in getting a slate of Taft electors on the ballot. In the event, the Roosevelt slate was elected in Kansas, but Woodrow Wilson, the Democratic candidate, won the national election.

As it happens, there was one faithless elector in 2000, in the District of Columbia, who, instead of voting for Al Gore, as she was pledged to do, cast a blank ballot for president. But her vote had no effect on the outcome, other than making the final count, 270 for Bush and 267, rather than 268, for Gore. As we all know, this was a very close election, and might have gone the other way if three Bush electors could have been persuaded to switch to Gore. One prominent Democrat suggested that an effort be made to find such electors, but nothing came of this, either because no such effort was made or because no such electors could be found. But this sort of mischief—of electors being cajoled, or bribed, or blackmailed—remains a possibility, and it is this that accounts for the title of this essay: two-and-a-half (not three) cheers for the electoral college. We could make it three if, by amending the Constitution, the states were given electoral votes, rather than electors.

But its critics want more than that. Their complaints are familiar. The electoral college, they say, is a relic, an absurdly dangerous method of selecting a president, one that threatens to plunge the nation into political chaos. The presumed danger is that a candidate might receive a majority of the electoral vote while receiving fewer popular votes than his or her opponent. They speak of this discrepancy as a "time-bomb waiting to go off," but the last time it did go off, in 1888, it proved to be a squib, and nothing happened. There was hardly a ripple of popular discontent, no spate of editorials claiming that Benjamin Harrison was an illegitimate president, no complaints from the losing candidate, Grover Cleveland, that he had been cheated. Indeed, when asked by a reporter the day after the election to what he attributed his defeat, Cleveland smiled and said, "It was mainly because the other party got more votes."[3]

It was different in 2000. No sooner had the election results been reported—showing that Gore had won the popular vote but was likely to lose the electoral vote—when Al Gore's campaign chairman claimed fraud, and Democrat Hillary Rodham Clinton, and even Arlen Spector, nominally a Republican, called for the abolition of the electoral college in favor of a direct popular vote.

Now, one of the virtues of the electoral college is, or was, that it regularly produces a president with a clear, immediate, and legitimate claim to the office, in part because it amplifies the margin of victory in the popular vote. In 1960, for example, John F. Kennedy won only 49.72 percent of the popular vote (as opposed to Richard Nixon's 49.55 percent), but Kennedy's margin in the electoral college was 303 to 219. In 1968, for another example, Nixon won 43.42 percent, Hubert Humphrey 42.72 percent, and George Wallace 13.53 percent of the popular vote, but Nixon's electoral college margin was 301 to 191 to 46. This did not happen in the 2000 election. Not only did our system not amplify the popular vote margin, but, for the first time since 1888, the candidate with a plurality of the popular vote did not win the electoral vote. In fact, the electoral vote was so close that we did not know, immediately, who was president; everything turned on Florida, where the popular vote was too close to call, and, as we all know, the outcome was not determined until the Supreme Court acted on December 12, six days before the electors were scheduled to meet in their state capitals to cast their votes.

Is there, then, any reason to believe that the country would have been spared this situation, this uncertainty as to who was elected, if we had a system of direct popular election of the president? Before pursuing this subject, I want to say a few words in defense of the Supreme Court and its December 12 decision.

As we know, the Court was accused of interfering in a matter that was none of its business, that its decision to put an end to the vote recounts in Florida was both unprecedented and, because the recounts could have been completed in the time available, unnecessary; that it was nothing more than a decision rendered by Republican justices to ensure the election of a Republican president.

But consider what would have happened if the Court had not intervened. The recount would have continued, and, by counting all those "dimpled" ballots, Gore probably would have been declared the winner of the popular vote in Florida. The Florida Supreme Court, which ordered the recount, would then have ordered the governor to certify a Gore slate of electors. But in the meantime, the Florida legislature had convened for the purpose of certifying a slate of Bush electors. So there could have been two slates of electors, and the Congress of the United States, meeting on January 6 in joint session, would have had to determine which slate was "regularly given." Not surprisingly, there is a statutory rule governing even this situation. I quote from the statute:

> [In case] of more than one return or paper purporting to be a return from a State . . . then those votes, and those only, shall be counted which the two Houses [that is, the House of Representatives and the Senate] shall concurrently decide were cast by lawful electors appointed in accordance with the laws of the State, unless the two Houses, acting separately, shall concurrently decide such votes not to be the lawful votes of the legally appointed electors of such State. But if the two Houses shall disagree in respect of the counting of such votes, then, and in that case, the votes of the electors whose appointment shall have been certified by the executive of the State, under the seal thereof, shall be counted. [And suppose there are two slates, each certified by the executive of the State?][4]

All clear? Actually, yes. But clearer still is the *probability* of nasty partisan wrangling with the *possibility* of a delay in reaching a decision—and all this just two weeks before the new president, whoever he is, and his cabinet, whoever they are, are scheduled to take office! There was talk in 2000 that the transition period, the time during which the new administration prepares to take office, was too brief. But suppose, instead of six weeks, it had been two? I don't *know* if the Court had this in mind when it decided to intervene, but I suspect it did, and, in any case, we, Democrats and Republicans alike, should be grateful.

But, to return to that other matter. I asked earlier whether there is any reason to believe that the country would have been spared the Florida situation—meaning the delay and the uncertainty as to who was elected president—if, instead of by the electoral college, presidents were selected by a direct popular vote. Under the present system, the delay and uncertainty were caused by the necessity to recount in Florida; we did not have to recount in Texas, New York, or California, to say nothing of Illinois, even though there is no reason to believe there were no dimpled ballots in Texas, or hanging chads in New York, or deliberate miscounts in Cook County, Illinois, where the Daley machine is still in power. Why not? Because the margin of victory for Bush in Texas, and for Gore in these other states, almost surely exceeded the number of miscounted, or uncounted, ballots. But under the alternative proposed, every vote, everywhere would matter, in a way they do not matter under the present system. And in any close election—and most of our presidential elections are very close—we would have reason to recount everywhere, not only in Florida.

This would plainly be the case with the system favored by the reformers. Under that system, the nation forms a single electoral district; the candidate with the most popular votes wins, provided he wins at least 40 percent of the votes cast; failing that, the plan calls for a runoff between the top two candidates. In this one national electoral district would be 180,000 local polling places, all equally important because, as I said, every vote everywhere matters—and not only the votes cast for one or the other of the major party candidates, but those cast for any of the minor party candidates. No longer could the argument be made that a vote cast for Ralph Nader, for example, or Pat Buchanan, or, thirty-two years earlier, for George Wallace, is a "wasted vote"; under the proposed system, there would be no such thing as a "wasted vote." In 1968, the 4.1 million votes cast for Wallace outside the states he carried were "wasted," because they gained him no electoral votes; but they would not have been wasted under a system of direct popular vote. Indeed, there probably would have been more such votes because Wallace's support faded from a high of 23 percent, in a September opinion survey, to an actual popular vote of 13.5 percent in the November election, at least in part because of the wasted vote argument.[5] So, if not three, then at least two-and-a-half cheers for the electoral college.

The critics of the electoral college are unmoved by any of this. The present system is undemocratic, they say, and, so far as they are concerned, this is all that matters.

But have we really reached the point where the right to hold a public office depends *solely* on the suffrage of a popular majority? Are the friends of direct popular election really willing to say that a candidate with a *constitutional* but not a popular majority is an illegitimate president? Perhaps, but only if the moral authority of the electoral college—indeed, of the Constitution itself—has been undermined by the persistent efforts to get rid of it, especially the efforts of members of Congress and what the British call the "chattering class."

The electoral college, they say, is a violation of the democratic principles of one man, one vote, and the majority rules. In fact, of course, the majority now rules, not necessarily nationally, but at the state level where (except in Maine and Nebraska) the popular votes are aggregated. As it happens, this is where the vote of any particular minority looms larger, or carries more weight, than it is likely to do in the country as a whole. So long as a minority is not evenly distributed throughout the country, it is in its interest to oppose direct popular elections; civil rights leaders used to understand this. And is there not something to be said for an electoral system that threatens to penalize a political party and its candidate for failing to respect the rights of minorities? Furthermore, is there not something to be said for an electoral system that protects the interests of states as states, which is to say, a system with an element of federalism built into it? Only twice in the twentieth century (1960 and 1976) has the candidate with an electoral college majority failed to win a majority of the states. (Bush, the electoral college winner in 2000, won thirty of the fifty states.) And is there not, then, something to be said for a system that threatens to penalize sectional candidates?

The American idea of democracy cannot be expressed in the simple—simple but insidious—formula, the greatest good of the greatest number. What the greatest number regards as its greatest good might very well prove to be a curse to those not part of that number. The American idea of democracy, which is expressed in the Declaration of Independence and embodied in various provisions of the Constitution—the principle of representation in the Senate, for example, and the district system in the House, as well as the electoral college—is that government is instituted to secure the rights of all. To this end, we also have a Bill of Rights. Finally, what is constitutionalism if not a qualification of majoritarianism?

The men who founded this country surely recognized the entitlements of a popular majority, but, with an eye to the qualifications for or the qualities required of an office, they devised institutions—the electoral college is one of them—that modify or qualify the majority principle. Nothing could be clearer than that the Founders sought institutions or ways—Alexis de Tocqueville called them "forms"—that would protect the country from what has come to be called populism. As I said, the organizing principle of the Senate is surely not majority rule, nor are its procedures simply democratic. Federal judges are not elected at all. They are appointed by the president, with the advice and consent of the Senate, and they serve for life. If legitimacy springs only from the principle of one man, one equally weighted vote, upon what meat do these, our judicial Caesars, feed? For that matter, if populism is our only principle, why should we have elections? Why not select all public officials by lot? This would be truly democratic, because it pays no attention whatever to the qualifications of officeholders—or assumes that everyone is equally qualified.

In short, the issue that ought to engage our attention is the one the Framers debated over the entire course of the Constitutional Convention, from May 1787 to September, namely, what way of election is more likely to produce a president with the qualities required of the person holding this great office? In all the years I have been engaged in this debate, in all the times I have testified on this issue before a House or Senate committee, I have yet to encounter a critic of the electoral college who argues that a president chosen directly by the people is likely to be a *better* president. And that, surely, is the issue.

My argument was best made by an old and close friend, the late Professor Herbert Storing, when, in 1977, in testimony before the Subcommittee on the Constitution of the Senate Judiciary Committee, he said,

> To see the case for the present system of electing the president requires a shift in point of view from that usually taken by the critics [of the electoral college]. They tend to view elections in terms of *input*—in terms of the right to vote, equal weight of votes, who in fact votes, and the like. The framers [of the Constitution] thought it at least as important to consider the *output* of any electoral system. What kind of man does it bring to office? How will it affect the working of the political system? What is its bearing on the political character of the whole country?[6]

If, then, James Madison, Alexander Hamilton, James Wilson, Benjamin Franklin, Gouverneur Morris, and the rest thought it important to consider *output* as well as *input* when designing the electoral system, I think that we today are obliged to do the same when considering proposals to amend it.

11

Civil Not Natural Rights

There is a question as to why the Beacon Press would choose to publish a collection of Wendy Kaminer's essays, *Free For All: Defending Liberty in America Today*.[1] It is not enough to say, as she does in a prefatory note, that "civil liberties are always in jeopardy and always require attention."[2] Fair enough, but she and her libertarian colleagues have made a career of saying just that. So why say it again? There is nothing new in these essays, all of them previously published and none of them distinguished in any way.

Numbering about fifty, they deal with such topics as sexual freedom, abortion rights, gay marriage, assisted suicide, and the medical use of marijuana, all of which she supports; as well as racial profiling, the death penalty, the war on drugs, "flag worship," and censorship, all of which she opposes. In still others—"An Imperial Presidency," for example, and "Safety and Freedom"—she comes to grips (so to speak) with the exigencies of our present situation. While written before 9/11, all the essays were "updated" later; she makes a point of this, presumably, to assure us that she appreciates the greater relevance after 9/11 of national security considerations. In any event, this appreciation amounts to very little.

The most that might be said is that Kaminer is not unmindful of the importance of national security, but she speaks disdainfully of every measure designed to promote it. The airport security measures are not only intrusive, she says, but "unnecessarily" so; moreover, they were adopted only because of the untoward influence of large but otherwise unidentified corporations. The requirement to display a photo ID card before boarding a plane is a useless security measure, in fact, an "idiotic" security measure, and was adopted only because it is "an effective revenue enhancer that enables the airlines to catch passengers using other people's discount tickets."[3] As she sees it, the whole security business is something of a scam; she

117

refuses to believe the (unidentified) officials who tell us that sacrificing freedom will make us more secure. "Most of them," she says, really want us "to have less freedom just so they can have more power, regardless of security."[4] This is a serious, in fact, a reckless charge, but she apparently sees evidence enough to support it in the laws enacted after 9/11, particularly the Patriot Act, and the way the laws, old and new, are being enforced. Her conclusion is that, while we don't yet inhabit a police state, "it is not paranoia that imagines one taking shape."[5] Her friend, Katha Pollitt, may have had statements like this in mind when she said, on the book's back cover, "Wonderful Wendy Kaminer! With wit and style and cold hard facts, she skewers contemporary credulity."

After all this, it comes as something of a surprise to learn that Kaminer's views on this subject do not differ all that much from those of the general public. "Ask people to choose between freedom and security," she says, "and almost all will choose security."[6] But, nominally at least, so does she. She does so because, like them, she believes that "freedom depends on peace and some measure of order, after all."[7] So it does, after all; but, perhaps because the American Civil Liberties Union spends its time defending the rights of unpopular minorities—anarchists, pornographers, flag-burners, left- and right-wing zealots—she overlooks the fact that the popular majority also has rights, specifically and of most consequence here, the right to peace and some measure of order—in a word, to security. This right deserves as much respect and protection as freedom of speech and the other rights explicitly mentioned in one or another provision of the Constitution, and more respect and protection than that so-called right of privacy derived from "penumbras formed by emanations" from a potpourri of provisions.[8] But she says nothing about this. Beyond that, it should be said that freedom and security are not so much at odds as she sometimes makes them out to be.

The key here is how we understand freedom, or, more precisely, our constitutional rights. For example, correctly understood, it is not a denial of a defendant's right to due process if, thanks to the Patriot Act, the government is allowed to avail itself of foreign intelligence information in a domestic criminal case. Kaminer thinks otherwise.[9] Nor, correctly understood, is it an abridgment of our First Amendment right of freedom of speech and press to prohibit child pornography on the Internet. But Kaminer, ever mindful of the alleged slippery slope, insists that the right is meaningless unless it protects, say, "A Child's Deep Throat" as well as "Anne of Green Gables."[10] Wonderful Wendy, indeed. But this can truly be said of her: She treats civil rights as if they were natural rights and, by doing so, exaggerates their extent or reach.

She is not the first of her tribe to do this, just as she is not the first to speak repeatedly of "autonomy" and "autonomous individuals."[11] The autonomous individual is said to have "antecedent rights against the state," including the right to say or print whatever he pleases, irrespective of its effect on the state.[12] In principle, this means (as the fashion now has it) that the right has priority over the good, a principle given at least quasi-official status in an opinion written by Justice Oliver Wendell Holmes (Kaminer's favorite jurist) in a free speech case decided by the Supreme Court of the United States in 1925. Holmes said, and among libertarians became famous for saying, "If in the long run the beliefs expressed in proletarian dictatorship are destined to be accepted by the dominant forces of the community, the only meaning of free speech is that they should be given their chance and have their way."[13] If we take him at his word, as libertarians are wont to do, this means that it is worse to suppress the advocacy of Stalinism or Hitlerism than to be ruled by a local Stalin or Hitler. So much for autonomy and its principle. The fact is, of course, there are no autonomous individuals in this country, none at all; leaving aside visitors, there are, instead, only citizens and aliens, all of them living under the jurisdiction of the law and expected to obey it, and with the collective right to peace and some measure of order under it.

There was a time when, in theory—venerable liberal theory—all of us were autonomous individuals, when there were nothing but autonomous or radically independent and self-governing individuals. Living then in the state of nature, we had nature's rights, but these rights were not secure, and could not there be secured. The state of nature proved to be a state of war, with the consequence that our lives were "solitary, poor, nasty, brutish, and short."[14]

The way out of this most unhappy situation was found by Thomas Hobbes, the political philosopher who coined that phrase. Hobbes, followed by John Locke, asked the political question, What sort of society or *social* bond can be established among persons who are by nature asocial and with the right (the "antecedent" right) to do as they please?[15] To put the question otherwise, what are the preconditions of a society formed of naturally autonomous individuals, or what portion of that autonomy is retained after society is formed? Or, again, since the autonomy is defined by natural rights, which rights does the individual retain, and which must he surrender when entering society?

These are not questions of interest only to theoreticians; on the contrary, they were asked and answered at our beginning as a people. Writing in *Federalist* 2, Publius—John Jay in this case—said, "Nothing is more certain than the indispensable necessity of government; and it is equally undeniable that whenever and however it is instituted, the people must cede to it some of their natural rights, in order to vest it with requisite powers." Which rights are ceded (or surrendered), and which are retained?

Strictly speaking, the only one retained is "the Right of the People" we exercised in 1776 and, if necessary, stand prepared to exercise again. All other natural rights are surrendered, in exchange for the civil rights that society promises to secure.[16] A civil right is a civilized version of a natural right, by which I mean, it is the result of reflections on what is necessary, first, to constitute a society, and then to govern it. By treating them as natural rights, Kaminer would deprive the government of the powers required in times of danger. And to do this would be to deprive the people of their right to peace and some measure of order.

12

Flag-Burning and Other Modes
of Expression

The summer of 1989 brought no peace to Washington. Thanks to the Supreme Court, the issue of abortion went back to the states whence it had come sixteen years earlier. But, as if in return, Washington was given patriotism and obscenity when the Court upheld the burning of the flag by an angry Gregory Johnson[1] and when an embarrassed Corcoran Gallery canceled an exhibition of Robert Mapplethorpe photographs.

Johnson was angry with the United States, which proved to be his salvation because, as the Court explained, the First Amendment protects angry political expression, but not, if such exists, pointless political expression—for example, flag-burning just for the fun of it. The Corcoran was embarrassed, not by the Mapplethorpe photographs themselves, but by its decision to cancel the exhibition, thereby surrendering its principles to a phalanx of angry congressmen led by "the unspeakable [Senator] Jesse Helms," as he was called by the *Washington Post*, "America's Number One Yahoo."[2] After all, the Corcoran is an art gallery, and Robert Mapplethorpe was an artist, and it follows, at least in the art world it follows, that everything done by an artist is art. Art, like angry flag-burning, is one of the modes of expression, and expression is said to be protected by the First Amendment.

According to Robert McCormick Adams, the head of the Smithsonian Institution, even graffiti are (or is) art—including, we are entitled to ask, even graffiti spray-painted on the exterior walls of one of the Washington museums entrusted to his care, for example, the National Gallery's East Wing, of which he is a trustee? After all, by definition graffiti are words or pictures scratched or painted on a public surface, and the East Wing provides public surfaces much grander, cleaner, and, one would think, much more inviting than any available in New York City subways. So grand, in fact, and so clean, that one wonders why no one has yet taken advantage of them. (Perhaps we can thank the corps of dogs employed by the Smithsonian to police its grounds and buildings.) Still, notoriety awaits the first to do so, just as noto-riety, of a sort, was won by the anonymous New York subway "graffitists" when, with the help of a grant in the amount of some $160,000 from the National Endowment for the Arts ("Your Tax Dollars at Work!"), a film was made depicting their work, and not only depicting but celebrating it.

Rather than celebrate it, Adams would surely call the police, the FBI, or the U.S. Attorney's office, if someone were to spray graffiti on any of the Smithsonian buildings. Graffiti may be an art, and art may be a form of expression, and expression may be protected by the First Amendment; but surely, he would protest, there are limits. He might cite a few Supreme Court decisions having to do with time, place, and manner. At a minimum, we would expect him to be outraged; but outrage was all Jesse Helms was expressing, at least initially. He thought it outrageous that public money, like public surfaces, should be made available to the likes of Robert Mapplethorpe.

One doesn't have to be a "yahoo" to agree with Helms on this point. Like Gregory Johnson, Mapplethorpe was undoubtedly expressing himself; indeed, unlike Johnson, he was expressing himself in the etymologically precise sense of the term. According to the unabridged Oxford English Dictionary, expression originally meant "the act of pressing or squeezing out," hence, "to expel or get rid of by force." Just so, in one of his photo-graphs Mapplethorpe shows one man artfully urinating into the mouth of another, expelling urine by force of the sphincters, so to speak (or so to express). In another of his photographs he also shows a bullwhip thrust handle-first into a man's anus. As a *Washington Post* writer explained, Mapplethorpe "set out to celebrate this domain of sexual experience, to ele-vate it, even to a transcendent level."[3] It was their failure to appreciate this higher purpose that caused the *Post* to be indignant with Jesse Helms and his "yahoo" colleagues in the Congress who threatened to cut off funding. Expression, the *Post* insisted, even apparently shocking expression, is protected by the First Amendment. (In its own expression of indignation, the *Post* reproduced a Mapplethorpe photograph of a couple of tulips and, a week or so later, a Mapplethorpe self-portrait of his face, but for some reason, it never got around to reproducing what the art critic Hilton Kramer, writing in the *New York Times*, referred to as "those disputed pictures.")[4]

In fact, of course, the First Amendment protects not freedom of expression, but freedom of speech. "Congress shall make no law," it reads, "abridging the freedom of speech." But, it might be asked, what is expression if not one of the forms of speech? Indeed, to refer again to the dictionary, the word soon acquired the meaning familiar to us, "the utterance of feelings." Besides, in our postmodernist world, speech and expression are easily confused and just as easily identified. In his massive and widely acclaimed book, *The System of Freedom of Expression*, for example, Thomas I. Emerson of the Yale Law School, no doubt inadvertently, removed the word "speech" from the First Amendment and put in its place the word "expression." In construing specific legal doctrines that govern concrete issues, he wrote, "The main function of the courts is . . . to define the key elements in the First Amendment: 'expression,' 'abridge,' and 'law.'"[5]

It would be foolish, however, to insist on this distinction between speech and expression when confronting the issue of censorship of the arts. Whatever the authors of the First Amendment intended by choosing the word "speech," there are sound practical reasons for the law to leave the arts alone. Even assuming that not everything carrying the label is, in fact, art, the courts are unable, and have proved themselves unable, to make the aesthetic judgments necessary to mark the distinction. And since the kind of restrictions proposed by Jesse Helms would inevitably end up in the courts, it would be best to forget about dealing with the problem through legislation.[6]

Thus, for example, Helms, like the legendary Anthony Comstock, would have drawn the line between art and obscenity, but many a work of art, and many a literary masterpiece, is obscene. Aristophanes's *Assembly of Women* is so obscene that the English translator of the play preferred to remain anonymous. (That was a long time ago.) Hilton Kramer finds it noteworthy that Manet's painting, *Le Déjeuner sur l'herbe*, now one of the Louvre's "treasured classics," was considered indecent when first exhibited in 1863. Treasured classic or not, it is indecent; no one, however, not even Jesse Helms, I suspect, would say that about the painting that inspired it, Giorgione's *Concert Champêtre*. The two paintings—each of them a masterpiece—are both strikingly similar and dissimilar, but what distinguishes them cannot, I think, be expressed in any category known to the law.

Manet, the greatest of the French Impressionists, shows a woman without a stitch of clothes on, and in the background another partially clothed woman, the two of them sharing a picnic lunch with two fully clothed men. Giorgione, some 350 years earlier, shows two women, without a stitch of clothes on, also in the company of two men who are fully clothed. But Manet's women are undressed; he shows their clothes in a heap. Giorgione's are simply nude; their clothes are nowhere to be seen. Manet's women are playful, even wanton, as if it is no big deal, as we would say, for women to undress before men in a public park. Giorgione's women appear serene, even noble; one of them is holding a pitcher and pouring water from it *into* a well. Manet's men look bored; sharing a picnic lunch with undressed women would appear to be something they do every day. Giorgione's men are innocent and appear to be engaged in serious musical conversation. Nothing indecent is being depicted here; as is evident to someone who knows how to look at it, the young men cannot see the women because the women, like Oberon in Shakespeare's *A Midsummer Night's Dream*, are invisible, not to us but to them. The women are not human; they are woodland nymphs who, attracted by the music and charm of the young men, have joined in their pastoral concert, their *Concert Champêtre*.

There is no reason to believe that a judge cannot be taught to see this—I myself learned it from an art critic, Philipp Fehl—but there is also no reason to believe that a judge could state the difference between the two paintings (or, more to the point, between Manet and Mapplethorpe) in a rule of law. When required to make such distinctions, judges are inclined to mutter something about "redeeming social value" (and find it in *Fanny Hill*, the highly explicit life story of a whore), or to throw up their hands and say, with the late Justice John Marshall Harlan, "One man's vulgarity is another's lyric."[7] This was said in 1971 for a divided Supreme Court, but it is a foolish statement at best and, at worst, it is pernicious. For if Harlan is right, there is no such thing as vulgarity (and therefore no reason to censor); but, by the same token, there is also no such thing as art (and therefore no reason not to censor).

Better, as I say, for the law to leave the arts alone. Better for society to express its disapproval of a Robert Mapplethorpe by simply refusing to fund his work. Presumably—although, goodness knows, there is reason to doubt it—the National Endowment for the Arts, unlike the courts, can do this without a Helms amendment and without jeopardizing the work of Giorgione or Manet.

Political expression is another matter, but unfortunately, our judges hardly do much better in that area. In the Skokie case, the Illinois Supreme Court even quoted Harlan's aphorism, thereby implying that what went for the brandishing of four-letter words in a courthouse (the issue in Harlan's case) applied equally well to an invasion of Nazis brandishing their swastikas in a community of Holocaust survivors.[8]

This sort of moral relativism is a feature of our First Amendment law: Distinctions, whether between the art of the tulip and the art of the anus, or between flag-burning and sober political speech, are not to be made because, so it is thought, they cannot be made except arbitrarily. Just as beauty is in the eye of the beholder, so truth is relative, a proposition that found its way into our law through the good offices of two of our most famous twentieth-century Supreme Court justices, Oliver Wendell Holmes and Hugo L. Black. If, said Holmes in 1925, "the beliefs expressed in pro-letarian dictatorship are destined to be accepted by the dominant forces of the community, the only meaning of free speech is that they should be given their chance and have their way."[9] So, too, Black in 1961: "Education and contrary argument [may provide an adequate defense against Communist and fascist speech, but if that] remedy is not sufficient, the only meaning of free speech must be that the revolutionary ideas will be allowed to prevail."[10] In other words, it is worse to punish the advocacy of Stalinism or Hitlerism than it is to be ruled by Stalin or Hitler.

According to the historian Arthur M. Schlesinger Jr., relativism is the peculiar American virtue; everyone we admire—not only Holmes, but Learned Hand, Ralph Waldo Emerson, William James, Reinhold Niebuhr, even (astonishingly enough) Abraham Lincoln—in fact, everyone except Allan Bloom and, presumably, the "yahoos" represented by the "unspeak-able Jesse Helms"—was or is a relativist. Relativism, Schlesinger says, "is what America is all about."[11]

It was, of course, otherwise at our beginning. John Locke was the first to teach us the importance, not of speech—Aristotle did that—but of free-dom of speech, by which he meant freedom of religious speech, or liberty of conscience. Locke, writing in the seventeenth century, aimed this doc-trine at the clergy (for example, the Archbishop of Canterbury, William

Laud) who, with the support of the government (for example, King Charles I), used *their* speech to instruct people in the proper care of their souls and threatened to punish anyone who disobeyed. The consequence, especially in Locke's own time, was civil war and revolution. Locke taught, and succeeded in teaching Thomas Jefferson and the other American Founders, that "the care of each man's soul belongs unto himself alone," and that "liberty of conscience is every man's natural right." Government is instituted to secure that right, which means, so far as government is concerned, that there is no right way to care for souls and that all religious speech is equal. As Jefferson put it, "It does me no injury for my neighbor to say there are twenty gods, or no god. It neither picks my pocket nor breaks my leg." In fact, he added, "difference of opinion is advantageous in religion."[12]

Freedom of speech may be advantageous in religion and, as Jefferson said elsewhere, harmless in physics and geometry; but he never said that, nor anything resembling it, with respect to political speech. On that subject, and unlike Schlesinger, he and the other Founders were not relativists. As they saw it, we might lack knowledge concerning the right way to care for souls, but we had firm knowledge concerning the fundamental principles of government: We knew that governments were instituted to secure rights, and that they derived their just powers from the consent of the governed. If this were a matter on which men might rightly disagree, it would be impossible to protect the right of freedom of conscience. For then the opinion that government must instruct men on the care of their souls would be equal to the opinion that the care of each man's soul belongs to himself alone, and the issue could not be decided (and, in the Britain of Locke's time, was not decided) other than by force of arms.

Thus, at our beginning, there was understood to be a difference between religious and other kinds of speech, which is why the First Amendment distinguishes them. With respect to religion, we were to be a house divided, and the Constitution was designed to keep us divided. With respect to the fundamental principles of government, we were to be a house united, and the Constitution was designed to keep us united: "The United States shall guarantee to every State in this Union a Republican Form of Government" (article 4, section 4).

Fulfilling this mandate is not an easy matter. Republican government is representative government, but, in the words of James Madison in

Federalist 10, the people to be represented are by no means unified; in fact, they are divided into "factions," the causes of which are "sown in the nature of man." By nature, men are selfish, each of them moved by "self-love"; and while they are endowed by nature with the same rights, they are also endowed by nature with different and unequal faculties. The consequence is that they have different interests. Republican government must bring these naturally self-interested persons together to form a whole while also respecting the diversity of their interests and, at the same time, securing their right to have different interests. Not, to repeat, an easy thing to do. The Founders' solution was representative government based on the consent of the people. Such a government must, first of all, represent the diversity of interests in the society. Therefore, the First Amendment guarantees that each person has a voice in the selection of the representatives who make the laws and form the policy. Stated otherwise, each member of the society registers his consent by debating, organizing, and then choosing his representatives. Freedom of speech plays an essential part in this process.

Secondly, such a government must make it possible for agreements to be reached with respect to the policies adopted in the laws and otherwise pursued. To do this, it must gain the consent of these representatives, or at least a majority of them, each of whom has a right to withhold it. This, too, requires speech, but speech of a certain kind, which is why every representative assembly has rules governing the manner of debate. Kings may speak haughtily and tyrants cruelly, insultingly, or even contemptuously, but the members of a republican assembly must adopt a mode of address that reflects a disposition to respect the interests of others because, as a matter of constitutional right, they are equally respectable. The speech of political representatives will be self-interested speech, of course, but it will be speech that recognizes the difference between self-interest and the common interest and the necessity to agree on a common interest. And given the fact that men are divided by their interests (which derive from their self-love and different faculties), the common interest here takes the form of an aggregation of partially satisfied self-interests.

Gregory Johnson wanted no part of this. On the contrary, he had nothing but contempt for the flag and "the republic for which it stands." To adopt the locution of the day, he was "into" self-expression, and as Harvard's Harvey Mansfield has reminded us, there is nothing in self-expression that requires or encourages one "self" to seek the consent of the other.[13] Self-expression is almost always angry expression, and anger provokes anger, as it did in this instance, not agreement or accommodation.

The reason self-expression is almost always angry is that it is self-assertion. According to Nietzsche (the founding father of self-expression and the man from whom all this derives), the "self" lacks innate definition; it acquires identity, or "authenticity," only by assertion against others.[14]

In this sense, the "self" is a neologism; we speak of "selfs" where our fathers, or at least our Founding Fathers, spoke of souls, and the difference is decisive. "The soul may be responsible for its being good or bad," as Leo Strauss wrote a number of years ago when addressing a somewhat similar issue, "but it is not responsible for its being a soul."[15] Rather, the soul is (or was) understood to be part of an order for which God was responsible. But in Nietzsche's words, "God is dead," and with his death went the ordered universe of which the soul was a part. "Nature's God," the God of the Declaration of Independence, is also dead, and with his death went the laws and rights of nature, because, lacking definition, the "self" is governed by no moral laws and is incapable of having rights.

This means that constitutionalism is also dead, an event announced by Sanford J. Levinson of the University of Texas Law School. "The death of 'constitutionalism,'" he declares, "may be the central event of our time, just as the death of God was that of the past century (and for much the same reason)."[16] Nature's God endowed us with rights and the Founders provided us with a Constitution that, in order to secure these rights, put constraints on the popular will. With His death, those constraints are deprived of all moral authority. In Levinson's words, "law is stripped of any moral anchoring," with the consequence that there is nothing "to which the will [is] bound to submit."[17] No moral order, no moral laws, and, as Nietzsche said, no reason to be burdened by guilt.

The "self" exists in this void; it is merely will; it becomes what it is only by asserting—in Nietzsche's formulation—"the will to power," and the strongest will must prevail. This prospect does not frighten Levinson: "Political institutions," he says, "thus become the forum for the triumph of the will," the phrase first uttered by Hitler's minister of propaganda, Joseph Goebbels, and rendered memorable (appallingly so, one would have thought) by Hitler's favorite filmmaker, Leni Riefenstahl, in *The Triumph of the Will.* When it comes to "self-expression," no one has yet been able to top Adolf Hitler. On the other hand, considering the condition of our legal and political thought—Levinson claims his view of our situation is held by "most major law schools"—there is no guarantee that someone might not yet succeed in doing so.

All this should serve to convince us that the Supreme Court was ill-advised to treat flag-burning as unimportant. The flag is the symbol of what we think about ourselves and what we think we are about, much more so than the presidential seal, to adopt Justice William Brennan's silly analogy. As Judge Robert Bork said after reading Brennan's opinion for the Court in this case, no one, save perhaps the members of the White House staff, salutes the presidential seal.[18] Nor, unlike the case with the flag, does the *United States Code* devote page after page prescribing when and where it should be displayed—"The flag should be displayed during school days in or near every schoolhouse"—or how it should be displayed, or how it should be folded and disposed of, or how and when it should be saluted.[19] Nor, again unlike the case with the flag, does the code make it a federal offense to "desecrate" the presidential seal. Like the American people, Congress has always looked upon the flag as something special. Why, then, is the Supreme Court unable to draw a line in favor of the flag and against its desecration?

The Court's answer is that the First Amendment forbids the drawing of such a line. Writing for the five-judge majority, Brennan said that "if there is a bedrock principle underlying the First Amendment, it's that the government may not prohibit the expression of an idea simply because it finds the idea itself offensive or disagreeable."[20] But surely it is possible to distinguish between an idea and the manner in which it is expressed. Judges may not be able to devise a rule of law marking the difference between Manet and Mapplethorpe, but it is not beyond their capacity as jurists to distinguish between speech and at least some forms of expression or, for that matter, among the various kinds of speech. Libelous speech is not protected by the First Amendment, nor are "fighting words," perjury, false advertising, verbal agreements to restrain trade, vulgar speech in a student assembly, or contemptuous speech in a courtroom. The list is not endless but it is long, and commodious enough to include flag-burning.

Within these limits, Gregory Johnson could say whatever he wanted to say; that is the "bedrock principle." He could, with impunity, denounce

Ronald Reagan and George Bush and call down a plague on the Republican Party; he could hurl his imprecations against the United States and the American people; he could scream his disgust with life in the twentieth century. He could also make a fool of himself by burning the presidential seal—no law forbids it—but he should not have been permitted to do whatever he wanted to do by way of expressing his "self."

Of course, deprived now of flag-burning—because it is no longer illegal—Johnson and his friends would have to find new and, of necessity, more egregious ways to aggress against the symbols, the conventions, or the mores which, as Tocqueville argued, provide the foundation of America's laws and its political life. For this they might have found inspiration in some of Robert Mapplethorpe's photographs, which may explain why Johnson immediately flew to Washington in order to be among the first to visit the private gallery exhibiting them.

13

Blue Movies

Hollywood Censored, we are told on the book's dust jacket, "examines how hundreds of films—Mae West comedies, serious dramas, and films with a social message—were censored and often edited to promote a conservative political agenda during the golden age of studio production in the 1930s."[1] It goes on to explain how, because of a series of sex scandals that took place in Hollywood in 1922, Will Hays was hired by the movie industry to clean up its image. Hays's solution was to adopt what came to be known as "the Production Code." Written by a St. Louis priest and a Catholic layman, it "stipulated that movies stress proper behavior, respect for government, and 'Christian values'—thereby challenging the moguls' staunch belief that movies entertain, not preach morality." The dust jacket continues:

> The Catholic Church further reinforced these efforts by launching its Legion of Decency in 1934. Intended to force Hays and Hollywood to censor movies more rigorously, the legion engineered the appointment of Joseph Breen as head of the Production Code Administration. For the next three decades, Breen, Hays, and the Catholic Legion of Decency virtually controlled the content of all Hollywood films.

In addition to this accurate summary of the book, the dust jacket also points out that its author, Gregory D. Black, is a professor, which, without more, is enough to assure opponents of censorship that the subject will be treated in the manner they have come to expect. The censors are depicted as knaves—or, with good reason in the case of Joseph Breen, anti-Semitic bigots—and the filmmakers as fools interested only in making money. But, since advertising is a good way of promoting a film, and therefore of making money,

131

one of the surest (as well as the cheapest) ways of advertising may be to resist, or pretend to resist, the strictures of the censors. This was proved in the case of *Klondike Annie*, starring the ludicrous Mae West; the attempts to ban it, Professor Black reports, "caused a flood of eager customers to storm box offices across the country."[2] Maybe the filmmakers weren't so dumb after all.

Black says the filmmakers during the "Golden Age" of studio production "worshiped revenue more than they respected honesty," and would have us believe that they would have made better films (presumably, films like those now being made) had they been honest.[3] Yet among the films that were made by these "dishonest" producers, which he does not so much as mention, were *Casablanca*, *The Maltese Falcon*, *Philadelphia Story*, *Mutiny on the Bounty*, *Top Hat*, *High Noon*, *Shane*, *Brief Encounter*, *The Lady Vanishes*, and (when the censors were dozing) *Le Diable au Corps*, starring Micheline Presle and the young Gerard Philipe. But Professor Black's concern is with the films that might have been made but were not, and "how different those films that were made might have looked," had they not been censored.[4]

With this in mind, he makes much of the censoring of *Anna Karenina*. He says:

> Breen realized that the industry would look foolish if it banned Tolstoy and other pieces of classic literature simply because they contained sexual themes [but he also knew that] any reasonably accurate film of Tolstoy's novel was sure to invoke howls of protest from [the Legion of Decency].[5]

In the earlier (1927) screening of the novel, MGM gave exhibitors a choice of endings by releasing two versions, one, true to the novel, in which Anna commits suicide, and the other, in which she and Count Vronsky are reunited and, presumably, live happily ever after. But, Professor Black points out, "Audiences in 1935 would have no such choice: The Anna of the Breen era would be thoroughly chastised and fatally punished for her sinful transgressions against family, church, and state."[6]

But Breen was not the fool (or not quite the fool) he is made to seem. Sure, Anna was in love, and love is a wonderful thing, but by committing adultery, abandoning her child, and running off with Vronsky, she did transgress against family, church, and state; and sure, Karenin (Professor

Black calls him "Karenina") was a clod, but he was Anna's lawfully wedded husband and father of her child, and that used to count for something. But, whatever Breen's reasons for insisting on it, Tolstoy knew that a happy ending would have made the novel pointless. Besides, how is the author of a love story going to depict the power of love except by putting it in competition with something equally compelling?

Professor Black wonders what an uncensored *Anna Karenina* would have looked like. The answer is, probably much as it would look if it were made today. Anna (Sharon Stone?) would casually pack her bags, dash off (or perhaps not bother to dash off) a short note to Karenin and, with Vronsky (Michael Douglas) at her side, catch the train to Portofino where, against a background of the blue Mediterranean, the two of them pull off their clothes, hop happily into the sack, and (she moaning and he grunting) commence their revels. But, with nothing at risk and nothing to suffer—when sex is "no big deal"—who could believe that this Anna was really in love?

The point escapes Professor Black, but the real fools in this business were those who thought it possible to produce a film of Tolstoy's novel for an audience for which drama is only a form of recreation. Such an audience simply wants to be entertained without having to wonder what it is that makes Vronsky a foolish but interesting man and Anna (but not the carelessly adulterous Betsy Tverskoy) an interesting woman, a woman under the sway of conflicting passions: romantic love and devotion to child, eros and duty, promise and necessity. Tolstoy could depict all this in the written word, and there was a time when, even in bourgeois and democratic America, he was read by a handful of us. But, given their cost, films— movies, as we say—are made for a larger and less patient audience. As Tocqueville said in a chapter devoted to the drama in a democratic age, "The great authors of a preceding age may be read, but pieces written for a different public will not attract an audience."[7]

What, then, will attract a democratic audience? Tocqueville anticipated the problem when he said, "There are no dramatic subjects in a country which has witnessed no great political catastrophes and in which love invariably leads by a straight and narrow road to matrimony," to which he added, "People who spend every day in the week making money, and Sunday in going to church, have nothing to invite the Muse of Comedy."[8] He suggested, but only in passing, that democratic dramatists would meet this problem by making their productions "more striking, more vulgar, and more true [to democratic experience]," but, considering his prescience, it is strange that he did not anticipate our apparently insatiable appetite for violence and pornography, and, once the censors were put out to pasture, that our dramatists would supply us with a steady stream of it.

That doesn't bother Professor Black. In one place, he suggests that it might make sense to take account of the susceptibility of children by rating some films "unobjectionable for adults." Under this sort of rating system, he says, it would be up to parents to decide whether "youngsters could attend [such] films."[9] But what gives him confidence that parents will be able to make these decisions, or, having made them, be able to enforce them? In our day, when the law is forbidden to make moral judgments—this because the Supreme Court effectively put the censors out of business some twenty-five or thirty years ago—and when, especially in the public schools, students are told that the only self-evident truth is that there is no such thing as truth, and, therefore, that all moral judgments are "relative," our parents will be on their own. In this situation, a dialogue between a father and his teenage son would be likely to go something like this:

> Father: "Your mother and I are going off for the weekend, and we don't want you watching any X-rated videos while we're away."
>
> Son: "Why not? You and Mommy do."
>
> Father: "Well, yes, but they're for adults only. Look at the label."
>
> Son: "But if they're okay for you and Mommy, why can't me and my girlfriend watch them?"
>
> Father: "Well . . . well, because I said so, that's why."
>
> Son: (but *sotto voce*) "Up yours."

Farfetched? Perhaps, but to paraphrase a line from Allan Bloom's *The Closing of the American Mind*, when no one else is seriously concerned with it, parents will lose control over their children's moral education.[10]

The film-rating system has been likened to the warning on cigarette packages, but the analogy is faulty. The latter tells us that cigarettes are bad for children and bad for adults; the former tells us that sex and violence are bad for children but okay for adults, perhaps even good for adults, something children can look forward to when they are "grown up," as we say.

But why should our teenage son have to wait until he is an adult? Unlike his father, he may not yet be capable of earning a living or caring for a family, but, like his father, he is perfectly capable of enjoying an X-rated film. The only reason to deprive him of this pleasure is that, by doing so, he might be prevented from becoming like his father, and this might be done only by declaring that obscenity and pornography (like cigarettes) are bad for father and son alike. This is why the censors preferred the Motion Picture Production Code to a rating system.

According to the code—I'm quoting the 1956 revision—"No picture shall be produced which will lower the moral standards of those who see it." Its specific provisions included the following (and how quaint they seem today!):

> Excessive and inhumane acts of cruelty and brutality shall not be presented. This includes all detailed and protracted presentations of physical violence, torture and abuse. . . . The sanctity of the institution of marriage and the home shall be upheld. No film shall infer that casual or promiscuous sex relationships are the accepted or common thing. . . . Lustful . . . kissing and embraces, suggestive postures and gestures are not to be shown. . . . Complete nudity, in fact, or in silhouette, is never permitted, nor shall there be any licentious notice by characters in the film of suggested nudity.[11]

The prohibitions of the 1950s (and before) have become the standard fare of the present day; the people like it and, with their custom, show their approval of it. With us, as Jean-Jacques Rousseau would have said, vice has taken on the likeness of decency. (What he did say is this: "Vice hardly insinuates itself by shocking decency but by taking on its likeness.")[12]

Does it matter? Some people (typically parents) think so, and occasionally call upon Congress to do something. Before her husband became vice president—in fact, in 1988, before he campaigned for the presidency—even Tipper Gore thought so; see her *Raising PG Kids in an X-Rated Society*.[13] But anyone who believes that the prohibitions might be reimposed today should ponder another of Rousseau's aphorisms: "Censorship can be useful for preserving morals, but never for reestablishing them."[14] As we say, that dog won't hunt.

14

Hail, New Columbia

"No taxation without representation" is a venerable principle. In December 1753, it inspired what we remember as the Boston Tea Party, then, in short order, the Revolution and the nation born in 1776. Surely, one might think, the Constitution of this nation would recognize the claims of the taxpayers resident in its capital city. Are they not, like the residents of the various states, entitled to be represented?

Admittedly, they are not altogether unrepresented now. The District of Columbia has elected city government—mayor, city council, and the rest—and, under the Twenty-third Amendment, its residents are fully represented in the electoral college. But in the national Congress they have, at best, a "virtual" representation—two "shadow senators" and a single "delegate" in the House of Representatives—even though they outnumber the residents of the states of Alaska, Delaware, and Vermont (to say nothing of Wyoming). This situation might be amended only by amending the Constitution, and, as the District's residents were to learn, this is not easily done.

In 1978, an amendment was proposed providing that, "for purposes of representation in Congress . . . the District constituting the seat of government of the United States shall be treated as though it were a State."[1] The amendment bill was approved by the required two-thirds vote in both House and Senate and sent on to the states for their ratification, with the stipulation that this be done within seven years. As it happened, however, only sixteen of the required thirty-eight states ratified the proposed amendment.

Partisan reasons had much to do with this outcome. The Republicans could not have been pleased with the proposal, and while they are as scarce as hens' teeth in the District—in the presidential election of 2004, for example, over 90 percent of the District voters favored the Democrat John Kerry—they are well represented in the various state legislatures. And they had good reason to believe that the adoption of the amendment would give the Democrats two more senators and two or three more members of the House.

But aside from these partisan considerations, the amendment may have failed because it was itself, or was said to be, a violation of the Constitution, specifically, of the clause in article 5 which provides that "no State, without its Consent, shall be deprived of its equal Suffrage in the Senate." This means, or is said to mean, that only states may be represented in the Senate.

I confess that I myself made this argument in testimony before the relevant committee of the House of Representatives. Briefly stated, the argument is that states are (as they originally were) manifestly unequal in wealth, industry, husbandry, virtue and vice, flora and fauna, and, most significantly, size of population. This inequality of states—"their respective numbers"—is duly recognized in the House of Representatives. In what respect are they equal? What is it that entitles them to equal representation in the Senate? The answer is clear: They are equal in their "stateness," a quality not possessed by the District of Columbia. Accordingly, the District may be represented in the Senate only if it is made a state.

The time allotted for ratification of the representation amendment expired in 1985, and, immediately on its expiration, a bill was introduced in Congress proposing another amendment to the Constitution, this one making the District a state, to be called New Columbia. It, too, failed of adoption; in fact, no action was taken on the bill. But there were plans to try again in the new Congress, and, if necessary, the Congress after that.

Who would oppose it? Not the District's residents, a majority of whom gave it their support in a special referendum. Not the city council, which was eager to become a state legislature and, to that end, had declared its readiness to write the required republican constitution. Not the Democrats, in or out of Congress, and not, in his time, President Bill Clinton; he may have kept his daughter out of the District's schools, but he supported its bid for statehood. All those foreign embassies located in the District might have preferred things to remain as they were, but, presumably, the grounds they occupy would, under the laws of New Columbia, retain the same status they then enjoyed under the laws of the United States. So why should they object? This leaves the Republicans. But who among them was likely to say publicly what Senator Edward Kennedy accused some of them of saying privately, namely, that the District is "too liberal, too urban, too black, and too Democratic"? The answer seemed clear: If Alaska, in addition to being too cold, might be said to be too rural, too white (leaving out the Eskimos), and too Republican, why not New Columbia?

Strangely enough, however, the Twenty-third Amendment stands as an obstacle to statehood and will have to be repealed. Until it is, "the District constituting the seat of Government of the United States" will continue to be entitled to three electoral votes, but it will be much reduced in size, so reduced that the number of its residents may not exceed the number of electoral votes. Given the name National Capital Service Area, the new "seat of Government of the United States" will comprise that part of the present District which lies outside the boundaries of the state of New Columbia.

The statehood bill devoted seven pages to defining those boundaries:

> Beginning at the point on the present Virginia-District of Columbia boundary due west of the northernmost point of Theodore Roosevelt Island and running due east of the eastern shore of the Potomac River; thence generally south along the shore at the mean high water mark to the northwest corner of the Kennedy Center; thence east along the north side of the Kennedy Center to a point where it reaches the E Street Expressway; thence east on the expressway to E Street Northwest and thence east on E Street Northwest to Eighteenth Street Northwest . . .[2]

The area thus defined comprises the White House (and Lafayette Square), the District Building (which will give New Columbia the dubious distinction of being the only state whose capitol is located outside its boundaries), the Mall, the Capitol, the Supreme Court, the Library of Congress (except the Annex), and most of the major federal office buildings (but not that part of the Department of Labor building which lies to the west of "Third Street Northwest").

Who lives in this shrunken District? Or, to speak more formally, who are the residents of this National Capital Service Area? George, Laura, and intermittently, Jenna and Barbara Bush, and, stretching the definition of resident, a handful of the itinerant homeless. And who will cast its electoral votes? Since the president is ineligible to serve as an elector—he holds an

"Office of Trust or Profit under the United States"—the three electoral votes will have to be cast by other District residents.[3] Whoever they are—Bushes or homeless—they will have as much power in the choice of a president as the voters in each of seven of the states. While not unconstitutional, this is surely not what the Supreme Court had in mind when it announced the one-man, one-vote rule.

As I said, the Twenty-third Amendment is an obstacle to statehood and would have to be repealed; it is a formidable obstacle because the repealing amendment, like the statehood amendment itself, would require the consent of three-fourths of the states. And that consent is not likely to be forthcoming. In fact, since 1789 and the adoption of the ten amendments comprising the Bill of Rights, only seventeen proposed amendments have won the support of three-fourths of the states.

The only certain way for residents of the District to gain representation in the Congress is to return the District of Columbia to the state of Maryland whence it came. There is precedent for this; that part of the District lying on the west bank of the Potomac was ceded to the federal government by Virginia in 1790 and "retroceded" to it by act of Congress in 1846. Retrocession of the Maryland portion would give the residents of the District all the rights and privileges enjoyed by citizens of Maryland, including representation in the state legislature, and Maryland would gain at least one more member of the federal House of Representatives.

For some reason, and despite the many attractive qualities the District is said to possess, Maryland seems to want no part of it. Perhaps Baltimore, the state's largest and, in many ways, its favored city, sees its position threatened by the absorption of Washington. Or perhaps, with Baltimore, its representatives believe the state has all the problems it can handle.

15

Teaching Patriotism

Back in 1776, Tom Paine said that commerce "diminishes" the spirit of patriotism, and we are the most commercial of peoples. Yet we are also one of the most patriotic; every public opinion survey shows this to be a fact. Not only that, but our patriotism is anything but selfish or parochial; Lincoln had this in mind when he said that we were "the last, best hope of earth." This was true in 1862 when he said it, and it is more obviously true today. Like it or not (and it is something of a burden), our lot is to be the one essential country—the one country with the power to defend liberal democracy against its enemies—and this ought to be acknowledged, beginning in our schools and universities, for it is only then that we can come to accept the responsibilities attending it. We owe it to our friends, as well as to ourselves, to be patriotic.

The word itself comes from the Latin *patria*, meaning country, and patriotism implies a love of country and a readiness to sacrifice for it, perhaps even to give one's life for it. This was well understood in the countries (or cities) of classical antiquity, especially in Sparta, where the words "citizen" and "patriot" were essentially synonymous. Thus, in the Spartan sense, patriots are citizens who love their country simply because it is their country—because it is "their birthplace and the mansion of their fathers," as Alexis de Tocqueville puts it in his famous *Democracy in America*.[1] Citizenship and patriotism were one and the same in Sparta; it was a kind of filial piety. But America is no Sparta.

Spartans were a homogeneous people, descended from the same ancestors, few in number, and inhabiting an area smaller than the District of Columbia. But we are many, not few—even in our beginning our numbers were many times those of Sparta—and we are no longer, if we ever were, a people descended from the same ancestors. In principle, whereas no stranger could become a Spartan, anybody can become an American, and millions of people from around the world have done so; this helps to explain why that patriotic word "fatherland" has no place in our vocabulary. Unlike Sparta in so many respects, we are, nevertheless, alike in our need of citizens who love this country and are willing to fight for it.

Citizenship for us has, first of all, a legal meaning. According to section 1 of the Fourteenth Amendment of the Constitution, a citizen is any person "born or naturalized in the United States, and subject to the jurisdiction thereof." But citizenship is, or is supposed to be, more than legal status and the enjoyment of the "privileges or immunities" attached thereto; in its larger sense, it is a sentiment or state of mind, an awareness of sharing an identity with others to whom one is related by nationality, if not by blood, a sense of belonging to a community for which one bears some responsibility. In a word, citizenship implies public-spiritedness, which is akin to patriotism, and has to be cultivated.

Both have to be cultivated because no one is born loving his country; such love is not natural, but has to be somehow taught or acquired. A person may not even be born loving himself—the authorities differ on this—but he soon enough learns to do so, and, unless something is done about it, he will continue to do so, and in a manner that makes a concern for country or fellow countrymen—or anyone other than himself—difficult or impossible to have. The problem is as old as politics, and no country is exempt from having to deal with it, but, for reasons having to do with our democratic principles, it could be especially difficult for us. To paraphrase a line from Abraham Lincoln's 1862 message to Congress, our case was new, so we had to think and act anew.

According to the motto inscribed on the Great Seal of the United States (and reproduced on every dollar bill), we are a *novus ordo seclorum*, which is to say, a new order of the ages. We were the first nation to declare our independence by appealing not to the past but to the newly discovered "Laws of Nature and of Nature's God," and this had (and has) consequences for patriotism. Whereas the God of Abraham, Isaac, and Jacob imposed duties on men (see Exodus 20:1–17), "Nature's God" endowed all men with rights, private rights; and, whereas the God of the Bible commanded all men to love God and their neighbors as themselves (see, for example, Matthew 22:37–40), "Nature's God" created a state of nature in which everyone was expected to take care of himself and, as John Locke said, take care of others only "when his own preservation comes not in competition."[2] And so long as he remains in the state of nature, he has the right to do what he is naturally inclined to do, and what he is naturally inclined to do is not to take care of others. To say the least, he is not naturally inclined to be a patriotic citizen.

It is, of course, true that a person is required to surrender his natural rights when leaving the state of nature—except the few unalienable ones, the surrender of which would contradict the very purpose of the flight from nature—but in exchange, as it were, he gains the security that only government can provide. For example, the Constitution makes it clear that he cannot be deprived of life, liberty, or property without "due process of law." As John Jay says in *Federalist* 2, "Nothing is more certain than the indispensable necessity of government, and it is equally undeniable that whenever and however it is instituted, the people must cede to it some of their natural rights, in order to vest it with requisite powers." Nevertheless, it remains true with us that rights are primary and duties are secondary and derivative. Designing a public-spirit curriculum for such a people is no easy task. Yet, according to the public opinion surveys, we are one of the most patriotic of peoples, more patriotic than the British, for example, or the Canadians, Swedes, Norwegians, Germans, Dutch, and Czechs, to say nothing of the French.[3] What accounts for this?

In *Making Patriots*, I wrote that the connection between war and patriotism, or better, between war and the making of patriots, is evident, perhaps even self-evident. I was speaking there of the Athenians and Spartans at the time of the Peloponnesian War, but, of course, I was thinking not only of them or of that time. The book itself is about making American patriots, or making patriots of Americans, and it was to be expected that I should be asked repeatedly—at a book forum, on radio and television, and privately by friends—whether I thought a war was required to make us patriots.

My answer then was a qualified no, but only so long as we remember past wars. To help us remember, we have a Memorial Day (Decoration Day, when I was young), a Flag Day, and the Lincoln, Vietnam, Korean, and World War II memorials. To the same end, we have national cemeteries filled with the graves of patriots, and a national anthem composed during, and reminding us of, a long-past war. This nation was born in an earlier war, and Abraham Lincoln referred to the men who fought it as "the patriots of seventy-six."⁴ Born British subjects, and living in thirteen separate British colonies, we became "one people" in 1776; we said so in our Declaration of Independence. We were made one because George III and our erstwhile British brethren were "deaf to the voice of justice and of consanguinity."

What the British did to rally American patriotism in 1776, the terrorists did on September 11, 2001. The signs of this are everywhere. It was only a few years ago that a divided Supreme Court held that Americans were entitled to burn the flag, that they had a constitutional right to do so. But no one is burning the flag these days (probably because it is no longer illegal to do so). Instead, millions of Americans are flying it, from their front porches and balconies, on their automobiles and the antennas of battered pickup trucks, even wearing it on their lapels. Flying the flag—the people seemed to know this intuitively—is the readiest way to demonstrate their love of country, and their pride in being Americans.

Not only that but, told it was in short supply, they rushed to give their blood, and to the scene of devastation in New York with food, blankets, masks of some sort, whatever they thought was needed. They grieved for those who had lost their lives, and some of them prayed for the bereaved left behind: the heroic police and firemen, and, especially, because it was not their job to do so, those passengers on United Airlines Flight 93 who gave their lives to prevent the plane from going on to Washington, there to destroy the White House or, worse, the citadel of our representative democracy, the Capitol on the hill. And for the relief of those left behind they donated prodigious sums. It was as if they remembered what the Apostle Paul said in his Epistle to the Romans, "We are members one of another."⁵

They had reason to believe this. The terrorists did not discriminate; they killed us all: black, white, and every shade between; rich and poor, investment bankers and blue-collar police and firemen; old and young; liberals and conservatives; Christian, Jew, Muslim, and "infidel"; some foreigners, as we soon learned, but all the others Americans, *unhyphenated* Americans—fellow citizens, if not personal friends or immediate neighbors.

There was no more talk of us and them, as in our usual political discourse; the only "them" were the terrorists. They surely did not intend it—and, I trust, will come to regret it—but by attacking us, intending to destroy us, they launched an unprecedented swell of patriotic sentiment among us. There was nothing like it during the years of Korea, Vietnam, or the Gulf War, and, although old enough, I cannot remember anything like it after Pearl Harbor. Not then did crowds gather in the streets or at ballgames shouting, "USA, USA, USA!"

Not all of us feel this way. For no good reason, there are Americans— mostly professors and New York intellectuals—who are inclined to despise rather than to love this country. For evidence of this, we need only to read the press. Looking down from their own Mount Olympus, they say, and this is the least of what they say, that only the bourgeois and right-wing fanatics wave the flag. We might ignore this, except that it is said by persons held in high esteem by the general public, and whose opinions, therefore, carry weight. Andy Warhol once said that "nothing is more bourgeois than to be afraid to look bourgeois."[6] If so, if it is a bourgeois thing to wave the flag, this may explain why some Americans are—or were—embarrassed to wave it, or otherwise to express their love of this country. Whatever its cause, this inhibition was obviously removed by the events of September 11. It turned out that there is patriotism enough in this country, and the people only needed an occasion to express it.

There is no denying that patriotism can be a problem; it can be misguided or a blind nationalism. This is why Aristotle refused to number it among the virtues along with justice, friendship, and courage, for example. But our patriotism is neither misguided or blind, nor is it a Spartan my-country-right-or-wrong patriotism. Ours was best described by Lincoln in his eulogy on Henry Clay. Clay, he said, "loved his country partly because it was his own country, but mostly because it was a free country, and he burned with a zeal for its advancement, prosperity and glory, because he saw in such, the advancement, prosperity and glory, of human liberty, human right, and human nature."[7] The American patriot is devoted to his country, of course, but he is also devoted to universal principles respecting the rights of man.

The twofold character of American patriotism is evident in our Pledge of Allegiance. We pledge allegiance to "the flag of the United States of America, and to the Republic for which it stands." The republic, in turn, stands not only for our country but for those principles, the principles expressed by Henry Clay, and, before him, by "the patriots of seventy-six"—

namely, that all men, not just Americans, are endowed by their Creator with certain "unalienable Rights," and that government is instituted "to secure these rights." In 1776 we declared our right to form a new nation by appealing to these principles, and, because we were the first to do so, it fell to us to be their champion, first by setting an example—Lincoln was ever mindful of this—and subsequently by defending them against their latter-day enemies, the Nazis and fascists in World War II and the Communists in the Cold War. Like it or not, America is the one essential country, the model as well as the arsenal of democracy.

The terrorists understand this, which is why they hate us (especially us) and want to destroy us. Our existence is a threat to them precisely because it gives hope to the oppressed people of the wretched and undemocratic lands from which they come. They hate us because we are a free country, a country that guarantees freedom of speech, freedom of association, freedom of enterprise, and—the freedom that best distinguishes us from the countries harboring the terrorists—freedom of conscience. This country is, as Lincoln said it was, "the last, best hope of earth."

He said this in his annual message to Congress in December 1862. He said much the same thing, but this time with supporting argument, in August 1864, when speaking—extemporaneously—to an Ohio regiment being disbanded and returning home:

> I almost always feel inclined, when I happen to say anything to soldiers, to impress upon them in a few brief remarks the importance of success in this contest. It is not merely for to-day, but for all time to come that we should perpetuate for our children's children this great and free government, which we have enjoyed all our lives. I beg you to remember this, not merely for my sake, but for yours. I happen temporarily to occupy this big White House. I am a living witness that any one of your children may look to come here as my father's child did. It is in order that each of you may have through this free government which we have enjoyed, an open field and a fair chance for your industry, enterprise, and intelligence, that you may all have equal privileges in the race of life, with all its desirable human aspirations. It is for this [that] the struggle should be maintained, that we may not lose our

birthright—not only for one, but for two or three years. The nation is worth fighting for, to secure such an inestimable jewel.[8]

When I was a schoolboy, we were expected to memorize Lincoln's words. Not those addressed to the soldiers, of course, but the 272 words of the Gettysburg Address, and the final paragraphs of his first and second inaugurals. And we had at least heard about his famous letter to Mrs. Bixby (which played a role in the recent film *Saving Private Ryan*), and we would have known what he was talking about when he referred to the "patriots of seventy-six." Our teachers—beginning in what grade, I cannot remember— thought it essential that we should be familiar with American history, and should respect, indeed honor, the men and women who made it, beginning with the Founders who declared our independence and wrote the Constitution.

Although it has been amended, formally as well as by judicial interpretation, the Constitution written in 1787 has ordered the affairs of this nation for more than two hundred years. We have become so accustomed to it that we might take its longevity for granted, but it is, in fact, remarkable, especially when compared with the experience of other peoples.

In a world where constitutions come and go with almost seasonal regularity, we have reason to wonder why ours has lasted so long, or to what we can attribute our good fortune. Various reasons account for it. In the first place, unlike France, we did not have to contend with a sullen nobility, dispossessed by a revolution of its property and privileges but not of its hopes to regain them. (Tocqueville had this in mind when he said that "the great advantage of the Americans is that they arrived at a state of democracy without having to endure a democratic revolution, and that they [were] born equal instead of becoming so.")[9] Then, unlike Poland, for example, we were not surrounded by powerful neighbors with hostile intentions; and we began, as John Jay said in *Federalist* 2, as a people speaking the same language (unlike Belgium), "professing the same religion" (unlike the former Yugoslavia), "attached to the same principles of government" (unlike France and Spain), and "very similar in their manners and customs" (unlike Canada). Jay exaggerated our unity, but his general point is valid. And, finally, we were more fortunate in our Founders. Many British colonies (to say nothing of others) have declared their independence since 1776—for example, Nigeria, Egypt, and Canada—but none can boast of men like George Washington, Thomas Jefferson, John Adams, James Madison, Alexander Hamilton, Benjamin Franklin, James Wilson, and others too numerous to mention. Again, we were fortunate.

Before vaunting our success, however, we should acknowledge that we came close to failing. We prevailed, and continue to exist as a nation "conceived in Liberty, and dedicated to the proposition that all men are created equal," only because Lincoln, who spoke these words at Gettysburg, insisted that we fight and win the Civil War. It proved to be the deadliest of our wars, but it was also the most necessary; at stake was the meaning of the Declaration of Independence. Like Lincoln, the Confederates appealed to it, but they insisted that its principle respecting the natural equality of all men did not apply to black people; worse, given their reading of the Declaration, the Confederates had no alternative but to say blacks were not human beings. Thus, to allow the South to secede from the Union, and to recognize its *right* to secede, would render the principle meaningless. And other peoples, beginning with their rulers, would draw this conclusion.

Lincoln saved the Union, and as the best of his biographers (Lord Charnwood) says, "Nobody else could have done it." By saving it, many good things were made possible, not the least of them being the abolition of slavery. This was something the Founders were unable to do.

It has become the custom, especially in academic circles, to denounce the Founders as hypocrites, who spoke ill of slavery but did nothing to put an end to it. Yet, it should be noted that no form of the word "slave" appears in their Constitution; in each case the word employed is "person" or "persons." Frederick Douglass, the one-time slave (who became one of the great men of his generation) understood the significance of this perfectly. He held that the government established under the Constitution was, "in its essence," an anti-slavery government. "Abolish slavery tomorrow, and not a sentence or syllable of the Constitution need be altered," he said.

> It was purposely so framed as to give no claim, no sanction to the claim, of property in a man. If in its origin slavery had any relation to the government, it was only as the scaffolding to the magnificent structure, to be removed as soon as the building was completed.[10]

By "scaffolding," Douglass meant the three constitutional provisions addressed to the slavery question: the provision in article 1, section 2, clause 3, whereby the southern states were allowed to count three of their five slaves for purposes of representation in the House of Representatives; the one in article 1, section 9, allowing them, for twenty years, to import more slaves from abroad; and, finally, the one in article 4, section 2, clause 3, providing for the return of fugitive slaves. These concessions to slavery, demanded by the southern states, were the original price of union, and the Framers of the Constitution did indeed pay that price—and to this day have been criticized for doing so—but they paid it grudgingly, out of what they thought was necessity. Anyone who says the price was too high is obliged to argue that the lot of the slaves would have been better if the southern states had been allowed to form (as in 1860–61 they did form) their own pro-slavery confederation.

It has also become the custom, in some circles, to accuse the Founders of being sexists. But, again, the words of the Founders' Constitution lend no support for this charge. The terms used throughout the document are, in addition to "person" and "persons," "electors," "citizens," "members," "inhabitants," "officers," and "representatives." There are pronouns—"he," "his," "himself"—but, as my colleague Robert A. Goldwin has pointed out, "There is not a single noun or adjective that denotes sex."[11] Frederick Douglass pointed out that slavery could have been abolished without changing a word or syllable of the Constitution (and not a word had to be changed before Thurgood Marshall could be made a justice of the Supreme Court, or might have been elected president). So, too, not a word had to be changed before women could vote, and in some places did vote, even before the Nineteenth Amendment (which merely *protects* the right to vote); and not a word had to be changed before Sandra Day O'Connor could be made a justice of the Supreme Court, or might be elected president.

One other point about the Founders' Constitution: Its article 6, section 3, says that "no religious test shall ever be required as a qualification to any office or public trust under the United States." Anyone—Christian, Jew, Muslim, or infidel (and European, Chinese, Arab, Polynesian, or whatever)— provided he satisfies the age and nationality requirements, might become president. To borrow a phrase from the (Episcopal) Book of Common Prayer, America is a haven "for all sorts and conditions of men" (and women), all of them with a right to pursue happiness as they themselves define it. No other country in 1776 could have made that claim, and very few (and none of our enemies) can make it now.

I devoted chapters of my book *Making Patriots* to the education that schoolchildren used to receive, to Lincoln, the greatest of our teachers, and to his colleague in the greatest of our struggles, Frederick Douglass. My purpose was to remind my readers that this country deserves citizens who love and honor it, and are prepared to defend it.

Especially after the events of September 11, it is appropriate that schoolchildren be taught the history of this country—and not be taught that all cultures are equal, that the greatest sin is to be judgmental, that our Founders were contemptible, that our history is nothing but a history of suppression of blacks, women, and American Indians. They should also— this is surely the time for it—be encouraged to read political biographies, of Washington, Jefferson, Adams, Madison, Hamilton, and especially of Lincoln; then, having acquired a taste for biographies, go on as adults to read those of Webster, Clay, and Calhoun; of Roosevelt and Wilson; of Truman and the second Roosevelt. Perhaps, then, all our citizens—young and old—can learn to appreciate the birthright Lincoln spoke of, and to understand better what he meant by this "inestimable jewel."

16

Religion and the Death Penalty

The best case for the death penalty—or, at least, the best explanation of it—was made, paradoxically, by one of the most famous of its opponents, Albert Camus, the French novelist, playwright, and World War II Resistance hero. Others complained of the alleged unusual cruelty of the death penalty, or insisted that it was not, as claimed, a better deterrent of murder than, say, life imprisonment, and Americans especially complained of the manner in which it was imposed by judge or jury (discriminatorily or capriciously, for example), and sometimes on the innocent.

Camus said all this and more, and what he said in addition is instructive. The death penalty, he said, "can be legitimized only by a truth or a principle that is superior to man," or, as he then made clearer, it may rightly be imposed only by a religious society or community, specifically, one that believes in "eternal life."[1] Only in such a place can it be said that the death sentence provides the guilty person with the opportunity (and reminds him of the reason) to make amends, thus to prepare himself for the final judgment which will be made in the world to come. For this reason, he said, the Catholic Church "has always accepted the necessity of the death penalty." This may no longer be the case. And it may no longer be the case that death is, as Camus said it has always been, a religious penalty. But it can be said that the death penalty is more likely to be imposed by a religious people.

The reasons for this are not obvious. It may be that the religious know what evil is or, at least, *that* it is, and, unlike the irreligious are not so ready to believe that evil can be explained, and thereby excused, by a history of child abuse or, say, a post-traumatic stress disorder or a temporal lobe seizure. Or, again unlike the irreligious, and probably without having read so much as a word of his argument, they may be morally disposed (or better, predisposed) to agree with the philosopher Immanuel Kant—that greatest of the moralists—who said it was a "categorical imperative" that a convicted murderer "must die."[2] Or perhaps the religious are simply quicker to anger and, while instructed to do otherwise, slower, even unwilling, to forgive. In a word, they are more likely to demand that justice be done. Whatever the reason, there is surely a connection between the death penalty and religious belief.

European politicians and journalists recognize or acknowledge the connection, if only inadvertently, when they simultaneously despise us for supporting the death penalty and ridicule us for going to church. We might draw a conclusion from the fact that they do neither. Consider the facts on the ground (so to speak): In this country, sixty-five convicted murderers were executed in 2003 (and fifty-seven in 2004), almost all of them in southern or southwestern and churchgoing states—Virginia and Georgia, for example, Texas and Oklahoma—states whose residents include the most numerous of deeply religious Americans.[3] Whereas in Europe, or "Old Europe," no one was executed and, according to one survey, almost no one—and certainly no *soi-disant* intellectual—goes to church, leaving, in Shakespeare's words, the "bare ruined choirs, where late the sweet birds sang."[4]

As for the death penalty, it is not enough to say that they (or their officials) are opposed to it. They want it abolished everywhere. They are not satisfied that it was abolished in France (in 1981, and over the opposition of some two-thirds of the population), as well as in Britain, Germany, and the other countries of "Old Europe," or that—according to a protocol attached to the European Convention on Human Rights—it will have to be abolished in any country seeking membership in the European Union; and its abolition in Samoa was greeted by an official declaration expressing Europe's satisfaction.[5] (To paraphrase Shakespeare's Hamlet, "What is Samoa to them or they to Samoa that they should judge for it?") In fact, their concern, if not their authority, extends far beyond the countries for which they are legally responsible.

Thus, the European Union adopted a charter confirming everyone's right to life and stating that "no one may be removed, expelled, or extradited to a State where there is a serious risk that he or she would be subjected to the death penalty."[6] They even organized a World Congress Against the Death Penalty which, in turn, organized the first World Day

Against the Death Penalty. They go so far as to intervene in our business, filing *amicus curiae* briefs in Supreme Court capital cases.[7]

What explains this obsession with the death penalty? Hard to say, but probably because abolishing it is one of the few things Europeans can do that makes them feel righteous; in fact, very few. They are now engaged in ratifying a new European constitution, and nowhere in this document— some three hundred pages long, not counting the appendages—is there any mention of religion, of Christian Europe, of God. God is dead in Europe and, of course, something died with him.

This "something" is the subject of Camus's famous novel, *The Stranger*, first published in 1942, sixty years after Nietzsche first announced God's death, and another sixty before the truth of what he said became apparent, at least with respect to Europe and its intellectuals. (As one of them said, and he claimed to be speaking for all Europeans, "Religion is the strangest and most disturbing feature about" America.)[8] The novel has been called a modern masterpiece—there was a time, and not so long ago, when students of a certain age were required to read it—and Meursault, its hero (actually, its antihero), is a murderer, but a different kind of murderer. What is different about him is that he murdered for no reason—he did it because the sun got in his eyes, *à cause du soleil*—and because he neither loves nor hates, and unlike the other people who inhabit his world, does not pretend to love or hate. He has no friends; indeed, he lives in a world in which there is no basis for friendship and no moral law; therefore, no one, not even a murderer, can violate the terms of friendship or break that law. The universe is benignly indifferent to how he lives.

It is a bleak picture, and Camus was criticized for painting it, but, as he wrote in reply, "There is no other life possible for a man deprived of God, and all men are [now] in that position."[9] But Camus was not the first European to draw this picture; he was preceded by Nietzsche who (in Zarathustra's "Prologue") provided us with an account of human life in that godless and "brave new world." It will be a comfortable world—rather like that promised by the European Union—where men will "have their little pleasures for the day, and their little pleasures for the night," but no love, no longing, no striving, no hope, no gods or ideals, no politics ("too burdensome"), no passions (especially no anger), only "a regard for health."[10] To this list, Camus rightly added, no death penalty.

This makes sense. A world so lacking in passion lacks the necessary components of punishment. Punishment has its origins in the demand for justice, and justice is demanded by angry, morally indignant men, men who are angry when someone else is robbed, raped, or murdered, men utterly unlike Camus's Meursault. This anger is an expression of their caring, and the just society needs citizens who care for each other, and for the community of which they are parts. One of the purposes of punishment, particularly capital punishment, is to recognize the legitimacy of that righteous anger and to satisfy and thereby to reward it. In this way, the death penalty, when duly or deliberately imposed, serves to strengthen the moral sentiments required by a self-governing community.

17

Under God

On March 24, 2004, the Supreme Court heard arguments in still another of what civil libertarians insist on calling establishment-of-religion cases, *Elk Grove Unified School District v. Newdow.*[1] While the previous cases dealt with school prayers, for example, or public religious instruction, or the public display of a creche or the Ten Commandments, this one had to do with the words "under God" in the Pledge of Allegiance.

Were it not for the law of these previous cases, this one could have been easily disposed of. The Court could have decided for the school district on the merits, confident that only the most zealous and unrelenting of libertarians would be likely to object. No one is required to make the pledge or utter the word God, and it is hard to believe that, as the plaintiff alleged, his daughter was somehow injured when hearing her classmates utter it. After all, the name of God is invoked on various public occasions by, or in the presence of, presidents, governors, members of Congress, even Supreme Court justices, and no one seems to be any the worse for it. So why may it not be uttered by schoolchildren when pledging allegiance?

The Court could also have sent the case back to the lower court with instructions to dismiss, on the ground that the plaintiff, Michael A. Newdow, lacked standing to sue and, therefore, the court had no jurisdiction because, constitutionally, there was no case. Newdow originally claimed to represent his daughter, of course, but in a formal custody hearing, the girl's mother (and *not* Newdow's wife) was awarded legal custody of the girl and the right to represent her interests, and she is on record as saying that "neither [she] nor her daughter objects to saying the Pledge."

In fact, the justices decided that Newdow lacked standing to bring suit. Instead, they might have seized the opportunity—the best they had had—to correct a pair of mistakes, dating back to the 1940s, when the

155

Court held that the First Amendment prohibited the states (as well as the national government) from making any law "respecting an establishment of religion."

Previously, everyone having anything to do with the subject understood that the prohibitions of the First Amendment did not apply to the states. This was not an oversight on the part of the men who wrote or ratified the amendment; on the contrary, they expected the states to be concerned with the moral character of the people and, to this end, would provide the young with religious instruction of some sort. In a word, the states would do, and would have to do, what the national government was forbidden to do.

There was a general agreement about this. For example, the same First Congress that forbade the national government to make any law respecting an establishment of religion also adopted an ordinance for the governance of the Northwest Territory which provided (in article 3) that "religion, morality, and knowledge being necessary to good government and the happiness of mankind, schools and the means of education shall forever be encouraged," and (in article 5) that the states to be formed out of the territory—these proved to be Ohio, Indiana, Michigan, Illinois, and Wisconsin—"shall be republican, and in conformity to the principles contained in these articles."[2] But the states needed no such encouragement; they took it for granted that religion was "necessary to good government," especially republican government, and, with that in mind, made it a part of the public school curriculum even as they established those schools. And so it remained, more or less, until the Supreme Court put an end to it in one of the cases decided in the 1940s. Prior to that time, it went without saying that schoolchildren, in the course of pledging allegiance, might be encouraged to utter the words "under God."

What is of interest in these 1940 cases, aside from the judgments rendered and the specious arguments used to support them, is the heedless manner in which they were decided. Not one of the Supreme Court justices gave any thought, *any* thought whatsoever, to the connection, or even the possibility of a connection, between religious training and the sort of citizen required by a self-governing republic. They simply did not address the issue, as if the cases being decided had nothing to do with it, or as if it were of no importance. They would have us believe that Jefferson was speaking for its authors—but he obviously was not—when he wrote to the Danbury Baptists that the First Amendment built "a wall of separation between church and state."[3] (Two days after issuing this letter [Sunday, January 3, 1802], Jefferson attended church services *in the House of Representatives* and heard the Baptist John Leland preach the sermon.) Indeed, one of them (Justice Wiley B. Rutledge) went so far as to say that the purpose of the First Amendment "was to create a complete and permanent separation of the spheres of religious activity and civil authority by comprehensively forbidding every form of public aid or support for religion."[4] Unless he intended deliberately to deceive, no one with any knowledge of our history could have written this.

As a consequence of these decisions, moral education, which had always been understood to be partly a public responsibility, was now held to be exclusively a private one, to be performed, in part, by the churches, but mostly by the parents in the home. Presumably, they will want to teach their children "values," as we now say, but, if so, they will get little help from the law.

At the oral argument, Michael Newdow, appearing for himself, demonstrated that the law of the Constitution favored him, that the Court could not decide for the school district without overruling the previous establishment cases—which is to say (but of course he did not say this), without returning to the correct understanding or meaning of the establishment clause; and this the Court refused to do. Instead, it held that he lacked standing to bring the suit. Nothing would be gained by explaining how the Court's majority reached that judgment; it is enough that I quote the chief justice who, with Justices O'Connor and Thomas, said, "The Court today erects a novel prudential standing principle in order to avoid reaching the merits of the constitutional claim." As he put it, the Court's holding is like the "proverbial excursion ticket—good for this day only."[5]

He is, of course, right about this. What Michael Newdow might not do, other self-styled (and self-righteous) "atheists" will be allowed to do—in fact, will be encouraged to do—and the issue will soon be before the Court again. There will then be no avoiding the constitutional issue, and it is likely that at least some members of the Court will, as Thomas said, take the opportunity to "begin the process of rethinking the Establishment Clause," and, in the process, reverse errors of long standing.[6]

Addendum

1. In the debates in the First Congress, James Madison offered an amendment to the speech and religious clause that would have applied its prohibitions to the states, as well as to the national government. His amendment was adopted in the House (where he served) but was defeated in the Senate.

2. Then, in 1876, Senator James Blaine, at the behest of President Ulysses S. Grant, proposed a somewhat similar amendment. This, too, passed in the House and went down to defeat in the Senate, coming up one vote short of the required two-thirds majority. But what Madison could not do in 1789, or Blaine and Grant in 1876, a divided Supreme Court, without so much as a by-your-leave, effectively did in the 1940s.

3. Quite apart from whether it applies to the states, the establishment clause was not intended to prohibit such practices as public references to God. As the chief justice said in his separate opinion in the Newdow case, "Examples of patriotic invocations of God and official acknowledgments of religion's role in our Nation's history abound."[7] He then mentioned a number of them.

18

What Does the Constitution
Expect of Jews?

The short answer to this question is that the Constitution expects of Jews what it expects of everybody. George Washington expressed this perfectly in his famous (and very familiar) response of August 17, 1790, to the Hebrew Congregation of Newport, Rhode Island:

> It is now no more that toleration is spoken of as if it was by the indulgence of one class of people that another enjoyed the exercise of their inherent natural rights. For happily the Government of the United States, which gives to bigotry no sanction, to persecution no assistance requires only that they who live under its protection should demean themselves as good citizens, in giving it on all occasions their effectual support. . . . May the Children of the Stock of Abraham, who dwell in this land, continue to merit and enjoy the good will of the other Inhabitants; while every one shall sit in safety under his own vine and figtree and there shall be none to make him afraid.[1]

All that is required of us, Jew and Christian alike, is a pledge of allegiance to Americanism, as Martin Diamond used to say, to the flag of the United States and "to the republic for which it stands."

The principle involved here is not that of the English Toleration Act of 1689 which, according to Thomas Babington Macaulay, "recognized persecution as the rule, and granted liberty of conscience only as the exception."[2] Here liberty of conscience is the rule, not an indulgence or a privilege granted to certain minorities. As Thomas Jefferson said in what became

159

the Virginia Statute for Religious Freedom, "Our civil rights have no dependence on our religious opinions, any more than our opinions in physics or geometry."[3] Liberty of conscience, he went on, is one of the "natural rights of mankind," and under a government instituted "to secure these rights," there are no religious minorities, because there is no recognized religious majority.[4]

Indeed, the Constitution speaks not of Christian and Jew, but of "persons" (and "Indians, not taxed"), and emphasizes its neutrality by providing in article 6 that "no religious Test shall ever be required as a Qualification to any Office or public Trust under the United States." Persons of any religious persuasion—Jews, Turks, infidels, and (to speak the frequently voiced prejudice of the time) even "Papists"—are eligible to become citizens and to hold office under this Constitution. And, in principle at least, what the Constitution expects of one group it expects of all, no more and no less.

But that, of course, is the simple view of the matter, as Alexander Hamilton once said on another subject.[5] In 1776 we declared ourselves a nation, and a new order of the ages, by invoking "the Laws of Nature and of Nature's God," but we continued to acknowledge the biblical God of our fathers; unlike the French revolutionists who were shortly to follow us, we made no effort to obliterate every vestige of what we had been. Unlike the French, we did not revise the calendar to rid it of every element of religious tradition—beginning the year at the autumnal equinox, rather than January 1 (the day on which the church celebrated the Feast of Circumcision), replacing the seven-day week of the Bible with a "decade" of ten days, giving the months new names drawn from nature and related to the seasons (Vintage, Mist, Frost, Snow, Rain, Wind, Seedtime, Blossom, Meadow, Harvest, Heat, and Fruits), celebrating not holidays (or holy days) but festivals named Virtue, Genius, Labor, Opinion, Rewards (and, in the leap year, the Festival of the Revolution), and, finally, designating 1792, the year of the first republican constitution, Year One. Napoleon put an end to this nonsense on the tenth of Snow, year fifteen, or on what we call the first of January, 1806.

Unlike, as I say, the French, the Americans of 1787 expressed no overt hostility to religion in general or Christianity in particular. Article 7 of the Constitution marked the occasion in a traditional and quite undramatic fashion: "Done in Convention, by the Unanimous Consent of the States present, the Seventeenth Day of September, in the Year of our Lord one thousand seven hundred and Eighty seven, and of the Independence of the United States of America the Twelfth."

What does the Constitution expect of Jews? What it expects of everybody. Among other things, it expects them to reckon the years from the birth of Jesus, and, in addition, and for one purpose at least, to recognize Sunday as the Sabbath. "If," reads a portion of the veto provision in article 1, section 7, "any Bill shall not be returned by the President within ten days (Sundays excepted) after it shall have been presented to him, the Same shall be a Law, in like Manner as if he had signed it, unless the Congress by their Adjournment prevent its Return, in which Case it shall not be a Law." America is not, as the Supreme Court once said it was, "a Christian nation," not officially; America is a country inhabited mainly by Christians, and in certain respects it is easier for Christians to live here.[6] They can more readily accommodate themselves to its ways—these two constitutional references serve to remind us of that—because in the determining of those ways it is inevitable that religious opinions carry more weight than do "opinions in physics or geometry."[7]

This was especially true at the beginning. Like the Constitution of the United States, most of the early state constitutions recognized the principle of liberty of conscience, but they also required oaths of office that only Christians could honestly take. Here, for example, is Delaware's: "I, A. B., do profess faith in God the Father, and in Jesus Christ His Son, and in the Holy Ghost, one God, blessed for evermore; and I do acknowledge the Holy Scriptures of the Old and New Testament to be given by divine inspiration."[8] A similar provision in the constitution of Pennsylvania caused the Jews of the city ("who are but few in number") to protest in 1793 that they, too, were patriots, that they, too, had "suffered for their attachment to the Revolution principles," and that "this religious test deprives [them] of the eminent rights of freemen, solemnly ascertained to all men who are not professed atheists."[9]

And unlike the Constitution of the United States, most of the early state constitutions, in one way or another, spoke of the necessity of morality or civic virtue and its dependence on some form of religious education. They encouraged religion, and indeed were encouraged by Congress to do so.

Here is article 3 of the Northwest Ordinance, adopted by the Continental Congress on July 13, 1787, and readopted by the First Congress, under the new Constitution, on August 7, 1789: "Religion, Morality and knowledge being necessary to good government and the happiness of mankind, Schools and the means of education shall forever be encouraged."[10] Should, that is, be encouraged by the states that would in due course be organized in that territory—Ohio, Michigan, Indiana, Illinois, Wisconsin, and part of Minnesota.

As I have indicated, most of the original states were already doing this; they needed no encouragement from Congress. Religion was a private matter, Maryland said in its Declaration of Rights, which meant that "no person ought by any law to be molested in his persuasion of profession, or for his religious practice"—so long, one might say, as he practiced religion, for, as that same article begins, "It is the duty [note: the *duty*] of every man to worship God in such a manner as he thinks most acceptable to him."[11]

Such statements were typical, and so, at the time, was the tendency to identify religion with Christianity. Under the Massachusetts constitution of 1780, "all men" had the right—as well as the *duty*—to worship as they pleased; and to facilitate the performance of that duty, the "several towns, parishes, precincts, and other bodies-politic" were expected to provide, "at their own expense," for the public worship of God and the support of "teachers ['*Protestant* teachers'] of piety, religion, and morality." In addition, the constitution guaranteed the protection of the law to "every denomination of Christians."[12]

But even at the state level there was little overt hostility to Jews. During the ratification debates in North Carolina, the Reverend David Caldwell complained that by prohibiting religious tests, the federal Constitution issued an invitation to "Jews and pagans of every kind to come among us," and he feared that at some future time "this might endanger the character of the United States."[13] But he was reassured by Governor Samuel Johnston that although it was possible that "Jews, pagans, etc." might emigrate to the United States, their numbers would not be "in proportion to the emigration of Christians." Besides, he went on, "In all probability, the children even of such people would be[come] Christians."[14] And Pennsylvania was more than willing not only to tolerate but to accommodate its Jewish citizens. In

1790, a mere seven years after the Jews of Philadelphia had issued their protest against it, the Trinitarian oath requirement was replaced in the new state constitution with a declaration to the effect "that no person, who acknowledges the being of a God and a future state of rewards and punishments, shall, on account of his religious sentiments, be disqualified to hold any office or place of trust or profit under his commonwealth."[15]

One historian of the subject, Morton Borden, says that by 1788 Jews had achieved toleration, but there is evidence that more than toleration was at work even then.[16] Speaking that year in the Massachusetts ratification debates, the Reverend Mr. Shute said this:

> Far from limiting my charity and confidence to men of my own denomination in religion, I suppose, and I believe, sir, that there are worthy characters among men of every denomination— among the Quakers, the Baptists, the Church of England, the Papists; and even among those who have no other guide, in the way to virtue and heaven, than the dictates of natural religion.[17]

And what was at work had little or nothing to do with Jews, who, in the event, numbered a mere two thousand in a total population (in 1790) of just short of four million.

What was at work was the right of liberty of conscience—and liberty of conscience meant equality of religious opinion in the eyes of the law, and eventually in the eyes of the people, legally, and, in due course, socially.[18] "The legitimate powers of government extend to such acts only as are injurious to others," Jefferson wrote, but "it does me no injury for my neighbor to say there are twenty gods, or no god. It neither picks my pocket nor breaks my leg."[19] That principle was embodied in the federal Constitution, but its influence was felt in the states long before it was formally applied to them by way of the Fourteenth Amendment. Indeed, even by Tocqueville's time it appears to have become pervasive. As he observed, public opinion may have obliged everyone to attend church services, but it obliged him to very little else. "Go into the churches (I mean the Protestant ones)," he wrote to his friend Louis de Kergorlay, "you will hear morality preached, of dogma not a word. Nothing which can at all shock the neighbor; nothing which can arouse the idea of dissent."[20] The same point was made by that earlier

Frenchman-turned-American, J. Hector St. John de Crevecoeur, who, having discussed how Europeans become Americans, went on to explain how "the various Christian sects [are] introduced, wear out, and how religious indifference becomes prevalent." That religious indifference, he concluded, "is at present one of the strongest characteristics of the Americans."[21] And this was in 1782.

What does the Constitution expect of Jews? What it expects of everybody: We all, Christians and Jews alike, have a "duty" to go to the church of our choice. To go to church, perhaps, because we are expected, but certainly not because we are required, to take care of our souls. A government with the latter concern would be required to prescribe the means appropriate to the care of souls; but our governments accept the truth of Locke's teaching that "the care . . . of every man's soul belongs unto himself."[22] Go to the church of your choice, and there acquire the habits of good citizenship. So long as that *political* purpose is met, the Constitution is indifferent as to mode of worship or the god worshiped.

Of course, the hope was that by favoring none, all would be "mild," to use Tom Paine's word. "All religions are in their nature mild and benign," Paine wrote in *Rights of Man*, and they lose this "native mildness, and become morose and intolerant" when connected with the state, when, as we say, they are established.[23] This point was repeated by Jefferson in his *Notes on the State of Virginia* and elaborated by his fellow Virginian, St. George Tucker, in his widely read edition of Blackstone's *Commentaries*, read by the lawyers who in turn made the laws. What is needed, Tucker said, is a "rational and liberal religion; a religion founded on just notions of the Deity, as a Being who regards equally every sincere worshipper, and by whom all are alike favoured as far as they act up to the light they enjoy." In other words, a God whose only command is, worship sincerely, a command that can be obeyed as well by Jew, Christian, Muslim, and even by those who know no other guide to virtue and heaven "than the dictates of natural religion." Worship sincerely, according to the light that you enjoy. "It is," Tucker goes on, "only this kind of religion that can bless the world, or be an advantage to society."[24] One is reminded of the Roman situation as described by Gibbon: "The various modes of worship which prevailed in the Roman world were all considered by the people as equally true, by the philosophers as equally false, and by the magistrates as equally useful."[25]

But this is too cynical a note to sound at the end. It is better to close with a reference to the "father of the Constitution," James Madison. Writing to Jefferson at the close of the Constitutional Convention, Madison referred to the danger of religious "enthusiasm," as he put it, how this enthusiasm, or excessive zeal, gives rise to political oppression, and, therefore, how it was necessary to guard against it.[26] He was confident that in the Constitution the Framers had found a way of tempering it. Now, two hundred years later, we are in a position to say that he was right about this.

What does the Constitution expect *of* us? Morality without Moral Majority. What does the Constitution permit *to* us? Piety without zealotry. Within these limits—and who can complain that they are too narrow?—America can be, in the words of the old Book of Common Prayer, a haven for "all sorts and conditions of men." And the foundation of this haven—this country safe for the Jews and safe for the rest of us—is not Christianity, certainly not the church of that prayer book, and not what we have come to call Judeo-Christianity, but that liberal Lockean right—liberty of conscience.

Part III

Academic Matters

Preface

Our word "school" derives from the Greek *scolé*, which means leisure. There is a lesson to be had in this. It tells us that, originally, schooling was an activity only a few might enjoy, those few who, because of their wealth, did not have to spend most of their waking hours working to provide themselves with the necessities of life: food, shelter, and the means of defense. This meant that most men were not free, and could not possibly be free. Without arguing the point here, there is a connection between leisure and freedom, schooling and freedom, the liberal (or liberating) arts and freedom, especially freedom of the mind. It was in the universities—if not there, where?—that these few were to be provided with a liberal education. That, at least, was the original idea,

But thanks to the Constitution and the free-market economy promoted and protected by it, we have created great wealth in this country, and so distributed it that almost all of our young go to school and almost half of them go on to college or university. It was almost inevitable that these numbers would have an impact on the ways of the university, on its governance as well as what is taught. So it was that the old liberal curriculum had to be scrapped and replaced by one more "relevant," and by relevance, professors meant dealing directly with what were considered to be the problems of the day: racism, sexism, and (in the 1960s) the Vietnam War. Then came student sit-ins, strikes, riots, and, at Cornell University, campus arson and students armed with guns.

Surprisingly—one would have thought—this met little resistance from within the university; administrators and professors, even (in fact, especially) liberal arts professors, acquiesced in the new order, some willingly or indifferently, and others cowardly. Allan Bloom, who witnessed all this at Cornell, deserves the last word here: "A few students discovered that pompous teachers who catechized them about academic freedom could, with a little shove, be made into dancing bears."[1]

169

19

The Assault on the Universities:
Then and Now

The assault on the university began with the student revolt at the Berkeley campus of the University of California in December 1964. Berkeley was followed by Columbia in 1968, Harvard and Cornell in 1969, and Yale and Kent State in 1970; during this same period, some three hundred universities were the scenes of student sit-ins, building takeovers, strikes, riots, and other forms of rebellious behavior. In addition to its violent character, what distinguished this assault from those of the past is that it came from within the university itself, and that it met little resistance from professors and administrators.

The issue at Berkeley, initially at least, was free speech, but free speech had little or nothing to do with the subsequent campus disruptions; here the issues were, or were said to be, university involvement in neighborhood deterioration, in the draft and the Vietnam War, and in racism, as well as university governance, especially in disciplinary matters, and the alleged irrelevance of the curriculum. Except for the neighborhood issue (so prominent at Columbia), all of these figured in the events at Cornell which, under pressure from gun-bearing students, proceeded to jettison every vestige of academic integrity.[1] In this respect, the Cornell of the sixties became the prototype of the university as we know it today.

Shortly after he was installed as Cornell's president in 1963, James A. Perkins formed a Committee on Special Educational Projects, charged with recruiting black students whose SAT scores were substantially below (as it turned out, 175 points below) the average of Cornell's entering class. Subsequently, it was revealed that many of these students were to be recruited from the slums of the central cities. Perhaps not surprisingly, they proved incapable of being, or were unwilling to be, integrated into or assimilated by the Cornell student body; assimilation, they said, threatened their identity and needs as blacks.

In 1966, they formed an Afro-American Society which, in short order, demanded separate living quarters, an Afro-American Studies Program— seizing a university building to house it—and ultimately an autonomous degree-granting college. To justify it, they issued a statement saying that "whites can make no contribution to Black Studies except in an advisory, non-decision making or financial capacity," and, therefore, that the program must be developed and taught by blacks and, as it turned out, only to black students.

This demand for an autonomous, degree-granting college took the form of an ultimatum, to which President Perkins responded by saying that he was "extremely reluctant to accept this idea of a college exclusive to one race, but [that he was] not finally opposed to it; it would involve a lot of rearranging of [his] own personality." In the event, and, as those who knew him had come to expect, his "personality" needed no rearrangement. As he said after the guns had brought him to his knees, "There is nothing I have ever said or will ever say that is forever fixed or will not be modified by changed circumstances." To head this college, or, as it came to be known, this Center for Afro-American Studies, the university, without the consent of the faculty, hired a twenty-eight-year-old graduate student in sociology at Northwestern University who, despite repeated requests, failed to submit a statement explaining the center's purpose and operation. (The closest thing to a statement of purpose came from the Afro-American Society, which said that the aim of the center "would be to create the tools necessary for the for-mation of a black nation.") To teach the first course in the program (on "black ideology"), the university, over the objection of two (and only two) faculty members of the appropriate committee, hired a twenty-four-year-old SNCC (Student Non-Violent Coordinating Committee) organizer who had completed a mere two years of college. This jettisoning of academic standards with respect to the courses to be taught and the faculty to teach them was largely the work of various members of the administration, only one of whom (the vice provost) was honest enough to admit that it was being done under pressure from the Afro-American Society—but, he assured the few dissenting members of the faculty, "It would never be done again." To refuse to accommodate the black "moderates," he said, would only strengthen the hands of the "militants."

Within a few months, these "moderates" were burning buildings; joining with the SDS (Students for a Democratic Society) to barricade Chase-Manhattan bank recruiters; removing furniture from a women's dorm and placing it in a building taken over by the Afro-American Society; disrupting traffic; overturning vending machines; trashing the library; grabbing President Perkins and pulling him from a podium (and, when the head of the campus police rushed to Perkins's aid, driving him off with a two-by-four); harassing campus visitors with toy guns; and, at five or six o'clock of a cold morning, seizing the student union building, driving visiting (and shivering) parents from their bedrooms—it was Parents Weekend—out onto the street. Justification for this seizure was said to be the burning of a cross on the lawn of a dorm for black women, which, the university now implicitly admits, was done by the "moderate" blacks themselves. They then brought guns—real, not toy, guns—into the student union and, two days later, at gunpoint, forced the university to rescind the mild (very mild) punishment imposed on the blacks found guilty of these various offenses by the student-faculty Committee on Student Affairs; in effect, they took control of the university. Photographs of the arms-bearing blacks, led by Thomas W. Jones, and of Vice President Steven Muller signing the surrender document, appeared on the covers of the leading national news magazines.

All that remained to be done was to get the faculty to agree to the surrender terms, but this proved to be easy. Jones went on the radio to say that Cornell had only "three hours to live," and that the "racist" professors—by which he meant those who opposed the surrender—would be "dealt with." (But Cornell's most famous philosophy professor was speaking for the majority of the faculty when he said, "You don't have to intimidate us.") The final act took place at a Nuremberg-like faculty-student rally at which one famous professor after another pledged his allegiance to the new order. So much for academic freedom, liberal education, and everything else the university was supposed to stand for.

No one should have been surprised by the faculty's willingness to capitulate to the armed students; the stage was set for it a year earlier when black students brought a charge of racism against a visiting professor of economics—he had made the mistake of employing a "Western" standard to judge the economic performance of various African countries—and, not satisfied with the professor's subsequent apology (which the administration required him to make), took possession of the economics department office, holding the chairman and the department secretary prisoner for some eighteen hours. The students were never punished, and, much to the relief of the dean of the college of arts and science, the accused professor left Cornell. On the basis of the findings of a special faculty-student commission, the dean then pronounced the professor innocent of racism, but went on to announce that the university and faculty were guilty of "institutional racism" and were obliged to mend their ways.

Nor should anyone have been surprised by the faculty's willingness to "reform" the curriculum, which is to say, to obliterate whatever differences there might still have been between the purposes of higher education and what were perceived to be the immediate, and pressing, concerns of the world outside. In the years immediately preceding the "crisis," one requirement after another of the old "core curriculum" had been dropped in favor of what can best be called "consumer freedom," or, in the jargon of the day, of allowing the students "to do their own thing." One of the university's most famous professors, Paul de Man (of whom, more later), argued that nothing of value would be lost by doing away with these requirements.

Begun as an assault on university "racism," the Cornell student uprising quickly became an assault on the integrity of the academic enterprise, an assault that was bound to succeed because it was met with only nominal resistance on the part of the faculty, and none at all from the administration. Although university rules were broken left and right, the dean of the law school supported the president and voted for peace (to paraphrase Shakespeare's Hamlet, "What was law to him, or he to law, that he should weep for it?"). At a special meeting of the arts college (in which, for the first time in its history, students were allowed to participate), the so-called humanists confessed their sins and called upon the president to do what he was not legally entitled to do—namely, nullify all the penalties imposed on black students "since the beginning of [the] spring term"—and the natural scientists, in the spirit of "better them than us," remained aloof from the battle, confident that none of it would reach the doors of their laboratories.[2] On the whole, just as George Orwell's Winston Smith came finally to love Big Brother, the typical Cornell professor came to admire the student radicals and sought their approval. From his perspective, theirs was the only moral game in town.

The black students, while threatening the lives of named members of the faculty, claimed to be putting "their [own] lives on the line"; others, inspired by Cornell's resident priest, Father Daniel Berrigan, insisted that they had "the moral right to engage in civil disobedience" and proceeded ceremoniously to burn their draft cards; the SDS, the vanguard of "the New Left," led the assault on the "irrelevant" curriculum, insisting that the university could not remain disengaged from the great moral issues, war, racism, and the rank injustice of "bourgeois society."[3] And the largely bourgeois faculty agreed, thereby demonstrating that Andy Warhol was right when he said that "nothing is more bourgeois than to be afraid to look bourgeois."[4]

With the faculty acquiescent and the students either triumphant or confused, Perkins had only to deal with the university trustees. They had been willing to fund the black studies program with a million dollars, and had remained quiet when Perkins placed the university airplane at the disposal of black students, enabling them to go to New York City to purchase, with $2,000 in university funds, a set of bongo drums for Malcolm X Day. The one thing they could not abide was negative publicity—could not abide and, as it turned out, could not prevent. Covering the Cornell story for the *New York Times* was a Pulitzer Prize–winning war reporter, Homer Bigart, who had learned to distrust official press releases, in this case those issuing from Muller's public relations office. Bigart's stories provided *Times* readers with a vivid account of what was, in fact, going on at Cornell; and when, despite Perkins's efforts to have it suppressed, the *Times* eventually ran on its front page a particularly damaging story summarizing the events (and the *Cornell Alumni News*, a publication with forty thousand subscribers over which Perkins and Muller had no control, hurried into print its own damaging account), the trustees called for Perkins's resignation—or, according to the story handed out, he chose to resign.

But Perkins and his friends survived, their reputations (at least in some circles) unblemished. Muller became president of Johns Hopkins University; in 1993, Thomas Jones, the erstwhile black revolutionist, having been named president of TIAA-CREF (Teachers Insurance and Annuity Association-College Retirement Equities Fund, the world's largest pension fund), was appointed to the Cornell Board of Trustees; and, in 1992, by way of recognizing "his outstanding leadership and extraordinary contributions to [the] University," Cornell established the James A. Perkins Professorship of

Environmental Studies. In 1995, Jones "made a large contribution to the University" enabling it to endow an annual Perkins Prize of $5,000 "for the student, faculty, staff member or program that has done the most during the preceding year to promote interracial understanding and harmony on campus."

To say the least, not everyone thought Perkins deserved this recognition—Bayard Rustin, the great civil rights leader, called him "a masochistic and pusillanimous university president"—but even his critics would have to admit that Perkins left his mark on the university, and not only on Cornell.[5] By surrendering to students armed with guns, he made it easier for those who came after him to surrender to students armed only with epithets ("racists," "sexists," "elitists," "homophobes"); by inaugurating a black studies program, Perkins paved the way for Latino studies programs, women's studies programs, and multicultural studies programs; by failing to support a professor's freedom to teach, he paved the way for speech codes and political correctness; and, of course, he pioneered the practice of affirmative action admissions and hiring. In a word, while it would exaggerate his influence to hold him responsible for subsequent developments, he did provide an example that other institutions found it convenient to follow. For evidence of this, consider these news items, culled from four months of the *Chronicle of Higher Education*:

- Bates College students protest admissions policy; student body only 8 percent minority; dean of admissions agrees with protesters (April 13, 1994).

- Cornell trustees approve a Latino Living Center and studies program after Hispanic students occupy administration building and block off sections of the campus (April 30, 1994).

- Under student pressure, University of Wisconsin (Milwaukee) is likely to approve gay and lesbian studies program (April 30, 1994).

- Howard University asks Yale professor David Brion Davis (Pulitzer Prize, National Book Award, for his studies of slavery) to cancel his lecture because of anti-Semitic atmosphere on campus (May 4, 1994).

- Vassar College found by U.S. District Court to have discriminated by denying tenure to woman; judge (not Vassar) found that her scholarship record was far superior to that of three men who received tenure (June 1, 1994).

- University of Oregon requires all students to take two courses meeting the "Race, Gender, Non-European American Requirement" (June 15, 1994).

- U.S. Department of Education, Office of Civil Rights, cites eighty-six colleges for violating rights of disabled, forty-four for sexual bias, forty-four for racial and ethnic bias, and one for age bias (June 22, 1994).

- Northeastern University accords gays and lesbians preferential treatment in hiring (June 29, 1994).

- National Endowment for the Humanities funds summer institute with $320,000 to help professors and administrators think about how diversity and democracy "should be dealt with in the classroom" (June 29, 1994).

- University of Wisconsin requires all students to take course in ethnic studies (June 29, 1994).

- Under pressure from U.S. Department of Education, University of Missouri will triple black enrollment by granting scholarship aid, despite low test scores or "marginal grades," to all but handful (July 13, 1994).

- University of Michigan criticized for failure to hire sufficient number of black and Hispanic professors (July 13, 1994).

- Georgetown Law School admits, then rejects, white student who, on application form, checked box marked "Black/A.A." (July 20, 1994).

When Perkins assumed the presidency of the university in 1963, there were only twenty-five black students at Cornell (out of a total of about eleven thousand students). Too few to be segregated, these twenty-five lived in the same dormitories and received the same education as the other students. By the time of Perkins' departure in 1969, there were two hundred and fifty black students on campus, but with their own, self-segregated living quarters and their own studies program.

What was true then remains true as I write this essay in 1997, and not merely at Cornell. Blacks are a visible presence on every campus, but, on every one I know or know about, so are the racial divisions. For example, black and white students at the University of Pennsylvania "tend to live in separate dormitories, beginning with the freshman year; they eat in separate portions of the dining hall; they belong to different clubs and campus organizations."[6] The only thing they seem to have in common, beyond their status as students in the University of Pennsylvania, is the desire to live apart from each other. This is not as the university would have it; on the contrary, it would prefer (or, at least, claims to prefer) an integrated student body, one where students associate regardless of race, sex, religion, national origin, or "sexual orientation"; such differences are supposed to be irrelevant, and on most campuses probably are irrelevant.

But there is one difference that is not irrelevant and the effects of which cannot be ignored, especially in a university: a difference in aptitude (or whatever it is that is measured by the SAT). Aptitude is directly, and predictably, related to success or failure in the university (and, since birds of a feather tend to flock together, at least indirectly related to campus social relations); and, because the SAT is a reasonably reliable measure of it, there is no denying that the difference between white and black students is huge. At Penn, the mean SAT score (verbal and math) of the whites is 150 points higher than that of the blacks; translated into centiles, the SAT score of the average black student is about equal to the SAT score of the tenth percentile of white students.[7] This means that 90 percent of the whites and 50 percent of the blacks are above that point (whatever it is), and 10 percent of the whites and 50 percent of the blacks are below it. What is true at Penn is true at the other so-called elite institutions—but less so at those that are able to attract the best black students—and, judging from the data from the universities of Virginia and California, the gap between blacks and whites may be even greater in the state universities.

In effect, as was the case at Cornell in the sixties, affirmative action means admitting students from different worlds, students with different capacities, interests, and habits, students who have little in common but, if left to their own devices, might be expected to live together peaceably even if separately; like members of the general public (65 percent of whom now approve of interracial dating, for example), students have come to be tolerant of differences. Unfortunately, they are not left to their own devices; instead, Penn subjects them to a steady drumbeat of propaganda—the students describe it as political indoctrination—urging them to be "sensitive and accepting of difference," the consequence of which, as the students themselves admit, is a campus "obsessed, mesmerized, driven by an unceasing battle between the various racial, ethnic, and sexual groups."[8]

This indoctrination begins with freshmen orientation when, in separate programs, black students are told, to put it simply, that the University of Pennsylvania is a racist institution, with a racist curriculum, a racist faculty and student body, and the whites, in turn, are harangued about their alleged racism.[9] Thus, as soon as they set foot on campus, students are informed, in effect warned, that, depending on their race, they will be treated differently and unequally; and so they are, and so are professors. The white student who shouts, "Shut up, you water buffalo," is charged with racial harassment, but the black students who steal and then destroy an entire pressrun of the student newspaper are not even reprimanded; the white Jewish professor who refers to himself and black students as "former slaves" is suspended for a semester without pay and is required to attend "sensitivity and racial awareness sessions," but the black professor who, in public, calls him an "asshole" is made head of the Center for the Study of Black Literature and Culture, and is named to the search committee charged with finding a new president to replace the man who had presided over these events, Sheldon Hackney, who, in turn, is named Chairman of the National Endowment for the Humanities by President Clinton.[10]

The situation at Penn is similar to that at Cornell in 1969 and, although not everywhere to the same extent, similar to that on most campuses today. Political correctness follows on affirmative action, and it is not at all clear that even its intended beneficiaries, to say nothing of the benefiting institutions, are the better off because of it. Many more black students are enrolled, but, despite grade inflation, their dropout rate greatly exceeds that of white students. What effect this has on their pride, or as we say today, their "self-esteem," is difficult to calculate, but not to imagine. The university encourages them to attribute their difficulties to white racism, but the honest among them know this not to be the case. Even those who would have been admitted without it are forced to bear the stigma attached to affirmative action; they can never be sure they are not perceived by their white fellow students as the beneficiaries of racial preference. No one, especially no one otherwise qualified, likes it to be thought he is being admitted because he is black (or is being hired or promoted to tenure rank because she is a woman); but where affirmative action is the rule, it is not easy to overcome the suspicion that this may indeed be the case. The highly qualified Susan Estrich, the first woman in ninety years to serve as president of the *Harvard Law Review*, said she did not know "a successful woman or minority who hasn't somewhere along the way, faced the assumption that they didn't quite deserve what they earned." As she put it, "We who are supposed to be its beneficiaries also pay the price of affirmative action."[11]

To say the least, these programs are of little use to the blacks, they breed cynicism among the whites, and they have a corrupting effect on the institutions; but, even if they were to be no longer required by the federal government, we are not likely to see the end of them in the private colleges and universities. They were initiated at Cornell and elsewhere because they were thought to be a way of alleviating a social problem, but they are retained probably because they make their champions feel good. They allow them to exhibit their compassion, and compassion, when detached from its religious foundations, is one way of expiating guilt. (Hence the "limousine liberal.") Compassion is also accompanied—not always, but frequently—by a sense of superiority; the healthy or wealthy one feels superior to the other who is sick or poor, both because it is the other who is suffering and the one who can provide relief. Sympathy, therefore, especially when one acts on it, is satisfying; it makes one feel good. As Clifford Orwin writes, "This is what lends credence to the Hobbesian view that sympathy is merely self-concern on vacation."[12]

Affirmative action for blacks was intended, ultimately, to bridge the economic and social gap between the races, but nothing similar to this can be said about women's studies courses which, by somebody's count, now number in the tens of thousands. The more radical among them—Christina Hoff Sommers calls them "gender feminist courses"—can have no other purpose but to teach women to hate or despise men, and in the process they threaten to transform the university into a sort of boot camp for culture warriors.[13]

Unaware that it takes two to tango, even the moderate programs proceed on the assumption that women can be studied apart from men, and have as their purpose to divide the sexes, not bring them together. Yet, there are few, if any, university presidents (still largely men) who object to the establishment of these programs. Like James Perkins before them, they apparently see no reason, or are too weak, to object; or perhaps they pretend ignorance of what is being taught in them.[14] Whatever the explanation, the situation brings to mind Tocqueville's prediction of what we can expect at the end of the women's project, namely, "weak men and disorderly women."[15]

Although a legacy of the sixties, affirmative action—for women or even for blacks—was not the principal cause for which the students took to the barricades in those turbulent times. True, they accused the universities of racism (as well as complicity in the draft and Vietnam War), but, like their counterparts in France and Germany—remember Rudi Dutschke?—they fancied themselves part of a mass movement against the "repressive system," or the "technological culture" being imposed on them by the universities. According to the chroniclers of the Berkeley "rebellion," the students of the sixties were searching for "authentic values," and could not find them in the courses available to them.[16] The same complaints were heard at Cornell (as well as at Columbia, Harvard, Yale, and the rest), where students paraded as New Left "revolutionists," all the while expressing their contempt for "bourgeois society."[17]

The antibourgeois sloganeering, so popular, so easy at the time, was mostly cant, as Richard Nixon demonstrated when he put an end to the draft and, with it, the so-called student movement. The radical students of the sixties may have hated bourgeois society (and despised its representatives), but, having no clear idea of what to put in its place, they abandoned politics for the drugs and sex of Woodstock. They should find the university much more to their liking today.

For the others, the sort of students who took no part in the sixties rebellions, the universities continue their bourgeois ways. According to a recent report, over 50 percent of the baccalaureate degrees in 1993 being awarded in our colleges and universities were in those most bourgeois of subjects, engineering, business, and other professional programs (excluding education).[18]

There is, of course, nothing despicable about learning how to make a living; on the contrary, providing for oneself (and for one's family) is, as Tocqueville points out, one of the things that distinguishes a free man from a slave.[19] But the radical students were justified in thinking that vocational training is not the proper business of the university. Americans have never had to be encouraged to look after the practical side of things; they do that for themselves. As Tocqueville said, "People living in a democratic age are quite certain to bring the industrial side of science to perfection anyhow," which is to say, without being encouraged to do so.[20] This explains why the taxpayers and alumni who pay the piper are disposed to call an industrial or vocational tune. Yet, perhaps uncharacteristically, they continue to support the universities even though so much of vocational training—basic economics, business, accounting, computer science, and the like—could be provided at less than half the cost by the community colleges. (Less than 18 percent of Maryland's higher education budget is allocated to community colleges, even though they enroll 57 percent of the state's undergraduates.) They probably support the universities because they think it important that students—even prospective engineers, bankers, lawyers, doctors, accountants, and the like—should have some acquaintance with the humanities, or, as they might say (but with only the vaguest idea of what they mean by it), with "culture." Before contributing to the annual fund drives, however, they would do well to learn how these "culture" courses are being taught these days.

Although not the first to define the term as it is used in this context, Thomas Carlyle (in the 1860s) spoke of culture as the body of arts and learning separate from the "work" or "business" of society. This definition has the merit of reflecting (and that very clearly) the problem that gave rise to the culture movement in the nineteenth century. Carlyle was preceded by Coleridge, Keats, and Wordsworth (who, in his role as poet, saw himself as an "upholder of culture" in a world that had come to disdain it); by Shelley (who said that society could do without John Locke "but not without Dante, Petrarch, Chaucer, Shakespeare"); by John Stuart Mill, for whom culture meant the qualities and faculties that characterize our humanity, or those aspects of humanity that he, like Tocqueville, foresaw might be absent in a utilitarian or commercial society; and Carlyle was followed by Matthew Arnold, for whom culture meant not only literary pursuits but—in a sentence that became familiar if not famous—the pursuit of "the best which has been thought and said in the world."[21]

These critics and poets had a concern for the sublime (or the aesthetic) and a complaint against the modern commercial and bourgeois society in which the sublime, they feared, would have no firm place. The philosophical founders of this new society—particularly John Locke and Adam Smith—promised to provide for the needs of the body (and in this they surely succeeded); culture was intended to provide for the needs of the soul. Coleridge made this the business of his "clerisy," an official body—originally (as in the case of the Church of England), but not necessarily, a religious corporation—set apart and publicly endowed for the cultivation and diffusion of knowledge. Unable, for constitutional reasons, to establish a "clerisy," America assigned this task to the universities and, more precisely, to their humanities faculties. Unfortunately, as Allan Bloom wrote, "The humanities are now failing, not for want of support but for want of anything to say."[22] Or, as he might have said, what the humanities are now saying is a sophisticated version of what the radical students used to say.

Shortly after Bloom published *The Closing of the American Mind*, a trenchant account of the state of the humanities in this country, and especially in the universities, the American Council of Learned Societies assembled a group of distinguished humanities professors and charged them with writing a response to it. Their report acknowledged the book's "disturbingly popular" success, but insisted that the attacks on the humanities (by Lynne Cheney and William Bennett, as well as by Bloom) "would be comic in their incongruity if they were not taken so seriously by so many people, with such potentially dangerous consequences." It goes on to say that "such attacks mislead the public [and] give students quite the wrong impression about what the humanities are doing." Contrary to what the critics are alleged to be saying, students are reading the great books (or, as the report puts it by way of casting doubt on their greatness, the "great books"), but they have "to learn to think about them in ways that do not suppress the challenges of contemporary modes of analysis."[23] But in making that statement about the humanities having nothing to say, Bloom was referring to deconstructionism, the most prominent of those "contemporary modes of analysis," the mode of analysis then favored by—to quote the ACLS report, "the best scholars in the humanities today."

Deconstructionism was brought to America by the Belgian-born Paul de Man (among others). When de Man died in 1983, Yale (where he had been teaching after leaving Cornell) is said to have gone into mourning, and President A. Bartlett Giamatti declared that "a tremendous light for humane life and learning is gone and nothing for us will ever be the same."[24] Giamatti himself was soon to resign and become, first, president of the National Baseball League and then baseball commissioner (neither one the most humane of vocations); but there is little doubt that in his eulogy on de Man he was speaking for the Yale literary faculties and, indeed, for the Modern Language Association, the governing body of contemporary humanities. When, in 1986, J. Hillis Miller became president of the MLA, he said, "The future of literary studies depends on maintaining and developing that rhetorical reading which is today called 'deconstruction.'"[25]

What, then, is deconstructionism?

An answer to this question is not easy to come by. As one might expect, there is a vast secondary literature on the subject, but, leaving aside the polemical and, therefore, unreliable attacks written by its enemies, most of it is either unintelligible or (at least, for someone not schooled in contemporary literary theory) incomprehensible. Consider the following passage from the pen of a Cornell professor of history:

> De Man's very understanding of language in his later works made dispossession, trauma, and mourning constitutive features of the linguistic process itself, and his continual critique of an "aesthetic ideology" of totalization, organicism, full rootedness, and the elimination of difference—in brief, the illusory realization of the imaginary—may in certain limited and problematic ways be read as applicable to the assumptions of the Nazi movement. I would also note that the undoing of the binary oppositions, while perhaps more marked in Derrida than in de Man, has been a crucial aspect of deconstruction in general and is very important for the critique of a scapegoat mechanism that resists internal alterity, is intolerant of mixed or hybridized forms, and requires a fixed, pure, and decisive divide between the integral self and the other.[26]

Any translation of this passage, indeed, any attempt to explicate its obscurity, would violate one of the principles of deconstructionism: Obscurity is supposed to be a sign of profundity, and, as such, is preferred over clarity.[27] Thus, to attempt to give a coherent account of deconstructionism requires one, like it or not, to enter a bizarre world where meaning is meaningless, where "all interpretation is misinterpretation," where words have no referents, where (to bring this to an end) a dog is not a kind of barking animal but a "concept."

As explained by de Man himself, deconstructionism is a way of reading that claims to be superior to other modes of literary criticism, because it is more cognizant of the problem of language and, therefore, of reading. "De Man," according to Geoffrey Hartman, one of his most devoted partisans, "always asks us to look beyond natural experience or its mimesis [its imitation or representation in a work of art or literature] to a specifically linguistic dilemma," and that dilemma derives from our inability to control "the relation between meaning and language."[28] The fact that it does not, and cannot, convey meaning in any objective sense is, de Man says, "the distinctive curse of all language." A "text" does not convey its author's meaning; it has its own "textuality," independent of the author. A work of literature cannot be "reduced to a finite meaning, or set of meanings," which means that the critic's task is not to elucidate but to interpret; in a way, the critic's interpretative skills are more important than the work (or "text") being read. "And since interpretation is nothing but the possibility of error, by claiming that a certain degree of blindness is part of the specificity of literature we also reaffirm the absolute dependence of the interpretation on the text and of the text on the interpretation."[29] In effect, there is no meaning, there is only interpretation—or as Gertrude Stein said of Oakland, "There's no there there"—and the more idiosyncratic the better. Like some other modern critics, deconstructionists treat a work of literature the way a figure skater treats ice: as a surface from which to launch their linguistic versions of camels, toe loops, and double axels. Put otherwise, criticism is exalted over literature, or readers over authors, and, according to one deconstructionist, whereas the history of criticism used to be part of the history of literature, "now the history of literature is part of the history of criticism."[30]

As explained by Hartman (quoting de Man),

The fields of critical philosophy, literary theory, and history have an interlinguistic, not an extralinguistic, correlative; they are secondary in relation to the original, which is itself a previous text. They reveal an essential failure of disarticulation, which was already there in the original. They kill the original, by discovering that the original was already dead. They read the original from the perspective of pure language [reine Sprache], a language that would be entirely free of the illusion of meaning.[31]

Translated, this means that what is written by the critic is related ("interlinguistically") to the work being criticized, but neither the work nor the criticism is related to anything in the world outside language. Language is not about anything except other language. This is true of a Shakespeare play, a Wordsworth poem, the Declaration of Independence, the Constitution of the United States, or a popular potboiler. As one deconstructionist admitted, even newspapers and almanacs can be deconstructed.

To say that nothing written has an "extralinguistic correlative" means that nothing written refers to, or is related to, anything existing outside the "text"; it means that love, friendship, and fidelity; envy and jealousy; justice, injustice, slavery, tyranny, and tolerance; natural rights and constitutional wrongs; all the things written about by poets, playwrights, philosophers, historians, statesmen, and Founders, are merely words, words without correlatives other than other words; it means—here I quote Roger Kimball—that "the atrocities we read about are merely literary phenomena, referring not to the sufferings of real people, real 'originals,' but only to a 'previous text'!"; it means that neither Matthew Arnold nor anyone else can speak of "the best which has been thought or said in the world" because there is no basis for such judgments, no basis for criticism.[32] There is nothing outside the text, and above all, as Allan Bloom put it, there is nothing higher. "This," he said, "is the final step in making modern man satisfied with himself."[33] The only thing the humanities can say to him is what the students were saying in the sixties: "Do your own thing."

Deconstructionism had its critics in the academy, but it ceased to be the reigning mode of critical analysis for another reason. It was discredited largely because de Man was discredited. In 1987, it was revealed (first in the pages of the New York Times)[34] that he had been a Nazi collaborationist during the German occupation of Belgium, having written one hundred and seventy articles for the French-language *Le Soir* and ten others in *Het Vlaamsche Land*, a Flemish-language daily.[35] What is of interest here, because it speaks volumes about the condition of the contemporary university, is how the academy responded to these revelations.

De Man had made no mention of his Nazi connections when he came to the United States in May 1948, and it is easy to understand why. His benefactor, novelist and critic Mary McCarthy, and his academic colleagues, first at Bard College, then at Harvard, Columbia, Johns Hopkins, Cornell, and Yale, could not have been expected to welcome him had they known of his Nazi connections. Communism is one thing, but being pro-Nazi, then and now, puts one beyond the pale. And, although many of the leading figures in the fields of comparative literature and literary theory were to deny it, some of them to excuse it as a product of youthful innocence, de Man had been pro-Nazi and, so long as the Germans were winning the war, had made no effort to conceal it. On the contrary, he had openly expressed his admiration of Hitler, had supported his war and his program; like Hitler, he had looked forward to a Europe without Jews.

He addressed the Jewish question in a *Le Soir* article of March 4, 1941, entitled "Les juifs dans la littérature actuelle" ("The Jews in Contemporary Literature"), at the end of which he proposed his own version of Hitler's "final solution." Modern literature, he wrote, has not been "polluted" by Jewish influence because Jewish writers, especially in France, have always been second-rate, but the Jews were at least partly responsible for the decadence of European political life. Thus, by banishing them to a "Jewish colony, isolated from Europe," the political problem could be solved without any "deplorable consequences for Western literary life." Banishing writers of only "mediocre value" would have the additional benefit of allowing Western literature to continue to develop or evolve "according to its own laws."[36]

In the October 28, 1941, edition of *Le Soir* he, like the notorious Martin Heidegger, rejected any attempt to distinguish between Germany and Hitlerism. Their similarity, or "closeness," he wrote, was evident from the beginning, and the war would only make it clearer that Hitler spoke for Germany; the war would unite "the Hitlerian soul and the German soul, making them into a single and unique power." He said this is an important phenomenon because it means that one cannot judge the fact of Hitler without at the same time judging the fact of Germany, and that the future of Europe can be foreseen only within the framework of the possibilities and needs of the German spirit. It is not a question of a series of reforms, but, rather, of the definitive or final emancipation of a people who, in turn, are called upon to exercise a hegemony in Europe.[37]

Question: From whom or what were the German people (and after them the people of Europe) to be emancipated?

In his essay "On the Jewish Question," Karl Marx had argued that the "emancipation of mankind from *Judaism*" (italics in original) depended on the "emancipation of the Jews" from Judaism—or, as he put it in the last line of the essay, "The social emancipation of the Jew is the emancipation of society from Judaism." It might be said that Marx was one of the first to think actively about a solution to the "Jewish question," or, as it came to be called, the "Jewish problem"; but, as he was later to say, mankind poses for itself only such tasks as it can solve, and because he thought that, at the time, mankind had no solution in hand, he was content to wait until the Jews ceased to be Jews. Not being content to wait for that to happen, Hitler devised a solution and, in his own way, so did Paul de Man.

As might have been expected, these revelations of his Nazi sympathies created a public scandal, but not among de Man's academic admirers. The charges against him were said to be "groundless" (Rodolphe Gasche); the fact that his "writings during the occupation contain certain disturbing statements and positions with no parallel in his other writings before or after the occupation makes it difficult to read his newspaper articles as straightforward expressions of deeply held beliefs" (Ian Balfour); it is impossible to "understand what this allusion to 'a Jewish colony isolated from Europe' meant at that moment" (Jacques Derrida); "Although [de Man] grants the maximum attention to the role that Germany or 'German genius' has played or ought to play in the destiny of Europe, although he recalls constantly the necessity of understanding thoroughly the history of the German nation in order to understand Hitlerism, although he is vigilantly opposed to the commonplace and the 'lazy and widespread solution' that comes down to 'supposing an integral dualism between Germany, on the one hand, and Hitlerism on the other [and] although his analysis leads him to judge German 'hegemony' in Europe to be ineluctable, this diagnosis seems rather cold and far removed from exhortation" (Jacques Derrida); "De Man's 'dirty secret' was the dirty secret of a good part of civilized Europe. In the light of what we now know, however, his [later] work appears more and more as a deepening reflection on the rhetoric of totalitarianism" (Geoffrey Hartman); "We are not now, and, in all likelihood, shall never be . . . in the position of being able to pass judgment on Paul de Man" (Leon Roudiez); de Man's so-called "collaborationist" journalism was "simply a job" (Fredric Jameson).[38]

Not content simply to defend de Man, his friends and intellectual neighbors proceeded to subject his academic critics (and there were many) to a torrent of abuse. To cite only the most extreme example, Northwestern University professor Andrzej Warminski accused them of not being able to read, of deliberate misrepresentation, of "stupidity," of being sick, of being philistines, of being primarily committed to "the institution and institutional values and criteria," which, they thought, were being threatened by de Man and "anyone with intellectual values (which, by the mere fact of being intellectual values always represent a potential threat to the institution and its creatures)." But, he went on, even this is not enough to explain the "hysteria" provoked by the revelations. "What could make so many of these creatures crawl out from under the rocks of their pathologies?" To this he attached the following footnote: "Anyone who thinks that the reptilian figure here is exaggerated should read some of the slime that has passed for [academic] 'journalism' these last months."[39] One might well ask what it was that caused him to crawl out from under the rocks of his pathologies.

But there is a nonpathological explanation for Warminski's anger, if not for the way he expressed it. He and his friends saw the revelations and the ensuing attacks as an attempt by the bourgeois "establishment" to discredit not only Paul de Man but also his way, which was their way, of doing literary criticism. By responding as they did, however, they disclosed the intellectual and moral bankruptcy of deconstructionism, with the result that few literary theorists today are willing to be associated with it.

The assault on the universities, begun by the radical students of the sixties, was continued in a more subtle fashion by the deconstructionists in the eighties. Unlike the students, they did not strike, riot, occupy buildings, or take up arms; nor, as one of the Berrigan brothers was accused of doing—even as he was nominated for a Nobel Peace Prize—did they engage in a plot to kidnap Henry Kissinger and blow up the heating system of federal buildings in Washington. (The case ended in a mistrial.) All they did was teach (and teach the next generation of teachers); but what they taught was that the universities have nothing of importance to teach. Matthew Arnold would have had the universities teach the books containing the best that has been thought and said in the world, and Thomas Jefferson wanted them to teach the Declaration of Independence and *The Federalist*, the "best guides [to the] distinctive principles of the government of the United States."[40] But, according to Paul de Man, there is no best thought and no best guide because there is no text; there is only interpretation. As he said, "the distinctive curse of all language" is that it cannot convey meaning in any objective sense.[41] Thus, about those things that mattered most to Arnold and Jefferson—all the things written about by poets, playwrights, philosophers, historians, statesmen, and Founders—the humanities, indeed the universities, would have nothing to say.

In a way, this is what the students were complaining about in the sixties: the irrelevance of the curriculum. For some of them, the solution was to remake the university into a kind of countercultural welfare agency, and the extent of their success is evident in the prevalence of black studies, women's studies, and multicultural programs. For the others—the ones searching for "authentic values," in which phrase there is, perhaps, a hint of a longing for an education of the sort proposed by Coleridge and Company—what does the university offer? In the humanities, it offers a politicized curriculum, the core of which is antirationalist, antihumanist, and antiliberal.

It used to be thought (and in some quarters is still thought) that Shakespeare is the greatest of our poets, the playwright who shows us, for example, the meaning of love and friendship, envy and jealousy, the character of good rulers and the fate of tyrants. In a word, he shows us human beings just as they are, a mixture of the high and the low; or as someone said, "His poetry gives us the eyes to see what is there." The political plays especially meant something for Abraham Lincoln. "Some of Shakespeare's plays I have never read," he said, "while others I have gone over perhaps as frequently as any unprofessional reader. Among the latter are Lear, Richard

Third, Henry Eighth, Hamlet, and especially Macbeth. It is wonderful."[42] But for the New Historicism, currently the dominant movement in the field of Shakespeare studies, his plays simply reflect the prejudices of his day. They are said to be worthy of study only because in them can be found the seeds of racism, sexism, capitalism, classism, all the evils that are said to characterize bourgeois society. Reading Shakespeare in this way has the effect of reducing his stature in the eyes of the students. "Safely entrenched in their politically correct attitude," writes Paul Cantor, a critic of the New Historicism, "students are made to feel superior to Shakespeare, to look down patronizingly at his supposedly limited and biased view of the world."[43]

For the students looking for something "wonderful," for something not available to them in the bourgeois world from which they come and to which they must, willy-nilly, return, these antihumanists have nothing to say.

20

Trashing Bourgeois America

I recall a faculty party at Cornell, the day after the annual Fourth of July celebration at the university football stadium. The wife of an economics professor, when asked if she had enjoyed the fireworks, replied, "Yes, but I could have done without all the flag-waving." This reminded me of that familiar old song—familiar in some circles, at least—"If you don't like my peaches, why do you shake my tree?"

As in Ithaca, New York, so, apparently, in Ann Arbor, the home of the University of Michigan. The following statement comes from an article by a professor of English, entitled, "Dissing the Middle Class":

> [Inhabited largely by professors], Burns Park is hardly a typical American middle-class neighborhood, as evidenced by the practice of one contentious colleague of flying the American flag on patriotic holidays so as, he claims, to annoy his neighbors.[1]

This phenomenon is not peculiar to America, nor to this time. Indeed, some sixty-odd years ago, George Orwell remarked much the same thing in England. "It is a strange fact," he said, "but it is unquestionably true, that almost any English intellectual would feel more ashamed of standing to attention during 'God save the King' than of stealing from a poor box."[2] What accounts for this?

Orwell attributed it to what he said was the fact that English intellectuals were ashamed of their own nationality. As to that, he would, of course, know better than I, but it seems to me that *shame* alone does not explain it, certainly not shame as Hobbes defined it—as grief caused by "the discovery of some defect of ability."[3] It was surely not because they

191

grieved for England that four of them—Guy Burgess, Donald MacLean, Kim Philby, and Anthony Blunt—spied for the Soviet Union. Orwell was probably closer to the truth when he said English intellectuals were Europeanized, taking "their cookery from Paris and their opinions from Moscow."[4] Of course, a Paris *crème caramel* rather than an English suet pudding is understandable, but why Moscow's Marxism rather than Britain's liberal democracy? The answer has something to do with the fact that, especially after Adam Smith, liberal democracy became bourgeois democracy.

Just as it was in England that the idea of liberal democracy was born— I refer, of course, to Thomas Hobbes and John Locke—so it was in England that opposition to, or dissatisfaction with, liberal democracy was first manifested. By this, I do not mean the champions of the old or traditional political idea, monarchy or divine right; Locke presumed to have disposed of that in the first of his *Two Treatises of Government*. I have in mind certain poets who defended what they called *culture*, and foresaw that John Locke's, and after him Adam Smith's, principles would lead to a commercial society, a society with no secure place for culture as they defined it, in a word, a "bourgeois" society.

Although not the first to use the term as it is now employed, the Scotsman Thomas Carlyle (in the 1860s) spoke of "culture" as the body of arts and learning separate from the "work" or "business" of society. This definition has the merit of reflecting (and that very clearly) the problem that gave rise to the "culture" movement in the early nineteenth century. Carlyle was preceded by the poets Coleridge, Keats, and, especially, Wordsworth (who, in his role as poet, saw himself as an "upholder of culture" in a world that had come to disdain it); and by Shelley (who said that society could do without Locke, but not without Dante, Petrarch, Chaucer, and Shakespeare); and by John Stuart Mill, for whom "culture" meant the qualities and faculties that characterize our humanity, or those aspects of our humanity that he foresaw might be absent in a liberal democracy. His famous essay, *On Liberty*, was written with this in mind.

But it was the great English historian and man of letters, Thomas Babington Macaulay, who explained the source of what the poets saw as the problem. I quote from his essay on Francis Bacon, where he compares the old philosophy with the new:

To sum up the whole, we should say that the aim of the Platonic philosophy was to exalt man into a god. The aim of the Baconian philosophy was to provide man with what he requires while he continues to be a man. The aim of the Platonic philosophy was to raise us far above vulgar wants. The aim of the Baconian philosophy was to supply our vulgar wants. The former aim was noble; but the latter was attainable.[5]

It was left to America to demonstrate the extent to which Macaulay and Bacon were right.

In 1776, we laid the foundation of a regime that would secure our unalienable rights to life, liberty, and the pursuit of happiness. What we did with these rights was up to us; more to the point, it was left to each of us to define the happiness he has the right to pursue. He might—we might—seek eternal salvation in another world, or, on the other hand, find happiness by acquiring the goods of this world. The government was to have nothing to do with this, other than to provide the conditions making it possible. This was to be done, in the one case, by guaranteeing liberty of conscience, and, in the other, by securing the property right—or as James Madison put it in the celebrated *Federalist* 10, by securing the "different and unequal faculties of acquiring property." He went so far as to say that this was "the first object" of government.

To repeat: Guided by the new political philosophy, we established a commercial republic, peaceful and prosperous, and peaceful, in part, because it is prosperous. The Constitution secures our rights, including the right to be—or not to be—cultured. The choice is ours. We can spend our leisure time reading the Bible, Petrarch, Dante, Shakespeare, and listening to the music of Bach, Mozart, Beethoven, or, on the other hand, by going to the movies, watching MTV or, thanks to modern science (which is protected by the Constitution—see article 1, section 8, clause 8), gaping at Internet porn. We enjoy the right to do the one or the other. As someone once said, the Constitution gives rights to vulgarity as well as to culture.

What began in nineteenth-century Britain as a serious critique of the new liberal democracy became, in twentieth-century America, a contemptuous "bourgeois-bashing," almost a way of life for some of our campus radicals. But if not American liberal democracy, with all its vulgarity, what?

What's the alternative? Our intellectuals might, with reason, prefer Parisian *crème caramel* to American apple pie, but they cannot, with reason, prefer Moscow's Marxism to America's liberal democracy, if only because Marxism suffered an un-Marxist—that is, unhistorical—death in Moscow.

Orwell, to get back to him, accused the intellectuals of his time of being nonpolitical, of living in the world of ideas and having "little contact with physical reality." The same might be said of some of ours—Martha Nussbaum, for example, a Harvard classicist but now a professor of law, as well as of ethics, philosophy, and divinity (a veritable polymath), at the University of Chicago, and author of the lead essay in a book entitled, *For Love of Country*. It ought to be entitled *For Love of Nowhere*.

Nussbaum is a cosmopolitan, and an advocate of what she calls cosmopolitan education, according to which students should be taught that "they are, above all," citizens not of the United States, but, instead, "of a world of human beings." Patriotism, as we ordinarily understand it, is a problem, she thinks, because it leads to parochialism, or "partisan loyalties." "Only by making our fundamental allegiance to the world community of justice and reason do we avoid these dangers."[6] But where is this world community to which we can pledge our allegiance? The United Nations?

In fact, of course, this country, however numerous its imperfections, is now, as Abraham Lincoln said it was in 1862, "the last, best hope of earth." It is this because the cause of justice, equality, tolerance, human rights—all the values Nussbaum favors—depends not on the so-called world community—Iran, Iraq, Saudi Arabia, North Korea, China?—but absolutely on this country and the willingness of its citizens to defend it against its enemies. She fails to appreciate this country and the fact that there is nothing narrowly partisan about its patriotism.

Lincoln made this clear in his eulogy on Henry Clay. Clay, he said, "loved his country partly because it was his own country, but mostly because it was a free country; and he burned with a zeal for its advancement, prosperity and glory, because he saw in such, the advancement, prosperity and glory, of *human* liberty, *human* right and *human* nature" (emphasis added).[7]

In closing, I refer to an article by John Judis, which appeared in *The New Republic* in 2000.[8] He had attended a conference in New York City on "globalization and independent politics," sponsored by the Nation Institute,

George Soros's Open Society Institute, the Carnegie Institute, Barnard College, Columbia University, and the City University of New York—in other words, a conference of academics. As one might expect in such a gathering, the speakers accused America of being racist, sexist, imperialistic, and, generally, a place where no decent person would choose to live. Among the speakers was a professor of politics at one or another branch of the University of California, who said the "two-party system is a sanctuary for middle-class, white-skin [that is, bourgeois] privilege." Not to be outdone, a female member of the audience repeatedly complained of "brown tap water."

Judis said he had intended to stay for Ralph Nader's luncheon address, but, instead, packed his suitcase, headed for Penn Station, and caught the first train back to his quiet home in the Washington suburbs where, he said, people think "white-skin privilege" is a kind of hand cream, and, when faced with "brown tap water," call the plumber. And also, I would add, where they love this country and, when necessary, are prepared to take up arms in its defense.

Part IV

Addendum: Personal Matters

Preface

The two chapters in this section have little or nothing to do with constitutional democracy; they are, instead, tributes to friends who in very different ways played major roles in my life. I met Frieda Lawrence soon after World War II at a time when I had illusions as to what I was going to do with my life; she rid me of those illusions. I met Herbert Storing soon after I entered graduate school and had begun the serious study of American politics. In the course of time, I came to recognize that he was an exceptional teacher and scholar.

21

Remembering Frieda Lawrence

Wind whispers through the pinon trees dotting the 160-acre mountain-top ranch that inspired writer D. H. Lawrence. . . . The scene is peaceful, yet melancholy: the property . . . is falling apart.
—*Washington Times*, March 27, 1998

It was a lovely place, that ranch, near (but not at) the top of a mountain a few miles from Taos, and so inaccessible that no one was likely to come upon it inadvertently. My wife and I spent our honeymoon at it in 1951, when Lawrence's wife Frieda still owned it. Alone, except when Frieda and Angie would come up from Taos for lunch or dinner—Angie was Angelo Ravagli, the model for the gamekeeper in *Lady Chatterley's Lover*, and soon to become Frieda's husband—we could sit on the wooden steps of the "big house" and look over the sage-brushed desert spread out below us, with the Rio Grande visible (and in that clear New Mexico air almost always visible) in the distance. And we could walk for hours along the crude aqueduct the Indians had built to carry water to the ranch—and to the concrete swimming pool (built by Angie) in which we could swim, naked as jaybirds. It was a perfect place for a honeymoon.

It had been owned by Mabel Dodge, a pretentious New Yorker with lots of money, who came to Taos, married a local Indian named Tony Luhan (whom I never heard utter a word), and settled in to become a patroness of the arts. The Lawrences acquired it from her in exchange for the manuscript of *Sons and Lovers*. I don't know what Mabel did with the manuscript, but Frieda, sole proprietor after Lawrence's death, left the ranch to the University of New Mexico, which, as the *Washington Times* tells us, allowed it to "decline from asset to eyesore."

I first met Frieda in 1946 at the Sagebrush Inn outside Taos where, with a friend from my wartime Navy days, I was working as a waiter and she had come to dine. That meeting led to an invitation to tea at her Taos home, and then to a visit, the first of many, at the ranch. There, usually at supper, she would ask us about the Navy and the war, and, in return, speak of her "wonderful days with Lawrence," of his precarious health, of his difficulties with publishers and editors, of their life in Germany, Italy, the south of France, Australia, and in England during the First World War, when she, born Frieda von Richthofen and cousin of the "Red Baron" Manfred von Richthofen, was suspected of being a German spy. And she spoke of her childhood at Metz where, after the Franco-Prussian War, her father, a German nobleman, served in some official capacity, and, sitting on the wall surrounding his estate, she and her two sisters would toss pears and apples from their orchard to the soldiers marching by; and of her days in a French convent school where she "did not learn very much" and the nuns would say, as she came dashing into class with her Hessian boots, "Toujours doucement, ma petite Frieda."

She was not petite when I knew her; in fact, she was rather lumpy and could have been mistaken for a peasant—walking around in her bare feet and an apron, feeding the chickens, answering questions with a throaty German "*Ja!*" (or when speaking Italian with Angie, "*Si!*"), and roaring with laughter when she came upon a laundry list, prepared by Angie, that included, among the items, "4 shits." Still, there was something of a queen or princess about her. Once, when some self-important Texas visitor to the ranch had bragged about his ancestors, she replied, "Mine were Silesian kings." And so they were. Her younger sister Johanna (Nusch, as Frieda called her) was lady-in-waiting to the empress queen of Kaiser Wilhelm II, and once, by way of declaring their love affair at an end, slipped off a pearl necklace given her by her suitor and casually dropped it into the Spree (or Seine, Tiber, or Thames). To hear Frieda tell it, Nusch had lovers everywhere, even (but not in her salad days) Hot Springs, Arkansas. This, because it says something of importance about Frieda, is a tale worth repeating.

In 1949, on Frieda's seventieth birthday, Nusch, at least sixty-five but doing a good job of concealing it, came to the ranch and announced that she had stopped at Hot Springs on the way and had met a "nice young man" there. Indeed, she continued, she had invited him to come to Taos and—

hoping her sister would not mind—had told him Frieda was her mother. Frieda thought this hilarious; she warned me not to give the game away.

After lunch on most days, Frieda would retire to her bedroom to read and take a brief nap, emerging with her impressions of what she had read. Writers, for her, were divided between those who had "*zut*" and those who didn't; somehow one knew what she meant. Nietzsche had "*zut*," according to Frieda, and, of course, Lawrence had it in abundance; but Aldous Huxley, though she loved him dearly, did not. She loved to read Lawrence's poems aloud, and subsequently recorded them; I have a copy of the recording still. A room in the "big house" was filled with his paintings, one of them showing a group of nuns looking furtively at a naked shepherd boy asleep under a tree.

Frieda enjoyed playing the piano, especially if we sang along with her; her specialty was a folk song that had been a favorite among the German soldiers at Metz, "*Wenn ich zu meinem Kinde geh*" ("When I go to my child"). Considering the fact that no tuner ever braved the rutted road to the ranch, the piano was in surprisingly good condition. Frieda was not the only one who thought so; to cite an even better authority, Leonard Bernstein did, too.

Bernstein visited the ranch in the summer of 1948 because Frieda had invited the poet Stephen Spender to spend some time there, and along with Spender came Bernstein and Bernstein's younger brother. For some reason—I never heard her try to play it—Frieda owned the complete score of Mozart's opera "Don Giovanni," and, seeing it, Bernstein immediately sat down and began to play and sing his way through it. I thought this extraordinary at the time, but Frieda, who had spent the better part of her life among unusually talented people, took it in stride. As I recall, Spender's crew lasted only a week, probably because, alone up there, they got tired of cooking for themselves or, in Bernstein's case, of having to do without the news from New York.

Frieda made it a practice to take fresh flowers and cedar and pine boughs to the tiny chapel where Lawrence's ashes are buried—the *Washington Times* refers to the place as a mausoleum. Angie, an expert mason, had built the chapel, and Georgia O'Keeffe, who lived not far away and was a great friend of Frieda's, had painted one of the pictures that hung in it. Famous people from around the world had entered their names in the registry that Frieda kept there.

There are interesting stories involving the chapel, but to tell one of them I have to introduce another inhabitant of Frieda's world, the Honorable

Dorothy Brett, daughter of the Viscount Esher (confidant of King Edward VII) and sister of the Ranee of Sarawak (now a part of Malaysia but, before World War II, ruled by Sir Charles Vyner Brooke, the Ranee's husband and the third and last of the Rajahs). Brett was a painter, and a rather good one, too; she lived in Taos across the road from Frieda, popping in on her at least once a day. She was therefore well placed to tell Mabel Dodge what Frieda was doing, and, of greatest interest to Mabel, what famous person—for instance, the poet William Carlos Williams—had visited Frieda without coming to visit her. To say the least, Mabel was jealous of Frieda and, beyond that, had persuaded herself that she better appreciated Lawrence's genius and would make a better custodian of his ashes.

Lawrence had died in the south of France, and, some years before my time in Taos, Frieda and Angie had gone there to recover the ashes. Arriving home, they were greeted by Brett, who asked, "Where's Lawrence?" It turned out that on their return to Taos they had stopped for a cup of coffee, and the ashes had been left on the counter. (Angie was dispatched to fetch them.) This proved to be the last straw for Mabel. Inviting Frieda and Angie to dinner, she instructed her husband Tony and some friends of his from the Indian pueblo at Taos to go up to the chapel and steal the ashes. They probably would have succeeded, had Brett, who was privy to the plot, not warned Frieda at the last moment.

In 1949, persuaded—by Frieda, among others—that I would never be a writer (I lacked "zut"), I left Taos for graduate school and became, of all things, a political scientist. I don't know about Mabel, but Frieda died in 1956, Brett in 1975, and my wife and I last saw Angie in 1966 on our way to Portofino in Italy. He had returned to his native Spotorno, near Genoa, but it was sadly obvious that he no longer belonged there and had nothing to do. On the other hand, without Frieda and the world she had built around her, he would have had nothing to do in Taos, either.

As for the ranch? I suspect that, after consulting some smart lawyers and developers, the University of New Mexico will turn it into still another of the area's ski resorts. What they will do with the chapel is a problem, though; it is too small for a bar, and a ski resort is no place for a shrine.

22

Remembering Herbert Storing

Almost thirty years have passed since Robert Goldwin called from Washington and said that Herbert Storing had died. I must have uttered a cry, because my wife, who was across the room, rose up startled; I then broke into tears. How else does one hear the news of the death—a sudden and unexpected death—of a child, for example, or, in this case, a dear friend?

Storing and I first met in 1950 as beginning graduate students in the political science department at the University of Chicago. He came from Colgate University, where his father was a professor and, for a while, had been acting president, and I from Reed College in Portland, Oregon, by way (for one year) of the London School of Economics and Political Science, where I learned little, other than to love London. We lived in different units of graduate student housing (converted Quonset huts) on the Midway across from the main campus. Because our wives, by chance, were away on the same night each week, one at work, the other at school, Storing and I would eat our evening meal together, one week at his place, the next at mine, but always discussing what we had learned that day or week. We studied constitutional law with Professor Herman Pritchett and political philosophy with Professor Leo Strauss, so there was much to discuss. These weekly suppers were, I believe, the real beginning of our friendship.

The Storings owned a property on Hatch Lake, a few miles from Colgate in Hamilton, New York. There were several houses on it. Nothing fancy about them, but they were capable of accommodating visiting friends, particularly, on several occasions, those of us from Chicago and our families. (They also had a bad-tempered cat named—for some reason—Walter.) Down by the dock, there was a very small structure—built, I suppose, to store life jackets and other boating paraphernalia—which Storing used as a summer office, exclusively for the reading of PhD dissertations. It seemed to me that he must have served on at least half of the department's dissertation committees, a disproportionate number as chairman. At any rate, I have a memory of manuscripts piled on his desk awaiting his attention. Unlike some professors I have known, Storing read them all with great care. His students will attest to this.

In July 1976, he organized a Bicentennial symposium at Colgate where we Chicago friends each gave a paper on some aspect of the Declaration of Independence. (Goldwin has a photograph of us sitting in a line on the platform.) That meeting was especially memorable because of the symposium, and also because of the Israeli raid and rescue at Entebbe, news of which reached us early in the morning of July 4. It was also the last time we were all together: Storing, Goldwin, Martin Diamond, Robert Horwitz, Robert Scigliano, and I, all professors, except Goldwin, who at the time was in the White House as special assistant to the president; and all, except Storing, who was younger than the rest of us, World War II veterans. (His Army service began in 1946. As he told it, he was a sort of itinerant bugler, blowing "taps" at veterans' burials, or reburials.) His death the following year (September 9, 1977) put an end to these summer gatherings and, of course, to much else of greater consequence: his teaching and scholarship.

Storing was one member of our Chicago group whose scholarship made a difference and, for that reason, will be remembered. This is especially true of his seven-volume study, *The Complete Anti-Federalist*, which was described by the *New York Times* reviewer as "a work of magnificent scholarship" and its publication a "civic event of enduring importance."

Except for a couple of years in London as a Fulbright Scholar, and an occasional visiting professorship, almost all his academic time was spent at the University of Chicago, first as graduate student, then, from 1956 to 1977, as assistant, associate, and professor of political science. He had no interest in going elsewhere; that changed when the University of Virginia contacted him respecting a position as professor and head of a new program on the American presidency. I learned about this when the chairman of the Virginia department asked me to assess his qualifications. This is the substance of what I wrote:

Dear ____ :

I know of no one who is better qualified to occupy the position you describe than Herbert Storing; in fact, I cannot imagine anyone who would be better qualified for it. Having begun in this immoderate fashion, I owe it to you to admit that Storing and I are close friends, and have been ever since 1950 when we first met as beginning graduate students at the University of Chicago, and that, therefore, I may not be an impartial judge. On the other hand, I would have to insist that the closeness of our relationship allows me to speak with unusual authority; I know him, I know his work, I know his students, I know his capacities—and, knowing all this, I know him to be the model of a university professor.

You know, or will quickly come to know, that the position you describe and seek to fill is exactly suited to his interests. The American constitutional system is his field; he has taught it and almost every aspect of it, and he has written about its Founding, and now proposes, in fact, to turn his attention to the institution of the presidency. It is also exactly suited to his talents. You want a scholar; Storing is one of the very few true scholars I know: he is thorough, comprehensive, unbiased, uncompromising in his search for all the evidence that research can uncover. You also want a profound man; Storing is the most profound man I have encountered in the field of American studies: He is a serious thinker, not an intellectual, he understands the deepest questions and problems involved in our politics, and he elucidates them with a clarity that is unsurpassed. You also want a teacher; Storing is an incomparable teacher. That, quite simply, is the unanimous judgment of all the students I have sent to him over the years. He tries to teach, and, therefore, never propagandizes; he listens to students, but never panders to them—he is too dignified, too much the man ever to do that or ever even to wish for popularity—and he has less of what we recognize as vanity than anyone I know. And he has an amazing capacity to gain the respect of an audience and even, when what he is discussing is contentious, to disarm the potentially most hostile of critics. I recall an astonishing performance at Cornell about ten years ago when a student group, which had been attracted to him through his essays on Booker T. Washington and Frederick Douglass, invited him to address a university audience on the subject of black power. There was a huge turnout, including, as one could have expected, many who denied on principle that any white man had a right to discuss the topic. Well, he made it an educational event by teaching everyone who was educable, gaining the respect of almost everyone, and angering no one. In the circumstances of that time and place it was a remarkable achievement, but altogether characteristic of him. In his quiet and careful way, he demonstrated that he knew more and had thought more deeply about the racial problem in the United States than anyone present, including, of course, all those who professed it either academically or politically.

One more word, this on his scholarship: The Chicago Press is publishing his seven-volume edition of the *Anti-Federalist Papers*, one of the seven being his essay on the ratification debates. I read—in fact, studied—this two years ago, and I can confidently say that with its publication he will be recognized as a preeminent authority on the Founding period. You should not expect a volume a year from him on the presidency—that is not his way—but you can expect work that will gain him the same sort of recognition in this area.

I close by repeating what I said at the beginning: I know of no one who is better qualified for the position than Storing. He's the best.

He was appointed, of course, and moved with his family to Charlottesville, but died (on the handball court) before he had begun to teach. He was forty-nine years old.

Publication Acknowledgments

"Ancients and Moderns: The Emergence of Modern Constitutionalism" was originally published by the University of London, Institute of United States Studies, in 2002.

"The Illegitimacy of Appeals to Natural Law in Constitutional Interpretation" was originally published in *Natural Law, Liberalism, and Morality*, ed. Robert P. George (Oxford: Oxford University Press, 1996), 181–94.

"Preserving a Living Constitution" was originally published in *Is the Supreme Court the Guardian of the Constitution?* ed. Robert A. Licht (Washington, D.C.: AEI Press, 1993), 34–45.

"The Demise of the Constitution" was originally a speech delivered at the National Constitution Center, Philadelphia, September 21, 1989.

"Solving the Problem of Democracy" was originally published in *South Africa's Crisis of Constitutional Democracy: Can the U.S. Constitution Help?* ed. Robert A. Licht and Bertus de Villiers (Washington, D.C.: AEI Press, 1994), 180–200.

"Constitutionalism and Multiculturalism" was originally published in *Multiculturalism and American Democracy,* ed. Arthur M. Melzer, Jerry Weinberger, and M. Richard Zinman (Lawrence, Kans.: University Press of Kansas, 1998), 91–111.

"States' Rights and the Union" was originally published under the title "Revisiting States' Rights Controversy at the Wrong Time, with Altered History" in the *Washington Times*, October 15, 2000. Copyright © 2000 News World Communications, Inc. Reprinted with permission of the *Washington Times*. This reprint does not constitute or imply any endorsement or sponsorship of any product, service, company, or organization.

"Talkers" was originally published under the title "The Prattling Presidency" in the *Wall Street Journal*, October 31, 1994.

"Why a Vice President" was originally published under the title "The Insignificant Office." Copyright © 2004 by National review Online, www.nationalreview.com. Reprinted with permission.

"Two-and-a-Half Cheers for the Electoral College" was originally a lecture delivered at Ashland University, February 20, 2001.

"Civil Not Natural Rights" was originally published under the title "The Libertarian Dodge" in *The Claremont Review of Books* 3, no. 4 (Fall 2003): 50–51.

Notes

Introduction

1. *The Federalist* (or *Federalist Papers*) began as a series of letters, eighty-five in number, which were published in New York City newspapers to persuade the people of the state of New York to ratify the Constitution drafted in Philadelphia during the summer of 1787. "Written with a haste that often bordered on the frantic," as the editor of a modern edition of the work says, and "printed and published as if it were the most perishable kind of daily news," *The Federalist* is, nevertheless, "the most important work in political science that has ever been written, or is likely ever to be written, in the United States." Clinton Rossiter, ed., *The Federalist Papers* (New York: Penguin Books, 1961), vii. In addition to its importance in the realm of political science, or theory, it is understood to be the most authoritative commentary on the Constitution; as a result, it is widely used as a college text and is probably one of the few books that can be found in most American libraries, including those located overseas.

2. *Grutter v. Bollinger*, 539 U.S. 306 (2003).

3. The majority opinion was written by Justice Sandra Day O'Connor. She did much the same thing—that is, play ducks and drakes with a statute—in a 1987 civil rights case, where she persisted in reading the statute so as to permit "what its language read literally would prohibit," even though, as she admitted, Justice Scalia (in his dissenting opinion) had pointed this out "with excruciating clarity." *Johnson v. Transportation Agency*, 480 U.S. 616, 647 (1987).

4. Walter Berns, *Making Patriots* (Chicago: University of Chicago Press, 2001), x.

5. Thomas Jefferson to Roger C. Weightman, 24 June 1826, in *Thomas Jefferson, Writings*, ed. Merrill D. Petersen (New York: Library of America, 1984), 1516–17.

Preface to Part I, Constitutionalism

1. Alexis de Tocqueville, *Democracy in America*, ed. Phillips Bradley (New York: Vintage Classics, 1945), 325–26.

Chapter 1: Ancients and Moderns:
The Emergence of Modern Constitutionalism

1. *Constitution of Athens* (New York: The Hafner Library of Classics, 1950).

2. After this the story becomes truly bizarre. Pisistratus returned from exile when Megacles "picked out a tall and beautiful woman by the name of Phya . . . dressed her up so that she looked like the goddess [Athena] and brought her into the city with Pisistratus. And so, Pisistratus drove into the city on a chariot, the woman standing by his side, and the citizens fell down in worship and received him with awe." *Constitution of Athens*, 82.

3. *Constitution of Athens*, 4–5.

4. Aristotle, *Politics*, trans. H. Rackham (Cambridge, Mass.: Harvard University Press, 1932), bk. 4, 331.

5. Cicero, *On The Republic, On The Laws*, trans. Clinton Walker Keyes (Cambridge, Mass.: Harvard University Press, 1928), bk. 2, sec. 33, 58.

6. Polybius, *The Histories*, trans. W. R. Paton (Cambridge, Mass.: Harvard University Press, 1927), bk. 6, sec. 11, 11.

7. Cicero, *On the Republic, On the Laws*, bk. 3, 30.

8. Montesquieu, *The Spirit of the Laws* (New York: Hafner, 1940), bk. 11, ch. 6.

9. 8 Coke Reports, 107a, 118a (1610).

10. "The main object of the Whig party in the early part of the eighteenth century was to establish in England a system of government in which the will of the people as expressed by Parliament should be supreme, and the power of the monarch should be subject to the limitations it imposed." William Edward Hartpole Lecky, *History of England in the Eighteenth Century* (London: Longman, 1925), vol. 1, 2–3.

11. Thomas Paine, *Rights of Man* (London: Watts & Co., 1937), 36. First published in 1791.

12. Henry St. John Bolingbroke, "Dissertation upon Parties, Letter X" in *The Craftsman* (London: R. Francklin,1754), 108.

13. Francis D. Wormuth, *The Origins of Modern Constitutionalism* (New York: Harper & Bros. 1949), 42.

14. Shakespeare, *Richard II*, Act 2, Scene I.

15. In such a system, he said, "laws are to be supported only by their own terrors, and by the concern which each individual may find in them, from his own private speculations, or can spare to them from his own private interests. In the groves of *their* academy, at the end of every vista, you see nothing but the gallows." Edmund Burke, "Reflections on the Revolution in France," in *The Works of Edmund Burke* (London: G. Bell and Sons, Ltd., 1911), vol. 2, 350. The publication of the "Reflections" led him to be denounced by the English friends of the Revolution, some of them fellow Whigs, but Edward Gibbon thought it "a most admirable medicine against the French disease."

16. Edmund Burke, *The Works of Edmond Burke*, vol. 2, 308.

17. Ibid., vol. 2, 362.

18. Ibid., vol. 6, 146.

19. Ibid.

20. Ibid., vol. 2, 422.

21. Ibid., vol. 2, 306–7.

22. Ibid., vol. 6, 21.

23. Ibid., vol. 2, 333.

24. Ibid., vol. 3, 85.

25. Ralf Dahrendorf, "Can European Democracy Survive Globalization?" *National Interest* 65 (Fall 2001), 17–22.

26. Treaty on European Union, signed on February 7, 1992, title I.

27. Treaty of Amsterdam, signed on October 2, 1997, article 2.

28. ". . . Providence has been pleased to give this one connected country to one united people—a people descended from the same ancestors, speaking the same language, professing the same religion, attached to the same principles of government, very similar in their manners and customs, and who, by their joint counsels, arms, and efforts, fighting side by side throughout a long and bloody war, have established their general liberty and independence." John Jay, *Federalist* 2.

29. Edmund Burke, "Speech on Conciliation with the Colonies," March 22, 1775, in *The Works of Edmund Burke*, vol. 1.

30. Both the federal and the various state constitutions are modern in this respect. The federal Constitution begins as follows: "We the People of the United States . . . do ordain and establish this Constitution for the United States of America." So compelling was this idea of a legitimate foundation of government that, in 1778, the people of Massachusetts, by a large majority, rejected a state constitution because, and only because, it was drafted by the legislature, not by the people. Then, in 1780, they voted in favor of a constitution because it was drafted in a convention of delegates chosen by the people.

31. Tocqueville, *Democracy in America*, introduction, 3–16.

32. *Federalist* 63.

33. Herbert J. Storing, ed., with the assistance of Murray Dry, *The Complete Anti-Federalist* (Chicago: University of Chicago Press, 1981), 224.

34. *Federalist* 49.

35. Felix Frankfurter, in *West Virginia State Board of Education v. Barnette*, 319 U.S. 624, 670 (1943). Dissenting opinion.

Chapter 2: The Illegitimacy of Appeals to Natural Law in Constitutional Interpretation

1. *Calder v. Bull*, 3 Dallas 386 (1798).

2. *Fletcher v. Peck*, 6 Cranch 87, 143 (1810).

3. *Griswold v. Connecticut*, 381 U.S. 479, 484 (1965).

4. Ibid., 511–12. Dissenting opinion.

5. Roscoe Pound, "Introduction," in *The Forgotten Ninth Amendment*, ed. Russell B. Patterson (Indianapolis: The Bobbs-Merrill Co., 1955), iii, iv.

6. Nature as guide or measure is, perhaps, best illustrated in this soliloquy spoken by the bastard son of the Earl of Gloucester (Shakespeare, *King Lear*, act 1, scene 2):

> Thou, Nature, art my goddess; to thy law
> My services are bound. Wherefore should I
> Stand in the plague of custom, and permit
> The curiosity of nations to deprive me,
> For that I am some twelve or fourteen moonshines
> Lag of a brother? Why bastard? Wherefore base?
> When my dimensions are as well compact,
> My mind as generous, and my shape as true,
> As honest madam's issue? Why brand they us
> With base? with baseness? bastardy? base, base?
> Who, in the lusty stealth of nature, take
> More composition and fierce quality
> Than doth, within a dull, stale, tired bed,
> Go to th' creating a whole tribe of fops,
> Got 'tween asleep and wake?—Well, then,
> Legitimate Edgar, I must have your land:
> Our father's love is to the bastard Edmund
> As to th' legitimate: fine word,—*legitimate*!
> Well, my legitimate, if this letter speed,
> And my invention thrive, Edmund the base
> Shall top th' legitimate. I grow; I prosper:—
> Now, gods, stand up for bastards!

7. Walter Berns, "Preserving a Living Constitution," in *Is the Supreme Court the Guardian of the Constitution?* ed. Robert A. Licht (Washington, D.C.: AEI Press, 1993), 34–45.

8. *Griswold v. Connecticut*, 515. Dissenting opinion.

9. *Roe v. Wade*, 410 U.S. 113 (1973); *Bowers v. Hardwick*, 478 U.S. 186 (1986).

10. Russell Hittinger, *A Critique of the New Natural Law Theory* (Notre Dame, Ind.: University of Notre Dame Press, 1987), 63.

11. John Quincy Adams, *Jubilee of the Constitution—a Discourse Delivered at the Request of the New York Historical Society . . . on the 30th of April 1839* (New York: Samuel Colson, 1839), 54.

12. John Courtney Murray, *We Hold These Truths: Catholic Reflections on the American Proposition* (New York: Sheed and Ward, 1960), 37–39.

13. John Locke, *Two Treatises of Government*, II, sec. 6. (Cambridge: Cambridge University Press, 1964).

14. Murray, *We Hold These Truths*, 53–54.

15. John Locke, "A Letter Concerning Toleration," in *Library of the Liberal Arts* (New York: Macmillan, 1950); Thomas Jefferson, "Notes on the State of Virginia," Query XVII, in *Thomas Jefferson, Writings*, 281.

16. Murray, *We Hold These Truths*, 299.

17. Ibid., 316.

18. Ibid., 305.

19. John Locke, *Questions Concerning the Law of Nature*, introduction, text, and translation by Robert Horwitz, Jenny Strauss Clay, and Diskin Clay (Ithaca, N.Y.: Cornell University Press, 1990), questions 4, 6.

20. Locke, *Two Treatises*, II, sec. 8–12, 87; Thomas Hobbes, *Leviathan, or the Matters and Powers of a Commonwealth Ecclesiastical and Civil* (Oxford: Basil Blackwell's Political Texts, 1960), 142.

21. Thomas L. Pangle, *The Spirit of Modern Republicanism: The Moral Vision of the American Founders and the Philosophy of Locke* (Chicago: University of Chicago Press, 1988), ch. 13–21.

22. Murray, *We Hold These Truths*, 307, 291, 37–39.

23. Jefferson, "Notes on the State of Virginia," Query XVII, in *Thomas Jefferson, Writings*, 285.

24. John Locke, *Essay Concerning Human Understanding*, ed. Peter H. Nidditch (Oxford: Clarendon Press, 1979), vol. 2, sec. 21, 55; vol. 1, sec. 3, 6; vol. 2, sec. 21, 42, 65, 55.

25. Locke, *Essay Concerning Human Understanding*, vol. 2, sec. 21, 43, 68; *Reasonableness of Christianity*, para. 245 ("pursuit of happiness"); *Two Treatises*, II, sec. 225 ("long train of abuses"); *Two Treatises*, II, sec. 230 (mankind "are more disposed to suffer").

26. James Wilson, in *The Debates in the Several State Conventions on the Adoption of the Federal Constitution*, ed. Jonathan Elliot (New York: Burt Franklin, 1888), vol. 2, 456. John Quincy Adams made the same point. The principles of the Declaration of Independence and the Constitution, he said, had been "especially expounded in the writings of Locke." Adams, *Jubilee of the Constitution*, 40. And, contrary to Murray, Adams says that "English liberties had failed them . . . the colonists appealed to the rights of man." Adams, *Jubilee of the Constitution*, 9.

27. "The Essex Result," in Philip B. Kurland and Ralph Lerner, eds., *The Founders' Constitution* (Chicago: University of Chicago Press, 1987), vol. 1, 112–18.

28. *Federalist* 49 and 43.

29. *Federalist* 51; Pangle, *The Spirit of Modern Republicanism*, 118–19.

30. Ernest L. Fortin, "The New Rights Theory and the Natural Law," *Review of Politics* 44 (1982): 590–612. For the presuppositions, see Heinrich A. Rommen,

The State in Catholic Thought: A Treatise in Political Philosophy (St. Louis and London: B. Herder Book Co., 1945), 169–70.

31. See Leo Strauss, "Natural Law," in *International Encyclopedia of the Social Sciences*, ed. David L. Sills (New York: Crowell Collier and Macmillan, Inc., 1938), vol. 2, 80–90.

32. Hobbes, *Leviathan*, ch. 14; Locke, *Two Treatises*, II, sec. 87, 128–31.

33. Randy E. Barnett, ed., *The Rights Retained by the People: The History and Meaning of the Ninth Amendment* (Fairfax, Va.: George Mason University Press, 1989).

34. *Annals of Congress*, 1st Cong., 1st sess., August 15, 1789, 775.

35. Patrick Henry, speech in the Virginia state ratifying convention, June 16, 1788, in *The Complete Anti-Federalist*, Storing, ed., vol. 5, 246–47.

36. Herbert J. Storing, "The Constitution and the Bill of Rights," in *Taking the Constitution Seriously: Essays on the Constitution and Constitutional Law*, ed. Gary L. McDowell (Dubuque, Ia.: Kendall-Hunt Publishing Co., 1981), 277.

37. George H. Reese, ed., *Proceedings of the Virginia State Convention of 1861* (Richmond: Virginia State Library, 1965), vol. 3, 24–25; vol. 1, 709.

38. The following statement from Mississippi is typical: "There is, however, a great principle underlying all constitutions and government . . . the right of the people to alter, to change, to amend, aye, to abolish the form of government whenever to them it shall seem proper. That, gentlemen of the Convention, is the great principle which underlies not only your federal constitution, but which lies at the basis of your State constitutions—the right of the people, the power of the people, aye, and the duty of the people, to resume the powers of government with which they have entrusted their agents whenever those agents have proven and manifested themselves to be unfaithful in the discharge of the trust." E. Barksdale, *Journal of the Convention and Ordinances and Resolutions Adopted in January*, 1861 (Jackson, Miss.: State Printer, 1861), 166.

Chapter 3: Preserving a Living Constitution

1. "Brutus," 15, March 20, 1788, in Kurland and Lerner, eds., *The Founders' Constitution*, vol. 4, 238–39.

2. *Calder v. Bull*, 387–88.

3. Ibid., 398–99. Concurring opinion.

4. *Fletcher v. Peck*, 139.

5. Ibid., 143. Concurring opinion.

6. *Savings and Loan Association v. Topeka*, 20 Wall. 655 (1875); L.Ed., 455, 461.

7. Ibid., 463. It should be pointed out that this case was decided long before the "takings" clause of the Fifth Amendment (or any other provision of the Bill of Rights) had been incorporated into the Fourteenth Amendment, which means that at the time the Constitution of the United States imposed no restrictions on state "takings." Thus, in effect, the Court held that the *state* constitution did not permit the state to do this; in

line with this, the cases cited in support of the judgment were all state cases. But, of course, the Court had no authority to expound the meaning of state constitutions.

8. James Madison, letter to Spencer Roane, September 2, 1819, in Marvin Meyers, ed., *The Mind of the Founder: Sources of the Political Thought of James Madison*, rev. ed. (Hanover, Mass.: Brandeis University Press, 1981).

9. James Madison, letter to Henry Lee, June 25, 1824, in *The Writings of James Madison*, ed. Gaillard Hunt (New York: G. P. Putnam's Sons, 1900–1910), vol. 9, 191. The passage cited in the text begins as follows: "I entirely concur in the propriety of resorting to the sense in which the Constitution was accepted and ratified by the nation. In that sense alone it is the legitimate Constitution."

10. *Marbury v. Madison*, 1 Cranch 137 (1803).

11. Thomas Jefferson, letter to Wilson Cary Nicholas, September 7, 1803, in *Thomas Jefferson, Writings*, 1140.

12. *Federalist* 78.

13. William Cranch and Joseph Story, in Kurland and Lerner, eds., *The Founders' Constitution*, vol. 4, 188.

14. Ibid., 206.

15. Ibid., 205.

16. Robert P. Kraynak, "Tocqueville's Constitutionalism," *American Political Science Review* 81, no. 4 (December 1987): 1191.

17. William J. Brennan Jr., "The Constitution of the United States: Contemporary Ratification," *South Texas Law Review* 27 (1986): 433–34.

18. *Lochner v. New York*, 198 U.S. 45 (1905).

19. See, for example, *Griswold v. Connecticut*.

20. *Buck v. Bell*, 274 U.S. 200 (1927). See Walter Berns, "*Buck v. Bell*: Due Process of Law?" *Western Political Quarterly* 6 (December 1953): 762–65.

21. *Jacobson v. Massachusetts*, 197 U.S. 11 (1905).

22. *Eugenical News* 19 (November–December 1934): 140–41.

23. *Lochner v. New York*, 75. Dissenting opinion.

24. *McCulloch v. Maryland*, 4 Wheat. 316, 407, 415 (1819).

25. See Walter Berns, *Taking the Constitution Seriously* (New York: Simon and Schuster, 1987), 207–8. The statement has been misquoted many times, beginning in Chief Justice Charles Evans Hughes's opinion for the Court in *Home Building & Loan Assoc. v. Blaisdell*, 290 U.S. 398, 443 (1934).

26. *Harper v. Virginia State Board of Elections*, 383 U.S. 663, 669 (1966).

27. Ibid., 676. Dissenting opinion.

28. "The idea of natural law rests on the following presuppositions. 1. A last and profound unity of mankind, a unity of conscience in the last and least of human beings. However darkened or enlightened by primitive civilizations and progressive cultures, by deleterious habits become traditions and by lack of serious efforts to live up to the demand of critical consciousness, there exists a unity and community of human conscience, of human nature through all the epochs, in all races, in all nations. 2. The ability

of the human intellect to perceive the essential and the unchangeable nature of things, in other words, the actual objective reality. The measure of our knowledge is the thing in its essence; it is not the categorical forms of the subjective mind, induced by the phenomena of the things that produce order out of the chaos of the phenomena. 3. Granted that the human mind recognizes the nature of things, this nature is for the existing thing at the same time its end and perfection. It is the degree of realized idea in an existing thing that determines the degree of its goodness. 4. Superiority of the intellect. The intellect recognizes the nature of things and presents to the will the concrete thing as a good that ought to be striven after." Rommen, *The State in Catholic Thought*, 169–70.

29. Carl L. Becker, *The Declaration of Independence: A Study in the History of Political Ideas* (New York: Vintage Books, 1942), 277.

30. "The enumeration in the Constitution of certain rights, shall not be construed to deny or disparage others retained by the people." Pound, "Introduction," in *The Forgotten Ninth Amendment*, ii, iv.

31. Ibid.

32. See Berns, *Taking the Constitution Seriously*, 23.

33. Leo Strauss, *Natural Right and History* (Chicago: University of Chicago Press, 1953), 1–2.

34. Sanford Levinson, *Constitutional Faith* (Princeton, N.J.: Princeton University Press, 1989), 172.

35. Ibid., 64–65.

36. Thomas L. Pangle, "Post-Modernist Thought," *Wall Street Journal*, January 5, 1989.

37. Levinson, *Constitutional Faith*, 191.

38. Michael J. Perry, *Morality, Politics, and Law: A Bicentennial Essay* (New York: Oxford University Press, 1988), 148–50.

39. Ibid., 162.

40. Three of these clauses are to be found in the Fifth Amendment (grand jury indictment, double jeopardy, and due process), one in the Fourteenth Amendment (due process), and one in article 1, section 2 (where the president is given the power to grant reprieves).

41. *Johnson v. Transportation Agency, Santa Clara County*, 480 U.S. 616, 647 (1987). Concurring opinion.

42. Fred Baumann, "Historicism and the Constitution," in *Confronting the Constitution*, ed. Allan Bloom (Washington, D.C.: AEI Press, 1990), 286.

43. Joseph L. Rauh Jr., "The Supreme Court: A Body Politic," *Washington Post*, March 5, 1980.

Chapter 4: The Demise of the Constitution

1. John Quincy Adams, "Inaugural Address," delivered March 4, 1825, in *Inaugural Addresses of the President of the United States from George Washington 1789 to Harry S. Truman 1949* (Washington, D.C.: Library of Congress, 1952), 43.

2. The Episcopal Church, *Book of Common Prayer* (Oxford: Oxford University Press, 2000).

3. *Marbury v. Madison*, 5 U.S. 137 (1803).

4. Perry, *Morality, Politics, and Law*,148–50.

5. Levinson, *Constitutional Faith*, 191.

6. Robert Bork, "Tradition and Morality in Constitutional Law" (Francis Boyer Lecture, Washington, D.C., December 6, 1984).

7. Ronald Dworkin, *Taking Rights Seriously* (Cambridge, Mass.: Harvard University Press, 1977), 149.

8. Ibid., 181.

9. Ibid., 152.

10. Bruce A. Ackerman, *Social Justice in a Liberal State* (New Haven, Conn.: Yale University Press, 1981), 158.

11. Levinson, *Constitutional Faith*, 52.

12. Ibid., 64–65.

13. *Federalist* 78.

Chapter 5: Solving the Problem of Democracy

1. Tocqueville, *Democracy in America*, vol. 2, bk. 4, ch. 7, 326.

2. *Federalist* 1.

3. *Federalist* 2.

4. Ibid.

5. *Federalist* 37.

6. Abraham Lincoln, "Address to the Young Men's Lyceum of Springfield, Illinois," January 27, 1838, in *Lincoln: Speeches and Writings, 1832-1858* (New York: The Library of America, 1989), 35.

7. "Le grand advantage des Américains est d'être arrivés à la démocratie sans avoir à souffrir de révolutions démocratiques, et d'être nés égaux au lieu de le devenir." Alexis de Tocqueville, *De la Démocratie en Amérique* (Paris: Garnier-Flammarion, 1981), vol. 2, 130.

8. "Pourquoi en Amérique, pays de démocratie par excellence, personne en fait-il entendre contre la propriété en général ces plaintes qui souvent retentissent en Europe? Est-il besoin de le dire? C'est qu'en Amérique il n'y a point de prolétaires." Tocqueville, *De la Démocratie en Amérique*, vol. 1, 333–34.

9. See Robert A. Goldwin, *Why Blacks, Women, and Jews Are Not Mentioned in the Constitution, and Other Unorthodox Views* (Washington, D.C.: AEI Press, 1990).

10. Interestingly enough, while the slaves were freed by the Thirteenth Amendment to the Constitution and made citizens of the United States by the Fourteenth, it was not until 1924 that Congress enacted a statute declaring all Indians "born within the territorial limits of the United States . . . to be citizens of the United States." (43 Statutes at Large 253.)

11. Berns, *Taking the Constitution Seriously*, 93–94.

12. Thomas Jefferson to John Adams, 30 August 1787, in *Thomas Jefferson, Writings*, 909.

13. There is no question that the liberties of Japanese-Americans were jeopardized during World War II. On the question of civil liberties during the Civil War, see Mark Neely, *The Fate of Liberty: Abraham Lincoln and Civil Liberties* (New York: Oxford University Press, 1991).

14. Harvey C. Mansfield Jr., *America's Constitutional Soul* (Baltimore: The Johns Hopkins University Press, 1991), 211. Some years after the Constitutional Convention, James McHenry, a delegate to the Constitutional Convention from Delaware, recorded the following entry in his Anecdotes: "A lady asked Dr. Franklin Well Doctor what have we got a republic or a monarchy—a republic replied the Doctor if you can keep it."

15. *Federalist* 9.

16. Ibid.

17. Hobbes, *Leviathan*, ch. 13; Locke, *Two Treatises*, II, sec. 101, 123.

18. Locke, *Two Treatises*, II, sec. 21.

19. Ibid., sec. 93.

20. Ibid., sec. 134.

21. Ibid., sec. 143.

22. Ibid., secs. 143–44.

23. Charles C. Thach Jr., *The Creation of the Presidency, 1775–1798: A Study of Constitutional History* (Baltimore: The Johns Hopkins University Press, 1969), 28–29.

24. Locke, *Two Treatises*, II, sec. 160.

25. "There is," Locke wrote,

> another power in every commonwealth which one may call natural, because it is that which answers to the power every man naturally had before he entered into society; for though in a commonwealth the members of it are distinct persons still in reference to one another, and as such are governed by the laws of the society, yet, in reference to the rest of mankind, they make one body which is, as every member of it before was, still in the state of nature with the rest of mankind. Hence it is that the controversies that happen between any man of the society with those that are out of it are managed by the public, and an injury done to a member of their body engages the whole in the reparation of it. So that, under this consideration, the whole community is one body in the state of nature in respect of all other states or persons out of its community.
>
> This, therefore, contains the power of war and peace, leagues and alliances, and all the transactions with all persons and communities without the commonwealth, and may be called "federative," if anyone pleases. So the thing is understood, I am indifferent as to the name (Locke, *Two Treatises*, II, sec. 145, 146).

26. Abraham Lincoln, for example, suspended the privilege of habeas corpus, a power that, from its place in the Constitution, would seem to belong to the Congress; and, acting in his capacity as commander in chief, he freed the slaves, which, he had argued when first taking the presidential oath of office, the Congress had no authority to do. To mention one more example, Franklin D. Roosevelt, without any authority from Congress, traded fifty of the navy's warships to the British in exchange for ninety-nine-year leases on some naval bases.

27. As one might expect, this is a recipe for conflict between the legislative and executive branches. Depending on the circumstances, each exercises the supreme power, and there is no rule—and in the nature of the case, there cannot be a rule—for determining those circumstances. Whether the executive has exceeded his authority is sometimes (but not always) determined by the Supreme Court, usually the final arbiter of constitutional questions; but if the executive defies the Court (as Abraham Lincoln did), the question of whether he exceeded his authority is determined, in principle, by the people, and, in practice, by a court of impeachment which, under the Constitution, is the Senate of the United States, with the chief justice of the United States presiding.

28. The importance of this principle was demonstrated when it was violated by President Ronald Reagan in the so-called Iran-Contra affair. He pleaded ignorance of the extraordinary actions undertaken by his subordinates, chiefly Colonel Oliver North and Admiral John Poindexter, setting off a lengthy controversy.

29. Walter Berns, "The Constitution as Bill of Rights," in *How Does the Constitution Secure Rights?* ed. Robert A. Goldwin and William A. Schambra (Washington, D.C.: AEI Press, 1985), 50–73.

30. *Dred Scott v. Sandford*, 19 How. (60 U.S.) 393 (1857); *Hepburn v. Griswold*, 8 Wall. (75 U.S.) 603 (1870); *Knox v. Lee*, 12 Wall. (79 U.S.) 457 (1871); *Pollock v. Farmers' Loan & Trust Co.*, 157 U.S. 429 (1895); *National Labor Relations Board v. Jones and Laughlin Steel Corp.*, 301 U.S. 1 (1937).

31. *United States v. Eichman*, 496 U.S. 310 (1990); *Korematsu v. United States*, 323 U.S. 214 (1944).

32. *Federalist* 63.

33. Storing, ed., *The Complete Anti-Federalist*, vol. 5, 224.

34. *Federalist* 49.

35. Amendment XVII.

36. Amendments XV, XIX, XXVI, and XXIV.

37. The advent of political parties ensured that presidential electors would be chosen by popular vote of the people; this became evident as early as 1800. Nevertheless, because these popular votes are aggregated at the state rather than at the national level, and because each state is given a number of electors equal to "the whole number of Senators and Representatives to which [it] may be entitled in the Congress," and because each state, regardless of the size of its population, is entitled to two senators, it is always possible that the person who wins a majority of the electoral votes will not have won a majority of the popular votes.

38. Michael Parenti, *Democracy for the Few*, 3rd ed. (New York: St. Martin's Press, 1980).

39. *Federalist* 10.

40. Party government would be possible in the United States only by amending the Constitution in fundamental respects. See James W. Ceaser, "Constitutionalism and a Semiparty System in the United States," in *South Africa's Crisis of Constitutional Democracy*, ed. Robert A. Licht and Bertus de Villiers (Washington, D.C.: AEI Press, 1994), 218.

41. Woodrow Wilson, *Congressional Government: A Study in American Politics* (New Haven, Conn.: Meridian Books, 1965), 91.

42. "We have in this country," Wilson complained (ibid., 142) "no real leadership," but real leadership, especially charismatic leadership, was precisely what the Framers sought to prevent (see *Federalist* 10). What is interesting here is the way Americans speak, or refuse to speak, of government. Whereas the British speak of the Major (or Thatcher or Wilson or Churchill or Chamberlain or Disraeli) government, and the Canadians of the Mulroney (or Trudeau or Diefenbaker or Mackenzie King) government, Americans speak of the Bush (or Reagan or Carter or Roosevelt or Lincoln or Jackson or Washington) administration. This, I think, is not by chance; rather, it derives from the Constitution.

43. American Political Science Association, *Toward a More Responsible Two-Party System*, a report of the Committee on Political Parties (New York: Rinehart, 1950); James MacGregor Burns, *The Deadlock of Democracy: Four Party Politics in America* (Englewood Cliffs, N.J.: Prentice-Hall, 1963).

44. Charles A. Beard, *An Economic Interpretation of the Constitution of the United States* (New York: Macmillan, 1936).

45. Robert E. Brown, *Charles Beard and the American Constitution* (Princeton, N.J.: Princeton University Press, 1956); Forrest McDonald, *We the People—The Economic Origins of the Constitution* (Chicago: The University of Chicago Press, 1958).

46. *Federalist* 12.

47. *Federalist* 10.

48. "Chacun ayant un bien particulier à défendre, reconnaît en principe le droit de propriété." Tocqueville, *De la Démocratie en Amérique*, vol. 1, pt. 2, ch. 6, sec. 3, 334 ("De L'Idée Des Droits Aux États-Unis").

49. See Allan Bloom, ed., *Confronting the Constitution*, especially chs. 10, 12, and 15.

50. *Federalist* 39, 63.

Chapter 6: Constitutionalism and Multiculturalism

1. For an account of the attempt to define culture, see Raymond Williams, *Culture and Society* (New York: Columbia University Press, 1958).

2. Allan Bloom, "Commerce and 'Culture'," in *Giants and Dwarfs: Essays 1960–1990* ed. Allan Bloom (New York: Simon & Schuster, 1990), 280.

3. Charles Taylor, *Multiculturalism and "The Politics of Recognition": An Essay by Charles Taylor with Commentary by Amy Guttman*, ed., Steven C. Rockefeller, Michael Walzer, and Susan Wolf (Princeton, N.J.: Princeton University Press, 1992), 3.

4. H. D. Forbes, "Multiculturalism: The General Principles in the Canadian Case." A paper presented at the 1990 Annual Meeting of the American Political Science Association, held in San Francisco, California, August 30–September 2.

5. Ibid., 16.

6. A news item of some years ago illustrates the problem: "Gojko Susak, the Croatian defense minister who three years ago was running a chain of pizza parlors in Ottawa, Canada, says the U.N. complaints about Croatian deception are 'their excuse for not doing what they are supposed to do.' In his Zagreb office, where a bear skin rug that once belonged to former Yugoslavian strongman Josip Broz Tito covers the floor, Mr. Susak [insists] that the Croats have stopped [the Serbian] offensive." *Wall Street Journal*, March 8, 1993, A6.

7. In this connection, it is interesting to note that "pluralism" as a political term is a neologism, one that made its first appearance in the *Oxford English Dictionary* only with the publication of the *Supplement* in 1982. There we are told that "pluralism," meaning "the existence or toleration of diversity of ethnic groups within a society or state, of beliefs or attitudes within a body or institution, etc.," was first used in 1956 by Horace Kallen in his book *Cultural Pluralism and the American Idea* (Philadelphia: University of Pennsylvania Press, 1956). Professor Rogers Smith informs me, correctly, that Kallen used the term "cultural pluralism" in 1924 in his *Culture and Democracy*.

8. *Annals of Congress*, 1st Cong., 2d sess., February 3, 1790, 1150; 3rd Cong., 2d sess., December 22, 1794, 1008.

9. Jefferson, "Notes on the State of Virginia," Query VIII, in *Thomas Jefferson, Writings,* 211.

10. Ibid., 212.

11. Goodwin Watson, quoted in Kallen, *Cultural Pluralism and the American Idea*, 166.

12. *Communist Party of Indiana v. Whitcomb*, 414 U.S. 441 (1974).

13. *Davis v. Beason*, 133 U.S. 334, 341–2 (1890).

14. *United States v. Macintosh*, 283 U.S. 605, 625 (1931).

15. Bernard Lewis, "Western Civilization: A View from the East" (Nineteenth Jefferson Lecture in the Humanities, Washington, D.C., May 1990).

16. Tocqueville, *Democracy in America*, vol. 2, bk. 1, ch. 5, 23.

17. Lord Swann, Committee of Inquiry into the Education of Children from Ethnic Minority Groups, "Education for All: Report of the Committee of Inquiry into the Education of Children from Ethnic Minority Groups," presented to British Parliament in March 1985, 71.

18. S. J. D. Green, "Religion and the Limits of Pluralism in Contemporary Britain," *The Antioch Review* 49, no. 4 (Fall 1991): 581. I am indebted to this article for my account of the British situation.

19. *Pierce v. Society of Sisters*, 268 U.S. 510 (1925).

20. Jefferson, "Notes on the State of Virginia," Query XVII, in *Thomas Jefferson, Writings,* 285.

21. John Locke, "A Letter Concerning Toleration," para. 6–7, 36, pp. 17, 30.

22. Jefferson, "Notes on the State of Virginia," Query XVII, in *Thomas Jefferson, Writings*, 285.

23. See Berns, *Taking the Constitution Seriously*, 162.

24. Elliot, ed., *The Debates in the Several State Conventions on the Adoption of the Federal Constitution*, vol. 2, 118. The point being debated was the article 6 provision forbidding religious tests for officeholders.

25. Gutmann, in Taylor, *Multiculturalism and "The Politics of Recognition,"* 5.

26. See *Holland v. Illinois*, 493 U.S. 474 (1990).

27. Selden Society, *Select Pleas, Starrs, and Other Records from the Rolls of the Exchequer of the Jews*, ed. J. M. Rigg (London: Bernard Quaritch, 1902), xxi, xl–xlii.

28. Kevin Boyle, Tom Hadden, and Paddy Hillyard, *Law and State: The Case of Northern Ireland* (London: Martin Robertson; Amherst, Mass.: University of Massachusetts Press, 1975), 175.

29. Ibid., 95.

30. Gutmann, in Taylor, *Multiculturalism and "The Politics of Recognition,"* 5.

31. Samuel P. Huntington, "The Clash of Civilizations?" *Foreign Affairs* 72, no. 3 (Summer 1993), 30–31.

32. Pierre Elliott Trudeau, *Federalism and the French Canadians* (Toronto: Macmillan, 1968), 178–79, as reprinted in Forbes, "Multiculturalism: The General Principles," 16.

33. Peter H. Russell, "The End of Mega Constitutional Politics in Canada?" *PS* (March 1993): 33. I am indebted to Professor Russell for much of this account.

34. CBC Archives, "Separation Anxiety: The 1995 Quebec Referendum," Canadian Broadcasting Corporation, http://archives.cbc.ca/IDCC-1-73-1891-12484/politics_economy/1995_referendum/ (accessed June 21, 2006).

35. Jefferson to Roger C. Weightman, in *Thomas Jefferson, Writings*, 1516–17.

36. Paul Richard, "Scrawling in the Margins: New York's Whitney Biennial Spits in the Face of Convention," *Washington Post*, March 4, 1993, C1; Deborah Solomon, "A Showcase for Political Correctness," *Wall Street Journal*, March 5, 1993, 7.

37. Leo Strauss, *Liberalism: Ancient and Modern* (New York: Basic Books, 1968), 262.

38. Werner J. Dannhauser, "Ancients, Moderns, and Canadians," *Denver Quarterly* 4, no. 2 (Summer 1969): 97.

Preface to Part II, Constitutional and Political Matters

1. Tocqueville, *Democracy in America*, vol. 1, 280.

2. John Milton, "Areopagitica," in *Complete Poems and Major Prose*, ed. Merritt Y. Hughes (New York: Odyssey Press, 1957), 746.

Chapter 7: States' Rights and the Union

1. Forrest McDonald, *States' Rights and the Union: Imperium in Imperio, 1776–1876*, (Lawrence, Kans.: University Press of Kansas, 2002).

2. Ibid., viii.

3. Ibid., vii.

4. James Madison, "Virginia Resolutions Against the Alien and Sedition Acts," in Hunt, ed., *The Writings of James Madison* (New York: The Library of America, 1999), 589.

5. McDonald, *States' Rights and the Union: Imperium in Imperio, 1776–1876,* 196.

6. Ibid., 197.

Chapter 8: Talkers

1. United States House of Representatives, "Articles of Impeachment exhibited by the House of Representatives against Andrew Johnson," 40th Cong., 2d sess. March 4, 1868, 6.

2. Jeffrey K. Tulis, *The Rhetorical Presidency* (Princeton, N.J.: Princeton University Press, 1987), 75.

3. John F. Harris, "Mr. Bush Catches a Washington Break," *Washington Post,* May 6, 2001.

4. Jimmy Carter, *A Government As Good As Its People* (Fayetteville, Ark.: University of Arkansas Press, 1996), x.

Chapter 9: Why a Vice President

1. John Adams to Abigail Adams, December 19, 1793, in *Bartlett's Familiar Quotations,* ed. Justin Kaplan (Boston: Little, Brown and Company, 2002), 351.

2. Max Farrand, ed., *Records of the Federal Convention of 1787* (New Haven, Conn.: Yale University Press, 1937), 176.

3. Ibid., 31.

4. Ibid., 32.

5. Ibid., 109.

6. U.S. Const. art 1, sec. I (superseded by amend. XII).

7. Farrand, *Records of the Federal Convention of 1787,* 537.

8. Ibid.

Chapter 10: Two-and-a-Half Cheers for the Electoral College

1. Farrand, *Records of the Federal Convention of 1787,* vol. 2, 515.

2. *Ray v. Blair,* 343 U.S. 214 (1952).

3. Henry F. Graff, *Grover Cleveland* (New York: Times Books, 2002), 95.

4. *Counting Electoral Votes in Congress,* U.S. Code 3 (2000), sec. 15 .

5. See Walter Berns, ed., *After the People Vote,* 2d ed. (Washington, D.C.: AEI Press, 1992), 4.

6. Herbert J. Storing, *Toward a More Perfect Union: Writings of Herbert J. Storing,* ed. Joseph M. Bessette (Washington, D.C.: AEI Press, 1995), 397.

Chapter 11: Civil Not Natural Rights

1. Wendy Kaminer, *Free for All: Defending Liberty in America Today* (Boston: Beacon Press, 2002).

2. Ibid., xx.

3. Ibid., 221.

4. Ibid., xvi.

5. Ibid., 210.

6. Ibid., xvi.

7. Ibid.

8. *Griswold v. Connecticut*, 484.

9. Kaminer, *Free for All*, 14.

10. Ibid., 54.

11. David M. Rabban, *Free Speech in Its Forgotten Years, 1870–1920* (New York: Cambridge University Press, 1999), 383.

12. Kaminer, *Free for All*, 55.

13. *Gitlow v. New York*, 268 U.S. 629, 673 (1925), dissenting opinion.

14. Hobbes, *Leviathan*, chs. 13, 82.

15. See Hobbes, *Leviathan*, chs. 13 and 14; Locke, *Two Treatises*, II, sec. 4.

16. Hobbes, *Leviathan*, ch. 14; Locke, *Two Treatises*, II, sec. 95.

Chapter 12: Flag-Burning and Other Modes of Expression

1. *Texas v. Johnson*, 491 U.S. 397 (1989).

2. Editorial, *Washington Post*, June 29, 1989, A24.

3. Hilton Kramer, "Is Art Above the Laws of Decency?" *New York Times*, July 2, 1989.

4. Benjamin Forgey, "The Power of Mapplethorpe's Pictures," *Washington Post*, June 25, 1989.

5. Thomas I. Emerson, *The System of Freedom of Expression* (New York: Random House, 1970), 17.

6. The Helms amendment would have barred federal arts money from being used to promote, disseminate, or produce obscene or indecent materials, including, but not limited to, depictions of sadomasochism, homoeroticism, the exploitation of children, or individuals engaged in sex acts, or material which denigrates the objects or beliefs of the adherents of a particular religion or nonreligion.

7. *Cohen v. California*, 403 U.S. 15 (1971).

8. *National Socialist Party v. Skokie*, 432 U.S. 43 (1977).

9. *Gitlow v. New York*, 673, dissenting opinion.

10. *Communist Party USA v. S.A.C.D.*, 367 U.S. 1, 147–48 (1961), dissenting opinion.

11. Schlesinger, commencement address at Brown University, as quoted by Allan Bloom, *Giants and Dwarfs*, 18.

12. Jefferson, "Notes on the State of Virginia," Query XVII, in *Thomas Jefferson, Writings*, 210.

13. Harvey C. Mansfield Jr., "Political Correctness and the Suicide of the Intellect," *The Heritage Lectures* (Washington, D.C.: Heritage Foundation, 1991), 3.

14. Friedrich Nietzsche, *The Philosophy of Nietzsche* (New York: Modern Library Edition, Random House, 1927), 7.

15. Leo Strauss, *Liberalism: Ancient and Modern*, 261.

16. Levinson, *Constitutional Faith*, 64–65.

17. Ibid.

18. Robert Bork, in conversation with the author.

19. USFlag.org, "United States Code," http://www.usflag.org/uscode36.html (accessed May 24, 2006).

20. *Texas v. Johnson*, 491 U.S. 397 (1989).

Chapter 13: Blue Movies

1. Gregory D. Black, *Hollywood Censored: Morality Codes, Catholics, and the Movies* (Cambridge: Cambridge University Press, 1994).

2. Ibid., 228.

3. Ibid., 300.

4. Ibid.

5. Ibid., 207.

6. Ibid.

7. Tocqueville, *Democracy in America*, vol. 2, 83.

8. Ibid.

9. Black, *Hollywood Censored*, 89.

10. Allan Bloom, *The Closing of the American Mind*, 57–58.

11. "Motion Picture Production Code" (Motion Picture Association of America, 1956).

12. Jean-Jacques Rousseau, *Politics and the Arts: Letter to M. d'Alembert on the Theatre*, trans. and ed. Allan Bloom (Glencoe, Ill.: The Free Press of Glencoe, Ill., 1960), 124.

13. Tipper Gore, *Raising PG Kids in an X-Rated Society* (Nashville, Tenn.: Abingdon, 1987).

14. Jean-Jacques Rousseau, *On the Social Contract*, ed. Roger Masters, trans. Judith Masters (New York: St. Martin's Press, 1978), bk. 4, ch. 7, 123.

Chapter 14: Hail, New Columbia

1. The D.C. Voting Rights Movement, "The 1978 D.C. Voting Rights Constitutional Amendment," http://www.dcvote.org/trellis/acting/1978amendmenthjres554.cfm (accessed May 19, 2006).

2. U.S. House of Representatives, "Proposed Amendments to the D.C. Statehood Bill," 99th Cong., 1st sess., April 15, 1985.

3. *Constitution of the United States*, Article 2, Section 1, Clause 2.

Chatper 15: Teaching Patriotism

1. Tocqueville, *Democracy in America*, vol. 1, ch. 14, 241.

2. See Locke, *Two Treatises*, II, sec. 6.

3. World Values Survey, "World Values Survey, 1989–1993," http://www.world valuessurvey.com (accessed May 25, 2006).

4. Abraham Lincoln, *Speeches, Letters, Miscellaneous Writings, Presidential Proclamations* (New York: Library of America, 1989), vol. 1, 32.

5. Rom. 12:5.

6. Tom Wolfe, *The Painted Word* (New York: Bantam, 1999), 71.

7. Lincoln, *Speeches . . . Writings*, vol. 1, 260.

8. Lincoln, *Speeches . . . Writings*, vol. 2, 624.

9. Tocqueville, *Democracy in America*, vol. 2, 101.

10. "Addresses of the Honorable W. D. Kelley, Miss Anna E. Dickinson, and Mr. Frederick Douglass, at a Mass Meeting, Held at National Hall, Philadelphia, July 6, 1863, for the Promotion of Colored Enlistments," first edition printing, Gettysburg College collection.

11. Robert A. Goldwin, *Why Blacks, Women and Jews Are Not Mentioned in the Constitution, and Other Unorthodox Views*, 17.

Chapter 16: Religion and the Death Penalty

1. Albert Camus, "Reflections on the Guillotine," in *Resistance, Rebellion, and Death*, trans. Justin O'Brien (New York: Modern Library Edition, Random House, 1960), 170.

2. Immanuel Kant, *The Metaphysical Elements of Justice*, trans. John Ladd (Indianapolis: Library of Liberal Arts, 1965), 100, 102.

3. Bureau of Justice, "Number of persons executed in the United States, 1930-2005," http://www.ojp.usdoj.gov/bjs/glance/tables/exetab.htm (accessed May 19, 2006).

4. William Shakespeare, "Sonnet 73."

5. Associated Press, "Around the World; French Lawmakers Vote To End Death Penalty," *New York Times*, September 19, 1981; Europa, "EU Presidency declaration on abolition of death penalty on Samoa," http://europa-eu-un.org/articles/en/article_3272_en.htm (accessed June 5, 2006).

6. Council of the European Union, "Charter of Fundamental Rights of the European Union," http://ue.eu.int/uedocs/cmsUpload/CharteEN.pdf (accessed May 19, 2006).

7. It is not clear what they intend to put in the place of the death penalty. Imprisonment for life, perhaps; but one could say that this is as cruel as sentencing someone to death. But, as the French might remember (and would probably prefer that we forget), there are ways of punishing offenders without even bringing them to trial. They (and especially foreigners) can be kidnapped. I happened to be living in Paris in October 1965 when a troublesome Moroccan was kidnapped by the police (or counterintelligence agents). They picked him up in broad daylight, on a very busy street corner (Saint-Germain-des-Prés, directly across from the Café de Flore), and whisked him away in a police car, whence he was never seen again. No trial, no appeal, no fuss, no muss, and no Mehdi Ben Barka.

8. Editorial, "Therapy of the masses," *The Economist*, November 6, 2003, http://www.economist.com/displayStory.cfm?story_id=2172112.

9. Albert Camus, *Carnet II* (Paris: Gallimard, 1964), 31.

10. Nietzsche, "Zarathustra's Prologue," in *The Philosophy of Nietzsche*, 7, 11.

Chapter 17: Under God

1. *Elk Grove Unified School District v. Newdow*, 542 U.S. 1 (2004), 1.

2. Paul L. Murphy, ed., *Liberty and Justice: A Historical Record of American Constitutional Development* (New York: Alfred A. Knopf, 1958), 53.

3. Thomas Jefferson, "Letter to the Danbury Baptists," in *Thomas Jefferson, Writings*, 510.

4. *Everson v. Board of Education*, 330 U.S. 1, 31–32 (1947).

5. *Elk Grove Unified District v. Newdow*, 25, concurring opinion.

6. Ibid., 45, concurring opinion.

7. Ibid., 26.

Chapter 18: What Does the Constitution Expect of Jews?

1. George Washington to Hebrew Congregation of Newport, Rhode Island, August 17, 1790, in *George Washington: A Collection*, ed. W. B. Allen (Indianapolis: Liberty Classics, 1988), 548.

2. Thomas Babington Macaulay, *The History of England, from the Accession of James II* (Leipzig: Bernh, Tachnitz, Jun. 1849), vol. 4, 88.

3. Thomas Jefferson, "A Bill Establishing Religious Freedom," in *Thomas Jefferson, Writings*.

4. Ibid., 346–48.

5. *Federalist* 78.

6. *Church of the Holy Trinity v. United States*, 143 U.S. 457 (1892).

7. Thomas Jefferson, "A Bill for Establishing Religious Freedom," in *Thomas Jefferson, Writings*.

8. Francis Newton Thorpe, ed., *The Federal and State Constitutions, Colonial Charters, and Other Organic Laws of the States, Territories, and Colonies Now or Heretofore Forming the United States of America* (Washington, D.C.: Government Printing Office, 1909), vol. 1, 566.

9. Anson Phelps Stokes, ed., *Church and State in the United States* (New York: Harper, 1950), vol. 1, 287–89.

10. Act of August 7, 1789, *Statutes at Large*, 1:50. The actual form of the action taken by the First Congress was to "adapt" the ordinance to the new "Constitution of the United States."

11. Thorpe, *The Federal and State Constitutions*, vol. 3, 1689.

12. Ibid., 1189–90.

13. Elliot, ed., *The Debates in the Several State Conventions on the Adoption of the Federal Constitution*, vol. 4, 191–200.

14. Ibid.

15. Anson Phelps Stokes and Leo Pfeffer, *Church and State in the United States*, revised ed. (New York: Harper, 1964), 80.

16. Morton Borden, *Jews, Turks, and Infidels* (Chapel Hill, N.C.: University of North Carolina Press, 1984).

17. Elliot, *Debates*, vol. 2, 117–19.

18. Thomas Jefferson to Roger C. Weightman, in *Thomas Jefferson, Writings*, 1517.

19. Jefferson, "Notes on the State of Virginia," Query XVII, in *Thomas Jefferson, Writings*, 210.

20. George Wilson Pierson, *Tocqueville and Beaumont in America* (New York: Oxford University Press, 1938), 106.

21. J. Hector St. John de Crevecoeur, "What Is An American?" in *Letters From an American Farmer* (London: T. Davies, 1782), 318.

22. Locke, *A Letter Concerning Toleration*, para. 36, 30.

23. Paine, *Rights of Man*, 54.

24. St. George Tucker, *Blackstone's Commentaries* (Philadelphia: William Young Birch and Abraham Small, 1803), vol. 1, 130.

25. Edward Gibbon, *The History of the Decline and Fall of the Roman Empire* (New York: A. L. Burt Co, 1845), ch. 2, 250.

26. James Madison, letter to Thomas Jefferson, October 24, 1787, in Hunt, ed., *The Writings of James Madison*, vol. 5, 30–31.

Preface to Part III, Academic Matters

1. Bloom, *The Closing of the American Mind*, 315.

Chapter 19: The Assault on the Universities: Then and Now

1. My account here of the Cornell crisis of 1969 is based on my notes made at the time, as well as on the extensive account written by Allan Sindler. A shorter version (unpublished) of Sindler's account—"How Crisis Came to Cornell"—was delivered at the 1971 annual meeting of the American Political Science Association. For an outsider's view of the events at Cornell, see Donald Alexander Downs, *Cornell '69: Liberalism and the Crisis of the American University* (Ithaca, N.Y.: Cornell University Press, 1999).

2. The scientists' turn came in 1971 when students blew up the Mathematics Research Center at the University of Wisconsin, killing a postdoctoral fellow and destroying the life work of five physics professors. Since then, science as such has come under attack from feminists, Afrocentrists, and a variety of "postmodernist" professors. For a detailed account of this anti-science campaign, see Paul Gross and Norman Levitt, *Higher Superstition: The Academic Left and Its Quarrels With Science* (Baltimore: The Johns Hopkins University Press, 1994).

3. Berrigan was a campus hero, famous for leading the band of grim ecclesiastics who wrested card files from the hands of the clerk of the Catonsville, Maryland, draft board office and burned them in the parking lot with homemade napalm. When, in a public debate in the law school auditorium, I asked him whether they had given some thought to the possibility that some harm might come to the defenseless and probably terrified clerk, he replied, "Yes, we gave that *prayerful* consideration, but we decided the protest was so important that we had to run that risk. . . . Besides," he added after a short pause, perhaps recalling that they had not bothered to solicit the clerk's opinion as to whether she was willing to run that risk, "anyone who works for the draft board deserves no more consideration than the guards at Belsen and Dachau."

4. Wolfe, *The Painted Word*, 71.

5. Bayard Rustin, "The Failure of Black Separatism," *Harper's*, January 1970, 30.

6. Richard Bernstein, *Dictatorship of Virtue: Multiculturalism and the Battle for America's Future* (New York: Alfred A. Knopf, 1994), 71.

7. Ibid.

8. Ibid., 64–65.

9. Ibid., for a detailed account of this haranguing.

10. Informed of the newspaper theft, Hackney said that "two important values, diversity and open expression, appear to be in conflict." That "conflict" was resolved as Perkins would have resolved it. Instead of punishing the students who stole the newspapers, the university punished the campus police who apprehended them. According to the official report of the university's Judicial Inquiry Office, the police should have known that they were dealing with "a form of student protest [and not] criminal behavior."

11. Susan Estrich, *USA Today*, February 23, 1995, 11A.

12. Clifford Orwin, "Compassion," *The American Scholar* (Summer 1980), 323.

13. Christina Hoff Sommers, *Who Stole Feminism?* (New York: Simon & Schuster, 1994), 28.

14. Students in a women's studies course at Georgetown University are required to read the "SCUM Manifesto," the flavor of which is contained in the following statement: "SCUM [Society For the Cutting Up of Men] is too impatient to hope and wait for the brainwashing of millions of [male] assholes. . . . SCUM will not picket, demonstrate, march or strike to attempt to achieve its ends. Such tactics are for nice, genteel ladies who scrupulously take only such action as is guaranteed to be ineffective. . . . SCUM will kill all men who are not in the Men's Auxiliary of SCUM." Valerie Solanas, "S.C.U.M. Manifesto," http://www.womynkind.org/scum.htm (accessed May 25, 2006).

15. "On peut aisément concevoir qu'en s'efforçant d'égaler ainsi un sexe à l'autre, on les dégrade tous les deux; et que de ce mélange grossier des oeuvres de la nature il ne saurait jamais sortir que des hommes faibles et des femmes déshonnêtes." Tocqueville, *De la Démocratie en Amérique*, vol. 2, bk. 3, ch. 12 ("Comment Les Américains Comprennent L'égalité De l'homme et de la Femme," or "How the Americans Understand the Equality of Men and Women").

16. Sheldon S. Wolin and John H. Schaar, *The Berkeley Rebellion and Beyond* (New York: New York Review of Books, 1970), 40.

17. The students took as their models Mao Zedong, Castro, and Che Guevara, but they might just as well have taken someone from Nazi Germany or Fascist Italy. I proved this when, to an American Government class at the height of the Cornell crisis, I read some speeches analyzing the situation and calling for what ought to be done. The radicals in the class were enthusiastic until I revealed that the speeches were by Mussolini.

18. Thomas M. Smith, Beth Aronstamm Young, Susan P. Choy, Marianne Perie, Nabeel Alsalam, Mary R. Rollefson, Yupin Bae, *The Condition of Education, 1996* (Washington, D.C.: National Center for Education Statistics, 1996), 132.

19. Tocqueville, *Democracy in America*, vol. 2, bk. 4, ch. 6 ("What Sort of Despotism Democratic Nations Have to Fear").

20. Ibid., vol. 2, bk. 2, ch. 10.

21. See Raymond Williams, *Culture and Society* (New York: Columbia University Press, 1958).

22. Bloom, *Giants and Dwarfs*, 293.

23. George Levine et al., "Speaking for the Humanities," ACLS Occasional Paper, No. 7 (1989), 2–3, 14.

24. A. Bartlett Giamatti, "In Memoriam," *Yale French Studies* 69 (1985): 6.

25. J. Hillis Miller, "The Triumph of Theory, the Resistance to Reading, and the Question of the Material Base," *PMLA* 102, no. 3 (1987): 289.

26. Dominick LaCapra, *Representing the Holocaust* (Ithaca, N.Y.: Cornell University Press, 1994), 114.

27. John M. Ellis, *Against Deconstruction* (Princeton, N.J.: Princeton University Press, 1989), 146–47.

28. Geoffrey Hartman, "Blindness and Insight," *The New Republic*, March 7, 1988, 30.

29. Paul de Man, *Blindness & Insight: Essays in the Rhetoric of Contemporary Criticism* (Oxford: Oxford University Press, 1971), ix, 11, 141.

30. Jonathan Culler, *Framing the Sign: Criticism and Its Institutions* (Norman, Okla.: University of Oklahoma Press, 1988), 40. See David Lehman, *Signs of the Times: Deconstruction and the Fall of Paul de Man* (New York: Poseidon Press, 1991), 262–63.

31. Hartman, "Blindness and Insight," 30.

32. Roger Kimball, "Professor Hartman Reconstructs Paul de Man," *The New Criterion* (May 1988), 42–43.

33. Bloom, *Giants and Dwarfs*, 293.

34. "Scholar's 40's Articles Debated," *New York Times*, December 1, 1987.

35. *Le Soir* was Belgium's most widely read paper, with a daily circulation of 255,000. After its Belgian owners had fled to France, its name and facilities were taken over by the German authorities. All its articles were censored by the *Militarverwaltung's Propaganda Abteilung* (the Propaganda Division of the Military Administration). The Flemish-language daily *Het Vlaamsche Land* was sponsored by the Germans, and began publication in January 1941; its circulation was 21,000.

36. "En plus, on voit donc qu'une solution du problème juif qui viserait à la création d'une colonie juive isolée de l'Europe, n'entraînerait pas, pour la vie littéraire de l'Occident, de conséquences déplorables. Celle-ci perdrait, en tout et pour tout, quelques personnalités de médiocre valeur et continuerait, comme par le passé, à se développer selon ses grandes lois évolutives." Paul de Man, "Les juifs dans la littérature actuelle," *Le Soir*, March 4, 1941.

37. "La guerre n'aura fait qu'unir plus étroitement ces deux choses si voisines qu'étaient dès l'origine l'âme hitlérienne et l'âme allemande, jusqu'à en faire une seule et unique puissance. C'est un phénomène important, car il signifie qu'on ne peut juger le fait hitlérien sans juger en même temps le fait allemand et que l'avenir de l'Europe ne peut être prévu que dans le cadre des possibilités et des besoins du génie allemand. Il ne s'agit pas seulement d'une série de réformes, mais de l'émancipation définitive d'un peuple qui se trouve, à sa tour, appelé à exercer une hégémonie en Europe." Paul de Man, "Voir la figure de J. Chardonne," *Le Soir*, October 28, 1941.

38. Quoted in Werner Hamacher, Neil Hertz, and Thomas Keenan, eds., *Responses: On Paul de Man's Wartime Journalism* (Lincoln, Neb.: University of Nebraska Press, 1989), 209, 7, 147, 139; Geoffrey Hartman, "Blindness and Insight," *New Republic*, March 7, 1988, 30–31; Leon Roudiez, "Searching for Achilles' Heel: Paul de Man's Disturbing Youth," *World Literature Today* (Summer 1989), 438; Fredric Jameson, *Postmodernism, or, The Cultural Logic of Late Capitalism* (Durham, N.C.: Duke University Press, 1991), 257. In 1991, Jameson's book won the Modern Language Association's James Russell Lowell Prize "for an outstanding literary or linguistic study."

39. Hamacher, Hertz, and Keenan, *Responses: On Paul de Man's Wartime Journalism*, 389, 395.

40. Thomas Jefferson, "Minutes of the Board of Ministers, University of Virginia," in *Thomas Jefferson, Writings*, 479.

41. Paul de Man, *Blindness and Insight: Essays in the Rhetoric of Contemporary Criticism*, 11, 141.

42. Abraham Lincoln, letter to James H. Hackett, August 17, 1863, in *Lincoln, Speeches . . . Writings*, 493.

43. Paul A. Cantor, "Shakespeare—'For All Time'?" *The Public Interest* 110 (Winter 1993) 44.

Chapter 20: Trashing Bourgeois America

1. Gorman Beauchamp, "Dissing the Middle Class," *The American Scholar* (Summer 1995), 336.

2. George Orwell, "The Lion and the Unicorn: Socialism and the English Genius," in *My Country Right or Left, 1940–1943*, vol. 2 of *Collected Essays, Journalism & Letters of George Orwell*, ed. Sonia Orwell and Ian Angus (Boston: Nonpareil Books, 2000), 74–75.

3. Hobbes, *Leviathan*, 36.

4. George Orwell, "The Lion and the Unicorn: Socialism and the English Genius," in *My Country Right or Left, 1940–1943*, 74.

5. Thomas Babington Macaulay, *Critical and Historical Essays* (London: J. M. Dent & Sons, 1953), vol. 2, 353.

6. Martha Nussbaum, "Patriotism and Cosmopolitanism," in *For Love of Country*, ed. Joshua Cohen (Boston: Beacon Press, 1996), 6, 8.

7. Abraham Lincoln, "Eulogy on Henry Clay," in Lincoln, *Speeches . . . Writings*, vol. 1, 264.

8. John B. Judis, "New York Diarist: Bad Trip," *The New Republic*, November 13, 2000, 46.

About the Author

Walter Berns is the John M. Olin University Professor Emeritus at Georgetown University and a resident scholar at the American Enterprise Institute. He has taught at the University of Toronto, the University of Chicago (where he earned a Ph.D. in political science), and Cornell and Yale universities. His government service includes membership on the National Council on the Humanities, the Council of Scholars in the Library of Congress, the Judicial Fellows Commission, and in 1983 he was the alternate United States representative to the United Nations Commission on Human Rights. He has been a Guggenheim, Rockefeller, and Fulbright Fellow and a Phi Beta Kappa lecturer. He is the author of numerous articles on American government and politics in both professional and popular journals; his many books include *In Defense of Liberal Democracy*, *The First Amendment and the Future of American Democracy*, *Taking the Constitution Seriously*, and *Making Patriots*. President George W. Bush awarded him the 2005 National Humanities Medal for his scholarship on the history of the Constitution.

Index